6.35

D1384328

Practical BUSINESS
STATISTICS

Practical BUSINESS

STATISTICS

FREDERICK E. CROXTON, Ph.D.

Professor of Statistics
Columbia University

DUDLEY J. COWDEN, Ph.D.

Professor of Economic Statistics
School of Business Administration
University of North Carolina

THIRD
EDITION

Englewood Cliffs, N.J.

PRENTICE-HALL, INC.

1960

©—1934, 1948, 1960, BY
PRENTICE-HALL, INC.
ENGLEWOOD CLIFFS, N.J.

All rights reserved. No part of this book
may be reproduced in any form, by
mimeograph or any other means, without
permission in writing from the publishers.

Library of Congress Catalog Card Number: 60–5376

PRINTED IN THE UNITED STATES OF AMERICA

68778

PREFACE TO THIRD EDITION

The material in a textbook on statistical methods may be arranged in various ways.

1. All the material dealing with a specified topic may be assembled in one section of the book. This method of arrangement is admirable for a reference book. But since all topics are interrelated it does not meet the needs of a beginning student. For example, a student cannot understand much about descriptive statistics until he knows a little about statistical inference, and he should know something about correlation in order to understand economic time series.

2. The material may be arranged in an effective teaching order. If the different topics are interrelated, and if the learning process consists in connecting new ideas with a variety of old ideas, then one should try to arrange the material so that the level of knowledge in all topics is gradually raised, rather than trying to completely fill one topical compartment before proceeding to the next. The difficulty with this method is that different teachers may not agree on the order and amounts to be directed to each compartment.

3. A compromise between the two methods may be attempted. The philosophy of method 2 has guided the writer, but some concession has been made to method 1. In order to assist the teacher, topics that could be postponed until a subsequent semester or quarter are marked with an asterisk.

This book differs from the second edition of *Practical Business Statistics*, and from many other books, in various respects.

1. Since the making of an inference is implicit in most statistical analysis, statistical inference is introduced almost at the beginning of the book, at a very simple level.

2. In the early part of the book the range is used in making statistical inferences, rather than the more complicated standard error of the mean. Thus the student can think about ideas rather than computations.

3. Conventional methods of statistical inference occupy the bulk of the pages devoted to that topic, but there is a brief introduction to non-parametric methods.

4. The power of a test, and the operating characteristic of a test, are explained. Without these tools of thought it seems to the writer that one has rather meager understanding of tests of hypotheses. There is also a small section devoted to decision theory, since most statistical tests lead to making some decision.

5. Most students of business administration are weak in mathematics. Therefore, short and simple chapters are interspersed, as needed, on arithmetic, rounding of numbers, algebra, probability, and equations and curves.

6. As a device for simplifying the computation of second and third degree polynomial trends, orthogonal polynomials are introduced, and a short table of orthogonal polynomials is given in an appendix.

7. There is a unified treatment of growth curves, though the treatment of the Gompertz and logistic curves has been curtailed in the interest of brevity.

8. The idea of a mathematical model, and its relation to the method of analysis, is extensively treated in Chapter 39.

In order to keep the size of the book moderately small, virtually no derivations are given, but the student is advised to look in other books, such as Dudley J. Cowden, *Statistical Methods in Quality Control*, Prentice-Hall, 1957, or F. E. Croxton and D. J. Cowden, *Applied General Statistics*, 2nd. ed., Prentice-Hall, 1955, for derivations in which he may be interested.

I am indebted to Professor Sir Ronald A. Fisher, Cambridge, to Dr. Frank Yates, Rothamsted, and to Messrs. Oliver and Boyd Ltd., Edinburgh, for permission to reprint portions of Tables III, IV, and V from their book *Statistical Tables for Biological, Agricultural and Medical Research*. I am similarly indebted to Professor E. S. Pearson and to the Biometrica Trustees for permission to reprint tables or portions of tables from *Biometrika* and from E. S. Pearson and H. O. Hartley's *Biometrika Tables for Statisticians*, Volume 1. Other persons, and organizations, who supplied data or gave permission to reprint material are acknowledged at the appropriate location.

The assistance of the many people who helped in the preparation of this book is gratefully acknowledged. I am particularly thankful to Barclay Jones for lettering many of the charts, to Mrs. Mary Jane LeNeave for typing much of the manuscript, to W. Allen Spivey for critically reading the entire work in its original form, and to my wife, Mercedes S. Cowden, for assistance in computing and preparation of charts and tables. My thanks also to R. M. Duvall for reading the page proofs and detecting several oversights of the writer.

The forthcoming second edition of *Practical Problems in Business Statistics*, by Dudley J. and Mercedes S. Cowden, intended for a one-semester course, is designed to accompany the third edition of *Practical Business Statistics*.

This third edition of *Practical Business Statistics* was prepared by Dudley J. Cowden.

Dudley J. Cowden

Chapel Hill,
North Carolina

CONTENTS

4. MISUSES OF STATISTICS

5. SELECTED TOPICS IN ARITHMETIC

Practical BUSINESS
STATISTICS

Chapter 1

THE NATURE OF STATISTICAL DATA

Nature, including persons and the behavior of persons, displays the characteristics of conformity and diversity. Uniformity is sometimes so great in the physical sciences that we overlook variability. But in the world of human beings, variability is so great that in the social sciences we must resort to the statistical method if we are to make valid generalizations.

Variability

It has been said that the most universal quality is diversity. No two objects are exactly alike. Compare two pieces of plate glass. They may look alike to you, but a microscope will reveal marked differences. No two actions performed by an individual are exactly alike. If you play golf, it is almost inconceivable that you have twice driven a ball the same distance, though several times you may almost have done so. Where the observations refer to different people the variability is likely to be greater. For example, it is reasonable to suppose that there is less variability in your scores on different days than there is in the individual scores of all persons using the course on the same day. Or look at the financial section of a metropolitan newspaper, and see what happened on the stock market. It is very likely that some stocks went up in price per share, while others went down; and of course some changed in price more than others. In timing the winning sprinter in a hundred-yard dash, the readings of experienced timers do not necessarily agree, and the official time is sometimes a more or less arbitrary average. Even in the physical sciences, which we think of as being so accurate, repeated measurements by the same person or by different persons may vary, and the accepted value is an average.

One great scientist and statistician has said:[1] "Absolute sameness is a purely conceptual notion, which is not in human experience."

Uniformity

To say that diversity is pervasive is to state only part of the truth. There is conformity as well as diversity, order as well as anarchy, cosmos as well as chaos, centripetal force as well as centrifugal force. Some degree of

---

[1] Karl Pearson, *The Grammar of Science*, 3rd ed., Macmillan Company, New York, 1911, p. 153.

1

uniformity is discernible for data of a given kind, as well as some degree of variability.

Consider the following observations of the time taken by a machine operator to pick up a bolt and put it in a chuck. Below are recorded the observations for 10 different bolts, in hundredths of a minute, taken in chronological order:

$$10, 10, 8, 9, 10, 10, 10, 11, 10, 9.$$

If we arrange the data in order of magnitude it is easy to see that the observations cluster around some central value, often referred to as an average. Thus we have the following array:

$$8, 9, 9, 10, 10, 10, 10, 10, 10, 11.$$

The average that is most commonly used is the arithmetic mean, which is obtained by dividing the sum of the values by the number of values. Thus:

$$\text{Arithmetic mean} = \frac{8 + 9 + 9 + 10 + 10 + 10 + 10 + 10 + 10 + 11}{10} = \frac{97}{10}$$

$$= 9.7 \text{ hundredths of one minute.}$$

The dispersion (variability) and the central tendency (uniformity) is seen even more clearly if we tally the items.

Time (hundredths of one minute)	Number of occurrences
8	/
9	//
10	ТНʬ /
11	/

We see that the values range from 8 to 11; i.e., the range is 3. Also, we see that the arithmetic mean is in this case a typical value, for it is approximately 10, the recorded time that occurs most frequently. Not only is there a tendency for the observations to cluster around some central value, but the number of occurrences becomes gradually smaller as we consider values farther and farther removed from that central value. Technically we can say that the probability of a large deviation from the mean is small.

If we should consider time trials for each of several different machine operators instead of several trials for one operator, the results would have been similar in one respect: both central tendency and dispersion would be observable.

Let us consider another business illustration. From the stocks listed on the New York Stock Exchange, a sample of 46 stocks was selected by a procedure intended to give a cross section of all the stocks. The price per share was noted at the end of 1954 and again at the end of 1955. Then the percentage change in the price of each stock was computed. Thus, for Admiral Corporation:[2]

$$\frac{1955 \text{ price} - 1954 \text{ price}}{1954 \text{ price}} = \frac{\$21.875 - \$28.250}{\$21.875} = \frac{-\$6.375}{\$21.875}$$

$$= -0.2257 = -22.57 \text{ per cent,}$$

which rounds to -23 per cent.

The percentage change for each of the 46 stocks is shown below, arranged in the alphabetical order of the names of the companies:

$-23, 2, 39, 7, -18, 5, 17, -2, 27, 13, 25, 31, 65, -1, 12,$

$-3, -7, -22, 37, 33, 4, 13, 10, 79, 20, 48, 29, 69, -4, 24,$

$6, 10, 3, 3, 10, 19, 33, 40, 9, -28, 35, 4, -14, -43, -5, 28.$

The appearance of the data in this form is rather chaotic. Therefore, we array the data in ascending order of magnitude:

$-43, -28, -23, -22, -18, -14, -7, -5, -4, -3, -2,$

$-1, 2, 3, 3, 4, 4, 5, 6, 7, 9, 10, 10, 10, 12, 13, 13, 17, 19, 20,$

$24, 25, 27, 28, 29, 31, 33, 33, 35, 37, 39, 40, 48, 65, 69, 79.$

Note that the values of items in the neighborhood of the two middle items[3] (each of which has a value of 10) do not differ greatly among themselves, but that the values of items near each end are more widely separated. This tendency is more apparent when we group the data into classes according to size, as in Table 1.1, which is called a *frequency distribution*. Finally, the data of Table 1.1 are presented in Chart 1.1 as a column diagram, known as a *histogram*.

The typical increase in stock prices during 1955, according to this sample, is obviously somewhere between 0 and 20 per cent, for values occur most frequently in that class. If we add the 46 values and divide by 46 we obtain a mean of 13.83 per cent.[4] If you had invested $10,000 in the 46 stocks at the end of 1954, dividing your money equally among the different stocks, you could have sold them for $11,383 at the end of 1955.

There seems to be one exception to the orderly pattern of Table 1.1 and

---

[2] Year end prices were obtained from Standard and Poor's Corporation, *Security Owner's Stock Guide*, January 1955 and January 1956. Adjustments were made for stock splits and stock dividends.

[3] The value of the middle item, or the average of the two middle items when there is an even number of items, is called the *median*.

[4] In making the computation two decimal places were used for each observation. Thus, Admiral Corporation was counted as -22.57 per cent rather than 23 per cent.

**Table 1.1—Distribution of Percentage
Changes Between End of 1954 and
End of 1955 of 46 Common
Stocks Listed on the New
York Stock Exchange**

Percentage change	Number of stocks
−60 to −40	1
−40 to −20	3
−20 to 0	8
0 to 20	18
20 to 40	12
40 to 60	1
60 to 80	3
Total	46

Source: See footnote 2.

**Chart 1.1—Percentage Changes Between End of 1954 and End of 1955 of Sample of
46 Common Stocks Listed on New York Stock Exchange**

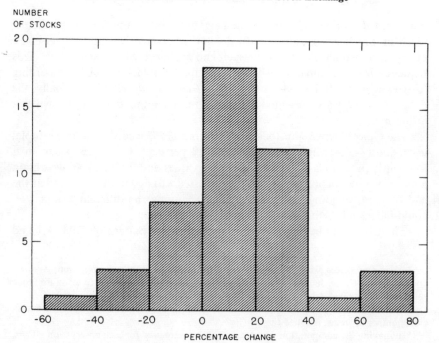

Source of data: Table 1.1.

Chart 1.1. There are more cases between 60 per cent and 80 per cent than there are between 40 per cent and 60 per cent. With a small sample, such as this one, there are often irregularities that are hard to explain.

The tendency towards uniformity as well as variability seems to be a law of nature. People are mostly neither very stupid nor very smart; they are mostly of moderate intelligence. This may perhaps be thought of as "the triumph of mediocrity."

For a given type of business, the merchandise turnover varies for different business units. But most of them do not get, and stay, very far out of line. The reason is that the mean is really golden. If a store keeps too small a stock of merchandise on hand it will frequently be out of stock on some items; if it keeps too large a stock, it will have money tied up unproductively, and the merchandise may deteriorate physically or become obsolete.

In human behavior it is a commonplace that persons who conform to the average in their appearance, who do not have extreme views, and who conform in their behavior to mass standards, get along better than do extreme individualists. This sometimes leads to the view that what is customary is right. In some countries and in some times attempts have been made to eliminate differences in opinion. Left deviationists and right deviationists have been liquidated. But although dispersion is thus often reduced, it is seldom, if ever, eliminated.

From the foregoing discussion it should not be concluded that there is any virtue in absolute uniformity. In most fields of endeavor a reasonable amount of variability is quite commendable. Political philosophy is to some extent concerned with the proper mixture of freedom and restraint. In the world of art we strive for a pleasing combination of pattern and variety, of order and disorder. The picture of the sound of an electric generator on the screen of an oscillograph is distinguished from that of a musical instrument by its much greater regularity. The object of acoustical design is to provide just the right proportion of direct sound from the platform and vibrations reflected from the walls and ceilings.

The Stability of Large Numbers

We have just remarked that measurable characteristics are subject to more or less variability, but that there seems to be something tending to pull them toward some "center of gravity." This central value is an average, around which the individual observations are dispersed in some characteristic manner.

Averages tend to become stable if they are obtained from a large number of observations, all taken from the same population. From game to game the batting average of nearly any baseball player varies considerably. From week to week there is usually less variability, and from month to month still less. There are apparent exceptions though. Some players may show a trend, gradually improving or deteriorating during the season; or they may show cycles, perhaps having occasional batting slumps. These are not real exceptions though; the population may be thought of as changing if the "cause system" is changing during the season.[5]

Here is another illustration that is simpler in some respects, for it avoids the disturbing effects of the passage of time. Table 1.2 lists, in presumably

Table 1.2—Kilowatt-Hours of Electricity Used in one Month
by 75 Residential Consumers

Item number	Kilowatt-hours	Item number	Kilowatt-hours	Item number	Kilowatt-hours
1	86	26	121	51	128
2	90	27	75	52	91
3	82	28	125	53	98
4	94	29	50	54	59
5	38	30	126	55	40
6	75	31	136	56	71
7	148	32	89	57	37
8	131	33	95	58	70
9	28	34	36	59	68
10	114	35	78	60	61
11	158	36	157	61	93
12	105	37	66	62	75
13	58	38	52	63	56
14	83	39	64	64	87
15	58	40	81	65	84
16	57	41	62	66	54
17	19	42	72	67	83
18	10	43	60	68	135
19	94	44	8	69	77
20	92	45	73	70	115
21	96	46	76	71	79
22	118	47	9	72	53
23	144	48	88	73	51
24	90	49	84	74	41
25	74	50	80	75	67

Source: Confidential

random order, the kilowatt-hours of electricity used in one month by 75 residential consumers. As an experiment we have first selected a random[6]

---

[5] The population must be thought of as the theoretically infinite number of possible appearances of a batter, of which the actual appearances during a season constitute a sample. Of the causes that may be changing, some may be weather changes, some may be physical and mental changes in the batter, some may be changes in the skill of the opposing pitchers, and some may pertain to knowledge that pitchers and batters acquire concerning each other's weaknesses.

[6] Random sampling is explained at length in Chapter 13. A random sample can be selected very easily by use of the random numbers of Appendix 28. For example, starting

sample of 4 observations from these data, and computed their mean. Continuing with the same procedure we have selected 40 such samples. (The same item appears in several samples, and occasionally more than once in the same sample.) We now have 40 averages. The results are shown in the first column of Table 1.3, the means being arrayed in descending order.

Table 1.3—Means of 40 Random Samples of 4 Items Each and 16 Items Each
(Kilowatt-hours)

Rank order	Sample size		Rank order	Sample size	
	4	16		4	16
40	123	106.5	20	76	78
39	115.5	106	19	75	77.5
38	109	96	18	74.5	77
37	102.5	93	17	74	77
36	102	90	16	73	76.5
35	101	90	15	73	76
34	100	90	14	73	76
33	99.5	89	13	72	76
32	95.5	88.5	12	71	75
31	89.5	87	11	71	74
30	87	85	10	69	73
29	86.5	84	9	69	72
28	85	82	8	66	71
27	83	82	7	65	70
26	81	82	6	65	69
25	80.5	80	5	63.5	69
24	80	79	4	63.5	68
23	80	79	3	53.5	66
22	79.5	79	2	49	64
21	77	78	1	48	62

Source: Table 1.2

Next we have selected 40 random samples of 16 observations each, and shown the means of these samples in column 2 of Table 1.3. The data of Table 1.3

at number 82 in the top row (a random start) and working down, the first 4 two-digit numbers between 01 and 75, inclusive, are 18, 20, 56, 11. The first sample, then, is

Item number	Kilowatt-hours
18	10
20	92
56	71
11	158
Total	331
Mean	82.75

are shown graphically in Chart 1.2. Straight lines connect the highs and lows of the two arrays, and also connect the extremes of the middle 36 (middle 90 per cent) and the middle 28 (middle 70 per cent). It is apparent that the means of the samples of 16 vary, roughly, one-half as much as do the means of the samples of 4. If we continue the experiment, selecting larger and larger samples for each set of 40 trials, we find that the variability among the means

**Chart 1.2—Means of 40 Random Samples of 4
Items Each and of 16 Items Each**

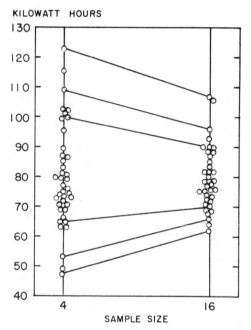

Source of data: Table 1.3.

tends to grow smaller and smaller. This dispersion eventually becomes so small that for practical purposes we can ignore it.

We should think of an average as being subject to some degree of uncertainty, but we can control the amount of uncertainty by choice of the sample size. But diminishing returns applies to sampling as well as to other activities. The reliability of sample means is not proportionate to the sample size. Theoretically it is proportionate to the square root of the sample size. Referring to the experiment described in the preceding paragraph, note that $\sqrt{4} \div \sqrt{16} = \frac{1}{2}$. By increasing the sample size we can decrease the uncertainty to any extent we wish, but we can never eliminate it.

At first it may seem shocking to speak of variability, approximation, and probability, rather than uniformity, exactness, and certainty. But it is better to be guided by probability than to be misguided by the misconception of certainty.

The statistical view of nature. There are several views of nature, including the mechanical and the statistical. The mechanical view is that the physical world is described by invariant laws. The statistical view is that laws are average relationships. These average relationships can be determined, more or less accurately, by experiment. The behavior of the individual molecule is unpredictable, but the behavior of physical objects consisting of almost innumerable molecules is often predictable within negligible limits of error. According to this view, the difference between the physical and the social sciences (including business) is one of degree, rather than of kind. The former exhibits much greater stability because the things measured are made up of such a tremendous number of molecules.[7] On the other hand, the totals and averages concerning which the economist and the businessman speak are made up of relatively few units. After all, there are fewer than 200 million people in the United States.

Physical laws are usually closer approximations for another reason. Physical experiments are usually carried out under closely controlled conditions, thus largely eliminating extraneous factors. For example, an experiment to test the relationship between the distance an object falls and the velocity of the object may be conducted in a vacuum. In agricultural experimentation, specified amounts and kinds of fertilizer may be applied to specified plots, in such a way that each type of plot receives a treatment of each type of fertilizer and of each specified quantity of fertilizer. But if we wish to learn the relationship between the amount of oranges offered for sale and the price that results, we cannot control any of the following: the amount offered for sale at different times; the prices of competing commodities; the income of buyers; changes in taste. We can perhaps select from the available data only the data that would be the equivalent of a well-designed experiment, but if we do this there may not be enough information left to permit us to make useful inferences. What we usually do is to utilize the data that are available, and try to allow statistically for the effect of the different variables.

Whether the statistical view of nature is valid is open to doubt. But numerical laws describing the behavior of aggregates of human beings are essentially statistical. Whenever the words "tends" or "tendency" are used, we are referring to average behavior. Averages computed from samples are

---

[7] "...[The] laws of classical physics are idealizations that are applicable only to the description of phenomena where the actions involved are sufficiently large to permit neglect of the quantum. Whereas this condition is amply fulfilled in phenomena on the ordinary scale, we meet in atomic processes regularities of quite a new kind." Niels Bohr, "Mathematics and Natural Philosophy," *The Scientific Monthly*, Vol. 8, February, 1956, pp. 86–87.

always subject to sampling error, and therefore only approximations to the "truth."

Summary

In economics and business we deal with masses of data. The individual units differ among themselves, but if the data are homogeneous, the items usually exhibit a tendency to "gravitate" toward some central value, with observations becoming progressively more sparse as the deviation from the central value increases.

These characteristics of uniformity and variability can be observed by the following devices:

(1) Arraying the data in order of magnitude;
(2) Grouping them in the form of a frequency distribution;
(3) Representing the grouped data graphically as a histogram (column diagram).

The central value around which the individual values tend to cluster is sometimes referred to as an average. The arithmetic mean is the most common average. It is obtained by dividing the sum of the values by the number of values.

Variability or dispersion has to do with the extent to which the individual items differ among themselves. Some idea of the amount of dispersion can be obtained by noting the range, or difference, between the largest value and the smallest value. Somewhat better is the range that includes the bulk of the items, excluding the more extreme values.

An average is never completely reliable, since different samples yield different averages; but it is more reliable for large samples than for small ones. The reliability of sample means is proportionate to the square root of the sample size. If the sample is large enough, the error is negligible.

It may be that the generalizations made in the physical sciences are more accurate than those in the social sciences because the objects that are under observation in the physical sciences are composed of such an enormous number of ultimate units.

Chapter 2

THE ANALYSIS OF STATISTICAL DATA

In Chapter 1 we saw that statistical data are characterized by uniformity and variability. Purposes of the statistical method are description, analysis, and inference. In this chapter we shall concern ourselves primarily with some elementary ideas about analysis, and only secondarily with statistical inference. We shall see how variability can sometimes be partly accounted for either by classification, or by discovering how the values of the data being analyzed tend to vary with the values of some associated variable.

Even though we can account for most of the variability in a set of data, there will almost always be a residue that is unexplained, and which exhibits a pattern of variability similar to that which we observed in Chapter 1.

The approach in this chapter will be mainly graphical and intuitive. Detailed computations and the application of probability theory will be deferred until later. Nevertheless this is a very important chapter. It contains the seeds of most of the ideas that, we hope, will subsequently be germinated. The illustrations are not all from the field of business, but are mostly from fields in which you already have some knowledge and interest.

Classification of Heterogeneous Data

Data are *homogeneous* if all the units are governed by the same system of causes. They are *heterogeneous* (nonhomogeneous) if not all the units are governed by the same system of causes. This does not mean that all the units of homogeneous data are alike with respect to some measurable characteristic. There is still variability.

When homogeneous data are grouped according to magnitude they usually display a pattern of variability somewhat resembling the frequency distributions illustrated in Chapter 1. The shape of a frequency distribution diagram composed of heterogeneous data is usually "peculiar" looking. In order to interpret such data it may be desirable to classify them in some rational way. Several methods of classification will now be considered.

Qualitative classification. If data that are of different *kinds* are lumped together it is difficult to extract much meaning. One would seldom find it useful, for example, to make a single frequency distribution of the weights of the cats and dogs in a community, or even of dogs of different breeds.

Wage data. Consider the wage data plotted in Chart 2.1. The histogram (column diagram) is constructed in a manner similar to Chart 1.1. A broken line connects the mid-points of the columns, forming what is known as a

11

**Chart 2.1—Distribution of Laborers and Mechanics by Average
Hourly Earnings, October 1954**

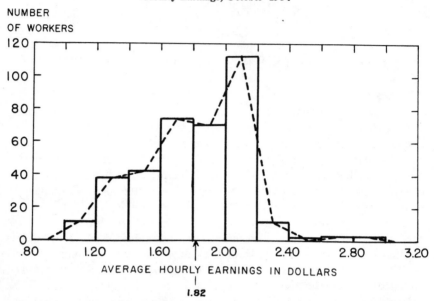

Source of data: United States Department of Labor, Bureau of Labor Statistics, *Monthly Labor Review*, Vol. 78
November 1955, pp. 1,254.

**Chart 2.2—Distribution of Laborers and Distribution of Mechanics
by Average Hourly Earnings, October 1954**

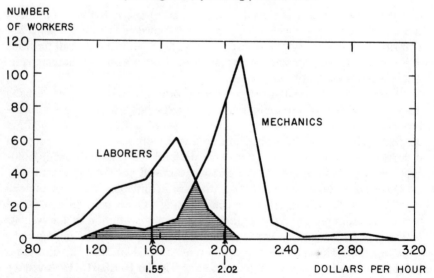

Source of data: See Chart 2.1.

frequency polygon. Note that this polygon has two peaks, a short one at
$1.65, and a tall one at $2.15. Such a curve is sometimes said to be bimodal,
for it has two modes,[1] a primary mode in the neighborhood of $2.15 and a
secondary mode in the neighborhood of $1.65. A bimodal distribution often
indicates heterogeneity. The reason for the bimodality is apparent. The
distribution consists of two kinds of workers, laborers and mechanics.
Chart 2.2 shows the distribution of laborers and mechanics separately. The
mean wage of the laborers is indicated on the chart to be $1.55 per hour,
while that of the mechanics is $2.02.

There can be little question concerning the significance of the classification.
The peaks of the two curves (and the two averages) are widely separated, and
there is not much overlapping (shown on the chart by the shaded area).
Or may we say that the difference between the two means is large compared
with the spread or dispersion of the two distributions around their respective
means. One would hardly ever select *at random* two samples from the same
population that differ as much in their mean values as those of Chart 2.2,
and at the same time show such small amounts of dispersion within each
sample.

Profits on corporation stocks. In Chapter 1 we considered the distribution
of percentage changes between the end of 1954 and the end of 1955 of a
representative selection of 46 stocks listed on the New York Stock Exchange.
Let us compare this distribution with the 46 stocks recommended for potential
price appreciation by a well-known securities analysis corporation. Chart 2.3
compares the two selections in the same manner as Chart 2.2 did the wage
data for the two classes of workers.

For the random sample the average price increase is 13.83 per cent,
while for the recommended stocks it is 14.26. The difference between the
two means is very small, especially in comparison with the large variability
within each sample. In taking pairs of random samples from one population
where the individual items vary as widely as these, one would usually find a
difference as great as 14.26 − 13.83 per cent = 0.43 per cent or greater.[2]
This experiment alone does not give us enough evidence to decide with much
confidence that the forecaster's recommendations tend to be better than
random selections of investment securities, so far as average price increase
during one year is concerned.

However, there is one way in which the forecaster's selection differs
from that of the systematic selection. There is not so much variability, or
spread, in the recommended selection as in the random selection. From

---

[1] The mode is the most typical value, the one that tends to occur the most frequently
within some range of values.

[2] How best to measure dispersion, and how greatly a sample mean must differ from
some other mean before the difference is considered significant, will be considered in later
chapters, especially Chapters 17 and 23.

the chart this can be seen by observing that the broken line runs from −30 to +70, a range of 100, while the solid line runs from −70 to +90, a range of 160. Judging from this experiment, the analyst's selection is less risky; the maximum profit on any one stock is not so large, neither is the maximum possible loss. Also, if one should follow the analyst's advice year after year, it is reasonable to suppose that the profits (or losses) on the year's speculation would not fluctuate as much as if random selections were made each year.

Chart 2.3—Percentage Price Changes during 1955 of 46 Common Stocks Recommended for Price Appreciation and 46 Common Stocks Selected at Random

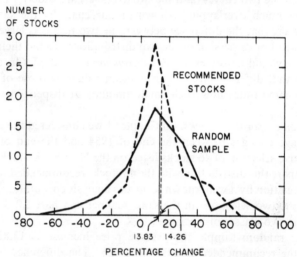

Source of data: Year end prices were obtained from Standard and Poors, *Security Owner's Stock Guide*, January 1955 and January 1956.

Temporal classification. Sometimes data are classified according to *time* because it is believed that significant differences in kind or magnitude may be associated with the passage of time.

A quality control illustration. In a branch of management known as *quality control*, small samples of manufactured product are taken at random, at more or less regular intervals, and the mean computed for each sample. These are plotted on what is known as a *control chart*, and if any point gets too far out of line this is considered as a danger signal. It indicates that there has been a change in the cause system, and that the process is therefore out of control. A search for the trouble is made, and if found the trouble is corrected.

As an over-simplified illustration, consider the warp-breaking strength of cloth for 6 consecutive samples of 4 items each, taken at hourly intervals. The data are shown in Table 2.1 and plotted in Chart 2.4, known as a *control chart*. The different observations in each sample are connected by a vertical line, so that some idea of the dispersion within each sample can be obtained.

**Table 2.1—Warp-breaking Strength in Pounds of 6 Samples of 4 Items Each,
Taken at Hourly Intervals**

Item number	Sample number					
	1	2	3	4	5	6
1	70	68	66	67	71	62
2	68	66	64	66	68	59
3	68	66	63	65	66	59
4	62	63	60	60	57	56
Sum	268	263	253	258	262	236
Mean	67.00	65.75	63.25	64.50	65.50	59.00

Source: Dudley J. Cowden and William A. Connor, "The Use of Statistical Methods for Economic Control of Quality in Industry," *Southern Economic Journal*, Vol. 12, October, 1945, pp. 115–129.

The circle in each sample array is the mean of that sample. If the process is in control, the means tend to fluctuate around the *central line* (which represents a standard value) running through the chart, and between the two broken lines known as *control limits*. As we shall see later, the location of these lines is determined by use of probability theory, and depends in part upon the amount of variation within the different samples. Therefore, if a point is

**Chart 2.4—Control Chart for Means, Showing also
Individual Items: Warp-Breaking Strength
of Cotton Cloth**

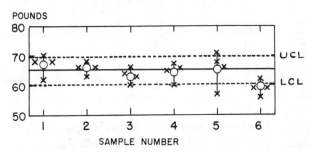

Source of data: Table 2.1.

outside of the control limits, it indicates a large departure from the desired central value compared to the variation within different samples. Since the dotted lines indicate the maximum amount of fluctuation that can reasonably be attributed to chance, a point outside these limits is a danger signal. It indicates a change in the cause system, and that the process is therefore "out of control." A search for the cause of the trouble is made, and if found, the trouble is corrected.

The mean of sample number 6 is below the lower control limit, and at this point a search was made for the cause of the apparent trouble. The trouble was found to be a progressive deterioration in the quality of the mix. This trouble was corrected by using in the mix a smaller proportion of strip from the cards, and the tensile strength immediately improved.

Chart 2.4 indicates that something may have gone wrong with sample 5 also. The dispersion of that sample is considerably greater than that of the

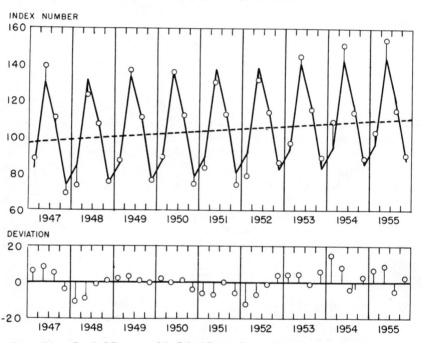

Chart 2.5—Graphic Analysis of Natural Cheese Production in the
United States, by Quarters, 1947–1955

Source of data: Board of Governors of the Federal Reserve System, *Federal Reserve Bulletin*, various issues.

others, indicating lack of uniformity in the items, though the sample mean is about right. Also it should be noticed that only one item in sample 5 is much out of line. It is not immediately apparent whether this one deviation is too large to be attributed to chance, nor whether the variability of sample 5 as a whole is significantly larger than that of the other samples. In order to resolve such doubts a more thorough analysis, based on probability theory, is required.

An economic time series. The objective of quality control is to discover *special* causes of variability, so that prompt action can be taken when needed.

Time series that are of an economic (as contrasted with industrial) nature usually show a *systematic* pattern of variability that is associated with time. The upper part of Chart 2.5 shows by small circles the production of natural cheese in the United States, by quarters, for the 9 years 1947–1955. The systematic character of the movements is immediately apparent, and is shown by the solid line that fluctuates around the slanting straight line. The broken line is known as a *trend* line, and indicates that cheese production has been gradually increasing. The fluctuations of the solid line around the broken line represent mainly the *seasonal* variation in cheese production. The chart shows that cheese production is much greater in the spring and summer than it is in the the fall and winter. Small vertical lines connect the observed values with the fluctuating solid line. These vertical lines indicate the amount of variability that is not accounted for either by trend or seasonal variation. As a visual aid these unexplained deviations are plotted in the lower part of the chart around a horizontal line.

The movements we have accounted for are undoubtedly significant. They are statistically significant, for the explained variability shown by the solid line in the upper part of the chart is large in comparison with the fluctuations shown in the lower part of the chart. Variability of that magnitude could hardly be attributed to chance. There are also economically significant, for we have been able to assign a logical reason for the fluctuations. But we should also notice that the residuals in the lower chart display a *cyclical* characteristic. If we could find some explanation of the cycles, little variability would remain unexplained.

Geographical classification. Corporations doing business on a national scale usually classify their sales according to sales districts. If each of the sales districts is reasonably homogeneous, estimation of sales potential and the establishment of sales budgets by districts is facilitated. Often it is found that sales in different regions tend to vary rather closely with regional differences, such as per capita income, density of population, per cent white, average temperature, and the like.

Table 2.2 shows the per capita income of the different states, District of Columbia, and regions in the United States in 1954. The states have been grouped into five classes according to per capita income, as follows:

Per capita income	Number of states
Less than $1,200	6
$1,200–1,499	12
1,500–1,799	16
1,800–2,099	7
2,100 or more	8
Total	49

In Chart 2.6 the per capita income of the different states is indicated by the darkness of the shading, the greater the income the darker is the shading. It is at once apparent that states with approximately the same per capita

**Table 2.2—Per Capita Personal Income in the United States,
by States and Regions, 1954**

State and region	Income	State and region	Income
Continental United States	**$1,770**	**Southwest**	**$1,544**
		Arizona	1,582
New England	**1,935**	New Mexico .	1,387
Connecticut	2,361	Oklahoma ...	1,466
Maine	1,492	Texas	1,574
Massachusetts	1,922		
New Hampshire	1,605	**Central**	**1,920**
Rhode Island	1,823	Illinois	2,155
Vermont	1,408	Indiana	1,834
		Iowa	1,667
Middle East	**2,000**	Michigan	2,017
Delaware	2,372	Minnesota ...	1,644
District of Columbia .	2,220	Missouri	1,747
Maryland	1,940	Ohio	1,983
New Jersey	2,219	Wisconsin ...	1,706
New York	2,163		
Pennsylvania	1,785	**Northwest**	**1,583**
West Virginia	1,232	Colorado .,..	1,686
		Idaho	1,433
Southeast	**1,233**	Kansas	1,689
Alabama	1,091	Montana	1,729
Arkansas	979	Nebraska	1,635
Florida	1,610	North Dakota	1,186
Georgia	1,237	South Dakota	1,332
Kentucky	1,216	Utah	1,483
Louisiana	1,302	Wyoming	1,779
Mississippi	873		
North Carolina	1,190	**Far West**	**2,094**
South Carolina	1,063	California ...	2,162
Tennessee	1,212	Nevada	2,414
Virginia	1,480	Oregon	1,757
		Washington ..	1,949

Source: U.S. Department of Commerce, Office of Business Economics, *Survey of Current Business,*
September, 1955, pp. 16–17.

income tend to cluster together. This of course indicates the obvious; geographical factors have a considerable influence on per capita income.

Not much information is lost if the states are classified geographically, as in Chart 2.7, for most of the states in a given region have approximately the same per capita income. There are some exceptions; Maine, West Virginia, North Dakota, and Florida are apparently affected by important special causes in addition to those common to their respective regions.

One problem that has occupied the attention of statisticians is how to classify states or counties into compact regions in such a way as to obtain the maximum difference among regions with respect to economic and other factors, and the minimum difference within each region.

Chart 2.6—Per Capita Income of the United States, 1954, by States

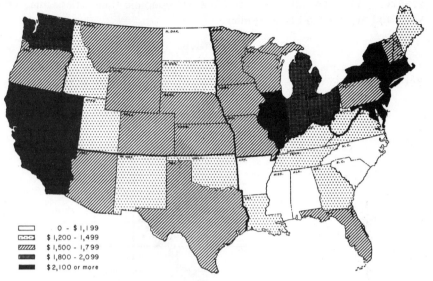

```
☐        0 - $ 1,199
☐☐☐    $ 1,200 - 1,499
▨▨▨    $ 1,500 - 1,799
▦▦▦    $ 1,800 - 2,099
■■■    $ 2,100 or more
```

Source of data: Table 2.2.

Chart 2.7—Per Capita Income of the United States, 1954, by Regions

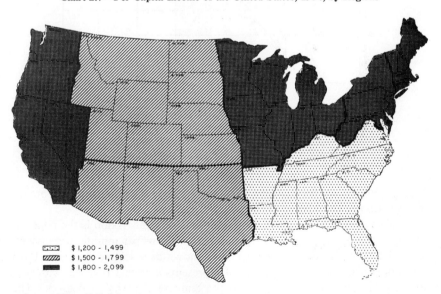

```
☐☐☐    $ 1,200 - 1,499
▨▨▨    $ 1,500 - 1,799
■■■    $ 1,800 - 2,099
```

Source of data: Table 2.2.

A similarity between geographical data and economic time series data should be noted. In the case of geographical data, adjacent states and counties tend to be similar; in the case of economic time series, adjacent years and months tend to be similar.

Correlation

One of the aims in the use of the scientific method is to show relationships. For example, the velocity of a falling body is proportionate to the distance

Chart 2.8—Temperature and Chirps per Minute of 115 Crickets

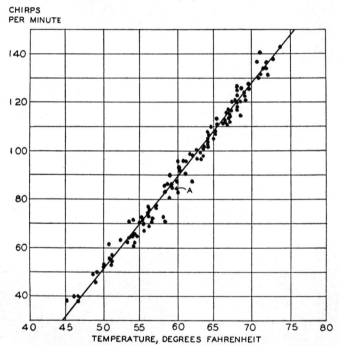

Source of data: Provided by Mr. Bert E. Holmes. See also Bert E. Holmes, "Vocal Thermometers," *The Scientific Monthly*, September 1927, pp. 261–264. This chart is reprinted from F. E. Croxton and Dudley J. Cowden, *Applied General Statistics*, 2nd. ed., Prentice-Hall, Inc., Englewood Cliffs, New Jersey, 1955, p. 452.

it has fallen. Also, the distance a car travels after the application of brakes is a function of the square of the speed of the car.

A biological illustration. A somewhat amusing illustration is the relationship between temperature and the number of chirps per minute of a cricket. The relationship is shown by Chart 2.8, known as a scatter diagram. Each dot represents a cricket. Thus dot *A* represents a cricket that was observed to chirp 85 times per minute when the temperature was 59 degrees. The diagonal line is an estimate of the relationship between temperature and chirps per minute. The relationship must be considered significant, for the variability in chirps per minute is accounted for almost completely by differences in temperature. This is evident by the fact that the observation points are very close to the line. The distances between the points and the line represent the amounts of variability that have not been explained. They could conceivably be attributed entirely to errors of measurement.

A football illustration. Table 2.3 shows the scores, rushing and passing

Table 2.3—Football Scores, Rushing and Passing Yardage, and First Downs Made by the Teams in 20 Games in 1955

September 24, 1955				October 1, 1955			
School	Score	Yardage	First downs	School	Score	Yardage	First downs
Oklahoma	13	483	26	North Carolina ...	25	284	14
North Carolina ...	6	123	5	N. C. State	18	295	14
Wake Forest	34	266	14	Duke	21	315	15
South Carolina	19	365	18	Tennessee	0	200	12
Duke	33	362	19	West Virginia	46	496	19
N. C. State	7	126	6	Wake Forest	0	169	7
Maryland	7	194	10	V. P. I.	14	147	5
U. C. L. A.	0	79	8	William and Mary	7	115	8
West Virginia	33	451	19	Clemson	26	351	19
Richmond	12	200	10	Georgia	7	132	10
Notre Dame	17	313	16	Oklahoma	26	412	18
Southern Methodist	0	256	13	Pittsburgh	14	227	15
Clemson	20	275	17	Notre Dame	19	280	16
Virginia	7	113	7	Indiana	0	188	11
Georgia Tech	14	224	15	George Washington	13	158	8
Florida	7	169	9	Virginia	0	169	9
Navy	7	303	11	Navy	26	369	16
William and Mary .	0	122	6	South Carolina ...	0	143	5
Ohio State	28	338	17				
Nebraska	20	327	16				
Army	81	567	18				
Furman	0	160	9				

Source: The *News and Observer*, Raleigh, N.C., September 25 and October 2, 1955.

yardage, and first downs made in 20 early season games in 1955. Specifically, these are all the games for which complete statistics were given by the Raleigh *News and Observer* on September 25 and October 2. It is thus not a random selection, but one that is heavily weighted with games considered important at that time, and with games participated in by Atlantic Coast Conference teams. Teams in odd-numbered rows are winners, while those in even-numbered rows are losers. For example, Oklahoma defeated North Carolina 13–6, while Wake Forest defeated South Carolina 34–19.

The data for yardage and scores are plotted in Chart 2.9. The winning teams are shown by black dots, while the losing teams are shown by hollow circles. The diagonal line is an estimate of the average score that results from any yardage.[3] For example, if a team makes 250 yards, the dotted lines indicate that 15 points would be a reasonable prediction for its score.

---

[3] A method of fitting a straight line to pairs of observations will be explained in Chapter 24.

Several interesting things are shown by the chart. First, football scores are not completely explainable by yardage, for the points do not cluster around the line very closely. Perhaps we could reduce the unexplained variability by considering the effect of other variables also, such as punting yardage, penalties, fumbles, and interceptions. This can be done statistically,

Chart 2.9—Yardage and Scores in 20 Football Games in 1955.

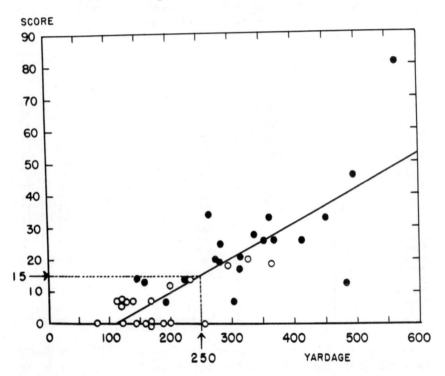

Source of data: Table 2.3.

and the method will be explained in Chapter 35. If you are a student of football, maybe you would like to speculate concerning the relationship between first downs and scores (1) for all teams and (2) for teams making the same yardage. For example, if we should consider teams making approximately 300 yards, would you expect teams with a large number of first downs or with a small number of first downs to have larger scores? Chapter 35 shows how to find the relationship between two variables after making adjustments for a third variable.

Second, the diagonal line indicates that until a team makes over 100 yards it ordinarily does not score, but for each 10 yards over that amount it picks up roughly 1 point. It is not unreasonable to suppose that most teams making a total of 100 yards will not score, for such yardage will ordinarily be dissipated in unproductive first downs. Still, there is no magic in the number 100, and it is ridiculous to assert that teams with zero net yardage will tend to have a total of —11 or —12 points, as indicated by the broken line. A line that is concave upward is more logical, and perhaps such a line, when fitted to these data, would conform better to the dots on the chart.[4] Methods of fitting curved lines to data of this type will also be explained in Chapters 27 and 36.

Third, it is worth noticing that the winners not only make more yardage and have larger scores, but they seem to get larger scores from the same yardage. This may be partly why they win. It would be of interest to fit two lines, one for the winners and one for the losers.

Summary

The underlying idea of statistical analysis is to explain variability. By reducing the unexplained variability we reduce our ignorance, or stated positively, we increase our knowledge. Variability can be explained by these devices:

1. Classification
   a. Qualitative
   b. Temporal
   c. Geographical
2. Correlation

Whether a classification or a correlation is statistically significant depends on the amount of variability that has been explained compared with the residual that is unexplained. If the explained variability is so large in comparison with the unexplained that it is unreasonable to suppose that it occurred accidentally, then we have a statistically significant classification or correlation. When we say that a classification or correlation is significant, we are making the inference that the classification or correlation is valid for the population or universe from which the sample is taken.

Without some consideration of probability we have no basis for deciding whether the results obtained from analyzing a sample are accidental. We must therefore acquire some knowledge of probability before we can understand statistical methodology very well.

---

[4] For some kinds of data, a curve that is concave downward would be more appropriate. Thus "Sugar Ray" Robinson, in an Associated Press release dated May 21, 1956, is reported as saying:

"Although certainly not the fighter I was five years ago, I haven't the least doubt of my ability to go (15 rounds) today."

"The best years of a fighter's life," Robinson conceded, "are between 25 and 30."

"After that you turn the bend, and should be on the downgrade," he said. "But the normal condition does not take in everyone. Each human being is different."

Note that Robinson recognized: (1) central tendency; (2) regressional relationship; (3) nonlinearity; (4) dispersion.

Chapter 3

USES OF STATISTICS IN BUSINESS

Since the material in this book is not organized according to business uses, but according to the nature of the statistical methodology, it is desirable to have a brief summary of business applications.

There are three major functions in any business in which the statistical method is useful:

1. *Planning of operations.* Plans may relate to special projects, or they may relate to the recurring activities of a firm over a specified period of time, such as a year.

2. *Establishment of standards.* Standards may relate to quality standards for manufactured product, standard rates of output per day, or standard operating or financial ratios.

3. *Control.* Control is attained by comparing achievement with plans or standards, and when the former is too far out of line with the latter, taking appropriate action. The amount of discrepancy between actual and desired results that calls for corrective action is, in practice, difficult to determine; but in theory when a discrepancy is too large to be attributed reasonably to chance, one should take cognizance of it. Appropriate action is discovering what is wrong and then correcting the trouble, or in some cases, revising the standards.

Planning, setting standards, and control are separate concepts, but are interwoven in practice. *Budgetary control* includes planning and control, while *quality control* includes standard setting and control.

Plans, standard setting, and control may involve the business as a whole, or mainly one of the major areas of a business:

1. Marketing
2. Production
3. Personnel
4. Finance
5. Accounting

Finally, the statistical method is especially useful in certain types of businesses, such as investment and insurance.

In this chapter we shall indicate how the statistical method is useful in each of these functions, areas, and types of business.

24

Project Planning

There are various types of decisions to be made occasionally or at irregular intervals, perhaps only once during the lifetime of a business. For example, there may be the question of locating a new plant. Things to consider include accessibility to raw materials, transportation facilities, nearness to market, availability of a satisfactory labor supply, wage rates, cost of living, climate, and tax laws. Some of these considerations require statistical information, and a sampling survey may be required. For example, some idea of wage rates and of rental costs may be obtained by interviewing a random sample of persons in the contemplated location.

Another type of project that involves the entire business is the expansion of plant and equipment. It is rather obvious that one must first try to forecast the trend in sales of one's product; otherwise sales orders will not be filled, or there will be idle equipment. Then one should try to forecast the cycles in general business as well as one's own business. Interest rates, construction costs, and the price of equipment are lower during depressions than during periods of prosperity. The economical time to expand plant and durable equipment is usually toward the end of a depression.

One method of forecasting business cycles involves the discovery of some economic time series that moves ahead of the series to be forecasted. When the leading series turns up, the forecast is that the lagging series will turn up after a specified time interval; when the leading series turns down, the forecast is that the lagging series will turn down after a specified time interval. One forecasting agency makes considerable use of data on unfilled orders to forecast productive activity. In this book, Chapter 37 is devoted to forecasting.

Other types of project planning include: introducing a new product; redesigning an old product; invading a new market area; changing selling methods; changing advertising media. Since these are all concerned primarily with marketing, they will be considered in connection with uses of statistics in marketing.

Budgetary Planning and Control

Budgetary planning and control is a device for planning all of the operations of a business and controlling the execution of these plans. Stated briefly, budgetary control comprises:

1. The formulation of a sales program for the budgetary period, which is quite likely to be one year.
2. The establishment, based on this sales program, of:
   a. Inventory requirements during this period.
   b. A manufacturing program.
3. A program of renewals, and perhaps expansion, of plant and equipment; this program is to be based in part upon plans involving a period longer than the budgetary period.

4. An estimate of receipts and expenditures that these plans will involve, and plans for obtaining the funds.
5. An estimate of the income and expense that will result from these plans.
6. The projection one year ahead of an estimated balance sheet and statement of profit and loss.
7. Enforcement of the budget by means of periodic (perhaps monthly) reports comparing actual results with budgetary plans. Any serious divergences should be investigated, their causes determined and, if possible, corrected.
8. Periodic revision of budgetary plans in the light of changing conditions and the divergences noted in the periodic reports.

Before being adopted as a budget, the sales estimate should be considered from various points of view. Perhaps the sales program is unsatisfactory from the production point of view, requiring additional equipment which cannot be provided in time, or perhaps necessitating that some remain idle. Perhaps it will be difficult to finance the program. Or possibly, though the program is expedient from the point of view of the production department and the treasurer, it is not a program that will result in maximum net profits.

The sales and production budgets require a number of subsidiary budgets which are prepared by specialized departments, such as the advertising department, personnel department, purchasing department, and so on. Based on all of these, however, and the objectives of all the budgetary plans, are (1) the financial budget, or an estimate of receipts and expenditures submitted by the treasurer, and (2) the projected financial statement, compiled by the controller.

Budgetary procedure is frequently in direct charge of the controller, although final decisions rest with a budgetary committee composed of the chief executive officers, or even with the board of directors.

Inventory Planning and Control

Inventory management may involve production planning as well as strictly merchandising functions. It is therefore considered under a separate heading here.

Coordinating production, sales, and inventories. If a firm is one which manufactures to stock, a manufacturing schedule can be set up permitting a fairly uniform rate of production, but with fluctuating inventories. In order to do this it is necessary to forecast sales, month by month, for at least 12 months ahead. The measurement of seasonal pattern is not difficult from a statistical viewpoint; the difficult task is to forecast the sales for the next year as a whole.

Maintaining minimum inventories. It may, however, be found more profitable to maintain minimum inventories at all times and to vary the rate of production. Indeed, if the firm is of the special order type, such a procedure is imperative.

Unit stores belonging to one large chain organization can often obtain delivery of canned goods overnight from the nearest warehouse. Therefore it is necessary to keep on hand only one day's stock. But the stock to be kept on hand is not merely an average day's sales, but an amount as large as the maximum sales which can reasonably be expected. If the central organization has kept careful records of sales by type of store, it can estimate the probabilities of selling various quantities during one day. If the probability is only 1 in 500 that more than 12 cans will be sold in one day, it is reasonably safe to reorder only when the stock is down to 12 cans.

Stocking different sizes. Another problem in inventory control is the proper distribution of sizes for such things as hats, suits, shirts, and shoes. Often a season's supply must be ordered in advance, and because of style changes must be disposed of during the current season. If records of past sales are kept it is usually possible to determine with reasonable accuracy the relative number of units of each size to order. This is especially easy if sales conform to some well-known probability distribution, such as the normal distribution. In Chapter 19 the method of fitting a normal curve is described.

Quality Control

Statistical control of quality is used in industry for three purposes:

1. To establish standards of quality for manufactured product;
2. To control the manufacturing process so that the standard of quality is maintained;
3. To give assurance that individual lots sold or purchased are of acceptable quality.

Thus, although quality control is concerned partly with production, it is concerned also with marketing (buying and selling).

Establishment of quality standards. Quality standards are initially embodied in engineering specifications. These usually state a desired quality, together with upper and lower specification limits. Thus a diameter may be specified as 5 mm $\pm$ 0.01 mm. The upper specification limit is then 5.01 mm and the lower specification limit is 4.99 mm. It is wishful thinking to expect that *all* the items will be within these limits; but it is hoped that nearly all of them will be. One of the functions of quality control is to determine statistically whether the manufacturing process is such that these specifications can be met. If it can be shown that (say) 10 per cent of the product will be defective (because it fails to come within the specification limits), either the manufacturing process should be improved or the specifications relaxed. But if the manufacturing process is capable of meeting specification limits for 999,999 out of 1,000,000 units, possibly the specification limits should be narrowed. On the other hand, perhaps the manufacturing process is too good, i.e., too costly.

Control of manufacturing process. This topic has already been discussed somewhat in Chapter 2 (pp. 14–16), and will be considered again in Chapter 20; so the discussion here is brief.

The statistical tool that is used in controlling the manufacturing process is the control chart. See Chart 2.4. A control chart typically has a central line around which the plotted points fluctuate in accordance with the laws of chance, and control limits inside of which nearly all the points are found when the process is in control. Small samples are taken at frequent intervals (say one hour) and the results plotted on the control chart. A point outside of a control limit is an indication of trouble. The control limits are established statistically with the use of probability theory. Usually there are two control charts, a control chart for means and a control chart for ranges. (The reader should recall that the mean is the sum of the values divided by the number of values, while the range is the difference between the largest value and the smallest value.) The purpose of the control chart for means is to control the average level of quality; the purpose of the control chart for ranges is to control the uniformity of the quality. For example, the control chart for means may be designed to insure that all items produced maintain an *average* diameter of 5 mm from hour to hour; the control chart for ranges is designed to insure that the different items produced are sufficiently *uniform* with respect to diameter, and to insure that the amount of variability does not change significantly from hour to hour. When either a mean or a range goes outside of its control limit, search for the cause of the apparent trouble is immediately undertaken, and if found it is corrected.

Lot acceptance sampling. A relatively small sample is taken from a lot of specified size. If the number of defectives in the sample is smaller than a number known as the *acceptance number*, the lot is accepted; if the number of defectives in the sample is larger than a number known as the *rejection number*, the lot is rejected. The acceptance and rejection numbers are established on the basis of probability.

If the rejection number is one larger than the acceptance number we have *single sampling*; for a lot must be accepted or rejected on the basis of a single sample. If the difference between the rejection number and the acceptance number is greater than one, the results of the first sample may be inconclusive and one or more additional samples may be required. Thus we may have *double sampling* or *multiple sampling*. In multiple sampling the individual samples are rather small, and we don't know in advance how many samples we will need. An advantage of multiple sampling is that the average amount of inspection required is usually small. If the lot is either very good or very bad it will usually be accepted or rejected before many samples are taken.

Sampling plans are usually designed to accomplish two or more of the following objectives:

1. Protect the consumer against accepting too many bad lots.
2. Protect the producer against having too many good lots rejected.
3. Give assurance that in the long run the proportion of defective items retained by the consumer from all lots will not be too large.
4. Minimize the average amount of inspection.

Marketing

Statistical methods are used in marketing for the following general purposes:

Sales analysis. By sales analysis is meant the study of sales records, properly classified. With the aid of sales analysis, results of sales campaigns can be evaluated, areas discovered where special attention is needed, and plans for the future formulated.

Market analysis. By market analysis is meant analysis of different markets and market areas in order to estimate potential sales.

Marketing analysis. By marketing analysis, marketing methods are studied, and results of different marketing methods analyzed.

In this section, discussion will be organized around specific problems, frequently cutting across these three categories.

Preparing sales budget. Since all other departmentai budgets depend on the sales budget, the first step in the preparation of a budget is usually the sales estimate. Methods of preparing the sales estimate vary. As a beginning, many concerns require estimates from salesmen or branch managers. It is believed that since they are in direct contact with the market, they are in a position to make practical estimates of sales possibilities in their respective territories. It is also believed that these salesmen will feel their responsibility for carrying out plans for the formulation of which they themselves are partly responsible. To assist them in making estimates, they should be provided with a record of their past sales for several periods, their past sales estimates, and their sales quotas as finally adopted. These data should be classified and sub-classified in reasonable detail, by commodities, terms of sale, types of customer, and so on. To be most useful, this information, as well as the estimates to be submitted, should be in terms of physical units rather than dollars. Each salesman should likewise be apprised of changes in policy that affect him, such as new lines to be added or old lines to be dropped, price changes, advertising campaigns to be undertaken, and the like.

Some concerns prefer to conduct market analyses by means of special investigators who survey sales territories and report on sales possibilities. Still another approach is to correlate industry sales and/or company sales by products with the measurable characteristics of different regions.[1]   Such characteristics may be size of population, race, age, education, degree of urbanization, average income, and climate.   Sometimes a formula can be developed that will account for the bulk of the sales in the different regions. Departures from the general pattern call for special consideration;   in particular, if sales are unusually low in some region, perhaps the sales quota for that region should be increased, and also special selling efforts concentrated there.   In any event, it will be necessary for the sales manager to change most of the estimates submitted by individual salesmen before adopting them as quotas, since some salesmen are chronically optimistic, while others are of the opposite psychological make-up.

Further modification of estimates may be made in the light of sales analysis: an examination of changes in sales classified by commodities, geographically, by terms of sale, and so on, will reveal certain important tendencies.   Merely to resolve, arbitrarily, to increase sales by a certain per cent in the ensuing year is totally inadequate.   An analysis of the trend of the different categories, modified by an estimate of cyclical changes and allowing for the effect of advertising campaigns, is a much more reliable indication of what can be expected.   The estimate of cyclical changes is of course a difficult task.

Investigating consumer preferences. From time to time a new product may be put on the market, or the specifications of an old one changed. Designing a product is partly an engineering problem;   but consumer preferences should be considered as well as cost of production. To determine consumer preferences may necessitate a sampling survey. Questionnaires or schedules must be prepared, information obtained from a cross section of prospective customers must be recorded on these schedules, and the schedules tabulated and analyzed. Chapter 10 is devoted to collection of data, while survey sampling is treated in Chapter 13.

Estimating potential market for a new product. Not only must consumer preferences be considered when introducing a new product, but the potential market must also be considered. This may involve a consumer survey in which various questions are asked that throw light on needs of consumers for a product of the type contemplated, and their plans for buying products of that general type.

Pricing a product. It is always advisable to consider the effect on sales of different prices for a product. This is especially important if a product is being redesigned in such a way as to affect cost of production. Determining a demand curve is always difficult, and is likely to require statistical methods of an intricate character.

Estimating potential market in a new region. If it is found that sales of a product vary from region to region in accordance with certain measurable

---

[1] Chapters 24–27 and 35–37 are devoted entirely or in part to correlation analysis.

characteristics, a reasonable value for total industry sales of the product in the contemplated region can be made. Of course this does not determine the sales of a particular company; among other things to consider is the strength of the competition.

Appraising effectiveness of alternative advertising media. A change in advertising methods may be under consideration. Often it is worthwhile to find out which magazine has the largest circulation among the type of people who buy your product. Or one may try to ascertain the types of television programs that have the greatest appeal to one's customers.

Testing effectiveness of different advertising or selling methods. Sometimes it is possible to use different methods in different regions, and compare the results. If different methods are used simultaneously in all areas it still may be possible to ascertain the origin of the different sales.

Production

Perhaps the most important use of statistics in production is quality control. This topic has already been treated briefly, and will require further consideration in later chapters.

Testing new methods or new products. Sometimes the question arises whether a new method or a new product should be substituted for the old method or product. Only if the new method or product is significantly different from the old should one seriously consider making the change. A difference need not be large in absolute magnitude to be considered significant; it needs to be large only in comparison with the variability that is attributable to chance. Testing the significance of a difference is done statistically.

Time study. Time studies are frequently made for various operations in order to establish a standard time for the accomplishment of a task, or a standard day's work load. Wage rates are often established in such a way that the volume of work done affects the amount of pay. A time study, statistically, is a problem in averaging the lengths of time taken in several trials for a given operation. The reliability of the average should also be considered.

Planning replacement of physical equipment. If a large number of units of equipment of a given kind are installed they will not all wear out at the same time. Though the bulk of them will have a span not greatly different from the average length of life, a few will have to be replaced rather soon, while a few will last for a long time. If proper records have been kept, a mortality table can be constructed indicating the proportion that can be expected to wear out each year. Thus purchases of new equipment can be estimated several years in advance. This is especially useful information for those who must plan the financing of equipment.

Personnel Administration

Personnel tests. Perhaps the most important use of statistics in personnel work is personnel tests. Before an employee is hired he is sometimes subjected to various tests to determine his interest, aptitude, or other qualifications. These tests must be developed statistically, to determine how *reliable* and how *valid* they are. One aspect of reliability pertains to whether the different items (usually questions) tend to test the same characteristic. If not sufficiently reliable, the test may be subjected to "item analysis" to determine which are the bad items. If a test is reliable, it must still be determined whether it is valid, that is, whether it tests the quality that is under consideration. Its validity is ascertained by correlating the test scores of a number of employees with some criterion of their usefulness to the firm.

Wage contracts. Often a contract with a labor union calls for automatic adjustment of wage rates, during the period between contract dates, on the basis of changes in retail prices. If prices go up wage rates are adjusted upwards by approximately the same percentage, while if prices go down wages are adjusted downward. Changes in prices are measured by a statistical device known as a *price index*. The one generally used is the Consumer's Price Index, often referred to as the C.P.I., constructed by the Bureau of Labor Statistics of the U.S. Department of Labor. The making of index numbers is discussed in Chapters 32 and 33.

Finance

Analysis ratios. Much can be learned about the financial condition and operating efficiency of a concern by studying ratios derived from accounting and other data. For example, the ratio of current assets to current liabilities is considered important by bankers. Of equal importance to management is the ratio of sales to average inventories.[2]

In order to determine a satisfactory ratio for merchandise turnover (for example), it is desirable to consider the merchandise turnovers of other firms of similar size and type. If these ratios are formed into a frequency distribution one can see what is a typical ratio, how much variability there is among different organizations in this respect, and how one's firm compares with the others.

Forecasting. Perhaps no one is as concerned with forecasting as the financial officer of the firm. He must not only borrow money from banks for current needs, but he must also plan the financing of additions and betterments. He is interested in timing these improvements so that they will not be too expensive, and can be utilized to good advantage when acquired. But he would also prefer to arrange for new financing to take place at a time when securities can be marketed easily. Finally, he must decide between bonds of different maturity dates. To do all of these things to best advantage he must be able to foresee the future.

---

[2] This ratio could reasonably be considered under the heading of marketing, also.

Accounting

Accounting records are kept for two purposes:

1. For reports to stockholders, banks, tax collectors, and others not actively participating in management.
2. For reports to company officials to aid them in management.

For the first purpose not much use is made of statistical methods; the procedures used are either conventional, usually prepared in such a way that fluctuations in book profits are minimized, or they are prescribed by law. It should be recognized, however, that although accounts are made to balance to the last penny, no such accuracy should be attached to them. Nor is such accuracy required for purposes of management. One prominent accountant has stated that it is doubtful whether any figure beyond the second digit has ever influenced a business decision.

For internal management several uses of statistics should be mentioned, most of which have to do with asset evaluation.

Auditing. Audits can be made more frequently if they are on a sampling basis. For example, if a company has 20,000 customers with charge accounts, a representative sample can be taken of (say) 1,000 customers. A comparison of the accounts of these customers with amounts verified by correspondence with customers will enable one to make an inference concerning the accuracy of the other 19,000 accounts.

Evaluation of accounts receivable. A study of the relationship between the length of time that accounts are delinquent and the per cent that are eventually collected provides some basis for deciding the probability of collecting each account, and consequently how large a net amount to carry on the books as accounts receivable.

Reserves for depreciation. Where several pieces of similar equipment are used, it is useful to determine average or normal values for:

1. Physical productivity during each year of life.
2. Cost of maintenance during each year of life.
3. Length of life.

It is usually found that physical productivity declines with age, while cost of maintenance increases, so that *net* productivity declines more rapidly than *gross* productivity. It is therefore good accounting practice to charge a relatively large amount for depreciation the first year, with progressively smaller amounts thereafter, in such a way that the entire value of the asset (cost minus salvage value) will be charged off by the time the average useful length of life has elapsed.

Adjustment for price change. If a reserve for depreciation is set up in such a way that the accumulated amount will equal the original cost of the asset when the property is worn out, and if prices go up, then the reserve will permit replacement of the asset by one that costs the same, but which is less productive. Therefore it is considered desirable by some accountants to adjust for changes in the price level the amount set up as reserve for depreciation each year. This will prevent paying out, as dividends, funds that are needed to maintain intact the real purchasing power of the company.[3]

Similar adjustments for changes in the price level should be made for inventory, and for materials used in manufacturing. These adjustments are

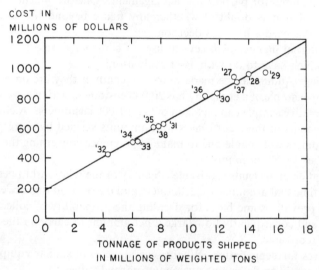

Chart 3.1—Relationship Between Total Cost of Operation
and Volume of Business, 1938 Conditions, United
States Steel Corporation and Subsidiaries
(Total costs adjusted to 1938 interest, tax, pension, and
wage rates; to 1938 price levels; and to 1938 efficiency.)

Source of data: United States Steel Corporation, *T.N.E.C. Papers,* Vol. 1, 1940, p. 253.

made by means of a price index. The effect of such adjustments is to reduce net income when prices are rising and increase it when prices are falling.

Relationship of cost to volume of production. It is well recognized that, up to a certain point, total cost of production increases less than proportionately to the volume of production. Historical data can be used to estimate statistically the relationship between the two variables. In order to make such estimates applicable to current use it is necessary, among other things, to adjust for the effect of two factors:

1. The trend of costs per unit of output.
2. The effect of price changes on costs.

―――――――

[3] Price adjustments do not affect current income, but are adjustments to surplus.

A well-known study along this line was made by the U.S. Steel Corporation, covering the years 1927–1938. The results are shown in Chart 3.1. Notice that the points are very close to the line, and therefore nearly all of the variability in costs is accounted for by volume of output.

One use for such information is the construction of a *break-even* chart, such as Chart 3.2. The solid line on this chart is the same as that of Chart

**Chart 3.2—Relationship of Sales and Total Costs to Volume of
Business, 1938 Conditions, United States Steel Corporation
and Subsidiaries**
(Break-Even Chart.)

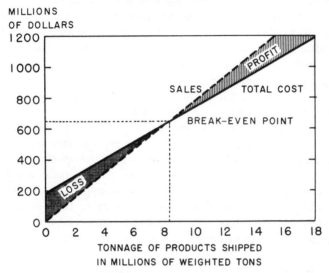

Source of data: See Chart 3.1.

3.1. The sales line is obtained by multiplying the tonnage figures by $77.64, the average selling price per ton.[4] The chart shows that when production (and sales) is 8.31 million tons, costs and sales are $645 million, and the company breaks even; smaller sales result in a loss, and larger sales result in a profit. Frequently break-even charts show not only total cost, but types of cost as well.

Investment Management

The successful management of investments requires many decisions aided by the use of statistical analysis.

It can be shown that historically an investor would usually have done well over a 20-year period if he had always kept a fixed proportion (say 2/3) of the value of his portfolio in corporation stocks, and the rest in United States

---

[4] In the absence of increased demand, an increase in sales can be brought about by lower prices per ton. In that case a given tonnage increase will not be accompanied by a proportionate increase in dollar sales.

Government bonds, selecting his stocks at random from the stocks listed on the New York Stock Exchange. Nevertheless he could have done still better if he had increased his proportion of bonds at the beginning of each cyclical downswing, and increased his proportion of stocks at the beginning of each cyclical upswing. To do this requires the forecasting of business cycles, which we have said before is not easy.

Also, instead of selecting stocks at random, it is obviously better to invest rather heavily in industries that are on the upgrade. To do this requires a greater knowledge of economics than of statistics.

Within each industry, successful investment management requires the selection of companies that are destined to be more successful than the average for the industry, and especially companies whose stocks are under-priced on the market. Although decisions concerning individual companies cannot be made mechanically, it is of some use to correlate stocks prices with past and present earnings and dividends. Stocks that are out of line are at least worth investigating.

Finally, one should not put all of his eggs in one basket, but should diversify not only as between stocks and bonds, but as between industries and companies within an industry. This principle contradicts the one we stated previously, that one should select the type of security, the industry, and the company that will be most profitable for the investor. Prudent and successful investment requires a compromise between these two principles. The principle of diversification is difficult to apply for another reason. Most stocks follow a somewhat similar pattern in their cyclical swings. Nevertheless there are some differences in amplitude and timing, and therefore some advantage to be obtained from diversification.

Insurance

All forms of insurance depend on statistics to determine the premiums that must be charged for policies. In life insurance this has been reduced to a science, requiring years of study for its mastery. Specialists in this field are known as actuaries. Actuaries must understand frequency distributions, and be well qualified in probability theory and various branches of mathematics, including of course compound interest theory.

Summary

There are many factors affecting business decisions that are not subject to counting or measurement. Frequently, also, the factors are so numerous and the relationships so complicated that they cannot easily be reduced to a formula. Consequently business decisions must depend to a considerable extent on judgment, aided by whatever information statistics can provide. The relative importance of judgment and statistics in decision making depends on the complexity of the problem and the extent to which probability theory is applicable.

There are some fields, however, where statistics can replace judgment. For example, the decision as to whether a lot of unknown origin and unknown fraction defective should be accepted (on the hypothesis that it is of good quality) or rejected (on the hypothesis that it is of bad quality) is better left to an acceptance sampling plan based on probability theory rather than to the judgment of the Chairman of the Board concerning the quality of the lot. Determination of life insurance premiums is another field where judgment is of minor importance.

Chapter 4

MISUSES OF STATISTICS

"Many speakers have the habit of saying, 'I know that you can prove anything with statistics but here are some figures that I want to give you' and then proceed to read off a long list to the edification or mystification of their hearers. To the experienced and competent statistician such a statement indicates a complete misapprehension of the function of statistics. It would be much nearer the truth to say that nothing can be proved with statistics, and that only the unwary are ever deceived into thinking that an array of figures in and of themselves constitute a sufficient and complete answer to any vital problem."[1]

It has also been said that some persons "lean on statistics like a drunk person on a lamp post, for support rather than illumination." More brutal sayings are "figures don't lie but liars figure," and "there are lies, damn lies, and statistics." The writer is more favorably disposed toward the sentiment expressed by Roger Babson who, upon obtaining a preponderance of reponses that were unfavorable to his political convictions, is reported to have said: "I hate to admit the above; but unfortunately I am a statistician and must tell the truth!"

In this chapter we shall indicate ways in which doubtful conclusions sometimes result from the misuse of statistics.

Defective Data

Inaccurate data. It must be remembered that numerical data, no matter how neatly printed, originate in measurements, records, or statements reported by some individual. If the original data are rough guesses, or worse, it is hard to see how valid conclusions can be refined out of them.

Vague definitions. It seems reasonable that before trying to measure something one should know what he is trying to measure. Put another way, the concept should determine the measurements rather than vice versa. This philosophy is not always adopted (even by statisticians), however.

In Chapter 3 we had occasion to mention that wage rates are sometimes adjusted on the basis of changes in the price level. But the exact meaning of the term "price level" is difficult to state. Consequently we cannot be sure that the wage rates have been adjusted properly. This is recognized by interested parties, and sometimes results in heated arguments concerning the

---

[1] H. H. Chapman, "The Business Man and Statistics," *University of Alabama Business News*, Vol. XVII, December, 1946, p. 1.

correct method of constructing index numbers with which to measure changes in the price level.

Unrepresentative Sample

There may be two sources of unrepresentativeness in a sample. In the first place, the sample may have been selected by a method that fails to give a good cross section. In the second place, the method of collection may have been such that certain classes fail to respond in proper proportion. Surveys of incomes of college graduates generally have an upward bias, for the financially unsuccessful are loath to divulge their incomes.

A study that caused considerable furor at the time it was published is Dr. Alfred C. Kinsey's, *Sexual Behavior in the Human Female*.[2] One criticism was that the sample was only 5,940, which was less than one hundredth of one per cent of the female population. The percentage of the population that is included in the sample is of minor importance, however, and considerable confidence can be attached to inferences drawn from samples as small as 5,940, provided the sample is a good cross section of the population. A religious leader pointed out that the 59 per cent of the American people who are church members were inadequately represented. Because these and other presumably conservative classes were under-represented, it is difficult to know how to interpret Dr. Kinsey's findings.

Unfair Comparisons

Statistics has been referred to as the "art of making comparisons"; and this is, to be sure, one of the things that the statistical method seeks to accomplish.

Making absolute instead of relative comparison. *Railroad Data*, a publication of the Eastern Railroad Presidents Conference, in its October 18, 1946 issue, quotes the Cleveland Press as follows: "You are much safer riding on the railroad than staying at home, thanks to the constant accident-prevention campaigns carried on by the nation's transportation lines. In fact, there were but 245 fatalities on the railroads of the country in one year as compared with 32,000 home fatalities." Obviously no fair comparison can be made between the number of accidents in the home and on railroads, for the reason that most of us spend more time at home than we do traveling on a railroad. If a comparison is to be made, it should be based on fatal accidents per man-hour at home and on the train.

Failure to classify data. The apparently fallacious conclusion drawn in the preceding illustration may have arisen partly also out of incomplete classification of data. An examination of fatal accident rates of persons classified by sex and age groups might lead to a further modification of conclusions.

---

[2] W. B. Saunders Company, Philadelphia, 1953.

There is a popular impression that the cost of living is higher in the North than in the South. This impression is apparently borne out by figures published[3] by the United States Bureau of Labor Statistics showing (among other things) family food costs in 34 large cities of the United States in June, 1947. If these cities are classified into 2 geographical groups, 22 Northern cities and 12 Southern cities (those in the South Atlantic, East South Central, and West South Central Divisions), and the simple arithmetic average computed for each region, we find that the average food price for the Northern cities is $1,048 per year and for the Southern cities, $1,044. More spectacular is the fact that the 8 cities with largest food cost are all Northern cities. The average food cost of these 8 cities is $1,071 as compared with $1,039 for the other 26. However, the 8 high-cost cities include New York, Philadelphia, and Detroit, all large cities. The average size of the 8 high-cost cities is 1,622 thousand, as compared with 570 thousand for the 26 low-cost cities.

Apparently food cost is correlated with size of city, the larger the city the higher is the cost of food. This is further borne out when we note that the average population of the 22 Northern cities is 1,085 thousand, while the average population of the 12 Southern cities is 329 thousand. Examining the data further, we notice that there are 5 Northern cities, but no Southern cities, with population over 900 thousand. If we compare the average family food cost of cities with less than 900 thousand population, we find that it is $1,043 for the 17 Northern cities, and $1,044 for the 12 Southern cities.

These results are not conclusive. The difference is so small that it is of doubtful significance. Also, it would be interesting to classify the cities according to population into smaller size groups, such as: under 200,000; 200,000–399,999; 400,000–599,999; and so forth. If the cost of food were greater in the South than in the North for each such group, we could have considerable confidence that there were geographical factors adversely affecting the South. It would be a still better procedure to adjust the family food cost figures for the effect of city size. The procedure for doing this is too complicated for illustration in this introductory chapter.

Failure to allow for changes in composition. It would be unfair to compare the death rates from heart disease for two states when the average age of the people in the two states is greatly different. Therefore death rates are often standardized for age distribution. Thus, the death rate is that which would have been obtained if the age distribution were taken as that of some "standard" population.

Consider next the data at top of page 41 for sales of a commodity of two different grades.

---

[3] *City Worker's Family Budget, 34 Cities of the United States, Spring 1946 (and) Summer 1947*, United States Department of Labor, Bureau of Labor Statistics, Washington, D.C., December, 1947, p. 45.

Grade [1]	1955				1956		
	Price per unit [2]	Number of units [3]	[2] × [3] [4]		Price per unit [5]	Number of units [6]	[5] × [6] [7]
A	$50	5	$250		$60	3	$180
B	10	3	30		15	5	75
Total	...	8	$280		...	8	$255
Average price	280 ÷ 8 = $35				255 ÷ 8 = $32		

Although the price of each grade increased between 1955 and 1956, the average price per unit declined. The paradox is explained by the fact that the composition of the sales changed; in 1955 the expensive grade was the big seller, while in 1956 more was sold of the cheaper grade. If we had used the same quantities each year in computing the averages, we would have obtained a larger average price in 1956 than 1955.

In July, 1947, a new labor contract was signed in the bituminous coal industry. The old contract called for $11.85 for a *nine-hour* day, time and one-half pay being allowed for hours in excess of seven hours in one day. (This means that the miners received $1.18½ per hour for the first seven hours, but $1.78 per hour thereafter.) By the new contract the underground basic pay was raised to $13.05 for an *eight-hour* day, with overtime at time and one-half pay for hours in excess of eight hours in one day. (This means that the miners received $1.63 per hour for the first eight hours, but $2.45 per hour thereafter.)

These facts were brought out by Irving G. Olds, Chairman of the Board of Directors of the United States Steel Corporation, in a release dated July 17, 1947. His conclusion was:

The increase in actual wages received by miners under the new contract is 15 cents an hour, or $1.20 for an eight-hour underground day (portal to portal).

I should like to place emphasis on this actual increase in the miners' "take-home pay," as erroneous reports have appeared to the effect that this increase amounts to 44½ cents an hour.

At the time, the United States Steel Corporation was being criticised by some for its part in granting such a large increase in pay, and the communication was partly in answer to these criticisms. The figure of 44½ cents is obtained by subtracting $1.18½ from $1.63. On the other hand, $13.05 — $11.85 = $1.20, and $1.20 ÷ 8 = 15 cents. But this is an unfair comparison because $13.05 is the pay for working eight hours while 11.85 was the pay for working nine hours. It seems elementary that we must hold the number of hours per day constant in making any comparison. Otherwise we will fail to distinguish between the effect of a change in pay and the effect of a change in hours worked.

Neither 15 cents nor $44\frac{1}{2}$ cents is the correct statement for the hourly increase. It depends on how many hours per day the miners actually work. Consider the following computations.

Hours	Old contract	New contract	Difference
7	$1.185	$1.63	$0.445
8	$\dfrac{7(1.185) + 1.78}{8} = 1.26$	$1.63	.37
9	$\dfrac{7(1.185) + 2(1.178)}{9} = 1.32$	$\dfrac{8(1.63) + 2.45}{9} = 1.72$	.40

The problem becomes more complicated if the actual number of hours worked was different in the two periods (before and after signing the contract).

Use of misleading base. One of the fears of persons with fixed incomes is that of inflation. It was easy to be lulled into a false sense of security during the years following 1950 by making such comparisons as the following. "Between 1952 and 1956 consumer prices rose only about 2 per cent." This is a true statement, for the Consumer Price Index was 113.5 in 1952 and 116.2 in 1956. However, if we compare 1956 with the pre-Korean War base of 1950 we find the price increase is 13 per cent, for $116.2 \div 102.8 = 113.0$ per cent. The price increase between 1952 and 1956 was smaller than for any other four-year period since 1939.

The sales of Sears, Roebuck and Company were 424.2 million dollars in December 1955 and 276.0 million dollars in July 1956, a decline of 35 per cent. December is not a good month to use as a base, however, for Christmas sales always result in December sales being high, and July sales are generally the low for the year. A better comparison is made by comparing July 1956 with July 1955. Thus

$$\frac{\text{July 1956 sales}}{\text{July 1955 sales}} = \frac{276.0}{273.2} = 101.0.$$

The increase is 1 per cent. If, however, one wishes to compare July 1956 with December 1955, he should adjust the sales of each month for seasonal variation. It is shown in Chapter 30 that the "seasonal index number" for December 1955 is 147.0 per cent while that for July 1955 is 91.0 per cent. The proper procedure for adjustment is

$$\frac{\text{July 1956 sales}}{\text{July 1956 seasonal index number}} = \frac{276.0}{0.910} = 303.3;$$

$$\frac{\text{December 1955 sales}}{\text{December 1955 seasonal index number}} = \frac{424.2}{1.470} = 288.6.$$

It appears then that, after adjustment for seasonal variation, the best comparison is

$$\frac{\text{July 1956 adjusted sales}}{\text{December 1955 adjusted sales}} = \frac{303.3}{288.6} = 105.1.$$

The improvement during the seven-month interval is 5 per cent.

Unwarranted Conclusions

Conclusions based on false assumptions. In statistical reasoning, as in all other methods of reasoning, assumptions are involved. In the familiar syllogism,

All men are mortal;
Socrates is a man;
Therefore, Socrates is mortal;

the major premise is an assumption. In statistical reasoning there are usually two assumptions:

1. The population is "normal" (or has some other specified form).
2. The sample is a random one (or was taken in some other specified manner).

If either of these assumptions is untrue, the conclusions are vitiated to some extent. If the assumptions are approximately true, one can have considerable confidence in the conclusions. This is because statistics uses probabilistic, rather than deterministic, reasoning.[4] In deterministic reasoning false assumptions lead to false conclusions. Bertrand Russell is alleged to have "proved" that he was the Pope, it being assumed that $2 + 2 = 5$, in this manner: "You admit $2 + 2 = 5$; but I can prove $2 + 2 = 4$; therefore $5 = 4$. Taking two away from both sides; we have $3 = 2$; taking one more, $2 = 1$. But you will admit that I and the Pope are two. Therefore, I and the Pope are one, *Q.E.D.*" (The quotation is from Garrett Birkhoff, *Lattice Theory*, Revised Edition, American Mathematical Society, New York, 1948, p. 194, footnote 10.)

Use of wrong average. Suppose a fraternal order consists of 29 members whose income is not greater than $500 per month, and one member whose income is $50,000 per month. The mean income could be nearly $\frac{29(500) + 50,000}{30} = \$2,150$ per month. Knowing only the mean income, a Cadillac salesman might think that the fraternal order was a fertile field

---

[4] Some of the theoretical work in statistics has to do with determining the quantitative effect of departures of the data from the customary assumption. A test of significance that is not much affected by the departure of the data from normal form is said to be a "robust" test.

for his sales efforts. Actually he would be unlikely to sell more than one car.
If he had known that the median income was less than $500 per month his
enthusiasm would have been dampened.

Confusion of Correlation and Causation

The Charlotte Observer, in its April 5, 1947 issue, argues as follows:
"That the educational level determines the prosperity of the community is
unquestionable. In North Carolina, where we spend only $68.91 a year on
each school child, our average income is $732.00 a year. In California, where
they spend $163.38 on a pupil, the per capita income is $1,480.00, and in
New York, where $194.47 is spent on each pupil, the income is $1,595.00, or
more than twice the income level of North Carolina." While there is good
reason for supposing that education is a good long-run investment, one
could also argue plausibly that the reason more is spent on education in
New York than in North Carolina is because the income is higher in the
former state. One might even argue that there is some other (perhaps
unknown) cause at work that results in concomitant variation in the two
series, income and expenditure for education.

Inadequate Sample

Inferences concerning a population based on the evidence afforded by a
sample are not very reliable unless the sample is large enough and is properly
selected. In Chapter 1 it was pointed out that the reliability of the arithmetic
mean of a random sample varies with the square root of the number of items
included in the sample. Thus, of two random samples selected from the
same population, a sample of 1,600 items will yield an arithmetic mean twice
as reliable as a sample of 400 items.

The importance of an adequate representative sample is often recognized
even by those who are not statistically trained. In some parts of the country
an individual who proposes to purchase a stationery store spends a week in
the store with the present owner before the sale is finally consummated, in
order to make certain that the amount of business is as claimed by the owner.
The prospective purchaser does not base his observation on a single day,
but on seven days, which will reveal to him the intra-week fluctuations of
the business.

According to E. L. Grant,[5] a common sampling acceptance procedure in
quality control "calls for inspecting 5 articles from each lot of 50 articles.
If every article in this 10% sample conforms to specifications, the lot is
accepted. If one or more defective articles are found in the sample of 5, the
lot is rejected."

It is obvious that even though there are no defectives among the 5 articles
that comprise the sample there could be several defectives among the other

[5] *Statistical Quality Control*, 2nd ed., McGraw-Hill Book Co., Inc., New York, 1952,
p. 35.

45 articles in the lot. Grant's computations indicate that if the manufacturing process produces 4 per cent defective articles, the proportion of defective articles in accepted lots should average 3.6 per cent as compared with 5.75 per cent in rejected lots. The sampling plan thus accomplishes very little, in spite of the fact that 18.5 per cent of all lots submitted for inspection tend to be rejected (if the process average is 4 per cent).

Chart 4.1—Employment in a Group of Counties in 1930, 1940, and 1950, and Trend of Employment Projected through 1970

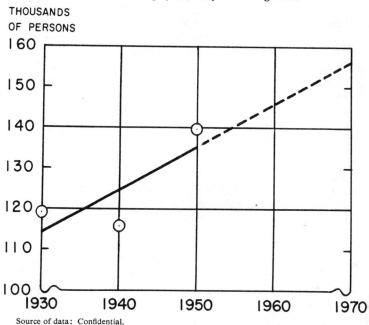

THOUSANDS
OF PERSONS

Source of data: Confidential.

As Grant points out, a sample of 5 articles is far too small for deciding whether to accept or reject a lot, when the only information available is whether an article is good or defective. Better protection against accepting defective articles would be given if both the lot size and the sample size were increased several-fold. If the lot were very large, a sample of less than 10 per cent could be used and several defective articles could be allowed in a sample without rejecting the lot. Actually it doesn't make much difference whether a sample is 5 per cent or 10 per cent of the population. The actual number of items is usually the important thing.

The director of a business research project sponsored by a state government found it desirable to forecast total employment in 1970 for a group of counties. Data were available for 1930, 1940, and 1950. A trend was fitted to these data by a conventional method (the method of least squares) and extended through 1970. The results are shown in Chart 4.1. There are three objections to this procedure. (1) A trend fitted to only three observations is very unreliable. (2) The extension of a trend beyond the range of the data becomes increasingly hazardous the farther it is extended. In this case it was extended two time periods on the basis of data for three time periods. (3) It is perhaps unreasonable to assume that the factors governing employment in 1970 will be an extension of those factors developing during the period 1930–1950. New factors may appear that will change the trend.

The ultimate in inadequate data is perhaps contained in the following editorial from the Raleigh *News and Observer* of September 14, 1955.

Travel statistics are wonderful things all the time but *The New Yorker* properly classified under its "Higher Mathematics Department" the item from *Travel Trends*, published by the American Automobile Association, as follows:

" 'The Cape Hatteras Region, developed as America's first national seashore park, was visited by 306,238 persons, three times the attendance for the full year of 1954, when no attendance figures were kept.'

"Upward and Onward!"

Misunderstanding of the Law of Large Numbers

In Chapter 1 it was pointed out that the larger the sample is the less a sample mean tends to deviate from the population mean. To some people this suggests that if a run of luck in one direction occurs, it is quite likely to be offset by a counterbalancing run of luck in the opposite direction. Consider, for example, this news article by Larry Hirsch, published in the *Greensboro Daily News*, December 28, 1947.

If there are any local married folks hankering for little girl babies, they had better arrange to have them New Year Day. According to maternity nurses of Greensboro hospitals, it's likely to be a most propitious day for becoming parents of the sugar-and-spice offspring.

The nurses base their prognostication on what happened in the maternity wards Christmas Day. It was snakes, snails, and puppy-dog tails by a score of 4 to 1. Specifically, Piedmont Memorial Hospital had three baby boys, Wesley Long Hospital one baby boy, and Sternberger Hospital one baby girl. St. Leo's Hospital wasn't even in the running either way.

Now, according to the nurses, who are supposed to know about such things, the birth business works by opposites. If baby boys outstripped baby girls by 4 to 1 on Christmas, the baby girls should come back by the same score, and maybe even better, on the next holiday, which of course, is New Year.

The law of large numbers states that the sample mean tends to be closer and closer to the population mean as the sample size increases. It does not guarantee that the sample mean will be exactly equal to the population mean if the sample size is increased sufficiently.[6]

---

[6] A more precise statement of the law of large numbers is provided by the central limit theorem (see Chapter 19).

Putting the Cart Before the Horse

Although statistical reasoning often involves testing a hypothesis, it should not involve proving an opinion. A scientist should always attack a problem with an open, though not vacant mind, and should not twist the facts to fit his fancy. Sometimes one does this through mistake; in other cases it is done unconsciously; in a few cases it is done deliberately.

Selection of data. One must have a poor case, indeed, if there is no evidence to support it. Although a lawyer or a politician may be justified in withholding evidence unfavorable to his cause, a statistician is a scientist and must therefore consider all of the relevant data before coming to a conclusion. Data should be discarded only when it can be shown, beyond reasonable doubt, to be unrepresentative.

Suppression of unfavorable results. It is unusual, though not unknown, for a statistician to analyze his data and then divulge only those results that are in accord with his preconceptions.

Mistakes in Arithmetic

Sometimes results of investigations are announced that can be explained only by arithmetic errors. Here is a trivial, third hand account of such a result. *Time* magazine, September 28, 1953, quotes the London *Observer* as quoting a Finnish magazine as follows: "Thousands are getting married. Statistics show that 64,462 persons were married in Finland during 1952. Of these, 32,230 were women."

On the same interesting topic (marriage) the Chicago *Tribune* is said to have reported: "In Urbana there are three boys to every girl, and one out of every three Illinois men marries an Illinois co-ed." The obvious conclusion is that every Illinois co-ed marries an Illinois man. It would seem that either the data are wrong or the arithmetic is wrong.

Summary

Erroneous conclusions are the result of false assumptions, faulty information, or faulty reasoning. Faulty reasoning may result from ignorance of the rules of logic or from ignoring the rules of logic. Thus faulty reasoning may be attributable to lack of knowledge, lack of intellectual capacity, or lack of intellectual integrity. The desire to arrive at a predetermined conclusion facilitates illogical thinking: "None are so blind as those who will not see."

This chapter may well be concluded with a quotation from the October–November 1928 issue of the *Review of Midland Bank, Limited* (London):

... we have observed ... how carefully, and with what circumspection, mixed with scepticism, the data must be handled. It is not enough to seize upon the results of intermittent or continuous statistical inquiry and swallow them, with the faith of a dog in the *bona fides* of his beloved master, as unquestionably wholesome food.

The process of arriving at the results must be examined, and care must be taken to ensure that no more is read into the results than they are qualified to convey, either by themselves or in conjunction with other figures. And to this end it is very desirable that in putting forward any new series of sitatstics some authoritative guidance should be given as to how they are prepared and what significance they bear. The problem at the moment is not so much to increase the volume of available statistical data, but rather to learn just how to use the material to the best advantage and with the smallest risk of being lead astray. Statistics are like proposals of marriage—they should be, but rarely are, studied and considered, very deliberately, upon their all-round merits.

Chapter 5

SELECTED TOPICS IN ARITHMETIC

Many students beginning the study of business statistics have forgotten some of the rules of arithmetic. Signs and decimal points give particular trouble. Although this chapter does not constitute a complete review of arithmetic, it may be of help to some. Instead of stating formal rules we shall, for the most part, confine ourselves to very simple illustrations.

Another purpose of this chapter is to help the student to decide intelligently how many digits to record in his computations and answers. There is no virtue in recording an answer to 17 digits when only three are significant. On the other hand, if three significant digits are wanted in the final answer, one must decide how many digits to start out with, and how many to record at each step of the computations.

Signs

Addition and subtraction.

$$3 + 4 = 7.$$

$$3 - 4 = -1.$$

$$-3 - 4 = -7.$$

$$-3 + 4 = 1.$$

$$-3 - (-4) = -3 + 4 = 1.$$

$$3 - (-4) = 3 + 4 = 7.$$

Multiplication. The two numbers to be multiplied together are the multiplicand and multiplier. The answer is the product. Multiplicand and multiplier are interchangeable.

$$3 \times 4 = 3 \cdot 4 = (3)(4) = 12.$$

$$3 \times (-4) = -12.$$

$$(-3) \times (4) = -12.$$

$$(-3) \times (-4) = 12.$$

$$3 \times 0 = 0.$$

Division. When written as a fraction, the numerator is the dividend and the denominator is the divisor; the answer in the quotient.

$$\frac{5}{2} = 5/2 = 5 \div 2 = 2.5.$$

$$\frac{5}{-2} = -2.5.$$

$$\frac{-5}{2} = -2.5.$$

$$\frac{-5}{-2} = 2.5.$$

$$\frac{0}{2} = 0.$$

$\frac{2}{0}$ has no meaning, for no number multiplied by 0 is equal to 2.

$\frac{0}{0}$ is indeterminate, for any number multiplied by 0 is equal to 0.

Mixed computations.

$$3 \times 4 - 2 = (3 \times 4) - 2 = 12 - 2 = 10.$$
$$5 - 2 \times 4 = 5 - (2 \times 4) = 5 - 8 = -3.$$
$$4 \times (5 - 2) = 4 \times 3 = 12.$$
$$3 \times 4 - 2 \times 3 = 12 - 6 = 6.$$
$$4 + 3 \times 2 - 7 = 4 + (3 \times 2) - 7 = 4 + 6 - 7 = 3.$$
$$(4 + 3) \times (2 - 7) = (4 + 3)(2 - 7) = (7)(-5) = -35.$$

Decimal Points

Addition.
$$113.87 + 3.541 = 117.411.$$

Subtraction.
$$113.87 - 3.541 = 110.329.$$

Multiplication. There is the same number of decimal places in the product that there is in the multiplicand and multiplier together.
$$113.87 \times 3.541 = 403.21367.$$
(Two decimal places + three decimal places = five decimal places.)

Division. To locate the decimal point, simplify by moving decimal point in dividend and divisor to right or left, and rounding in such a way that divisor has only one or two digits.

$$\frac{113.87}{3.541} = 32.16 \text{ (to 2 decimal places)}, \quad \text{since} \quad \frac{114}{4} = 28.5.$$

If in doubt, prove by multiplying divisor by quotient:

$3.541 \times 32.16 = 113.87856$ (a little larger than dividend);

$3.541 \times 32.15 = 113.84315$ (a little smaller than dividend).

$$\frac{3.538}{213.87} = 0.0165, \quad \text{since} \quad \frac{0.035}{2} = 0.0175.$$

Proof:

$213.87 \times 0.0165 = 3.528855$ (a little smaller than dividend);

$213.87 \times 0.0166 = 3.550242$ (a little larger than dividend).

Square root. Appendix 2 tabulates squares and square roots. The student is urged to compare these illustrations with that appendix table.

$\sqrt{100} = 10$	$\sqrt{336} = 18.33$	$\sqrt{900} = 30$
$\sqrt{10} = 3.162$	$\sqrt{33.6} = 5.80$	$\sqrt{90} = 9.49$
$\sqrt{1} = 1$	$\sqrt{3.36} = 1.83$	$\sqrt{9} = 3$
$\sqrt{0.1} = 0.3162$	$\sqrt{0.336} = 0.58$	$\sqrt{0.9} = 0.949$
$\sqrt{0.01} = 0.1$	$\sqrt{0.0336} = 0.183$	$\sqrt{0.09} = 0.3$
$\sqrt{0.001} = 0.0316$	$\sqrt{0.00336} = 0.058$	$\sqrt{0.009} = 0.095$

Notice that the square root of a number that is less than 1 is larger than that number. It is a good idea to check square roots by multiplication. For example, assume you are in doubt whether $\sqrt{.336}$ is 0.58 or 0.183.

$0.183 \times 0.183 = 0.033489$ (much smaller than 0.336);

$0.183 \times 0.184 = 0.033672$ (much smaller than 0.336).

$0.58 \times 0.58 = 0.3364$ (a little larger than 0.336);

$0.58 \times 0.57 = 0.3306$ (a little smaller than 0.336).

Therefore $\sqrt{0.336} = 0.58$. It is between 0.57 and 0.58, but closer to 0.58 than 0.57, for

$0.57 \times 0.57 = 0.3249$ (which is even smaller than 0.3306).

If your computation leads to the square root of a negative number, you can be almost certain that you have made a mistake.

$$\sqrt{-64} = 8\sqrt{-1}, \quad (\text{not } -8).$$

$\sqrt{-1}$ is an imaginary number. We shall not deal with imaginary numbers in this book.

Significant Digits

Original data result from measurements (which can never be exact) or from counting. Measurements will therefore always be rounded; counts may be rounded. A number which is the result of rounding always represents a range of possible values rather than a single value. Thus, if such a number is recorded as 78 pounds, we know that the true value is not lower than 77.5 pounds nor higher than 78.5 pounds.

A digit is significant if the error in the next position to the right can not exceed ± 5. Thus, if a measurement is recorded as 172.3 pounds we may assume that the correct value does not lie beyond the limits of 172.3 ± 0.05, or 172.25 pounds and 172.35 pounds, and there are four significant digits. It is sometimes difficult to ascertain the number of significant digits, even in an enumeration. Thus, it is extremely unlikely that there were exactly 150,697,361 persons in the United States on April 1, 1950, as reported by the Bureau of the Census.

Below are given three illustrations of correct terminology for measurements that have been accurately made and properly recorded, or for rounded enumerations:

127.34 is said to contain five significant digits. It has been rounded to five significant digits, or to two significant decimal places.

4,125 thousand or 4.125 million or $4,125 \times 10^3$ is significant to four digits. If occurring in a table, usually 4,125 is recorded, with a prefatory note or column heading specifying thousands. The number of significant digits in 4,125,000 is ambiguous, since it may range from four to seven. The context, however, often indicates the number of significant digits. There is no ambiguity if a number ends in zero after a decimal point. Thus 4,125.0 and 4.1250 each have five significant digits.

0.00031 contains two rather than five significant digits (though 0.10031 contains five and 1.00031 contains six). This is because the choice of a unit of measurement is arbitrary. For instance, 0.31 meters is also 31 centimeters. The importance of this concept will be apparent when rules for multiplying and dividing rounded numbers are given.

Rules for Rounding

1. If the leftmost of the digits discarded is less than 5, the preceding digit is not affected. Thus 113.746 becomes 113.7 when rounded to four digits. Also, 87.3499999 becomes 87.3 when rounded to three digits.

2. If the leftmost of the digits discarded is greater than 5, or is 5 followed by digits not all of which are zero if carried out to a sufficient number of digits, the preceding digit is increased by one. Thus, 129.673 becomes 129.7 when rounded to four digits. Also, 87.2500001 becomes 87.3 when rounded to three digits.

3. If the leftmost of the digits discarded is 5, followed by zeros only, the preceding digit is increased by one if it is odd, and left unchanged if it is even. The number is thus rounded in such a manner that the last digit retained is even. For example, 103.55 becomes 103.6 and 103.45 becomes 103.4 when rounded to four digits. (However, 103.5499 becomes 103.5 as

explained in paragraph 1, and 103.4501 becomes 103.5 as explained in paragraph 2.) This rule is adopted in order to avoid the cumulation of errors in summations, which could result if the preceding digit were always raised or always left unchanged. The rule (making the last digit even) is more generally used than its reverse (making the last digit odd). It is more convenient than alternately adding and dropping the half, since one is spared the trouble of remembering which was done last. It is apparent that this rule is not of wide applicability, for most numbers do not fall in the category specified. Also, there is an assumption that the digit preceding the 5 is odd for approximately half of the numbers, and even for the other half. Where this is not true, the rule should not be invoked. For example, the rule is satisfactory if the numbers all end in 00, 25, or 75, and the last digit is to be rounded off, but not if they all end in either 00 or 25. Perhaps the best procedure, in many cases, is to retain the 5 instead of rounding it off, even though some answers will contain more digits (or more decimal places) than others.

Products and Quotients Obtained from Rounded Numbers

1. In the multiplication of two numbers (including squaring), division, or extraction of square root, one should never record as an answer more digits than there are in the original number with the fewest significant digits. The following illustrations thus indicate the maximum number of digits which it is good practice to record:

$$358 \times 412 = 147 \text{ thousand.}$$
$$14 \times 427 = 6.0 \text{ thousand.}$$
$$4,821 \times 0.00412 = 19.9$$
$$5,673 \times 8 \text{ (exactly)} = 45.38 \text{ thousand.}$$
$$25 \div 23 = 1.1.$$
$$42.7 \div 52 = 0.82.$$
$$52 \div 42.7 = 1.2.$$
$$\sqrt{0.354} = 0.595.$$

In the above illustrations the *maximum* number of digits that may be significant is recorded; in some instances the number significant will be fewer than the number recorded. In the case of the sixth illustration there is, strictly speaking, only one significant digit in the answer. Remembering that a rounded number recorded as 42.7 may vary between 42.65 and 42.75, while one recorded as 52 may vary between 51.5 and 52.5, we may compute:

$$42.75 \div 51.5 = .830 \text{ to three digits, the largest possible result;}$$
$$42.7 \div 52 = .821 \text{ to three digits, the result obtained;}$$
$$42.65 \div 52.5 = .812 \text{ to three digits, the smallest possible result.}$$

Since .830 and .812 are not included within .821 $\pm$ .005, it is apparent that the second digit in .821 is not significant. It is, of course, highly improbable that both of the numbers involved will be in error close to the maximum possible amount.

2. Since there is a tendency for digits to lose accuracy with each operation, it is a better rule to record *one less* digit in the answer than in the original number with the fewest significant digits.

3. If a given number of significant digits is required in the final answer, each of the original numbers and each of the intermediate results should have one more significant digit than the number of digits required in the answer. If any of the original data contain more digits than called for by this rule, the excess digits may be rounded off. For example, if three digits are required in the final answer, we first round each member to four significant digits. Thus

$$\sqrt{\frac{(2.7608)^2}{(13.195)(0.87367)}} \quad \text{becomes} \quad \sqrt{\frac{(2.761)^2}{(13.20)(0.8737)}}.$$

Then we compute

$$\sqrt{\frac{(2.761)^2}{(13.20)(0.8737)}} = \sqrt{\frac{7.623}{11.53}} = \sqrt{0.6611} = 0.813.$$

As is almost always the case, the final answer is the same as if we had retained all of the original digits and also one more digit in each intermediate step:

$$\sqrt{\frac{(2.7608)^2}{(13.195)(0.87367)}} = \sqrt{\frac{7.6220}{11.528}} = \sqrt{0.66117} = 0.813.$$

The rounding of the original data is justified because of the small probability that most of the numbers involved will be in error close to the maximum possible amount, and the large probability that there will be considerable offsetting of errors.[1]

---

[1] Where several computations involving multiplication, division, or extracting a square root are involved in working with one set of data, it is sometimes advisable to record one more digit in intermediate computations than there are in the original number with the fewest significant digits. While the extra digits may not be absolutely accurate, they are sufficiently close to contribute something to the final answer. For instance, if we want three digits in our final answer and have

$$\frac{(4.137)(0.684)}{(0.316)(7.821)} \quad \text{we write} \quad \frac{2.830}{2.475} = 1.14 \quad \text{rather than} \quad \frac{2.83}{2.47} = 1.15.$$

Sometimes more than one nonsignificant digit may be desirable. In this book we have sometimes carried more than one nonsignificant digit in order to obtain a formal check on the accuracy of our computations.

Some authorities advocate the extremely conservative rule that a digit be rounded off after each computation. If that rule were followed with the above illustration, it would be necessary that each of the three original numbers contain six significant digits.

4. When the correct product or quotient is known in advance, it should be recorded rather than the approximate product or quotient resulting from use of the rounded original numbers. Thus, although $0.125 \times 0.333 = 0.0416$, if it is known that the actual operation is $\frac{1}{8} \times \frac{1}{3} = \frac{1}{24} = 0.0417$, the answer should be recorded as 0.0417 rather than 0.0416.

5. If one of the numbers is an exact number, it is considered to have an infinite number of significant digits. Thus, the total weight of 4 bars of steel weighing 8.24 pounds each is $4 \times 8.24 = 32.96$ pounds, which is best recorded as 33 pounds (since 8.24 has 3 digits).

Sums and Differences Obtained from Rounded Numbers

Rules for addition and subtraction substantially parallel those for multiplication and division, except that it is the number of significant decimal places, rather than the number of significant digits, that must be considered.

1. In addition or subtraction, one should never record as a *final answer* more decimal places than there are in the original number with the fewest significant decimal places. The following illustrations thus indicate the *maximum* number of decimal places which it is good practice to record:

$$2,156.2 + 39 = 2,195.$$

$$2,156.2 - 39 = 2,117.$$

$$13 + 12 = 25.$$

$$13 - 12 = 1.$$

In some instances the number of significant decimal places will be fewer than the number recorded. For example, we have recorded $13 + 12 = 25$, but we check our results by computing $13.5 + 12.5 = 26$ and $12.5 + 11.5 = 24$. The second digit place is not significant, since the limits of error are ± 1.0 rather than ± 0.5. It is, of course, highly improbable that both of the numbers involved will be in error close to the maximum possible amount.

2. Since there is a tendency for decimal places to lose accuracy with each addition or subtraction, it is a better rule to record *one less* decimal place in the answer than in the original number with the fewest decimal places.

3. If a given number of significant decimal places is required in the final answer, it is desirable that each of the original numbers have one more significant decimal place than the number of decimal places required in the answer. If any of the original data contain more digits than called for by his rule, the excess digits may be rounded off. Thus, if no decimal place

(no digit to the right of the decimal point) is required in the final answer, we
may proceed as follows:

$$\left.\begin{array}{r} 122.34 \\ 81.7 \\ 293.826 \end{array}\right\} \quad \text{may be rounded to} \quad \left\{\begin{array}{r} 122.3 \\ 81.7 \\ 293.8 \end{array}\right.$$

$$\overline{497.866} \qquad\qquad\qquad\qquad\qquad \overline{497.8}$$

Both totals round off to 498.

The rounding of the original data is justified because of the small
probability that most of the numbers involved will be in error close to the
maximum possible amount, and the large probability that there will be
considerable offsetting of errors.

4. When the correct total is known in advance, it should be recorded,
rather than the approximate total resulting from addition of the rounded
numbers. Thus:

	Dollars	Thousands of dollars	Per cent of total*
	507,334	507.3	66.67
	126,832	126.8	16.67
	126,834	126.8	16.67
Total of recorded numbers:	761,000	760.9	100.01
Record the total known to be correct:	761,000	761.0	100.00

* Computed from column 1. Total would not be exactly 100, even if 7 digits were recorded for each percentage.

Mixed Computations Using Rounded Numbers

Where the computations involve both types of operations discussed in
this chapter, it is difficult to lay down simple rules. Each case must be
considered individually. As an illustration, however, consider the following
problem:

$$(59.23)(173.145) - (3,216.2)(1.31467).$$

For each term, round to one more than the fewest significant digits in that
term:

$$(59.23)(173.14) - (3,216.2)(1.31467).$$

Multiply each term:

$$10,255 - 4,228.$$

The first term can have only 4 significant digits; i.e., the last 5 is not significant. Therefore, subtract and round:

$$10,255 - 4,228 = 6,027 = 6.03 \text{ thousand.}$$

It is possibly better to round off the 3 also, because we are not sure that the
product of 59.23 and 173.145 has more than 3 significant digits.

Let us check our answer. The maximum possible answer is

$$(59.235)(173.1455) - (3,216.15)(1.314665) = 10,256.3 - 4,228.2$$
$$= 6,028, \text{ to 4 digits.}$$

The minimum possible answer is

$$(59.225)(173.1445) - (3,216.25)(1.314675) = 10,254.5 - 4,228.3$$
$$= 6,026, \text{ to 4 digits.}$$

Since both the maximum and minimum answers are within the range 6.027 ± 0.005 thousand, it is apparent that the answer of 6.03 thousand is justified. In order to be safe, however, it would be better if the original number recorded as 59.23 had one more digit.

Chapter 6

PRESENTATION OF DATA

Statistical data may be shown by four different methods: (1) The figures may be woven into a text statement. (2) A table may be made to present the data in compact, organized form. (3) A chart may be drawn to help interpret the data more easily. Graphic methods obliterate some of the details, but enable us to see the woods, rather than the trees. (4) The data may be summarized in the form of one or more statistical measures, such as average, range, ratio, trend equation, or correlation coefficient. In later chapters we shall be concerned extensively with descriptive measures. In this chapter we shall confine ourselves to statistical tables and statistical charts.

Statistical Tables

Statistical tables are usually preferable to a paragraph of text, though the latter method is useful for the purpose of emphasizing the facts that might otherwise be overlooked. The advantages of statistical tables are threefold. (1) They are concise, since repetition is eliminated, but relevant information is not sacrificed. (2) They are easy to understand since the data are logically arranged, classified, and often cross-classified. (3) Tables facilitate comparisons by means of the arrangement of the figures in columns and rows.

Types of tables. Before considering statistical tables in greater detail, we should note that data may be set forth in tables for either of two purposes. (1) Tables may be prepared for reference use. Such tables are customarily termed *reference tables*, because they do not attempt to emphasize specific findings but rather serve as a repository of information. In a report, these tables are usually relegated to the appendix. Since reference tables are tables to which research workers will frequently refer for data, it follows that they must be so constructed that any item or items desired may be selected with a minimum of effort. (2) Tables may be used to analyze or to assist in analyzing data. Tables of this sort are termed *text tables*. They should be designed so as to place the most important data in the most prominent position and, by the judicious placing of columns and rows, to bring together the figures that should be compared. Text tables are frequently rather limited in size because it is more effective to present only a few facts at a time.

Parts of a table. A complete table consists of at least four parts: the title, the stub, the box head, and the body, as shown. In addition, some tables have one or more prefatory notes, footnotes, or both.

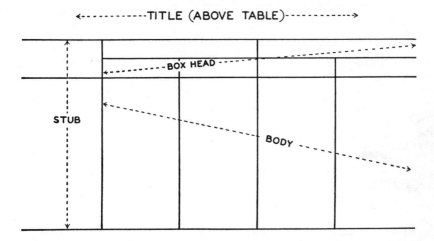

Every table should have a title, which should be clearly worded, indicating succinctly what is to be found in the table. A title usually states: *what, where, how classified*, and *when*, generally in that order. When the title of a table requires more than one line, it is customary to arrange the lines to form a sort of inverted pyramid. If a report contains several tables, it is advisable to assign a number to each table in order that it may be referred to in the discussion by number rather than by title. The prefatory note, placed just below the title, has general reference to all or a large part of the data in the table. Footnotes, placed just below the bottom line of the table, are specific in nature and usually refer to one or a few items in the table. If a table contains secondary data, a source reference should be placed below the table as the last footnote. A complete reference giving author, title, publisher, date of publication, and page should be given.

Table 6.1 illustrates the points mentioned in this paragraph.

Technique of making tables. In constructing a table, a number of points must be considered, some of the most important of which are explained below.

Simplicity. Tables should not be too complex. Many readers tend to skip tables; and complex tables are not only quite likely to be passed by unread, but may not be understood if they are read. It is usually preferable to use several relatively simple tables rather than one complex table.

Unity. A text table should be devoted to one topic, though the data may be cross-classified in several ways; and it should show the relationship of the parts to the whole. Table 6.1 is a unified table. There are three bases of classification, the individual items add up to column totals, the column totals add up to class totals, and the class totals add up to a grand total.

Table 6.1—Estimated Population of the United States by Age Groups,
Race, and Sex, July 1, 1956
(Thousands)

Age group (years)	All races			White			Nonwhite		
	Total*	Male	Female	Total*	Male	Female	Total*	Male	Female
All ages*	168,091	83,355	84,737	149,824	74,425	75,399	18,268	8,930	9,338
Under 5	18,680	9,517	9,163	16,147	8,249	7,898	2,534	1,269	1,265
5–14	31,768	16,207	15,561	27,740	14,187	13,553	4,028	2,020	2,008
15–24	22,132	11,172	10,961	19,383	9,811	9,572	2,750	1,361	1,389
25–44	47,056	23,124	23,932	42,125	20,805	21,319	4,932	2,319	2,613
45–64	34,028	16,676	17,353	30,988	15,188	15,799	3,041	1,488	1,554
65 and over	14,426	6,659	7,766	13,444	6,187	7,257	982	473	509

*Each total has been independently rounded to the nearest thousand from unrounded figures; hence, the sums of the parts shown may differ slightly from the totals shown.
Source: U.S. Department of Commerce, Bureau of the Census, *Current Population Report, Population Estimates,* Series P-25, No. 146, November 12, 1956, p. 7.

Table 6.2, on the other hand, is not unified, the data are classified by race and by sex, but race is not subclassified by sex, nor is sex subclassified by race. Actually, two different topics are considered: age groups classified by race, and age groups classified by sex. The individual entries do not add up to the grand total, but to twice the grand total. It would be better to split up Table 6.2 into two tables, with box head captions, *white, nonwhite, total* and *male, female, total,* respectively.

Table 6.2—Estimated Population of the United States by Age Groups,
Race, and Sex, July 1, 1956
(Thousands)

Age group (years)	White	Nonwhite	Male	Female	Total
Under 5	16,147	2,534	9,517	9,163	18,680
5–14	27,740	4,028	16,207	15,561	31,768
15–24	19,383	2,750	11,172	10,961	22,132
25–44	42,125	4,932	23,124	23,932	47,056
45–64	30,988	3,041	16,676	17,353	34,028
65 and over	13,444	982	6,659	7,766	14,426
All ages	149,824	18,268	83,355	84,737	168,091

Source: Table 6.1.

Making comparisons. It is important to arrange the figures in such a way that the desired comparisons can easily be made. In working toward this end, one should apply these principles: (1) Figures to be compared should be placed as close together as possible. (2) When only one set of figures is to be compared, they should be placed in a column rather than a row. (3) Two or more *series* of figures can best be compared through the use of adjacent columns. As an illustration of the last point, consider Table 6.1. The table is designed to facilitate comparison between the number of males and the number of females in each age group. If it had been designed for comparing the number of whites and number of nonwhites in each group, the arrangement of captions in the box head would have been:

Both sexes			Male			Female		
Total	White	Nonwhite	Total	White	Nonwhite	Total	White	Nonwhite

The comparison of items in a table may frequently be furthered by the use of computed values, such as ratios, percentages, and averages. Table 6.3 shows sex ratios computed from Table 6.1. These ratios could appropriately have been placed at the end of each section of Table 6.1, though this would have made the table rather long.

Table 6.3—Sex Ratio of Population of the United States,
by Age Group and Race, July 1, 1956
(Males per 100 females)

Age	All races	White	Nonwhite
All ages	98.4	98.7	95.6
Under 5	103.9	104.4	100.3
5–14	104.2	104.7	100.6
15–24	101.9	102.5	98.0
25–44	96.6	97.6	88.7
45–64	96.1	96.1	95.8
65 and over	85.7	85.3	92.9

Source of data: Table 6.1.

Table 6.4 shows the median[1] age of the population by sex and age. These figures were put at the bottom of the column in the reference table from which text Table 6.1 was derived. Putting them in a separate table facilitates comparisons. Thus it is apparent that the median age of females is greater than the median age of males, not only for the population as a whole, but

---

[1] The median is a type of average. It is so obtained that half of the values are equal to or greater than the median and half of the values are equal to or smaller than the median.

for each of the two racial classes. It is equally apparent that the median age of whites is greater than the median age of nonwhites, not only for the population as a whole, but also for each sex.

Table 6.4—Median Age of Population of
the United States, by Sex and Race,
July 1, 1956
(Years)

Sex	Race		
	White	Nonwhite	Total
Male	, 29.8	23.6	29.1
Female	31.3	25.0	30.7
Total ...	30.6	24.3	29.9

Source: See Table 6.1.

Emphasis. One or more of the following devices may be used to emphasize items in a text table:

A common method of securing emphasis consists in placing the important item or items in the most prominent position. Since it is customary for Occidentals to read from left to right and from top to bottom, it follows that the most prominent position in the caption is to the left, just beside the stub, whereas the most prominent position in the stub is at the top. (See Table 6.1.)

A column of figures, a row of figures, or an individual figure may be emphasized by the use of distinctive—usually bold-face—type. Italics are usually used to indicate exceptions. For example, in a column of figures showing profits, any losses might appear in italics.

Arrangement. It has already been pointed out that statistical data may be classified according to qualitative, temporal, and geographical characteristics. The method of arrangement to be applied to the items in the stub or box head of a table will be determined by two considerations: first, the basis of classification; and second, the purpose of the table. The following methods of arrangement may be used: according to magnitude (in rank order, either ascending or descending); alphabetical (for reference tables); geographical; historical; progressive; customary.

Whatever arrangements are used in a table it must be borne in mind that, for a reference table, the items should be arranged for greatest ease of reference, while for a text table the items should be arranged to place emphasis on the most important ones and to bring out the comparisons desired.

Some tables include a "miscellaneous" or "not reported" group, customarily placed at the bottom of the stub or at the right of the caption. If such a category embraces a large number of cases, readers may well question the adequacy of the classification.

Rounding. Numbers of many digits may sometimes be rounded in order to facilitate reading. If a number of seven digits be cut to four, the rounding should be to the *nearest* thousand. Thus 1,723,168 would become 1,723 (thousand) and 4,691,869 would become 4,692 (thousand). When numbers are rounded, a statement should be made to the fact either in the prefatory note or in the stub or caption, as in Table 6.1. Customary phrases are "thousands of ..." and "000 omitted."

Rounding off does not usually introduce a serious error in column or row totals. If a long series of numbers is rounded to the nearest thousand (or million or other convenient figure), some will be raised and some will be lowered, and the errors introduced will tend to offset each other. Nevertheless, the total of several rounded numbers will not necessarily exactly equal the rounded total of the unrounded numbers. Thus, in the first column of Table 6.1, the total of the rounded numbers is 168,090. However the number correctly recorded is 168,091, since the total of the unrounded numbers is 168,091, when rounded to the nearest thousand.

Statistical Charts

Most of the charts on the following pages are taken from annual reports of corporations. In some cases they are direct reproductions, while in other cases it was necessary to redraw them. In many cases the charts in the annual reports are in color, and the reproductions in black and white are less attractive.

Chart 6.1 shows that tractor production is increasing by *amounts* that tend to get larger each year. A special type of ruling is available (see Chart 6.3) for showing whether the *percentage* rate of growth is constant, getting larger, or getting smaller.

Notice that the line representing the data is a heavy line, since that is the most important part of the chart. The plotted points are connected by straight lines, since they refer to production for the entire year, and only the points have any validity. The only function served by the lines is to guide the eye. Shading below the plotted line results in a silhouette that enhances the effectiveness of the chart. This chart would be improved if the zero base line were ruled in. The base line should be more prominent than the other guide lines, but less prominent than the line representing the data. It is unusual to put the scale on the right, rather than the left, but this procedure is perhaps justified by artistic considerations, since the chart in the *Annual Report* was at the upper right corner of a page.

In choosing scales for a chart, one should avoid extremes. The movements

Chart 6.1—Simple Line Chart
(From International Harvester Company, *Annual Report*, 1956, p. 15.)

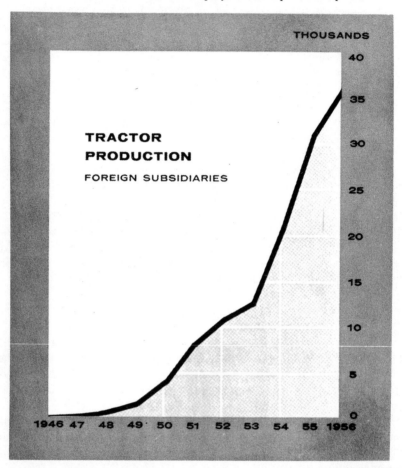

to be emphasized should be represented by an angle of roughly 45 degrees. Possibly the vertical scale for this chart is slightly too large in proportion to its width.

Chart 6.2—Simple Vertical Bar Chart
(From the Equitable Life Assurance Society of the U.S., 97th *Annual Report*,
1956, p. 7.)

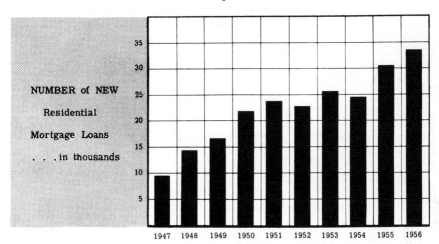

The vertical bar chart is a logical and effective way of presenting time series. These are *period* data, since they refer to the number of loans made *during* each year. They could have been plotted as a line diagram simply by connecting the mid points at the top of adjacent bars by a straight line. It would also have been correct to let a vertical line (rather than a space) refer to a specified year, and to connect points plotted on the vertical lines.

Point data refer to an *instant* of time. For example, the number of mortgages held at the end of each year would be point data. When plotting point data, a good method is to label the spaces on the horizontal axis, and to plot points at the point of time to which they refer.

Chart 6.2 would be improved slightly if 0 were placed to the left of the zero line, and if a scale label were placed above the vertical scale values, instead of letting the title also serve as a scale label.

Vertical bar charts are also used for frequency distributions, and are called *histograms*, or column diagrams. See Chart 1.1. Geographical and qualitatively classified data are generally represented by horizontal bars.

Chart 6.3—Ratio Chart
GROWTH OF SALES AND COMPANY INVESTMENT
Ratio Scale: Equal vertical distances represent equal percentage changes.
(Similar to chart appearing on p. 9 of the Eastman Kodak Company, *Annual Report*, 1956; data are on pp. 34–35.)

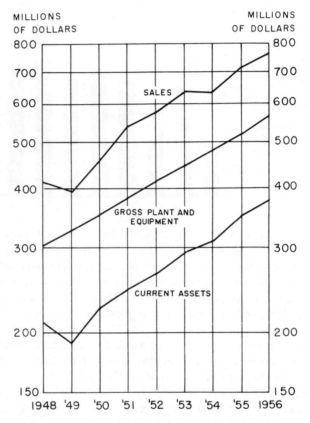

The type of paper on which this chart is drawn is usually referred to as *semi-logarithmic* paper. It is also called ratio paper, since equal vertical distances represent equal ratios. The use of logarithmic scales is considered in more detail in Chapter 9.

Because the line representing gross plant and equipment on this chart is almost a straight line, we know that these assets have been increasing at an almost constant percentage rate. The chart also shows that between 1949 and 1951 the percentage rate of growth was greater for sales than for gross plant and equipment. This we know because the slope of the curve for sales was steeper than that for gross plant and equipment. Finally, the chart shows that the ratio of sales to gross plant and equipment was larger in 1951 than it was in 1949. This is indicated by the fact that the two curves were further apart in 1951 than in 1949.

Chart 6.4—Net Balance Chart

U.S. SMELTER PRODUCTION AND APPARENT CONSUMPTION OF NEW COPPER

(Traced, with minor changes, from chart appearing in Kennecott Copper
Corporation, *Annual Report*, 1956, p. 21.)

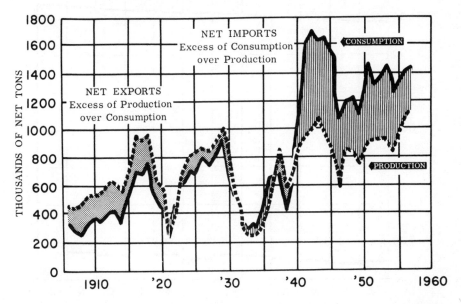

This chart shows four things: production; consumption; net exports; net imports. It is a little more complicated than a silhouette chart showing net exports above a straight, horizontal zero line and net imports below it. Below the chart the *Annual Report* stated: "With the growth in domestic consumption of copper, the United States changed from an exporter of copper to an importer. Since 1940 the country has been depending on imports for a substantial part of its copper needs."

Chart 6.5—Z Chart
SEARS, ROEBUCK AND COMPANY SALES, 1956
(Data of Table 30.5)

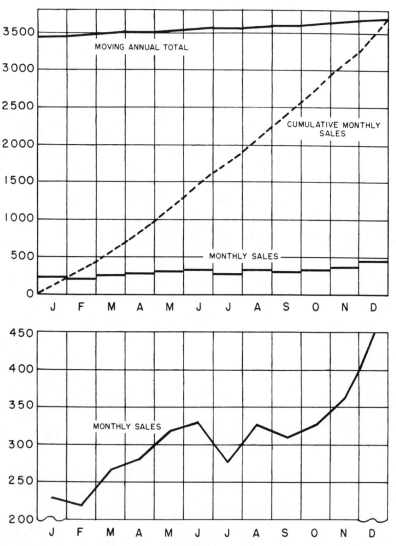

THOUSANDS OF DOLLARS

This chart permits one to see not only each month by itself, but also the sales for 1956 to date at the end of each month, and the total sales for any twelve month period. The moving total automatically eliminates the effect of seasonal movements, and shows a gradual increase during the year. Usefulness of the chart would be enhanced by plotting the cumulative budgeted sales as well as the cumulative actual sales.

In order to see the fluctuations in the monthly sales more clearly, they are plotted in the lower section with a vertical scale ten times as large. In the lower section monthly sales are plotted in the middle of each space, since they are period data, while in the upper section they are shown by horizontal lines. Cumulative monthly sales and the moving annual totals are plotted at the end of the different spaces, since they are point data, showing the situation at the end of each month.

Chart 6.6—Multiple Axis Chart
SEARS, ROEBUCK AND COMPANY SALES, AS PER CENT OF AVERAGE
(Data of Table 30.5)

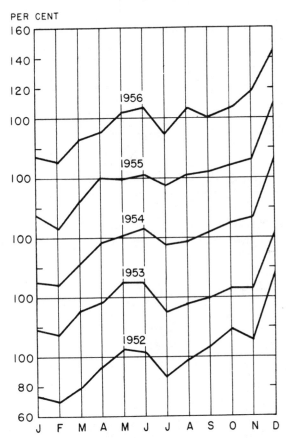

This type of chart is useful in showing similarities in pattern for different years. Note, for example, that sales are usually low in February and July, and high in June and December. The sales are expressed as percentages of average each year to make them comparable. If ratio paper were used this would not be necessary.

Chart 6.7—Profile Chart
PROFILE CHART FOR BOOKKEEPERS WITH PROFILE OF INDIVIDUAL APPLICANT

Dotted line is norm established for bookkeepers, while solid line is profile for Henry Smith.

(Freely adapted from Dale Yoder, *Personnel Management and Industrial Relations*, Prentice-Hall, Inc., Englewood Cliffs, N.J., 1943, p. 196.)

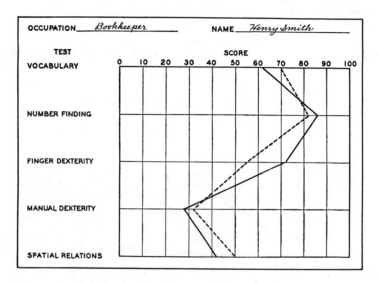

This is a specialized type of chart. If the profile of an individual closely resembles the norm for that class of workers, the presumption is that he is well suited for that type of work.

Chart 6.8—Simple Horizontal Bar Chart
(From The Cleveland Trust Company, *Business Bulletin*, Vol. 36, November 16, 1955, p. 3.)

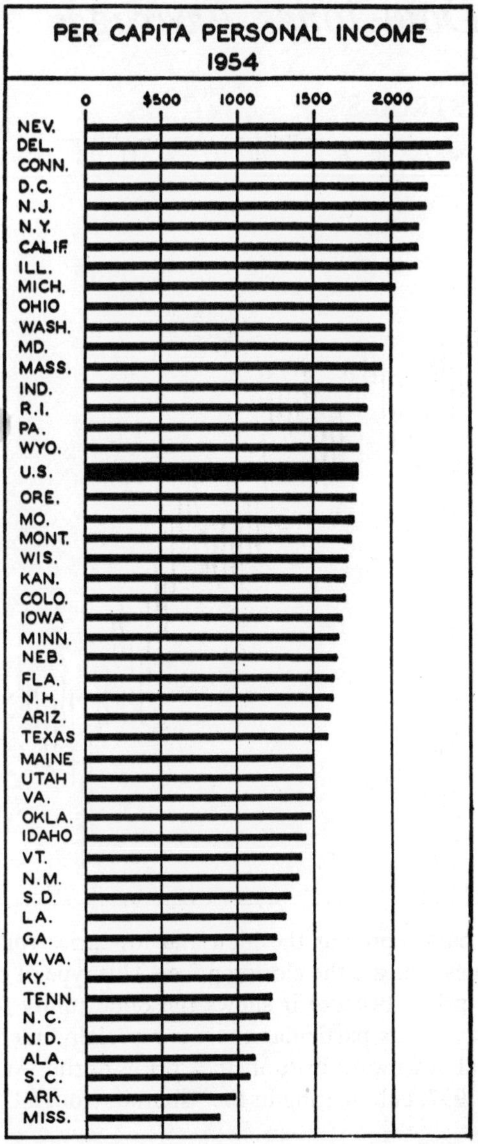

PER CAPITA PERSONAL INCOME
1954

Horizontal bars are used to represent data that are classified qualitatively or geographically. The arrangement is usually from largest to smallest. In this chart the per capita personal income for the United States is emphasized by using a thicker bar. Often the individual bars are shaded, and the bar to be emphasized is darker, or in color.

Chart 6.9—High-Low Bar Chart
(From the *Wall Street Journal*, October 31, 1957, p. 27.)

The Dow-Jones Averages

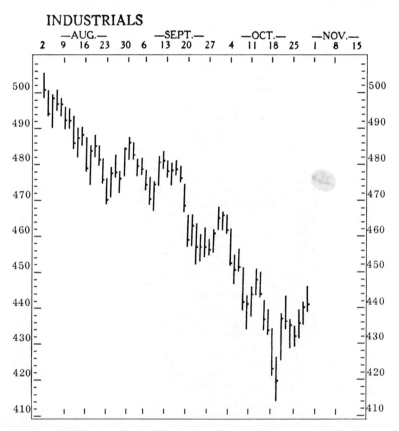

The vertical bars represent the high and low price for each day, while the horizontal lines indicate the closing price. This type of chart is especially useful for stock prices because it shows the opportunity for taking profits or losses each day. This particular chart is especially interesting because it shows the gradual downward drift of stock prices during August, September, and October of 1957, culminating in the "sputnik trough."

Chart 6.10—Per Cent Change Horizontal Bar Chart
**PER CENT CHANGE IN WHOLESALE PRICE INDEX FOR MAJOR COMMODITY
GROUPS BETWEEN AUGUST 1956 AND AUGUST 1957**
(Data from United States Department of Labor, Bureau of Labor Statistics,
Wholesale Prices and Price Indexes, July 1957 Final and August 1957 Preliminary.)

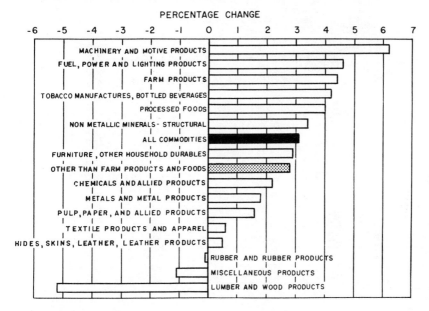

This is more effective than a chart showing each price as a per cent of
the preceding year, for it indicates clearly that some groups decreased while
others increased.

A similar principle can be used for a time series chart, with vertical bars
extending above or below a horizontal zero line. For example, profits can
be shown above the line and losses below the line. A silhouette curve showing
periods of prosperity and depression in American business activity is shown
by Chart 31.1.

Chart 6.11—Grouped Vertical Bar Chart
CAPITAL EXPENDITURES AND DEPRECIATION EXPENSE OF
MONTGOMERY WARD & CO.,
1952–1956
(From Montgomery Ward Annual Report, 1956, p. 8.)

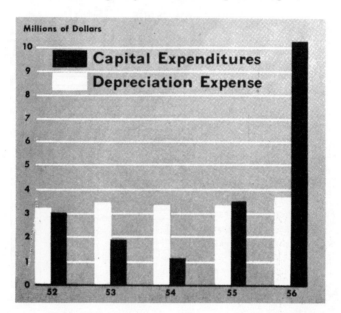

Aside from its technical aspects, this chart is interesting because it indicates a change in policy. Beginning in 1955 a more aggressive policy was decided upon, involving heavy capital expenditures.

For data classified qualitatively or geographically, grouped *horizontal* bars are appropriate for the primary classification. Thus we could show sales of a large number of retail stores for 1956 and 1957 by horizontal bars. The 1957 bar should be the more prominent, being placed above, or partly in front of, the 1956 bar, and being shaded or hatched more prominently.

Chart 6.12—Grouped Vertical Bar Chart with Overlapping Bars
CAPITAL EXPENDITURES AND PROVISION FOR DEPRECIATION, EASTMAN KODAK COMPANY
(Similar to chart on p. 9 of Eastman Kodak Company, *Annual Report*, 1956; data of pp. 34–35.)

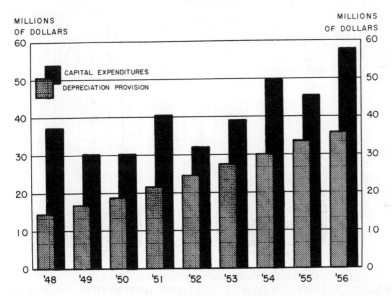

This chart is slightly unusual in that one of the bars is placed partly in front of the other. Not only does this add an artistic touch, but it facilitates visualization of the *net* amount of capital invested each year.

It is interesting to contrast Charts 6.11 and 6.12 in another respect. Chart 6.11 showed a change in administration policy on the part of Montgomery Ward & Co., while Chart 6.12 reveals a stable investment policy on the part of Eastman Kodak Company.

Chart 6.13—Component Part Time Series Bar Chart
EARNINGS BEFORE INCOME TAXES, AND DISPOSITION OF EARNINGS,
EASTMAN KODAK COMPANY
(Similar to Chart on p. 8 of Eastman Kodak Company *Annual Report*,
1956; data of pp. 34–35.)

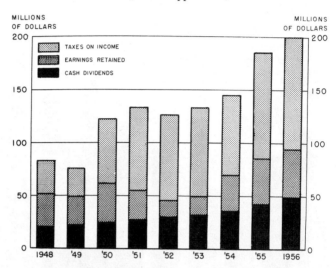

Chart 6.14—Component Part Time Series Band Chart
EARNINGS BEFORE INCOME TAXES, AND DISPOSITION OF EARNINGS,
EASTMAN KODAK COMPANY
(Data from Eastman Kodak Company, *Annual Report*, 1956, pp. 34–35.)

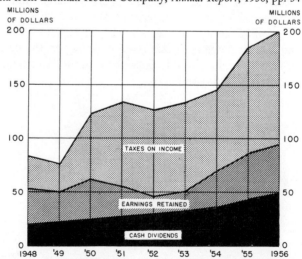

Here are two alternative methods of showing the same data. The bar
chart has a slightly more popular appeal. Also, attention can be directed
more easily to individual years, while the band chart focuses attention on
the changing relationships.

Chart 6.15—Percentage Part Time Series Bar Chart
DISPOSITION OF EARNINGS, EASTMAN KODAK COMPANY
(Data from Eastman Kodak Company, *Annual Report*, 1956, pp. 34–35.)

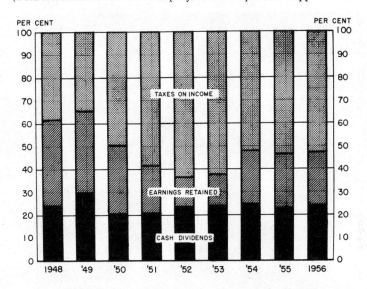

Chart 6.16—Percentage Part Time Series Band Chart
DISPOSITION OF EARNINGS, EASTMAN KODAK COMPANY
(Data from Eastman Kodak Company, *Annual Report*, 1956, pp. 34–35.)

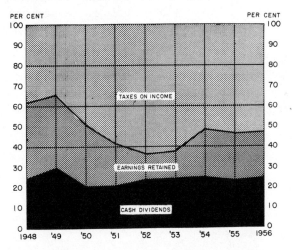

These two charts present the same data as Charts 6.13 and 6.14, but from a different point of view. Charts 6.13 and 6.14 show that all three components have been growing in absolute amount. Charts 6.15 and 6.16 show that dividends and retained earnings have been declining relative to total earnings, while taxes on income have been increasing relative to total earnings.

Chart 6.17—Pie Chart
GENERAL MOTORS SALES DOLLAR
(General Motors Corporation, *G M Annual Report*, 1956, p. 57.)

The pie chart is an effective way of showing percentage parts. This is perhaps because the relative size of the parts can be judged by the size of the angle, as well as the length of the arc and the area of the sector. Or perhaps it is because we have become experts at judging the size of a helping of pie. This type of chart lends itself to showing percentage parts of any kind of a circular object. It could appropriately be called a dollar chart, since it is used in business statistics for showing how the sales dollar was spent, more than for any other purpose. The Atchison, Topeka and Santa Fe Railway Company uses a wheel instead of a dollar.

Chart 6.18—Circle Chart
AMERICAN TOBACCO COMPANY SALES DOLLAR
(The American Tobacco Company, *Annual Report*, 1956, p. 6.)

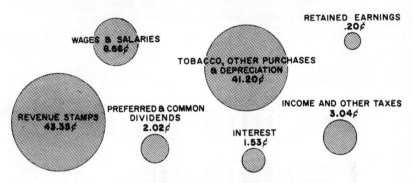

HOW OUR SALES DOLLAR WAS DISTRIBUTED

This type of chart, though perhaps attractive in appearance, may be misleading. Although the area of the different circles is the proper basis of comparison, many persons will compare the diameters of the circles, thus underestimating the size of the larger circles compared with the smaller ones. On the other hand, some persons will regard the objects as being spheres, and compare cubic content. But even if one correctly interprets size to mean area, comparisons are likely to be inaccurate. We can compare heights (one dimension) more easily than areas (two dimensions), and areas more easily than volumes (three dimensions).

Chart 6.19—In and Out Chart
TIAA'S DOLLAR:
WHERE IT COMES FROM—WHERE IT GOES
(Redrawn from Teachers' Insurance and Annuity Association,
College Equities Fund, *Annual Report*, 1956, p. 12.)

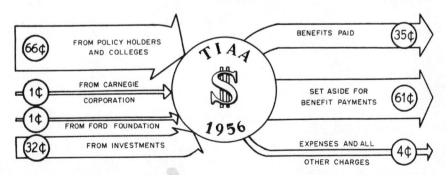

The in and out chart is an interesting method of showing where money comes from, and where it goes.

Chart 6.20—Pictogram
SHAREHOLDINGS OF SOCONY MOBILE OIL COMPANY
Each figure represents 5,000 shareholders
(Similar to chart appearing in Socony Mobile Oil
Company, *Annual Report*, 1956, p. 25.)

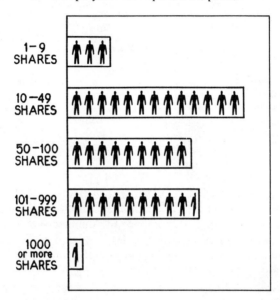

   The pictogram is a popular device for showing statistical data. "One picture is worth a thousand words." The pictures suggest the nature of the information, and thereby reduce the amount of thinking required.

   It is unusual for a histogram to be represented by a pictogram, since the bars in a histogram are usually vertical, while most pictures are naturally arranged in horizontal rows. Stacks of money are an exception to this statement. The frequency distribution pictured above is further discussed on pages 200–201.

Chart 6.21—Basic Rules for Pictograms
(From Rudolph Modley and Dyno Lowenstein, Pictographs and Graphs, Harper and Brothers, New York, 1952, pp. 25–26.)

SYMBOLS SHOULD BE SELF-EXPLANATORY

CHANGES IN NUMBERS ARE SHOWN
BY MORE OR FEWER SYMBOLS   NOT BY LARGER OR SMALLER ONES

EACH SHIP REPRESENTS 5 MILLION TONS

CHARTS GIVE AN OVER-ALL PICTURE   NOT MINUTE DETAILS

                                                          4,873,285

                                                          11,075,357

                                                          20,468,953

PICTOGRAPHS MAKE COMPARISONS   NOT FLAT STATEMENTS

1870

1900

1930   1930

The last two rules given in the above chart apply to all types of charts. A chart is intended to give an over-all picture, not minute details; the details should be presented by means of a table. The statistical method is not concerned with individual observations, but with data that are subject to variability, either systematic or random.

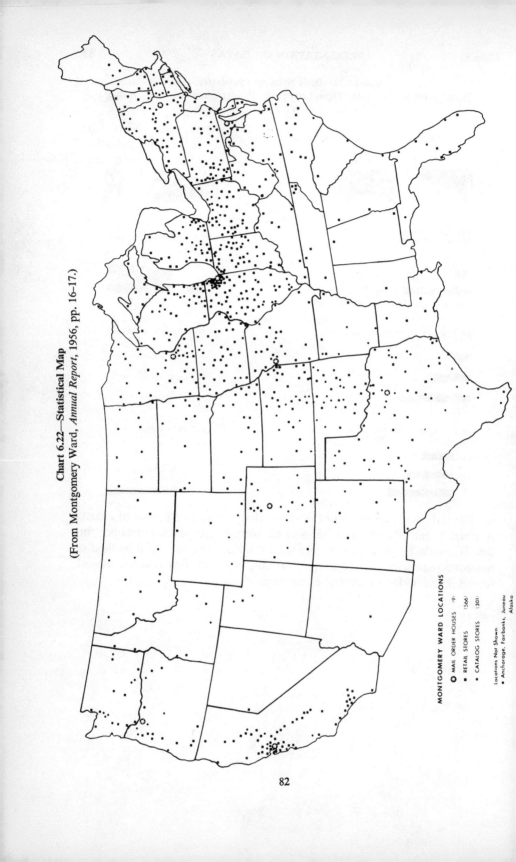

Chart 6.22—Statistical Map
(From Montgomery Ward, *Annual Report*, 1956, pp. 16–17.)

MONTGOMERY WARD LOCATIONS

⊙ MAIL ORDER HOUSES   (9)
■ RETAIL STORES   (566)
• CATALOG STORES   (301)

Locations Not Shown
• Anchorage, Fairbanks, Juneau
Alaska

This is essentially a dot map, showing the distribution of units over space. Pin maps are often used for this purpose, pins of various colors and shapes being used for showing different kinds of information.

Another type of statistical map is the cross-hatch map. See Charts 2.6 and 2.7. The cross-hatch map is used to show averages, rates, or ratios. The shading ranges from light to dark as the averages, rates, or ratios range from small to large.

Occasionally a map is distorted so that the areas of the different states will be proportional to their populations, or some other measures of importance.

Chapter 7

SELECTED TOPICS IN ALGEBRA

Algebra differs from arithmetic in that we use symbols, usually letters, to denote ideas and unknown numbers. An advantage of so doing is that it permits us to solve problems that would be too difficult for most of us if we had to use the cumbersome language of literature.

Another advantage of the algebraic method is that it permits us to make general statements, instead of (or in addition to) arithmetic illustrations. An arithmetic illustration is valid only for the numbers chosen. It usually takes many arithmetic illustrations to constitute a convincing proof.

In this chapter we shall consider the following: (1) summation signs; (2) factorials; (3) combinations; (4) logarithms.

Use of Summation Sign

Let us start with an example:

Item number	Value X	X^2
1	3	9
2	7	49
3	8	64
Sum	18	122

The symbol Σ means "sum of." Thus, for the above illustration,

$$\Sigma X = 3 + 7 + 8 = 18.$$

Sometimes, for clarity, each item is assigned a subscript corresponding to its item number i. Thus: $X_1 = 3$; $X_2 = 7$; $X_3 = 8$. Then we may write

$$\sum_{i=1}^{3} X_i = X_1 + X_2 + X_3 = 3 + 7 + 8 = 18.$$

If there were more than 3 items we would write

$$\sum_{i=1}^{n} X_i = X_1 + X_2 + \ldots + X_n,$$

where n is the number of items. If the item numbers started with 0 instead of 1 we would write

$$\sum_{i=0}^{n-1} X_i = X_0 + X_1 + \ldots + X_{n-1}.$$

An an illustration of the use of the summation sign in statistics, let us consider the computation of the arithmetic mean. This measure, which is perhaps the most important measure used in statistics, is defined to be the sum of the values divided by the number of values. The symbol and definition are much less cumbersome when stated algebraically, by means of symbols

$$\overline{X} = \frac{\Sigma\,X}{n}.$$

Referring to the data tabulated above,

$$\overline{X} = \frac{\Sigma\,X}{n} = \frac{18}{3} = 6.$$

In the next five paragraphs are given rules regarding the use of summation signs.

(1) *The square of the sum is not equal to the sum of the squares.* Square of sum:

$$(\Sigma\,X)^2 = (X_1 + X_2 + X_3)^2 = (3 + 7 + 8)^2 = 18^2 = 324.$$

Sum of squares:

$$\Sigma\,X^2 = \Sigma\,(X^2) = X_1^2 + X_2^2 + X_3^2 = 9 + 49 + 64 = 122.$$

One should be very careful to distinguish between $\Sigma\,X^2$ and $(\Sigma\,X)^2$, because they are both used a great deal in statistics. That $(\Sigma\,X)^2 \neq \Sigma\,X^2$ is easily shown algebraically. Take, for simplicity, the case where there are two observations:

$$(\Sigma\,X)^2 = (X_1 + X_2)^2 = X_1^2 + 2X_1X_2 + X_2^2.$$
$$\Sigma\,X^2 = \qquad\qquad X_1^2 \qquad\quad + X_2^2.$$

Therefore $(\Sigma\,X)^2 = \Sigma\,X^2 + 2X_1X_2.$

(2) *The product of two sums is not equal to the sum of the products.* Consider the following example:

X	Y	X²	XY	Y²
3	4	9	12	16
7	2	49	14	4
8	5	64	40	25
18	11	122	66	45

Product of sums:

$$\Sigma\,X\,\Sigma\,Y = (\Sigma\,X)(\Sigma\,Y) = (X_1 + X_2 + X_3)(Y_1 + Y_2 + Y_3)$$
$$= (3 + 7 + 8)(4 + 2 + 5) = (18)(11) = 198.$$

Sum of products:

$$\Sigma\,XY = \Sigma\,(XY) = X_1Y_1 + X_2Y_2 + X_3Y_3 = 12 + 14 + 40 = 66.$$

That $\Sigma\,X\,\Sigma\,Y \neq \Sigma\,XY$ is easily shown algebraically. Take for simplicity the case where there are two observations:

$$\Sigma\,X\,\Sigma\,Y = (X_1 + X_2)(Y_1 + Y_2) = X_1Y_1 + X_2Y_2 + X_2Y_1 + X_1Y_2.$$
$$\Sigma\,XY = X_1Y_1 + X_2Y_2.$$

Therefore $\Sigma\,X\,\Sigma\,Y = \Sigma\,XY + X_2Y_1 + X_1Y_2.$

(3) One simple rule is most easily stated algebraically:

$$\Sigma (X + Y) = \Sigma X + \Sigma Y.$$

Referring to our numerical illustration,

$$7 + 9 + 13 = 18 + 11 = 29.$$

(4) Suppose now we wish to square each value of $(X + Y)$ before summing:

$$\Sigma (X + Y)^2 = \Sigma (X^2 + 2XY + Y^2)$$
$$= \Sigma X^2 + 2 \Sigma XY + \Sigma Y^2.$$

Thus $\qquad 49 + 81 + 169 = 122 + 2(125) + 45) = 299.$

Obviously $\Sigma (X + Y)^2$ is larger than $\Sigma X^2 + \Sigma Y^2$ by the quantity $2 \Sigma XY$.

(5) Sometimes we wish to sum quantities that contain constants as well as variables. In the following illustration X is a variable, while a and b are constants, since they do not change.

X	$Y = a + bX = 10 + 2X$
$X_1 = 3$	$Y_1 = 10 + 2(3) = 10 + 6 = 16$
$X_2 = 7$	$Y_2 = 10 + 2(7) = 10 + 14 = 24$
$X_3 = 8$	$Y_3 = 10 + 2(8) = 10 + 16 = 26$
$\Sigma X = 18$	$\Sigma Y \qquad\qquad 30 + 36 = 66$

It is easily seen that

$$\Sigma Y = \Sigma (a + bX) = na + b \Sigma X.$$

Thus, $\qquad 16 + 24 + 26 = 3(10) + 2(18) = 30 + 36 = 66.$

Factorials

The exclamation point after a symbol or number means *factorial*. Thus $X!$ is read X factorial and $5!$ is read 5 factorial. By definition

(7.1) $\qquad\qquad X! = X(X - 1)(X - 2) \ldots 1.$

The three dots means that some of the multipliers have not been recorded.

$$5! = 5 \cdot 4 \cdot 3 \cdot 2 \cdot 1 = 120.$$

In order to make use of factorials (see next section) we must define $0! = 1$.

Combinations

The symbol $\binom{n}{d}$ means the number of combinations of n things taken d at a time. By definition

(7.2) $\qquad\qquad \binom{n}{d} = \frac{n!}{d!(n - d)!}.$

For example, if there are six objects

$$A, B, C, D, E, F,$$

and we wish to take a sample of 2, how many different samples are possible? Applying formula (7.2) we obtain

$$\binom{6}{2} = \frac{6!}{2!4!} = \frac{6 \cdot 5 \cdot 4 \cdot 3 \cdot 2 \cdot 1}{(2 \cdot 1)(4 \cdot 3 \cdot 2 \cdot 1)} = \frac{6 \cdot 5}{2 \cdot 1} = 15.$$

Notice that in computing $\binom{n}{d}$ we divide the product of the first d numbers in the series $n(n-1)(n-2) \ldots 1$ by the product of the last d numbers in the series.

Let us verify formula (7.2) by enumerating the different combinations. They are

$$
\begin{array}{lllll}
AB & AC & AD & AE & AF \\
   & BC & BD & BE & BF \\
   &   & CD & CE & CF \\
   &   &   & DE & DF \\
   &   &   &   & EF
\end{array}
$$

Let us compute the number of samples of different sizes that can be taken from a collection of 6 objects.

Sample size[1] (d)	$\binom{6}{d}$	Number of samples
0	$\binom{6}{0}$	$= 1$
1	$\binom{6}{1} = \frac{6}{1}$	$= 6$
2	$\binom{6}{2} = \frac{6 \cdot 5}{2 \cdot 1}$	$= 15$
3	$\binom{6}{3} = \frac{6 \cdot 5 \cdot 4}{3 \cdot 2 \cdot 1}$	$= 20$
4	$\binom{6}{4} = \frac{6 \cdot 5 \cdot 4 \cdot 3}{4 \cdot 3 \cdot 2 \cdot 1}$	$= 15$
5	$\binom{6}{5} = \frac{6 \cdot 5 \cdot 4 \cdot 3 \cdot 2}{5 \cdot 4 \cdot 3 \cdot 2 \cdot 1}$	$= 6$
6	$\binom{6}{6} = \frac{6 \cdot 5 \cdot 4 \cdot 3 \cdot 2 \cdot 1}{6 \cdot 5 \cdot 4 \cdot 3 \cdot 2 \cdot 1}$	$= 1$

[1] Ordinarily we use the symbol N to mean number of items in the population and n to mean number of items in the sample.

Notice that the distribution of results is symmetrical; i.e., that

$$\binom{n}{d} = \binom{n}{n-d}.$$

Values of $\binom{n}{d}$ are also known as *binomial coefficients*, since they are used in computing the coefficients of the terms in the binomial expansion. Some knowledge of combinations is necessary for an understanding of probability and sampling.

Logarithms

A logarithm is the exponent of that power of a fixed number, called the base, which equals a given number, called the antilogarithm. In general, if $b^Y = X$, then $\log_b X = Y$. Thus, because $10^2 = 100$ we may write $\log_{10} 100 = 2$. Or we may say: the logarithm of 100 to the base 10 is 2. Conversely, the antilogarithm of 2 is 100. Or since $10^{0.30103} = 2$, we may write $\log_{10} 2 = 0.30103$. The antilog of 0.30103 is 2.

Common logarithms are to the base 10. These are the ones most commonly used. For some purposes, however, it is necessary to use logarithms to the base e, where

$$e = \lim_{X \to \infty} \left(1 + \frac{1}{X}\right)^X = 2.71828...$$

Since $2.71828^2 = 7.389$, we may say $\log_e 7.389 = 2$. Often the simpler expression ln is used instead of $\log_e$, since logarithms to the base e are referred to as natural logarithms. In this book we use generally common logarithms, instead of natural logarithms, and write $\log X$ instead of $\log_{10} X$.

The chief use of logarithms is for computations.

To multiply 2 numbers, add their logs, and look up the resulting antilog. Example: multiply 100 by 1,000.
Logarithmic notation:

$$\text{Log } 100 + \log 1{,}000 = 2 + 3 = 5;$$
$$\text{Antilog } 5 = 100{,}000.$$

Exponent notation: $10^2 \times 10^3 = 10^5 = 100{,}000.$

To divide, subtract the log of the divisor from the log of the dividend, and look up the antilog of the difference. Problem: divide 100,000 by 100.
Logarithmic notation:

$$\text{Log } 100{,}000 - \log 100 = 5 - 2 = 3;$$
$$\text{Antilog } 3 = 1{,}000.$$

Exponent notation: $10^5 \div 10^2 = 10^3 = 1{,}000.$

To extract the square root, divide the log of the number by 2, and look up the antilog. Problem: find the square root of 1,000,000.

Logarithmic notation:

$$\text{Log } 1,000,000 \div 2 = 6 \div 2 = 3;$$
$$\text{Antilog } 3 = 1,000.$$

Exponent notation: $10^6 \div 10^3 = 10^3 = 1,000.$

These are extremely simple examples, given as an aid to understanding the meaning of logarithms, rather than as examples of their practical use. Appendix 1 is a table of logarithms. See the text accompanying that table for further information.

Chapter 8

RATES, RATIOS, AND PERCENTAGES

Absolute and Relative Comparisons

Comparisons are of two kinds, absolute and relative. As one illustration of the distinction between the two, consider standings in the American League on April 28, 1956.

Team	W.	L.	Pct.	Games behind
Chicago	5	1	.833	$\frac{1}{2}$
New York	8	3	.727	...
Cleveland	5	4	.556	2
Washington	6	5	.545	2
Boston	4	5	.444	3
Detroit	3	5	.375	$3\frac{1}{2}$
Kansas City	3	6	.333	4
Baltimore	3	8	.273	5

Source: The *News and Observer*, Raleigh, N.C., April 29, 1956.

The table shows that Chicago was $\frac{1}{2}$ game behind New York, since $\frac{1}{2}[(5-1)-(8-3)] = \frac{1}{2}(4-5) = -\frac{1}{2}$. We really have two absolute comparisons here. The *difference* between games won and games lost, which is the net number of games won, is an *absolute* comparison; so is the difference between the net number of games won by Chicago and New York. The table also shows the *percentage* of games won by each team. These are *relative* comparisons. Notice that the absolute comparison is favorable to New York, while the relative comparison is favorable to Chicago.

Incidentally, it is worth noting that the per cent of games won by Chicago is not 0.833 as reported by the newspaper, but 83.3.

The sales of two corporations were as follows:

Company	1956	1957	Amount of growth	Percentage of growth
A	$ 200	$ 300	$100	50
B	2,000	2,500	500	25

The amount of growth is an absolute comparison, the percentage growth is a relative comparison. Company B had a larger amount of growth, but company A had a larger percentage growth.

The 1956 *Annual Report* of Sears, Roebuck, and Company indicates that the net working capital of that company was $744 million at the end of January, 1957, and that the sales during the fiscal year ending on that date were $3,556 million. The relationship existing between these two large figures is difficult to grasp, and therefore a further statement may be made to the effect that working capital turned over 4.78 times during the year, or that working capital was 20.92 per cent of sales. Here, as in the case of all relative figures, whether rates, ratios, or percentages,[1] the purpose is to facilitate comparison.

Suppose the data of department store companies shown in Table 8.1 are to be studied. The basic figures given relate to the current assets and

Table 8.1—Net Working Capital and Current Ratios of Thirteen
Department Stores as of January 31, 1957
(000 omitted)

Company	Current assets	Current liabilities	Net working capital	Current ratio
Marshall Field & Co.	$89,532	$26,199	$63,333	3.41
Associated Dry Goods Corp.* ...	77,941	23,367	54,574	3.34
Federated Department Stores, Inc.*	185,274	59,082	126,192	3.14
Mercantile Stores Co., Inc.	46,136	17,653	28,483	2.61
Gimbel Brothers, Inc.	121,675	43,820	77,855	2.78
Lerner Stores Corp.	35,380	14,368	21,012	2.46
Best & Co., Inc.	16,005	5,327	10,678	3.00
May Department Stores Co.	178,848	66,061	112,787	2.71
Allied Stores Corporation	208,137	59,358	148,779	3.51
Abercrombie & Fitch Co.	4,821	1,456	3,365	3.31
Arnold Constable Corp.	9,771	3,759	6,012	2.60
National Department Stores Corp.	21,716	4,026	17,690	5.39
Hoving Corporation	10,897	3,023	7,874	3.60

* As of February 2, 1957.
Source: Moody's Investors Service, *Moody's Industrial Manual*, 1957.

current liabilities of a number of companies of diverse size. Instead of comparing the dollar figures for current assets and current liabilities for each firm, it is much more useful to calculate a "current ratio" by dividing current

---

[1] A *rate* is a quantity expressed relative to some other quantity, as 3 cents per kilowatt-hour, 40 miles per hour, $3.06 current assets per $1.00 current liabilities, 2 per cent interest, or 1 per cent defective. Miles per hour may be an average obtained by dividing the total number of miles by the total number of hours. Current assets per dollar of current liabilities, the rate of interest, and per cent defective are also *ratios*, since the numerator and denominator are in the same units. A ratio expressed relative to 100 is a *percentage*. Per cent defective is also an average, in which each good unit is assigned a value of 0 and each defective unit is assigned a value of 1. It is apparent that a *ratio* is a particular type of rate, a *percentage* is a ratio expressed in a particular manner, and a rate may often be an average.

assets by current liabilities. Thus the current ratio for Abercrombie & Fitch Co. was 3.31, and for the other concerns, the figures shown in the last column of the table. An *absolute comparison* obtained by considering the dollar figures may be misleading. For example, the difference between the current assets and the current liabilities of May Department Stores was $112,787,000, while National Department Stores showed an excess of but $17,690,000 of current assets over current liabilities. This quantity may be referred to as net current assets or net working capital. But a *relative comparison*, obtained by the use of current ratios, shows that while May Department Stores had a current ratio of 2.71, the current ratio for National Department Stores was 5.39, or nearly twice as large.

It will be noticed that the current ratio expresses the current assets to the current liabilities as a ratio to one. That is, for Best & Co., Inc.,

$$\$16,005,000 : \$5,327,000 :: 3.00 : 1.$$

Frequently, the base is expressed as 100, and the ratio is then termed a percentage. For Best & Co., Inc., current assets were 300 per cent of current liabilities.

Ratios may also be expressed in relation to 1,000 (per mille), 10,000 100,000, 1,000,000, or any other convenient figure. Death rates are expressed on these larger bases. Deaths from all causes are usually given per 1,000 of the population. Deaths from a specific disease such as scarlet fever, for example, are relatively infrequent. If, in a city of 217,644 population, there were 12 deaths from scarlet fever during a year, the death rate from that disease would be 5.5 per 100,000.

Method of Calculation

A ratio is determined by dividing the base figure into the figure that is being compared with that base. Thus the figure is expressed in terms of, or in relation to, that base. Ratios (including percentages) are therefore sometimes spoken of as relative numbers or simply as "relatives."

The New York Life Insurance Company paid $372,626,212 to its policy-holders in 1956, and $352,423,230 in 1955. If the 1956 payments are to be expressed in terms of the 1955 payments, then 1955 is the base. The division of $372,626,212 by $352,423,230 gives 1.057; the payments in 1956 were, therefore, 1.057 to 1 in relation to those in 1955.

Of the various forms of ratios mentioned previously, the percentage form is most frequently used. The figure just given showed the payments as a ratio to 1. To transform this figure to a percentage (ratio to 100), it is necessary only to move the decimal point two places to the right. Thus, 1.057 to 1 becomes 105.7 to 100, and payments in 1956 were 105.7 per cent of those in 1955.

To repeat: in calculating ratios and percentages, remember (1) always divide by the base and (2) the base is the figure with which the others are being compared.

Bases of Comparison

The data in the first two columns of Table 8.2 give the operating income of the William Wrigley, Jr. Company for 1949–1956. For comparative

Table 8.2—Operating Profit of the William Wrigley, Jr. Company, 1949–1956

Year [1]	Operating income (thousands of dollars) [2]	Per cent of 1949 [3]	Per cent increase over 1949* [4]	Per cent of preceding year [5]	Per cent over preceding year* [6]
1949	19,642	100.0	. . .	. . .	. . .
1950	20,369	103.7	3.7	103.70	3.7
1951	18,978	96.6	−3.4	93.17	−6.8
1952	18,597	94.7	−5.3	97.99	−2.0
1953	21,261	108.2	8.2	114.32	14.3
1954	22,111	112.6	12.6	104.00	4.0
1955	22,496	114.5	14.5	101.74	1.7
1956	21,891	111.4	11.4	97.31	−2.7

* A minus sign denotes a decrease.
Source: Moody's Investors Service, *Moody's Industrial Manual*, 1957.

purposes, the income of each year may be expressed as a percentage of the income in 1949. This is accomplished by dividing each of the income figures by the one for 1949. In this manner the figures in column 3 are obtained. When a large number of items are to be divided by the same number, the speed of computation is greatly increased by the use of reciprocals. Thus the reciprocal of 19,642, which is .000050911, is multiplied in turn by 20,369, by 18,978, and so on. In this table two types of comparisons are made: in columns 3 and 4, the operating income for each year from 1950 through 1956 is compared with that for 1949; in columns 5 and 6 the operating income for each year from 1950 through 1956 is compared with that for the preceding year, the income for each year being divided by that for the preceding year. As is customary, in columns 4 and 6 a minus sign denotes a decrease. (If the column headings had contained the words "per cent change," both plus and minus signs would be shown.) When comparisons are made with the 1949 figures, we are using a fixed (1949) base; when comparisons are with the preceding year, we are using a shifting base.

The percentages in column 5 of Table 8.2 are sometimes referred to as "link relatives." These link relatives can be chained together to form a series of percentages with a fixed base. Thus if the fixed base is 1949:

$$103.70 \times 0.9317 = 96.62$$
$$96.62 \times 0.9799 = 94.68$$
$$94.68 \times 1.1432 = 108.24$$
$$108.24 \times 1.0400 = 112.57$$
$$112.57 \times 1.0174 = 114.53$$
$$114.53 \times 0.9731 = 111.45$$

Averaging Percentages

Occasionally data such as are shown in Table 8.3 may be met with, and it may be desirable to obtain a figure for the per cent of spoilage for the entire plant. The three percentage figures added together give 33.3 per cent,

Table 8.3—Production and Spoilage in Three
Departments of a Manufacturing Plant
Making the Same Items

Department	Units produced	Units spoiled	Per cent spoiled
1	150	15	10.0
2	300	10	3.3
3	225	45	20.0
All departments	675	70	10.4

Illustrative data.

and division by 3 (the number of departments) yields 11.1 per cent. A per cent spoilage figure for the plant may also be obtained by totaling the units produced (675) and the units spoiled (70) and determining the per cent spoiled by dividing the units spoiled by the units produced. This time the result is 10.4 per cent. The first of these answers is a simple arithmetic mean, but it is not a useful average in the present instance, since we are interested in the average spoilage rate for the plant as a whole. If the three percentages are to be averaged, each should be given its proper importance; that is to say, each should be weighted according to the number of units produced. If this is done, the result is 10.4 per cent, as just found.[2]

For certain purposes, ratios may sometimes be averaged, ignoring the size of the categories from which each ratio has been computed. This might

---

[2] A weighted arithmetic average is obtained by multiplying each value by its weight, summing these products, and dividing this sum by the sum of the weights. Thus,

$$\frac{(150)(0.100) + (300)(0.033) + (225)(0.200)}{150 + 300 + 225} = 0.104 = 10.4 \text{ per cent.}$$

be the case if we were averaging the current ratios of Table 8.1, in order to find a typical value to use as a standard of comparison.[3]

A person owns several shares of stock in three different automobile corporations and wishes to ascertain his average percentage yield. This is a slightly more complicated illustration of averaging percentages, for weighting according to importance, in this case, means to weight each percentage not according to the number of shares held, but according to the value of the holdings in each corporation. The weighted average is more easily obtained, however, by dividing total dividends by total value of shares shown in Table 8.4. Thus the average yield is $3,260 ÷ $79,698 = 0.0409 = 4.09 per cent. The reason the average yield is only slightly greater than the yield on Chrysler is that most of the money was invested in that corporation.

Table 8.4—Computations of Average Yield on Common Stock Holdings
in Three Automobile Corporations, 1956

Corporation	Number of shares	Average* price per share	Dividends per share	Percentage yield	Total value of shares	Total dividends on shares
Chrysler	1000	$73.50	$3.00	4.08	$73,500	$3,000
Ford	100	57.50†	2.40	4.17	5,750	240
General Motors .	10	44.75	2.00	4.47	448	20
Total	...	....	...	...	$79,698	$3,260

* Average of high and low for year, known as mid-range.
† Average of high and low since it was listed in 1956.
Source: Moody's Investors Service, *Moody's Industrial Manual*, 1957, and the Fitch Publishing Co., Inc., *The Annual Fitch Stock Record*, January 1, 1957.

Comparing Percentages

If one branch office sells 40 per cent of its quota and a second office 60 per cent of its quota, there are several ways in which a statement may be worded concerning the two figures. First, it may be stated that the per-cent-of-quota figure for the second office was 150 per cent *of* that for the first office. Second, it may be said that the per-cent-of-quota figure for the second office was 50 per cent *greater than* that for the first office. Third, it may be noted that the per-cent-of-quota figure for the second branch was 20 *percentage points* more than that indicated for the first branch. The first two statements are relative comparisons of relatives; the third is an absolute comparison of relatives obtained by subtracting one percentage from the other.

In an advertisement appearing in *The Country Home*, the Firestone Tire and Rubber Company in referring to a study made by a publishing house

---

[3] When this is done the geometric mean may be used. Thus,

$$\sqrt[3]{0.100 \times 0.033 \times 0.200} = 0.082 = 8.2 \text{ per cent.}$$

For a discussion of the geometric mean, see Chapter 16.

said: "They found that 68% of those interviewed are going to buy tires this summer, and that 27.2% of these car owners are going to buy Firestone Tires—the next highest is only 20.6%, which shows the demand for Firestone Tires is 32% more than for any other make." In saying that the demand for Firestone tires is 32 per cent more than the demand for any other make, a relative comparison of the two particular percentages, 27.2 and 20.6, has been made. It would also be correct to say that the demand for Firestone tires was 132 per cent of that for any other make. Upon an absolute basis it might be said that, as a per cent of total, the demand for Firestone tires was 6.6 percentage points more than for any other make.

Errors and Misuses

If careful attention is given to published material, errors will occasionally be discovered in the use of percentages. Sometimes the wrong base is used. Occasionally percentages are based on too few items. At times arithmetic errors, often involving misplaced decimal points, will occur.

A sheet advertising a sale of $10,000 worth of imported and domestic gifts said, "Buy your Christmas presents now and save 100%!" This would seem to be the world's biggest sale—things appear to be given away. The reduction, however, was 50 per cent, and the use of the 100 per cent figure was due to a confusion of base. If an article priced at $3.00 is reduced to $1.50, the reduction is $1.50, or 50 per cent of the original price. The reduction is 100 per cent of the new price, but the base for the comparison indicated requires that the original price be used, not the new price.

A similar slip was made by the president of a flower growers association when he announced in a newspaper interview, "Flowers are 100 per cent cheaper than four months ago."

Another instance of an impossible percentage decrease is given in Ida M. Tarbell's *History of the Standard Oil Company* (Vol. II, p. 222). Here she says, "... prices [were] dropped at once by Standard agents on the introduction of an independent oil. A table offered to Congress in 1888, giving the extent of price cutting in the southwest, shows that it ranged from 14 to 220 per cent." A decrease of 220 per cent in the price of an article would mean that it was selling for less than nothing, for a negative amount; or in other words, that the seller was paying to have the article taken away!

In the July 2, 1932 issue of the *New York Times*, an Associated Press dispatch stated, "The depression took a stiff wallop on the chin here today. Plumbers, plasterers, carpenters, painters and others affiliated with the Indianapolis Building Trades Unions were given a 5 per cent increase in wages. That gave back to the men one-fourth of the 20 per cent cut they took last winter." The 5 per cent increase gives the men *less* than one-fourth of the 20 per cent cut. If a man originally received $25 a week, and was cut 20 per cent to $20 a week, then an increase of 5 per cent would mean that he would be getting $21 a week. The 5 per cent increase is not one-fourth, but one-fifth, of the 20 per cent decrease, because the decrease is figured upon the $25 base, whereas the 5 per cent increase is calculated upon $20 as a base. To carry this illustration a little further, it must be clear that a 50 per cent decrease would be offset not by a 50 per cent increase but by a 100 per cent increase, and that a 33.3 per cent decrease would be offset by a 50 per cent increase.

A certain manufactured product was selling at a profit of 3,800 per cent, according to the *Columbus Dispatch*. The cost of manufacture was given as $1.75 per unit and the selling price as $40 per unit. The percentage of profit is not correct, whether cost or selling price be used as the base. Just how the figure of 3,800 per cent was obtained is not at all clear. Perhaps a "rough and ready" comparison was made in which the profit was called "approximately $38" and the cost "about a dollar." If the profit in the preceding instance is figured on cost, then it is 2,185.7 per cent; if figured on selling price, it is 95.6 per cent. Both methods of calculating profit margin are in use, and it is not within the province of this book to go into the merits of the two methods. However, it must be obvious that if profit is figured upon selling price as a base, the percentage of profit can never be so great as 100 per cent unless the cost is zero. When profit is compared to cost, the per cent of profit may exceed 100 per cent.

In the *Monthly Labor Review*, published by the United States Department of Labor, it was stated that 4.9 per cent of the offers of part-time household employment with provision for carfare, in Washington, D.C., during the period September 16–October 15, 1944, were at $18.00 per week. It is perhaps surprising to learn that there were 2 such offers, there having been 41 offers of this category at various weekly wages. It is often misleading to compute a percentage where the number in the base is small, especially if carried out to one or more decimal places.[4] In the present instance it must be said, in justice to the editors of the *Monthly Labor Review*, that the absolute number of cases was given as well as the relative number, and percentages were not given where the base was as small as 24 cases.

A news item appearing in the *New York Herald Tribune* during the depression of the 1930's stated that times may be hard but silk hosiery is still being worn. A department store buyer is quoted: "We still sell lisle and flat black cotton hosiery. But the figures from February to June, 1931, show that 31 per cent of all sales were plain lisle hose, 1.59 per cent were fancy lisle, and more than 98 per cent were silk and chiffon." A bit of simple arithmetic reveals that the percentages total not 100 per cent, as they should, but 130.59 per cent! Perhaps the sales of plain lisle hose were 0.31 per cent. To avoid such errors as this, it is well to say "31 hundredths of 1 per cent."

The *New York Times* stated that for the fiscal year ended June 30, 1930, air mail "lost through fire was 4,863 pounds, or a percentage of but 0.00063."

---

[4] When a percentage is calculated from a small sample, it is also misleading because it is unreliable.

If an insurance company had based its rates for air-mail fire insurance on this percentage it would have found itself in serious difficulties. The amount of mail carried by air was 7,715,741 pounds. Dividing the pounds lost by fire by the total pounds carried yields 0.063 per cent, a figure 100 times that quoted in the paper!

Misuses and errors such as these are found all too frequently.

Ratio Analysis

The analysis of business ratios is widely employed in business. Among the ratios frequently used are the following:

Current ratio: current assets ÷ current liabilities.

Merchandise turnover: cost of goods sold during a year ÷ average inventory, also at cost.

Receivables turnover: net sales ÷ accounts receivable at end of year.

Net worth to debt.

Net worth to fixed assets (after depreciation).

Sales to fixed assets (after depreciation).

Margin of profits: Earnings from operations ÷ net sales.

By a careful examination of business ratios and their interrelations over a period of years, and by a comparison of the ratios with typical ratios for firms in the same industry, much can be learned about the liquidity, general condition, and prospects of the firm being analyzed. The principles of ratio analysis are appropriate for study in business administration (perhaps in accounting or business finance) rather than in statistical methods. The statistical part of ratio analysis is related to setting standards for business ratios.

Setting standards. Sometimes business ratios for different firms are averaged, in order to obtain a standard with which a given firm can make comparisons.[5] Before averaging ratios, however, the firms should be classified, so that the data will be reasonably homogeneous. Some bases of classification that are pertinent are:

1. Whether manufacturing, wholesaling, or retailing.
2. Type of product. If store, type of store.
3. Size group, according to sales.
4. Geographical location.
5. Type of sales area, such as city or rural.
6. Whether selling for cash or credit.
7. Size and stability of earnings.

When averaging ratios, the type of average must be determined and whether it is to be a simple or weighted average. Since the ratios are for

---

[5] For sources of ratio studies, see Richard Sanzo, *Ratio Analysis for Small Business*, Small Business Administration, Washington, D.C., 1957, Ch. 4.

different companies, rather than parts of a single organization, the method of averaging illustrated in Table 8.3 is not necessarily the best. But since we are dealing with ratios (which theoretically can vary from zero to infinity), and since we wish to obtain typical ratios, there is much to be said in favor of a simple geometric mean (discussed in Chapter 16).

In comparing the ratio for one's own firm with that of a standard for the industry, one should not necessarily think that the larger (or smaller) a ratio the better it is. One must remember that usually two factors are involved, safety and profitability. If one insists on too high a degree of safety (say by having a very large current ratio), his business may become unprofitable (by having too much tied up in merchandise). Usually a successful firm will have ratios not too far out of line with the typical. One should also remember that each business has individual characteristics that justify some departure from the average.

Much is to be learned also by a study of the relationship among ratios. A ratio should not be judged in isolation, but its interpretation is colored by the magnitude of the other ratios.

Chapter 9

LOGARITHMIC SCALES

In Chapter 8 it was stated that there are two kinds of comparisons: (1) absolute comparisons, and (2) relative comparisons. Absolute comparisons are made by taking the difference between two numbers; relative comparisons are made by taking the ratio of one number to another number. When presenting data graphically, in order to make absolute comparisons one uses arithmetic scales, and the paper is sometimes called difference paper. But in order to make relative comparisons, one uses a logarithmic scale for one or both axes. Paper that has only one logarithmic scale is called semi-logarithmic paper, or sometimes ratio paper. A chart drawn on ratio paper is often called a ratio chart.

There is only one principle to remember concerning each of these two types of paper:

On *arithmetic*, or *difference*, paper, equal spaces anywhere on the paper indicate equal differences.

On *semi-logarithmic*,[1] or *ratio*, paper, equal spaces anywhere on the paper indicate equal ratios.

Arithmetic and Geometric Progressions

For the conventional type of chart, using arithmetic scales, a given distance on any one axis always indicates the same *amount*. Reference to Chart 9.1 will reveal that nine-sixteenths of an inch on the vertical scale always represents 5 units, whereas seven-sixteenths of an inch on the horizontal scale indicates a year. The conventional type of curve is useful for showing absolute differences, whether they are between points on one curve or between points on two or more curves on the same axes.

In the series of figures 2, 4, 6, 8, 10, 12, 14, 16, 18, it will be noticed that each succeeding figure is 2 greater than the figure before. There has thus been a constant *amount* of increase. A series which increases or decreases by a constant amount is termed an *arithmetic progression*. Table 9.1 shows the series just mentioned, and Chart 9.1 shows how the figures appear when plotted. They yield a straight line, as will any arithmetic progression when plotted in relation to the conventional scales. Scales such as those used for Chart 9.1 are usually referred to as "arithmetic" or "difference" scales. An arithmetic progression increasing by a greater amount than the one

---

[1] It is called semi-logarithmic, rather than logarithmic, because only one of the two axes has a logarithmic scale; the other scale being arithmetic.

shown (for example, 2, 6, 10, 14, and so on) would result in a curve with greater slope. A decreasing arithmetic progression (such as 24, 22, 20, 18, and so on) would slope downward. Since an arithmetic progression gives a

Table 9.1—An Arithmetic Progression

Year	Units produced	Amount of increase
1947	2	. . .
1948	4	2
1949	6	2
1950	8	2
1951	10	2
1952	12	2
1953	14	2
1954	16	2
1955	18	2

straight line when plotted in reference to arithmetic scales, it follows that the eye can readily ascertain whether or not a given curve represents an arithmetic progression.

Chart 9.1—Arithmetic Progression of Table 9.1,
Plotted on Arithmetic Paper

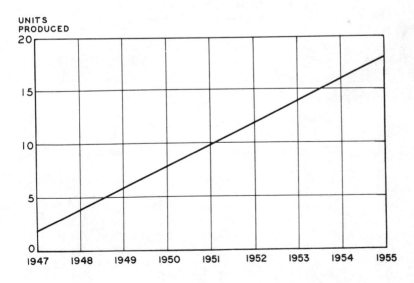

Frequently we are interested in the *percentage* change rather than the *amount* of change, and it is desirable to have some way by which a constant

Table 9.2—A Geometric Progression

Year	Units produced	Per cent increase
1947	2	...
1948	4	100
1949	8	100
1950	16	100
1951	32	100
1952	64	100
1953	128	100
1954	256	100
1955	512	100

percentage change may easily be visualized, and by which a large percentage change can be distinguished from a small percentage change. Many statistical series show a fairly constant percentage growth, at least through a portion of their duration. Table 9.2 illustrates a series having a constant percentage change. Such a series, whether increasing or decreasing, is termed a *geometric progression*. When the series of Table 9.2 is plotted in reference to arithmetic scales, it describes the curve shown in Chart 9.2. This curve is far removed from a straight line. It is concave upward, bending

**Chart 9.2—Geometric Progression of Table 9.2,
Plotted on Arithmetic Paper**

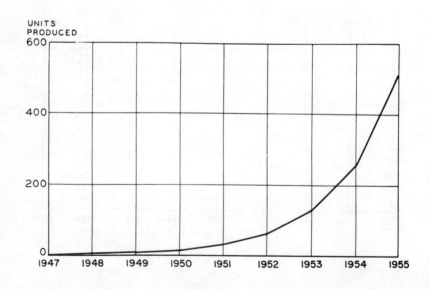

upward more and more steeply as we move from left to right along the
X axis.[2] This is characteristic of all increasing geometric progressions,
the degree of curvature being determined by the rate of increase. Similarly,
in the case of a decreasing geometric progression (as 100, 90, 81, 72.9, and
so on), the curve bends downward less and less steeply, that is, it slopes
downward but it also is concave upward.

Table 9.3—Increasing Values

Year	Units produced
1947	20
1948	62
1949	147
1950	300
1951	536
1952	811
1953	1104
1954	1425
1955	1755

Chart 9.3—Increasing Values of Table 9.3, Plotted on Arithmetic Paper
(The series plotted is not a geometric progression, but the
curve may appear so to the eye.)

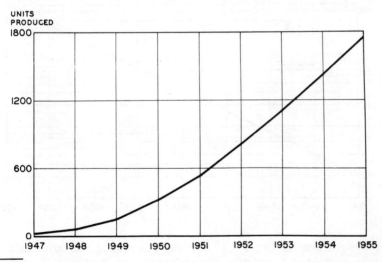

UNITS PRODUCED

[2] Such a curve is termed an *exponential curve*, known also as a compound-interest curve,
and is represented by the equation $Y = AB^X$. A straight line is indicated by $Y = a + bX$. The
exponential curve can be put in linear form as $\log Y = a + bX$, where $a = \log A$ and
$b = \log B$.

Any series of figures that increases *more* rapidly than an arithmetic progression bends upward when plotted on arithmetic paper and might readily give the visual impression of a geometric progression. A series of this nature is shown in Table 9.3 and is presented as a curve in Chart 9.3. It is virtually impossible for the eye to determine whether a curved line such as this one is the result of plotting a geometric progression or merely the representation of a progression which is increasing by increasing amounts. Similarly, a series that decreases *less* rapidly than an arithmetic progression (for example successive Y values of 25, 19, 14, 10, 7, and 5) slopes downward but is concave upward when drawn on arithmetic paper and might easily be mistaken for a decreasing geometric progression.

Semi-logarithmic Paper

A geometric progression is a straight line when plotted on semi-logarithmic paper. Thus, the data of Table 9.2, which was concave upward on Chart 9.2,

Chart 9.4—Geometric Progression of Table 9.3, Plotted on Semi-Logarithmic Paper

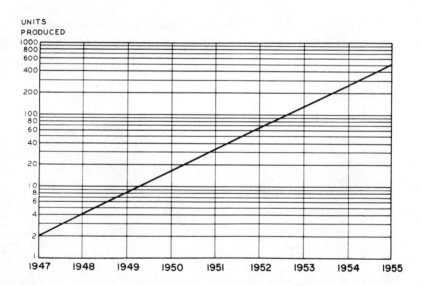

is a straight line on Chart 9.4.[3] On the other hand, the arithmetic progression of Table 9.1, which was a straight line when plotted on arithmetic paper as Chart 9.1, becomes concave downward when plotted on semi-logarithmic paper as Chart 9.5. However, it cannot be visually identified

---

[3] This follows from the fact that the exponential curve, $Y = AB^x$, which describes a geometric ratio, can also be written $\log Y = a + bX$, where $a = \log A$ and $b = \log B$.

as an arithmetic progression, since any curve increasing at a decreasing rate is concave downward when plotted on semi-logarithmic paper. The series of Chart 9.3, which looked in that chart as if it might be a geometric progression, is now clearly seen in Chart 9.6 not to be a geometric progression, but rather a series that is increasing by increasing amounts but by decreasing percentages.

Chart 9.5—Arithmetic Progression of Table 9.1, Plotted on Semi-Logarithmic Paper

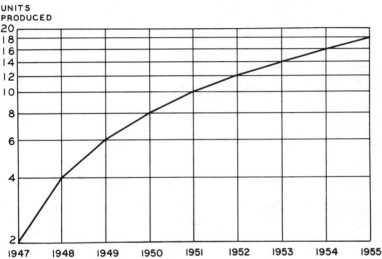

Ratio explanation. Although the grid that we shall use involves a logarithmic vertical scale, it is easy to understand and to use semi-logarithmic paper even though one has no knowledge of logarithms. It will be remembered that on arithmetic paper equal vertical distances on the vertical scale represent equal *amounts*. On semi-logarithmic paper, however, equal vertical distances represent equal *ratios* or *proportions*. The geometric progression of Table 9.2 has been plotted on semi-logarithmic paper in Chart 9.4, and it will be seen that the distance on the vertical scale from 2 to 4 is the same as the distance from 1 to 2. Similarly the distance from 6 to 8 is the same as the distance from 30 to 40. Likewise, any other ratio is represented by a constant vertical distance, and therefore a series of figures exhibiting a constant ratio of increase, such as those in Table 9.2, will produce a straight line as is shown in Chart 9.4. It should be noted that the slope of the curve in Chart 9.4 is constant throughout. This is especially important when two or more curves are to be compared, since, irrespective of the position of a curve on a given semi-logarithmic grid, equal slopes will represent equal relative changes, and curves may be placed close together to facilitate comparison. It is because of the foregoing characteristic that the term "ratio chart" is used.

Chart 9.6—A Series Increasing by Increasing Amounts, but by Decreasing Percentages, Plotted on Semi-Logarithmic Paper

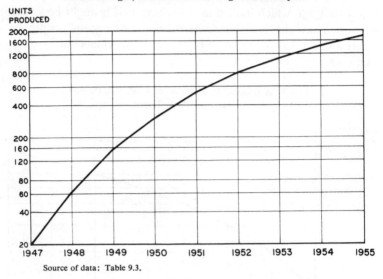

Source of data: Table 9.3.

A home-made slide rule. Because equal spaces represent equal ratios, two pieces of semi-logarithmic paper can be used for a slide rule. Chart 9.7 shows two such pieces placed alongside of each other. The sheet on the right has the scale value for 1 opposite the scale value for 2.5 of the sheet on the left. This places the 8.4 of the sheet on the right opposite the 21 of the sheet on the left. Thus, the home-made slide rule shows for this setting

$$2.5 \times 8.4 = 21;$$

$$21 \div 8.4 = 2.5.$$

The accuracy with which multiplications and divisions can be made depends on the size of the logarithmic scales and their accuracy.

Logarithmic explanation. Table 9.4 repeats the data of the geometric progression of Table 9.2 but shows also the logarithms[4] of the values. It may be observed that the logarithms form an arithmetic progression. If, now, we plot the values of the logarithms as in Chart 9.8, we find that a straight line results, and it is easy for the eye to grasp the fact that we are dealing with a series of figures that increases at a constant percentage. The visual effect is the same as that of Chart 9.4, and the two charts may be thought of as equivalent methods of presenting the same information. The semi-logarithmic chart has the advantage, however, that the numerical values, rather than their logarithms, are shown as scale values.

---

[4] A table of logarithms is given in Appendix 1.

**Chart 9.7—Use of Home-Made Slide Rule to
Compute 2.5 × 8.4 and 21 ÷ 8.4**

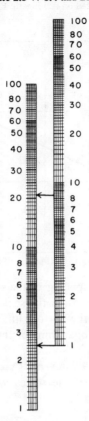

**Table 9.4—A Geometric Progression and
Logarithms of a Geometric
Progression**

Year	Units produced	Logarithm of units produced
1947	2	.30103
1948	4	.60206
1949	8	.90309
1950	16	1.20412
1951	32	1.50515
1952	64	1.80618
1953	128	2.10721
1954	256	2.40824
1955	512	2.70927

**Chart 9.8—Logarithms of Geometric Progression of Table 9.4,
Plotted on Arithmetic Paper**

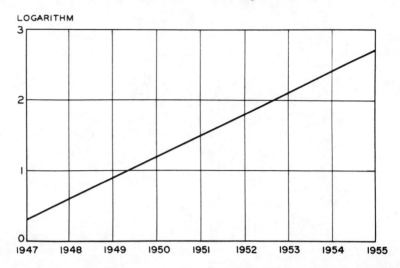

On a logarithmic scale the spacing of the scale is according to the logarithms of the scale values, rather than the scale values themselves. Thus on Chart 9.9, the distances above the bottom line for the scale values shown at the right are indicated by the logarithms of those scale values shown at the left.

An examination of Chart 9.9 reveals that as the scale values increase geometrically, the logarithms of the scales values increase arithmetically. For example:

Scale value	Logarithm		Scale value	Logarithm
1	.000		1	.000
2	.301		3	.477
4	.602		9	.954
8	.903			

The above statement follows directly from the definition of a logarithm, which is "the exponent of that power of a fixed number (called the base) which equals a given number." The base of the common logarithm is 10. Thus, for the expressions

$$10^0 = 1, \quad 10^1 = 10, \quad 10^2 = 100, \quad 10^3 = 1,000,$$

the given numbers are 1, 10, 100, 1,000, and the logarithms are 0, 1, 2, 3. The numbers are increasing geometrically, but the logarithms are increasing arithmetically. Also,

$$10^0 = 1, \quad 10^{0.301} = 2, \quad 10^{0.602} = 4, \quad 10^{0.903} = 8.$$

This is one of the sets of numbers and their logarithms tabulated above. The reason equal spaces represent equal ratios on semi-logarithmic paper is because the logarithms increase arithmetically as the numbers increase geometrically (i.e., by a constant ratio).

Chart 9.9—Scale Values and Logarithms of Scale Values

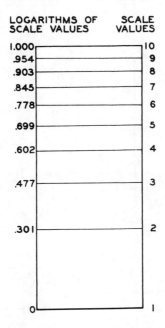

LOGARITHMS OF   SCALE
SCALE VALUES   VALUES

Labeling the vertical scale. It will be noticed that the vertical scale of Chart 9.4 is divided into three major sections called *cycles* or *phases*. Thus the paper upon which Chart 9.4 was drawn is termed "three-cycle (or three-phase) semi-logarithmic paper." The values on the vertical scale may begin at the bottom with any positive number. The value placed at the top of the first cycle in Chart 9.4 must be 10 times the value at the bottom of that cycle; the value at the top of the second cycle must be 10 times the value at the bottom of the second cycle (top of first cycle); the value at the top of the third cycle must be 10 times the value at the bottom of the third cycle (top of the second cycle), and so on. Chart 9.10 shows several three-cycle log scales with the scale values resulting from beginning with 0.1, 1, 2, 5, 10, 13, 25, and 50, respectively. It should be observed that any of these scales may be obtained merely by multiplying each of the scale numbers on the first scale by the proper constant.

Chart 9.10—Logarithmic Vertical Scales
(The scale beginning with 13 would be very difficult to use.)

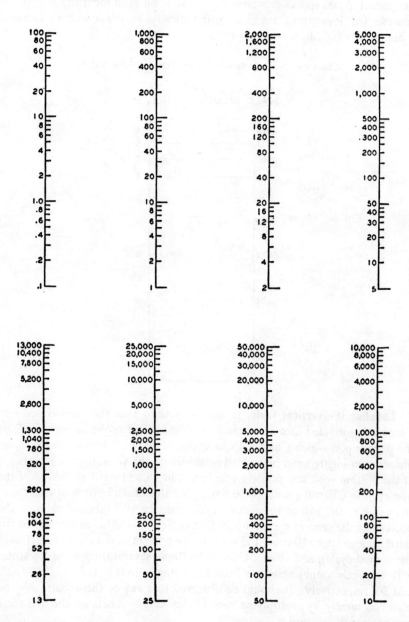

Chart 9.11—Comparisons of Series of Various Types Plotted in Relation to Arithmetic and Logarithmic Vertical Scales

(Series plotted as shown on one scale become as indicated on the other. The comparisons refer to increasing series only.)

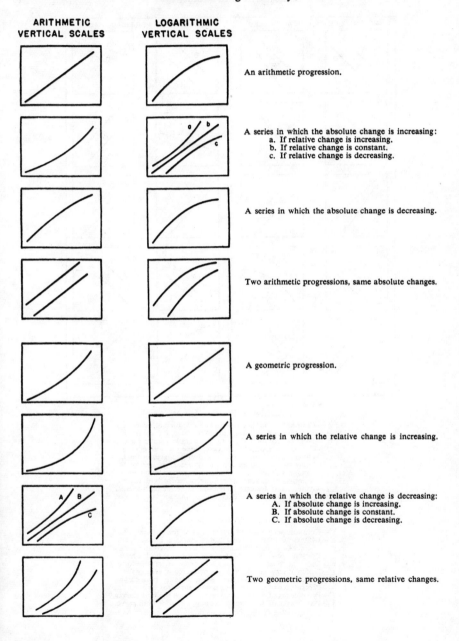

ARITHMETIC VERTICAL SCALES   LOGARITHMIC VERTICAL SCALES

An arithmetic progression.

A series in which the absolute change is increasing:
   a. If relative change is increasing.
   b. If relative change is constant.
   c. If relative change is decreasing.

A series in which the absolute change is decreasing.

Two arithmetic progressions, same absolute changes.

A geometric progression.

A series in which the relative change is increasing.

A series in which the relative change is decreasing:
   A. If absolute change is increasing.
   B. If absolute change is constant.
   C. If absolute change is decreasing.

Two geometric progressions, same relative changes.

Chart 9.12—Pairs of Curves on Arithmetic and Semi-Logarithmic Grids
(The two curves in each of the lower eight squares are equidistant
vertically from each other.)

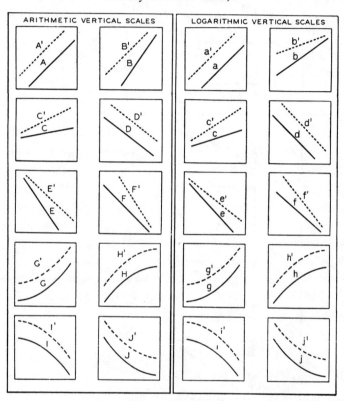

ARITHMETIC VERTICAL SCALES

A, A'—Constant amounts of increase, same for both curves.
B, B'—Different constant amounts of increase, greater for B.
C, C'—Different constant amounts of increase, greater for C'.
D, D'—Constant amounts of decrease, same for both curves.
E, E'—Different constant amounts of decrease, greater for E.
F, F'—Different constant amounts of decrease, greater for F'.
G, G'—Amounts of increase increasing, same for both curves.
H, H'—Amounts of increase decreasing, same for both curves.
I, I'—Amounts of decrease increasing, same for both curves.
J, J'—Amounts of decrease decreasing, same for both curves.

LOGARITHMIC VERTICAL SCALES

a, a'—Constant percentage of increase, same for both curves.
b, b'—Different constant percentages of increase, greater for b.
c, c'—Different constant percentages of increase, greater for c'.
d, d'—Constant percentages of decrease, same for both curves.
e, e'—Different constant percentages of decrease, greater for e.
f, f'—Different constant percentages of decrease, greater for f'.
g, g'—Percentages of increase increasing, same for both curves.
h, h'—Percentages of increase decreasing, same for both curves.
i, i'—Percentages of decrease increasing, same for both curves.
j, j'—Percentages of decrease decreasing, same for both curves.

While it is mathematically correct to begin the vertical scale at any positive value, it is customary to begin with a value that renders easy the interpolation of intermediate values. The scale of Chart 9.10, which begins at 13, would be very awkard to use. Such a choice should be avoided; ordanarily by starting at 10 instead.

Use of two vertical scales. A logarithmic scale cannot show zero because $\log 0 = -\infty$. If a zero were placed at the bottom of the first cycle, the top of that cycle would be 10 times $0 = 0$, and the top of the second and succeeding cycles would also be zero. Since there is no zero base line, the semi-logarithmic chart does not enable us to visualize the distance of a curve above a base line. In other words, it gives us no adequate visual impression of the absolute magnitude of the values plotted. We can, of course, read the plotted values back against the vertical scale, but this is not the sort of use for which charts are intended. There is no zero base line on a semi-logarithmic chart, and therefore distance above the bottom of the chart is not important, as it is for the arithmetic chart. Because equal vertical distances always represent the same ratio, we are at liberty to use two (or more) different vertical scales, as in Chart 9.14, in order to bring curves close together for comparison.

Interpretation of curves. Since equal vertical distances on a logarithmic scale represent the same ratio, it follows that for a given semi-logarithmic grid equal slopes anywhere on the grid represent the same percentage change. Also, the steeper the slope the greater the percentage change. Finally, if two lines are parallel on semi-logarithmic paper, they bear a constant ratio to each other; but if they are not parallel, the farther apart the two curves, the greater will be the ratio of the upper curve to the lower. Charts 9.11 and 9.12 should be studied before proceeding to the following section dealing with applications of the semi-logarithmic chart.

Applications

Comparing percentage rates of growth. Chart 9.13 shows, on an arithmetic grid, sales of General Electric Company and of McGraw Edison Electric Company. Because of the great difference in the size of these two series, it is difficult to compare them with respect to growth, except that the average *amount* of growth is greater for General Electric Company.

Chart 9.14 permits a more useful comparison. There are two scales on this chart. The one on the left applies both to General Electric Company and to McGraw Edison Company. It puts the two curves so far apart, however, that comparison is difficult. The scale on the right, which is only one-tenth as large as the one on the left, applies only to McGraw Edison. The upper curve for McGraw Edison is parallel to the lower one; it is also closer to the General Electric curve. This latter fact makes it easier to compare them. It is apparent that although the percentage growth of McGraw

**Chart 9.13—Sales of General Electric Company and McGraw Edison Company,
1944–1955**
(Arithmetic Vertical Scale)

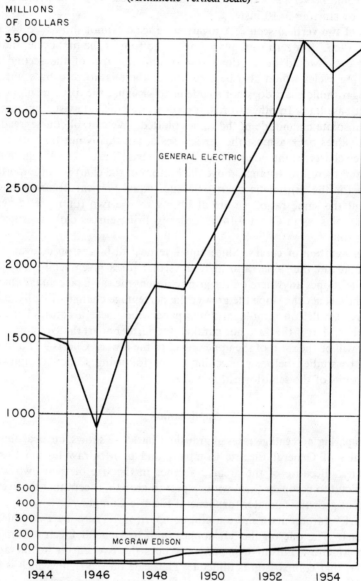

MILLIONS
OF DOLLARS

GENERAL ELECTRIC

MCGRAW EDISON

1944   1946   1948   1950   1952   1954

Source of data: Moody's Investors Service, *Moody's Industrial Manual,* various issues.

**Chart 9.14—Sales of General Electric Company and McGraw Edison Company,
1944–1955**
(Logarithmic Vertical Scale)

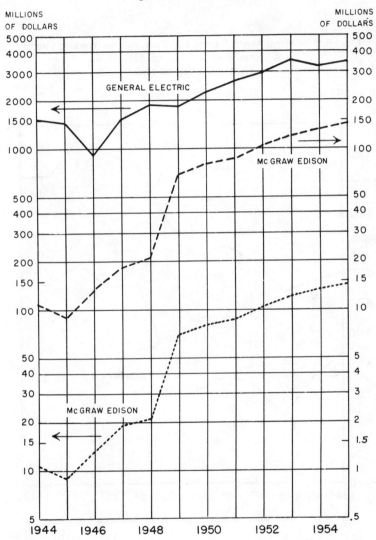

Source of data: See Chart 9.13.

Edison has been greater over the period as a whole, it is also apparent that this is accounted for by the tremendous increase between 1948 and 1949 (resulting from an important merger). Otherwise the trends of the two series are substantially parallel, and their percentage rates of growth nearly the same.

Chart 9.15—Current Assets, Current Liabilities, and Net Working Capital, of General Electric Company, 1944–1955
(Arithmetic Vertical Scale)

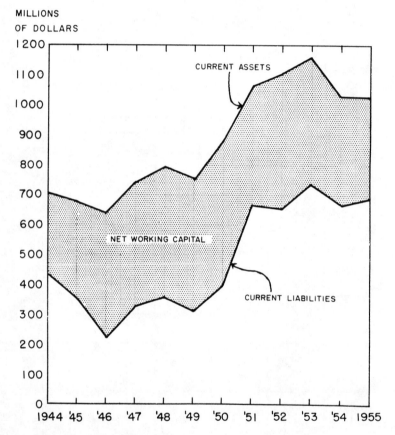

Source of data: Moody's Investors Service, *Moody's Industrial Manual*, various issues.

It must be obvious that the semi-logarithmic chart enables one to compare the percentage growth during one period of time with that during another period of time. Thus, the percentage growth for McGraw Edison was greater during the period 1944–1949 than it was during the period 1949–1955.

Percentage rates of growth can also be compared when the two series are in different units, such as sales and stores, or kilowatt-hours and tons.

It would of course be impossible to say which represents a greater annual growth, 100 kilowatt-hours, or 5 tons, though it might be of interest to note that an increase of 100 kilowatt-hours in one series tends to be accompanied by an increase of 5 tons in another series.

Comparing amplitude of fluctuations. Referring to Chart 9.13 again, it is apparent that the absolute fluctuations from year to year are greater for

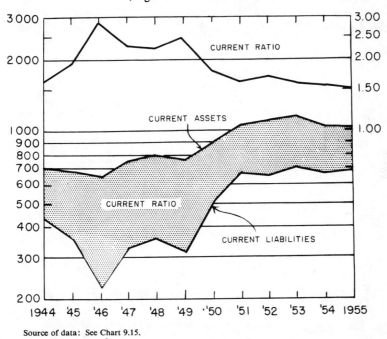

Chart 9.16—Current Assets, Current Liabilities, and Current Ratio, of General Electric Company, 1944–1955
(Logarithmic Vertical Scale)

General Electric than they are for McGraw Edison. But Chart 9.14 shows that the percentage fluctuations in the two series are about the same.

As another illustration, notice Charts 9.15 and 9.16. The amount of year-to-year fluctuation seems to be about the same for current assets and current liabilities. However, Chart 9.16 indicates that the percentage fluctuations in current liabilities are more violent than those in current assets.

Percentage fluctuations can be compared by use of semi-logarithmic paper just as easily when the series being compared are in different units.

Showing ratios. The amount of working capital, shown by the distance between the current assets line and the current liabilities line of Chart 9.15, seems to be about the same, with no perceptible trend.

Chart 9.16 indicates that changes in the current ratio are attributable more to changes in current liabilities than to changes in current assets. Changes in the current ratio can be observed either by noting changes in the distance between current assets and current liabilities, or by observing the movements of the broken line. The distance between the broken line and the 1.00 line on the current ratio scale is always the same as the distance between the current assets line and the current liabilities line.

Interpolation and extrapolation. Since many series show a fairly constant percentage growth, at least during part of their existence, and therefore appear almost as straight lines when plotted on semi-logarithmic paper, a reasonable forecast (extrapolation) can sometimes be made for a few years in the future simply by projecting the plotted curve. Chart 9.17 shows an

**Chart 9.17—Gross National Product, Total and Per Capita,
1910–1953, and Projection through 1965**

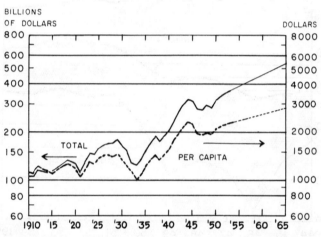

Source of data: Joint Committee on the Economic Report, *Potential Economic Growth of the United States During the Next Decade*, p. 35.

extrapolation of gross national product in 1953 dollars and gross national product per capita in 1953 dollars, made by the staff of the Joint Committee on the Economic Report. If plotted on arithmetic paper, these data would yield a curve bending sharply upward, especially in the later years. On semi-logarithmic paper, however, the upward slope shows a slight tendency to decrease. Such extrapolations may be made either graphically or mathematically. A forecast of this type will be correct only if the causes of the past growth continue to operate in the future. Also, as pointed out in Chapter 37 and elsewhere, no forecast should be a blind graphic or mathematical procedure. A thorough knowledge of the series being studied and of associated economic, social, and other allied factors is essential. It should be apparent that interpolation (reading between two plotted points) may be more reliably done than may extrapolation (forecasting). Intercensal population estimates are sometimes made by logarithmic interpolation, and the interpolated values may be determined approximately from a semi-logarithmic chart.

There is nothing inherent in semi-logarithmic paper that makes inter-polation or extrapolation more accurate on that kind of paper than on arithmetic paper. It is only when a series plotted on semi-logarithmic paper is more nearly straight than when plotted on arithmetic paper that the former type of paper is better. It so happens that most economic series are increasing in a way that is more nearly constant geometrically than arith-metically.

Constructing Logarithmic Scales

Ruled semi-logarithmic paper, with one cycle, two cycles, three cycles, and four cycles may be obtained from numerous sources. Occasionally, however, one may wish to use a scale that is different from those available on ready-ruled forms.

If one wishes to alter the logarithmic scale shown on a sheet of graph paper, it may be done readily. As shown in Chart 9.18, the scale may be expanded by placing a piece of paper at such an angle on the semi-logarithmic paper that the desired scale is obtained, and then marking the divisions thereon. The scale may be contracted by placing the logarithmic scale at such an angle on the other sheet as to produce the desired scale, as shown in Chart 9.19.

Chart 9.18—A Method of Expanding Logarithmic Scales

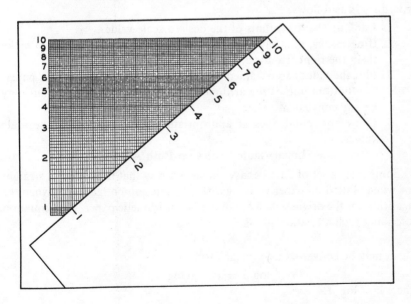

Chart 9.19—A Method of Contracting Logarithmic Scales

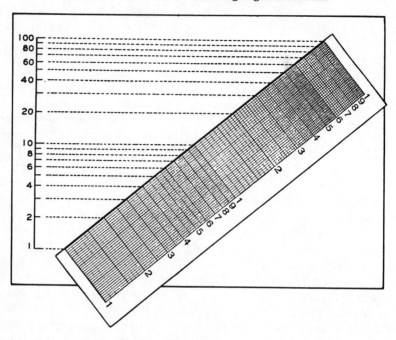

If it is necessary to construct a large semi-logarithmic grid such as would be used for a wall chart, neither of the above methods would suffice. By the use of a table of logarithms a scale of any size may be constructed. The procedure is as follows:

1. Look up the logarithms of the desired scale values.
2. If necessary, multiply the logarithms by a constant suitable to make them the right size for convenient plotting.
3. Plot the values so obtained on the vertical axis of arithmetic paper. The bottom line of the arithmetic paper need not be zero, but may be any convenient value.
4. Draw horizontal lines at appropriate intervals and print the scale values.

Logarithmic Scales on Both Axes

Sometimes a set of data behaves in such a way that it becomes a straight line when plotted on paper with logarithmic scales on both axes, or when the logarithms of the original data are plotted on arithmetic paper. The equation describing such a relationship is

$$Y = AX^b,$$

which may be converted into linear form as

$$\log Y = a \not\sim b \log X,$$

where $a = \log A$.

Chart 9.20 shows the relationship between net profits of 24 aircraft manufacturing companies and total compensation of their chief executives. Both scales are logarithmic. If arithmetic scales were used the points would spread apart more and more as we proceed upward and to the right on the

**Chart 9.20—Net Profits and Total Compensation of Chief Executives
in 24 Aircraft Manufacturing Companies in 1956**
(Logarithmic Scales)

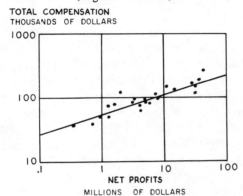

Source: Arch Patton, "Annual Report on Executive Compensation," *Harvard Business Review*, Vol. 35, September, October 1957, p. 128.

chart. Chapter 27 contains another illustration of the use of logarithmic scales. It would be worthwhile to study Charts 27.1, 27.2, and 27.3 at this point.

Other types of ruling are also available, such as paper ruled on one axis according to reciprocals of the scale values. Such types of paper are too specialized, however, for inclusion in this book.

Chapter 10

SOURCES AND COLLECTION OF DATA

The data used in statistical work may be obtained from various sources. Accounting records contain much information that is useful for purposes other than merely the evaluation of assets, liabilities, and proprietorship, and the determination of profit and loss. The various departments of a business, also, in the course of their routine activity maintain records of a statistical nature. It may be, however, that the internal records do not yield all the information necessary to solve a particular problem. For instance, if one wishes to account for a decline in sales, it would certainly be helpful to know whether other firms in the industry are experiencing the same difficulty. Perhaps there is some agency that assembles this sort of data, and the figures may be available in either published or unpublished form. Of course, it may be desirable to pursue the question further and seek to learn the opinion of consumers concerning the various features of the product, and this makes necessary a direct canvass of consumer habits and attitudes.

The purpose of this chapter is to consider in turn these three methods of obtaining statistical data.

Internal Records

The accounting records furnish what is probably the most important source of internal data, since every dollar received and every dollar spent must be accounted for in some fashion, as well as every dollar earned and every dollar of expense incurred.

The keeping and using of such records for statistical purposes is greatly facilitated by the use of electric tabulating equipment. With such equipment one can maintain a complete accounting system. But more important for the purposes under consideration is the fact that these records may be kept in such a way as to facilitate their use by the statistician.

The use of electric tabulating equipment involves several machines and processes. Assuming that we are dealing with sales analysis, the original records would be sales invoices similar to the one on page 123. Each time a sale of 0301 Beauty Soap regular is made, it is necessary to transfer the information by means of a card-punch machine, similar to that illustrated on page 124, to a small sales-analysis card. Information on the sales invoice is summarized by code numbers and transferred to the sales-analysis card shown on page 125 by means of holes punched in appropriate columns and rows. As each card is punched it is filed according to customer, or in chronological, geographical, or other appropriate order. If more than one method of filing is to be used, the cards may be punched in duplicate.

Cards differently ruled and labeled may be used for the various accounting and statistical needs. Such cards may provide for: sales analysis; accounts and notes receivable and cash receipts; accounts payable; journal voucher; duplicate voucher check; traveling expense analysis; inventory card; job ticket; insurance policy record; patent, research, and investigation expense analysis; and so on. Cards may be obtained with no rulings and headings or may be printed so as to fit the individual needs of the business.

These cards are, of course, a complete record for the accounting department. Suppose, however, it is desired to classify the sales according to salesmen. This is done by a process of sorting. The cards are fed into a sorting machine (see page 125), which automatically separates them into groups according to the punched numbers representing the numbers of the salesmen at the rate of about 450 cards per minute. All the cards representing salesmen the last digit of whose number is 0, go into the first compartment; those with 1 as the last digit are deposited into the second compartment, and so on. A second sorting of each pile in respect to the tens' digit is then necessary to separate 10, 20, 30, 40, and so on, into separate groups. Notice that the sorting began with the numbers in the "units" column and then proceeded to the "tens" column rather than the reverse. The final numerical

Sales Invoice

REPRESENTATIVE COMPANY
INVOICE

SOLD TO	ACE DRUG CO 1412 STATE ST LUDINGTON MICH		1 3 BRANCH 6 7 CUSTOMER
SHIP TO	ACE DRUG CO 811 MAIN ST MUSKEGON MICH		
VIA	ACME TRUCK PREPAID		
TERMS	2% 10 DAYS NET 30		

SALESMAN	ORDER NUMBER	ORDER DATE	REF. NO.	INVOICE	INVOICE DATE
G DRISCOLL	AM 8462	06 07	7142013420		0 62 0

COMMODITY		UNIT PRICE	QUANTITY		AMOUNT
CODE	DESCRIPTION		NUMBER	UNIT	
0301	BEAUTY SOAP REGULAR	2 00	12	DZ	2 4 00
0302	BEAUTY SOAP GUEST	2 10	12	DZ	2 5 20
1314	SHAVE SOAP LARGE	2 90	24	DZ	6 9 60
1411	OIL SHAMPOO MEDIUM	3 00	50	DZ	15 0 00
1421	REG SHAMPOO SMALL	1 10	24	DZ	2 6 40
3242	SUPER PASTE MEDIUM	1 85	6	DZ	1 1 10
	BACK ORDERED				
0302	BEAUTY SOAP GUEST	2 10	12	DZ	
5410	LAUNDRY SOAP BAR	2 40	24	DZ	
5420	LAUNDRY SOAP CHIP	2 50	12	DZ	
	FREIGHT				2 43
					3 08 73 *

Electric Card Punch

This card punch is made in a nonprinting model, and in a printing model for simultaneous interpretation of the information punched in the cards. It is available either for punching numerical data only, or for punching both numerical and alphabetical information.

arrangement is achieved more easily in this way. Although the sorting machine may count the cards that it sorts into the different categories, it is necessary to run each group of cards through the accounting[1] machine (see page 126) in order to total the value of sales from the punched holes on each card. As a matter of fact, the machine will summarize not only these facts but several others, such as costs and commissions. The illustration shows an accounting machine; it counts and totals items from the punch cards and also prints the information on analysis sheets, several of which are shown on page 127.

---

[1] The devices shown are manufactured by the International Business Machines Corporation. Similar devices are manufactured by Remington Rand, Inc., Burroughs Corporation, and Underwood.

Punched Sales-Analysis Card

Card-Operated Counting Sorter

Arranges the punched cards in numerical or alphabetical sequence according to any classification punched in the cards, such as *Salesmen*, *Towns*, *Classes of trade*, and other required statistical or accounting groups. Also counts the number of cards in each class, and prints the results

Electric Punched-Card Accounting Machine

Prepares reports and records after cards have been arranged in the proper sequence. May be used to list both alphabetical and numerical details from every punched card or from selected punched cards and to accumulate and print the various classifications of totals, together with dollar signs, commas, and periods. All such compilations can be printed automatically as finished reports with complete descriptive information.

A mechanical device, useful for small studies, is known as the McBee Keysort. Cards on which facts are to be recorded have holes around the edges:

Information is recorded by punching out a portion of the card between the hole and the edge of the card, making a notch:

When rods are inserted at a chosen position on the cards, all cards with a notch in this position will not be held by the rod but will drop when the rod is raised. Multiple selection may be made by using two or more rods.

Suppose it is desired to know how many bakers are represented in the file. A rod is thrust through the front of the case and through the hole in the cards at the top of the slot used to designate bakers, and all cards for bakers will drop down. If it happens that information is desired concerning

Analysis Sheets

COMMODITY SALES BY SALESMAN								
BRANCH	NO	SALESMAN	QUARTER ENDED				SALES PREVIOUS QUARTER	SALES YEAR TO DATE
	CLASS	COMMODITY	FIRST MONTH	SECOND MONTH	THIRD MONTH	TOTAL		
13	32	G DRISCOLL						
	03	BEAUTY SOAP	1 0 6 9 4 0	1 1 0 0 1 0	6 6 5 5 0	2 8 3 5 0 0	3 7 7 6 2 0	6 6 1 1 2 0
	13	SHAVING SOAP	1 9 6 5 6 0	1 7 0 1 2 0	1 9 3 6 8 0	5 6 0 3 6 0	5 0 6 0 3 0	1 0 6 6 3 9 0
	14	SHAMPOO	1 2 7 4 4 0	1 0 6 2 0 0	1 3 6 8 0 0	3 7 0 4 4 0	2 9 1 0 4 0	6 6 1 4 8 0
		[FOR THE PURPOSE OF THIS EXHIBIT ONLY] [A FEW COMMODITIES ARE ILLUSTRATED]				1 8 0 9 3 0 0 ❋	1 8 6 4 8 0 0 ❋	3 6 7 4 1 0 0 ❋
13	45	R M EDWARDS						
	03	BEAUTY SOAP	9 6 0 0 0	4 7 3 5 0	5 7 1 5 0	2 0 0 5 0 0	1 4 6 5 0 0	3 4 7 0 0 0

NET REVENUE ANALYSIS BY SALESMAN								
BRANCH	SALESMAN		GROSS SALES	RETURNS AND ALLOWANCES	NET SALES	COST SALES	TRAVEL AND EXPENSE	COMMISSION	NET REVENUE
	NO	NAME							
13	29	A ANDREWS	5 4 0 3 0 0	3 7 5 0 0	5 0 2 8 0 0	2 9 6 0 0 0	2 5 7 0	4 2 5 0 0	1 6 1 7 3 0
13	32	G DRISCOLL	6 1 1 9 0 0	4 3 5 0 0	5 6 8 4 0 0	3 8 2 5 0 0	2 6 4 0	5 7 4 1 4	1 2 5 8 4 6
13	45	R M EDWARDS	3 9 0 5 0 0	3 4 0 0 0	3 5 6 5 0 0	2 2 4 0 0 0	2 9 0 0	3 4 0 0 0	9 5 6 0 0
13	47	A H FRANKLIN	7 5 1 3 0 0	4 5 0 0 0	7 0 6 3 0 0	5 1 3 5 0 0	2 8 0 0	6 2 5 0 0	1 2 7 5 0 0
13	51	J A HOLLAND	6 2 5 7 0 0	4 4 1 0 0	5 8 1 6 0 0	3 8 5 5 0 0	2 6 2 5	5 9 5 5 0	1 3 3 9 2 5
13	55	L B LAWSON	6 1 2 0 0 0	4 2 9 0 0	5 6 9 1 0 0	3 8 5 0 0 0	2 5 7 5	5 7 5 2 5	1 2 4 0 0 0

only those bakers who speak Spanish, a second rod is thrust through the cards at the top of the slot used to designate Spanish-speaking persons. Then only those cards drop which represent bakers who speak Spanish.

Accounting records are not the only internal business records. Individual records of employees maintained by the personnel department, production orders, idle equipment reports, and stores requisitions are some illustrations of internal records of a nonaccounting nature. These and others will be drawn upon by the statistician from time to time.

External Sources

It is customary to distinguish between two types of sources: *primary* and *secondary*. The source of data is said to be primary when the data are published or released by the same organization that collected them; it is secondary when the data are published or released by another organization. Census volumes are primary sources, since the data shown therein are the result of enumerations conducted by the Bureau of the Census. The *Statistical Abstract of the United States*, also published by the Bureau of the Census, is, for the most part, a secondary source: the data contained in this volume are merely brought together from numerous sources, governmental and otherwise, only part of the contents originating with the Bureau of the Census.

Although it may frequently be more convenient to go to secondary sources for material, it is often much safer to go to the primary source. The reasons for this preference are:

1. A primary source often shows more detailed information than does a secondary source.

2. Definitions of terms and units are more likely to be found in primary sources. It is essential that the user of data understands what is meant by the units in which the data are recorded. The terms "profit," "farm," "dwelling," and so on, are sometimes used in several ways.

3. When a secondary source is used, there is a slight additional risk of errors of transcription, since the data have been reprinted from a primary source.

4. In a primary source may be included copies of the forms (schedules or questionnaires) used to collect the information, together with a description of the procedure used in the investigation, such as the method of collection, the type of sample, and the size of the sample. This information may give the user some idea of the degree of reliance which may be placed in the data.

When taking figures from an existing source, either primary or secondary, certain questions must always be asked: *Is the collecting agency biased?* If an organization has been set up for the avowed purpose of furthering some objective, data supplied by this organization may be biased, consciously or unconsciously. *If a sample was used, was it representative?* More will be said about the problem of sampling in Chapter 13. For the present, an example will suffice: A representative sample of the homes of a city cannot be had by selecting names from a telephone directory, since many of the homes of poorer families would be omitted. Are figures comparable from year to year? There are many reasons for lack of comparability, among which may be mentioned: changes from fiscal to calendar year or vice versa; revisions of data (such as including more firms in a reporting list), which are not, and sometimes cannot, be carried into the earlier years of a series; changes in definitions.

When data are being combined from several sources, the additional problem of comparability is present. Lack of comparability may exist because two organizations have used different definitions, such as different formulas for computing labor turnover. As another example, the Bureau of Mines, in reporting coal production in the United States, uses short tons of 2,000 pounds, whereas the Bureau of Foreign and Domestic Commerce, when showing data of coal exports, uses long tons of 2,240 pounds.

External sources of data are of several kinds:[2]

---

[2] A selected list of readily available sources of data is given as Appendix U in F. E. Croxton and D. J. Cowden, *Applied General Statistics*, 2d ed., Prentice-Hall, Inc., Englewood Cliffs, N.J., 1955.

1. *Trade associations.* Many industries in the United States are organized into trade associations. One important function of such associations is to collect data concerning the industry from the members, to summarize them for the industry, and to disseminate them exclusively among the members. Some trade associations make public a great deal of data, as in *Automobile Facts and Figures*, published annually by the Automobile Manufacturers Association, in *Steel Facts* published by the American Iron and Steel Institute, in *A Yearbook of Railroad Information*, issued each year by the Eastern Railroad Presidents Conference Committee on Public Relations, and in the *Rayon Organon*, a monthly publication of the Textile Economics Bureau, Inc. Such information may concern capacity, production, shipments, unfilled orders, prices, wages, payrolls, employment, and the like. At the present time, trade associations are of increasing importance as sources of data.

2. *Trade and financial journals.* Frequently there are several periodicals devoted to news of importance to a given industry or profession. These may be issued by a publishing house or by an important firm in the industry. Thus *The Iron Age* is published by the Iron Age Publishing Company. Several financial journals are devoted largely to the reporting of financial and industrial statistics; among these the *Commercial and Financial Chronicle*, *Barrons*, and *Dun's Statistical Review* should be mentioned.

3. *Daily newspapers.* From this source day-to-day information may be obtained, especially concerning reports on prices and volume of stocks and bonds sold in the security markets, prices on the commodity exchanges, interest rates, and foreign exchange rates. Each year the New York *World-Telegram* publishes also a statistical summary known as *The World Almanac*.

4. *Private statistical organizations.* Several important organizations of this type publish, as part of their service, a wide variety of numerical data. Standard and Poor's *Trade and Securities Statistics* supplies a wide variety of business and economic time series. Standard and Poor's Corporation and Moody's Investors Service publish each year the financial statements of all important corporations. In the present text much use has been made of *Moody's Industrial Manual*. Of especial interest to persons engaged in marketing is the *Sales Management Survey of Purchasing Power*. Published each year, this publication contains a wealth of information by counties, cities, and other geographical divisions.

5. *Governmental sources.* Voluminous information concerning population is published every ten years by the Bureau of the Census. This agency also conducts, at irregular intervals, a *Census of Business*, which includes the following: *Census of Manufacturers*; *Census of Retail Trade*; *Census of Wholesale Trade*; *Census of Service Industries*. Of great interest to the businessman is information concerning commodity prices: the Bureau of Labor Statistics provides this information in the form of monthly index numbers of wholesale prices, retail food prices, and consumers' prices which appear in the *Monthly Labor Review*.

Four publications that bring together data covering a wide range of activity should be mentioned. The *Statistical Abstract of the United States*, published annually by the Bureau of the Census, contains data concerning nearly any field in which one may be interested. If more details are required, the investigator may turn to the sources given under the tables in this volume. A supplement called *Historical Statistics of the United States* covers time series on an annual basis over many years. Still another important supplement to the *Statistical Abstract* is the *County and City Data Book*. For data on a monthly basis the Office of Business Economics of the U.S. Department of Commerce publishes the *Survey of Current Business*. Annual supplements summarize the data on a monthly basis for several years, and on an annual basis for a longer period. There is also a special supplement on National income. *Economic Indicators*, issued by the Joint Committee (of Congress) on the Economic Report, contains monthly and annual data, and charts. Supplements on special topics are issued from time to time. Also general in scope, but with more attention to financial data, is the *Federal Reserve Bulletin*, issued by the Federal Reserve Board. These four publications are, of course, secondary sources as regards most of their information.

Steps in a Statistical Investigation

It is not often that the business statistician will need to collect original statistical data, but he may occasionally need to do so. Furthermore, a working knowledge of the proper procedure in collecting data will enable him to evaluate data taken from other sources.

When a businessman must attempt to obtain information directly from the consuming public, the study may be conducted by his own staff or may be assigned to a research organization.

The steps in a statistical investigation may be described as follows:

1. General formulation of the problem.
2. Preparation of schedule.
3. Designing the sample.
4. Collecting the data.
5. Editing schedules.
6. Tabulating the data.
7. Presentation, analysis, and interpretation.

General formulation of the problem. The first step in making a statistical study consists of a detailed consideration of the problem to be studied. Other investigations in the same and allied fields should be examined, since they may contain some of the information sought. Frequently it is important to examine these other studies carefully in order that one's own investigation may be carried on in such a way that it will be comparable to these others. Sometimes, for comparative purposes, it will be desirable to define units in the same way as in earlier studies; sometimes the previously used definitions do not seem logical and must be discarded.

A manufacturer of toilet soap wishes to know more about the retail market for his product, and the information is to be obtained from a representative sample of housewives. So far as can be ascertained, no other studies of a like nature are available, and it is therefore necessary for him to formulate the problem upon the basis of his own experience. One fact of importance is the number of cakes of soap used per year by each family; but this information would mean little unless the number of persons in the family were also known. It might be worth while to know how many members of the family are adults and how many are children. Perhaps it would be well to know whether or not daily baths are taken by each member of the family and whether they are shower baths or tub baths. It would be well to know what brands of soap the family uses. It would probably not be possible to find out how many cakes of each brand are used, but the housewife can probably list the brands 1, 2, 3—according to their relative importance. Some housewives may prefer a floating soap, some a nonfloating soap; some may prefer scented, some an unscented soap; some may like a colored soap, some a white soap. Are housewives willing to pay more for a wrapped soap? Perhaps some of the answers to the above points might be related to the occupation of the husband or to his income level.

Devising the questions and making the schedule. The points that have been mentioned in the preceding paragraph are now listed as a preliminary step to the construction of the schedule, which is the form used to collect statistical information:

1. Number of cakes of soap used per year
2. Number of persons in household
    (a) Roomers
    (b) Adults in family
    (c) Children in family
3. Brands of soap used in order of amount
4. Reason for choice
5. Housewife's soap preferences
    (a) Floating or nonfloating
    (b) Scented or unscented
    (c) White or colored
    (d) Wrapped, or unwrapped at a lower price
6. Occupation of husband
7. Income of husband

In some localities it may be desirable to determine (by test) the degree of hardness of the water supply; and, where hard water is used, to ascertain which brands of soap are especially satisfactory or unsatisfactory, possibly also to find out how many families use water-softening devices or compounds. If the inquiry extended beyond toilet soaps to include soap used for dish-washing and laundry, inquiry would also have to be made concerning the use of detergents which may make suds but are not soap.

Attention must now be given to the definition of units, since there must be no doubt as to the meaning of any of the terms used. A cake of soap seems at first not to need defining, even though there is marked variation in size and weight. Some families, however, buy soap in bars rather than in cakes, and occasionally small, individual, hotel-style cakes may be used. It is very rare for families to use the small cakes, and it is easily possible to write "bars" after the answer to the first question when necessary.

Upon reflection it is decided to separate the members of the family into those eighteen or over and those under eighteen years of age, since the purpose of this question is to ascertain if families with children use more or less soap than those whose members are older.

The questions listed may now be arranged, with slight changes in wording, into a schedule form. For ease of handling it is advisable to use a good grade of light cardboard, of standard filing size, and printed on one side only, in order to facilitate the later tabulation of the information. The schedule may appear as shown; and it may be noted that a space for remarks has been added. What is meant by a cake of soap is not stated on the schedule itself because these forms are intended to be taken from house to house by enumerators, who must be carefully instructed and trained in advance. More detail is, of course, needed when a schedule is sent to the informant through the mail.

Soap-Study Schedule

Before putting a schedule into actual use, it is advisable to try it out with a representative group of people and to revise it in the light of what is learned in the tryout. Sometimes it is found that one or more questions are poorly framed, or that other clarifying questions should be added. If it is not possible to try out the schedule, an alternative procedure consists of submitting it to a qualified expert for criticism and suggestions.

There are a few general cautions concerning the questions to be used on schedules. These cautions are especially important when the schedules are sent to the informant to be filled out instead of being filled out by a trained enumerator.

1. *Questions should be clearly stated.* For example, the question "Married or single?" might be answered "Yes," which is meaningless. It would have been equally meaningless had the answer been "No." The question, as stated, often yields such ambiguous answers; furthermore, there are other categories which should be considered. There are several correct ways of asking such a question. One may say, "State whether married or single." Better and more complete is the following form:

Check whether:

____Single   ____Widowed

____Married   ____Divorced

This question is easy to answer, as are all questions designed to be answered by *yes* or *no*, a number, a check mark, or an underscore.

2. *"Leading" questions should never be asked.* Putting the answer into the mouth of the informant is not a scientific attempt to arrive at facts, but rather an attempt to support a preconceived idea. The enumerator is asking a leading question if he starts with, "Why do you like Our Soap best?" instead of asking first, "Which soap do you prefer?" and second, "Why do you prefer it?"

Occasionally an investigator will call upon or telephone a number of housewives and ask each if she uses a certain product. If she answers in the affirmative, the investigator asks if she prefers this product. In this way he builds up a large total of persons who prefer the product.

3. *Except when studying attitudes, an objective reply is always preferable to a subjective reply.* If a question is to be asked concerning the condition of a roof, it should not read, "Is condition of roof excellent, good, fair, or poor?" Rather, a set of definite questions should be asked as to whether or not the roof leaks, as to the age of the roof, the material used in the roof, and so on.

4. *If questions cannot be answered accurately, approximate answers may be useful.* Some types of questions are nearly certain to be answered only approximately. Thus the question as to how many cakes of soap are used in a year could not be answered accurately by very many housewives. Possibly she could state more accurately when she last bought soap, and how much. From many such replies an estimate of the average amount of soap purchased per year could be estimated.

Another interesting illustration is that of the reports of ages received by the United States Census. Reference to the published reports of the Census will reveal that a great many people have a tendency to report ages in multiples of five years. Strange as it may appear, more people are reported to the Census as being (for example) 35 years of age than are reported as 34 or 36 years old. It is almost certain that more exact information on age is obtained when the inquiry asks for the date of birth than when it merely asks for age. There are, of course, other reasons also which account for the "fives concentration," among them being that census information is often supplied by one member of a household for all of the other members.

5. *It is sometimes desirable to use check questions on a schedule.* When an applicant for life insurance is being examined, he is asked his age. Later during the examination, he is asked his date of birth and, if he has falsified his age, he is almost certain to be embarrassed in an attempt to supply a date of birth consistent with the falsified age. When such incompatible answers are received as to age and date of birth, it is customary to regard neither as correct. If the matter is important, as in the granting of insurance, it is best to require documentary evidence in the form of a birth certificate or otherwise.

6. *Any questions that may offend the person being interviewed should be studiously avoided.* Questions of an unnecessarily prying nature should also be avoided. If questions involving personal or confidential information are to be asked, it is important that extreme tact be used. Such questions, when asked, are usually placed at the end of an interview. This is the reason that the question concerning income was placed last on this soap-study schedule.

Designing the sample. One of the problems that is usually dealt with early in an investigation has to do with the inclusiveness of the enumeration. A complete enumeration (such as the Decennial Census of Population) is usually not feasible for the businessman, even when he is concerned with only a single city. Neither is a complete enumeration necessary, since a properly selected sample will ordinarily yield sufficiently reliable results at a relatively moderate cost.[3] Also, if the sampling method is used, an investigation can be made at more frequent intervals. It may be very important for information to be up to date. An adequate sampling plan enables a businessman to obtain information efficiently and at minimum expense. One organization manufacturing a product of high cost per unit, and in which pattern is an important factor, spends large amounts of money to find out *ahead of time* which of its proposed patterns for the next year will be most likely to sell well. These are the ones that are then manufactured.

---

[3] Sometimes a sample is more accurate than a complete enumeration. For a given amount of money it may be more accurate to devote more effort to obtaining a relatively few accurate responses, rather than a large number of less accurate ones. In quality control work, 100 per cent inspection often results in the inspector overlooking defects or defectives because of "inspection fatigue," whereas if fewer pieces are inspected more thoroughly, perhaps only devoting a part of one's time to inspection, the net result will be better.

Before a sampling plan can be adopted, it is necessary to define the population which we wish to include:

All persons?
All adults?
All adult males?
All adult male clerical workers?
All adult male clerical workers with a college education?
All adult male clerical workers with a college education who have been employed less than 5 years?

It would be easy to mention other related categories. The precise meaning of some of the words used is not obvious; for example, "clerical," "college," and "education."

The size of the sample and method of sampling must also be determined. The basic method of sampling is random sampling. Sampling is random when each possible *sample* has the same probability of being selected. The emphasis here is on the word *sample*. A sample is made up of *items*. It is not sufficient to say that each possible *item* has the same probability of being selected.

Sampling methods and sample design will be considered in more detail in Chapter 13.

Collecting the data. Schedules requesting information may be sent out by mail or some other method, or may be taken by enumerators to the people to be interviewed. Schedules filled out by the informant without supervision, and returned by the informant at his option, are usually called questionnaires. Of course, a schedule to be sent by mail must be not only much more completely self-explanatory than one to be taken by enumerators, but must also be accompanied by a courteous letter of explanation and a self-addressed, stamped (or business-reply) envelope. It might appear that use of the mails is an inexpensive means of collecting data, but it must be noted that many people fail to reply and that, therefore, a certain amount of follow-up work is necessary. The follow-up may consist of personal letters and, if the additional expense is warranted, special delivery letters, registered letters, telephone calls, telegrams, and personal calls. When only some of the questionnaires are filled in and returned, the statistician must assure himself that those returned represent a fair cross section of the group canvassed. Almost never will the returns be a fair cross section. A larger than average proportion of some classes of persons will respond, and a smaller than average proportion of other classes. For example, the upper income brackets may be over-represented, or the better educated persons, or those who are dissatisfied with current practices. The difficulty of obtaining a representative sample by the use of questionnaires is undoubtedly the greatest weakness of that method.

The bias resulting from nonresponse can be partially corrected if one can estimate the differential response rate for the different strata and the characteristics of those not responding originally. It may be discovered, for example, that certain kinds of persons who do not originally respond, tend, on a follow-up, to respond in a particular way. A program of follow-ups is therefore highly desirable, not only to augment the sample, but to aid in interpreting the results and sometimes in correcting for differential response bias.

One advantage of the use of enumerators is that they may patiently explain, to the people being interviewed, the purpose of the study and the meaning of each question. The result is that a larger proportion of the questions will be answered than when the questionnaire method is used, and the answers are more apt to be valid. The enumerators should be persons of unquestioned integrity. The enumerator's task may be made much easier if, before his visit, a letter is sent explaining why he is coming. The approach to the housewife (or other person being interviewed) should be carefully planned to explain as quickly as possible what is wanted and why. The enumerator must be polite and tactful, and he must not lose his politeness and tact when he meets with curt refusal.

It will be noticed that the schedule on page 132 asks a question concerning the occupation of the husband and another concerning his income. Questions like this are more frequently answered if the inquiry is impersonal—that is, if the name is not requested. The enumerator would do well not to ask bluntly, "What is the yearly income?" but rather, more tactfully, "Would you mind telling me the yearly income? The information will be regarded as confidential and we do not ask your name." Even with most careful planning and the exercise of extreme tact, answers to questions as to income will naturally often be refused. However, the co-operation of housewives in answering questions on such a schedule as the one illustrated may sometimes be insured by the presentation of a small gift.

Another advantage of using enumerators is that unintelligible responses will be avoided. A person filling out a questionnaire that has been mailed to him may not know how to fill out the form, and may care even less.

Enumerators sometimes fill in the schedule form after the interview is over, in order not to be writing while talking with the person being interviewed. This is not a good practice when many facts are to be remembered, but may be the only practicable way when it is desired to obtain varying shades of opinion from the different respondents.

Enumerators should always carry adequate credentials to satisfy the persons visited as to their official connection. When requesting information from organizations, it is advisable to obtain the promise of co-operation from the highest official available. Occasionally, when the original contact is made with a minor official (who may perhaps have to go to some trouble to dig out the facts), he may find it all too easy to refuse to co-operate.

Occasionally data are obtained by a process slightly different from that just described. Instead of enumeration the procedure involves registration.

In effect, the informants come to the investigator instead of the investigator going to the informants. If an automobile manufacturer institutes a prize contest and requires the contestants to procure entry blanks from dealers, the entrants may be required to register. At that time the dealers may ask each contestant not only his name and address but also what car he is driving (if any), how old it is, and other questions. This is an inexpensive method of getting facts and sometimes is the only practical one, though the population that the sample represents may be difficult to determine.

Editing the schedules. As the filled-out schedules come into the office, they are not in shape to be tabulated. The editor may have to undertake one or more of the following tasks:

1. *Since it is not satisfactory to allow enumerators or informants to make computations, these may now be necessary.* Some housewives, answering the question in the soap inquiry as to number of cakes used, would reply in terms of the number of cakes used per week or month; the editor must convert these figures to an annual basis. The edited soap-study schedule, shown below, shows 8.3 encircled on line 2. This refers to the number of cakes used per person per year, and was obtained by dividing 50 (the number of cakes per year) by 6 (the number of persons in the household). It was necessary for the editor also to total the roomers, the number of members of the family under eighteen years of age, and those eighteen and over to show the total number of members of the household. For this soap-study schedule the total was 6, which is encircled immediately below the entries for number of persons in household. If income is stated upon some basis other than a year, it is necessary to show the income on an annual basis.

Soap-Study Schedule Filled Out and Edited

Tally Sheet Showing Brand Preferences, and Occupations of Husbands, of Soap Purchasers

DISTRICT ..3..   SOAP PREFERENCE AND OCCUPATION, BALTIMORE   SCORED BY ..*wither*.. / CHECKED BY ..*dundee*..

OCCUPATION CODE	FIRST CHOICE					SECOND CHOICE						THIRD CHOICE					
	SNOWHITE	PALMO	VELVET	CORAL	OTHERS	SNOWHITE	PALMO	VELVET	CORAL	OTHERS		SNOWHITE	PALMO	VELVET	CORAL	OTHERS	
10																	
11																	
12																	
13																	
20																	
21																	
22																	
30																	
31																	
40																	
41																	
42																	
43																	
44																	
45																	
46																	
50																	
60																	
70																	

2. *Coding may be helpful; it is usually necessary if electrical equipment is to be used.* For the occupations listed on the soap-study schedules, it may be desirable to design a code in order to standardize the terms and facilitate later classification. Thus the code number 11, encircled after the word "lawyer," refers to the husband's occupation. (See occupational classification give below.) If the schedules are to be tabulated by punch-card machines, all of the entries must be transformed into such a numerical code. Sometimes a schedule can be devised so that it will be precoded, check marks on the schedule indicating the code numbers.

3. *It may sometimes be necessary for the editor to decipher "unreadable" writing.* Schedules filled out by enumerators hastily and sometimes in the rain or snow are not always graced with the best chirography. If the editor is unable to read some of the entries on the schedule it may be necessary to refer the matter to the enumerator and possibly even have another call made on the informant.

4. *When the entries are missing, the editor must enter N.R.* ("not reported") or, if it seems worth while, return the schedule for more complete data.

5. *Checking may be required.* Inconsistent replies and obvious errors must be watched for and, when found, must be resolved, usually by a revisit to the informant. One of the most often encountered inconsistencies is that resulting from age and date-of-birth information which do not agree.

Tabulating the data. After the schedules have been edited, it is necessary to count the number of items, or to sum the values of the entries, in the different categories or classes, and to arrange the data in some logical order. This may be done by tallying the information on a tally sheet, by sorting the schedules by hand, or by the use of tabulating machinery. After this work is done, tables and charts can be made.

1. The accompanying tally sheet shows a set-up by means of which it is possible to determine the preferences for various brands of soap and, at the same time, indicate these preferences in relation to occupation of the husband. It will be noted that the facts on a schedule are transferred to the tally sheet by the use of tally marks. To facilitate counting, each group of five marks is shown as four vertical tallies and one diagonal tally. It is necessary to tally the schedules twice and compare the results in order to assure accuracy. The totals, which are entered on the tally sheet, may then be transferred to a table form.

A somewhat oversimplified occupational classification, but one that might prove useful in the soap study, is used on the tally sheet and is given below, together with code numbers:

Professional group:
  10 Clergymen
  11 Lawyers
  12 Doctors
  13 Teachers
Sales group:
  20 Salesmen in stores
  21 Salesmen, traveling
  22 Storekeepers
Office group:
  30 Insurance agents, bankers, and brokers
  31 Clerks in offices

Mechanical group:
  40 Carpenters
  41 Electricians
  42 Painters
  43 Plumbers
  44 Machinists
  45 Engineers (stationary)
  46 Chauffeurs and truck drivers
Others:
  50 Laborers
  60 Miscellaneous
  70 Occupation not reported

2. Sorting the schedules by hand is a satisfactory and rapid procedure if there are not too many questions and if the schedule is small enough to be handled easily. The edited soap-study cards could be sorted into piles— first, according to number of cakes used per person per year; and then each of these groups could be sorted according to income (or income per member) in order to see if families at higher income levels use more soap per member. One sorting could quickly show the number of housewives preferring floating or nonfloating soap; a second, those preferring scented or unscented soap, and so on.

3. The use of mechanical tabulating devices was described in an earlier part of this chapter. It may be noted here that such machinery is relatively expensive to rent and therefore it may be advisable to have the work done by organizations that provide such service. Mechanical tabulation is desirable and expeditious (1) when a large number of schedules is being tabulated, (2) when there are many entries on the schedules, and (3) when many different table forms are to be prepared.

Analysis and presentation. When the data have been tabulated by hand or mechanical means, they can be analyzed by statistical methods, inferences arrived at concerning the population sampled, and business decisions made. The results can be presented by means of tables and charts.

Chapter 11

PROBABILITY AND PROBABILITY
DISTRIBUTIONS

Statistics is concerned, among other things, with the making of decisions by the application of the theory of probability to observed numerical data. Consider this problem. If you are willing to tolerate only one per cent of defective units in a lot of goods, would you accept or reject the lot if a random sample of 50 units from a very large lot contains 7 defective items? It can be proved that the probability of 7 or more defectives in a sample of 50 from an infinite population that is one per cent defective is .000001. What would be your decision?

Some of the most advanced and subtle methods of mathematics are used in probability, but we can develop the basic ideas without recourse to anything more advanced than high school algebra.

Probabilistic reasoning is sometimes used when deterministic reasoning cannot grapple with a problem. For example, if we know the total assets of a firm and the total liabilities, we can easily calculate the total value of the proprietary section of the balance sheet. This is deterministic reasoning. On the other hand, if we see an honest man about to throw a pair of honest dice, we do not know what total will turn up on the dice; but probabilistic reasoning can be applied to find the most probable total, i.e., the total that will turn up most often. Probabilistic reasoning is used in such various fields as gambling, insurance, theoretical physics, biology, economics, and many others.

Definitions of Probability

The classical definition. To make the idea of probability concrete, consider an experiment in which an event can occur in a certain number of ways, say r different ways, and can fail to occur in a certain number, say s different ways. If A is a success and B is a failure, the probability of a success is

$$\text{Prob } (A) = \frac{r}{r+s}.$$

That is, *probability of an event is the ratio of the number of ways an event can occur to the total number of possible outcomes, when each possible outcome is equally likely.*

Similarly the probability of a failure is

$$\text{Prob } (B) = \frac{s}{r+s},$$

or the ratio of the number of ways the event can fail to the total number of possible outcomes.

Notice that Prob (A) and Prob (B) are both fractions because r is equal to or smaller than $r + s$, as is s. Notice also that

$$\text{Prob } (A) + \text{Prob } (B) = \frac{r}{r+s} + \frac{s}{r+s} = 1.$$

That is, the probability of success plus the probability of failure equals one.

As an example consider the tossing of an unbiased coin. Suppose we agree that a head is a success and a tail is a failure. Then a success can occur in only one way; that is, by a head showing on a toss, and a failure can occur in only one way, that is, by a tail showing on a toss. Hence the total number of possible outcomes is two (head or tail). Then for this example:

$$r = 1; \quad s = 1;$$

$$\text{Prob } (A) = \frac{r}{r+s} = \frac{1}{1+1} = \frac{1}{2};$$

$$\text{Prob } (B) = \frac{s}{r+s} = \frac{1}{1+1} = \frac{1}{2};$$

$$\text{Prob } (A) + \text{Prob } (B) = \frac{1}{2} + \frac{1}{2} = 1.$$

As another example consider the matching game. You win if a match occurs when two coins are tossed and your opponent wins if a match does not occur. Is the game fair? The possible outcomes of the game are

$$TT \quad TH \quad HT \quad HH.$$

Hence there are four possible outcomes. You win if TT or HH show. You lose if TH or HT show. Consequently:

$$r = 2, \quad s = 2; \quad r + s = 4;$$

$$\text{Prob } (A) = \tfrac{2}{4} = \tfrac{1}{2};$$

$$\text{Prob } (B) = \tfrac{2}{4} = \tfrac{1}{2};$$

$$\text{Prob } (A) + \text{Prob } (B) = 1.$$

The game is obviously fair.

These are among the most elementary examples of the use of probability, and when problems become slightly complicated, finding the solution may become greatly complicated. For example, what is the probability that the player who casts the dice in a crap game will win ?[1]

---

[1] It is approximately .493. See Paul Peach, *An Introduction to Industrial Statistics and Quality Control*, 2d ed., Edwards & Broughton, Raleigh, N.C., 1947, p. 6.

Another definition of probability. We tentatively defined probability as the ratio of the number of ways an event can occur to the total number of possible outcomes, when each possible outcome is equally likely. This definition is not completely satisfactory because it involves circular reasoning, for equally likely is only another way of saying equally probable. Also, if we are playing with loaded dice, each possible outcome is not equally likely. Another interpretation of the meaning of probability is given by saying that *probability is the limit of the relative frequency of successes in an infinite sequence of trials.* This definition also involves logical difficulties, for we cannot be sure that a limit exists, but it permits us to estimate a probability experimentally.[2] For example, if an urn contains a very large number of balls, some of which are red and the others white, and we draw a sample of n balls from the urn after thorough mixing, always replacing each ball before the next is drawn, we should expect the ratio of red balls to total balls in the sample—the relative frequency of the red balls—to be almost the proportion in the urn if n is large enough. As n approaches infinity p approaches P, where p is the proportion of red balls in the sample, and P is the proportion of red balls in the urn population. Probability can also be estimated experimentally when the different outcomes are not equally likely, and therefore the first definition of probability is not applicable. For example, we can estimate the probability of obtaining a one-spot from a six-sided die when the die is loaded in a manner unknown to us.

Chart 11.1—Probability Distribution of Results of Throwing one Six-Sided Die

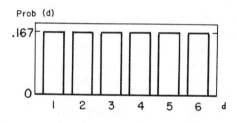

Probability Theorems

Since a die contains six sides, with 1, 2, 3, 4, 5, and 6 spots, respectively, the probabilities for the different numbers of spots are as given in Table 11.1 and shown graphically in Chart 11.1. Such a distribution is known as a probability distribution.

---

[2] Quoting from S. S. Wilks, *Elementary Statistical Analysis*, Princeton University Press, Princeton, N.J., 1948, p. 61 (with slight change in symbols):

"If (1) whenever a series of many trials is made, the ratio of the number of times A occurred to the total number of trials is nearly P, and if (2) the ratio is nearer to P when longer series of trials are made, then we agree in advance to define the probability of A as P, or more briefly, Pr $(A) = P$."

Addition theorem. Referring to Table 11.1, it appears that the probability of a one-spot is $\frac{1}{6}$; the probability of a three or a four is $\frac{1}{6} + \frac{1}{6} = \frac{1}{3}$; the probability of more than 3 spots (4 or 5 or 6) is $\frac{1}{6} + \frac{1}{6} + \frac{1}{6} = \frac{1}{2}$, and so on. These obvious statements can be generalized into a formal theorem.

Table 11.1—Probability Distribution
of Number of Spots on One
Six-sided Die

Number of spots (d)	Prob (d)
1	$\frac{1}{6}$
2	$\frac{1}{6}$
3	$\frac{1}{6}$
4	$\frac{1}{6}$
5	$\frac{1}{6}$
6	$\frac{1}{6}$
Total	1

The probability that one of several mutually exclusive events will occur is the sum of their separate probabilites. Symbolically this may be stated as

(11.1) $\text{Prob}(A + B) = \text{Prob}(A) + \text{Prob}(B)$.

Two events are mutually exclusive if the occurrence of one of the events precludes the occurrence of the other. Thus, if a one-spot appears, a two-spot cannot also. On the other hand, if among 6 people one person is a German and three persons males, the probability that a person selected at random will be either a German or a male is not $\frac{1}{6} + \frac{1}{2} = \frac{2}{3}$, if the German is also a male.

Multiplication theorem. Another theorem that is of great interest is the multiplication theorem. If two dice (one colored red and the other white) are thrown, the probability that both will be one-spots is $\frac{1}{6} \times \frac{1}{6} = \frac{1}{36}$. The probability that the red die will turn up a one-spot and the white die a two-spot is also $\frac{1}{6} \times \frac{1}{6} = 36$. A formal statement of the pertinent theorem follows:

The probability that each of two independent events will occur is the product of their separate probabilites. Symbolically,

(11.2) $\text{Prob}(AB) = \text{Prob}(A) \times \text{Prob}(B)$.

This theorem is of course applicable where Prob (A) is not equal to Prob (B). For example, if the white die is four-sided, with 1, 2, 3, and 4 spots, the probability of a one for the red die and a two for the white die is $\frac{1}{6} \times \frac{1}{4} = \frac{1}{24}$.

Chart 11.2—Probability Distribution of Results of Throwing
two Six-Sided Dice

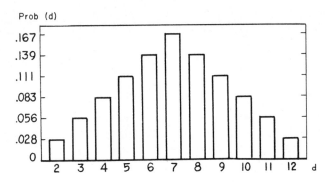

In using this theorem, we must be sure that the events are independent. This is true for two dice, since the number that turns up on the red die has no bearing on the number that turns up on the white die. On the other hand, the probability of a specified baseball player making a hit next Thursday against a left-handed pitcher is not the probability that the pitcher will be left-handed × the probability of making a hit, because the probability of making a hit depends partly on whether the pitcher is left-handed or right-handed.

In order to verify the multiplication theorem, let us tabulate the different combinations that can be obtained when tossing six-sided dice, two at a time. In the second column of Table 11.2, enclosed by parentheses, are the different

Table 11.2—Probability Distribution of Number of
Spots on Two Six-sided Dice

Number of spots (d)	Combinations	Prob (d)
2	(1,1)	1/36
3	(1,2; 2,1)	2/36
4	(1,3; 2,2; 3,1)	3/36
5	(1,4; 2,3; 3,2; 4,1)	4/36
6	(1,5; 2,4; 3,3; 4,2; 5,1)	5/36
7	(1,6; 2,5; 3,4; 4,3; 5,2; 6,1)	6/36
8	(2,6; 3,5; 4,4; 5,3; 6,2)	5/36
9	(3,6; 4,5; 5,4; 6,1)	4/36
10	(4,6; 5,5; 6,4)	3/36
11	(5,6; 6,5)	2/36
12	(6,6)	1/36
Total	. . .	1

combinations resulting in a specified number of spots (the number of spots showing on the red die always being recorded first). It is apparent that there are 36 different combinations, and since each combination has the same probability, this probability is $\frac{1}{36}$, which is of course $\frac{1}{6} \times \frac{1}{6}$. If we add these probabilities horizontally (Theorem 11.1) we obtain the probability for each possible number of spots. The results are shown graphically in Chart 11.2.

Binomial Distribution

Symmetrical distribution. Suppose a box contains a very large number of balls half of which are red, and the other half white. Symbolically, $P = .5$ and $Q = 1 - P = .5$. After thorough mixing, a paddle shaped like the following is slid into the box and a sample of three balls scooped up.

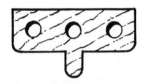

The different samples, each of which has a probability of $\frac{1}{2} \times \frac{1}{2} \times \frac{1}{2} = \frac{1}{8}$, that may result, are as follows.

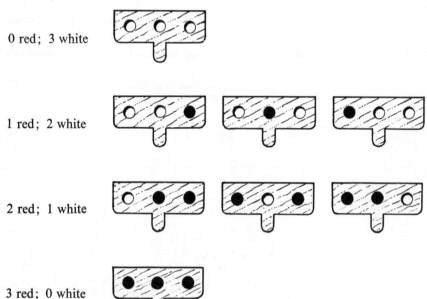

0 red; 3 white

1 red; 2 white

2 red; 1 white

3 red; 0 white

We see that in a sample of 3: there is 1 way of getting 0 red balls; there are 3 ways of getting 1 red ball; there are 3 ways of getting 2 red balls; there is 1 way of getting 3 red balls.

Or more generally, we may say:

$$\binom{3}{0} = \frac{3!}{0!3!} = \frac{3 \cdot 2 \cdot 1}{(1)(3 \cdot 2 \cdot 1)} = 1;$$

$$\binom{3}{1} = \frac{3!}{1!2!} = \frac{3 \cdot 2 \cdot 1}{(1)(2 \cdot 1)} = 3;$$

$$\binom{3}{2} = \frac{3!}{2!1!} = \frac{3 \cdot 2 \cdot 1}{(2 \cdot 1)(1)} = 3;$$

$$\binom{3}{3} = \frac{3!}{3!0!} = \frac{3 \cdot 2 \cdot 1}{(3 \cdot 2 \cdot 1)(1)} = 1.$$

As was stated in Chapter 9, values of $\binom{n}{d}$ are often called *binomial coefficients*. The symmetrical binomial distribution is obtained by dividing each binomial coefficient by the sum of the binomial coefficients, or by multiplying each binomial coefficient by the probability $.5^n$ of any sample. Thus the expression for the binomial probability distribution when $P = Q = .5$ is

(11.3) $$\text{Prob}(d) = \binom{n}{d} .5^n.$$

See Table 11.3. The results are shown graphically in Chart 11.3. This distribution is symmetrical, for Prob $(d = 0)$ is the same as Prob $(d = 3)$

Table 11.3—Probability Distribution of Number of Red Balls in Samples of Three, from a Population with Half the Balls Red and the Other Half White

Number of red balls (d)	Binomial coefficient $\binom{n}{d}$	Probability of any sample, $.5^n$	Prob (d), $\binom{n}{d} .5^n$
0	1	.125	.125
1	3	.125	.375
2	3	.125	.375
3	1	.125	.125
Total	8	...	1.000

and Prob $(d = 1)$ is the same as Prob $(d = 2)$. A binomial distribution is always symmetrical when the two classes (such as red balls and white balls) have the same number of items in the population.

**Chart 11.3—Probability Distribution of Number
of Red Balls in Samples of Three from a
Population of Balls that is Half
Red and White**

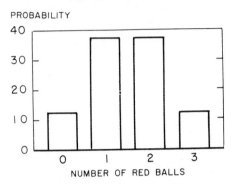

Skewed distribution. Now let us determine the probability distribution for samples of 3 from a population that is 40 per cent defective (bad) and 60 per cent effective (good). For convenience, let P be the proportion of defective items in the population and Q be the proportion effective.

**Table 11.4—Probability Distribution of Number of Defective in Samples of
3 from a Population that is 40 per cent Defective**

Number defective (d)	Proportion defective $p = \dfrac{d}{n}$	Binomial coefficient $\binom{3}{d}$	$P^d Q^{n-d}$	Prob (d) and Prob (p)
0	.000	1	$.4^0 .6^3 = .216$	.216
1	.333	3	$.4^1 .6^2 = .144$	.432
2	.667	3	$.4^2 .6^1 = .096$	.288
3	1.000	1	$.4^3 .6^0 = .064$	.064
Total	. . .	8	. . .	1.000

$P + Q = 1$. In the present case $P = .4$ and $Q = .6$. We proceed exactly as before, except that instead of multiplying $\binom{n}{d}$ by $.5^n$, we multiply it by $P^d Q^{n-d}$, which is the probability that a specified number of items will be bad, the others being good. Thus we have[3]

$$(11.4) \qquad \text{Prob } (d) = \binom{n}{d} P^d Q^{n-d}.$$

Table 11.4 shows the computations for the probability distribution. The

---

[3] Formula (11.3) is really a special case of formula (11.4), for if $P = Q = .5$, we have $P^d Q^{n-d} = .5^d .5^{n-d} = .5^n$.

column labeled p, the proportion defective in a sample, is not needed for computational purposes, but is nevertheless of some interest. The results are shown graphically in Chart 11.4. The distribution shown in Chart 11.4 is positively skewed. If P were .6 and Q were .4 the figure would be negatively skewed. It would appear as if Chart 11.4 were viewed from the reverse side of the page.

**Chart 11.4—Probability Distribution of Number of
Defectives in Samples of Three from a
Population that is 40 Per Cent
Defective**

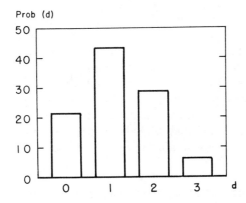

Actually all we have done in Table 11.4 is to expand the binomial $(Q + P)^n$, which is accomplished by substituting the different values of d in expression (11.4) for the general term of the binomial. In the present case we have the binomial $(.6 + .4)^3$, and the expression for the general term is

$$\text{Prob } (d) = \binom{3}{d}.4^d.6^{3-d}.$$

Therefore

$$(.6 + .4)^3 = \binom{3}{0}.4^0.6^3 + \binom{3}{1}.4^1.6^2 + \binom{3}{2}.4^2.6^1 + \binom{3}{3}.4^3.6^0$$

$$= .216 + .432 + .288 + .064 = 1.$$

Let us now return to the question raised in the first paragraph of this chapter. Summarizing the information, we have $P = .01$, $Q = .99$, $n = 50$, $d = 7$, $n - d = 43$. From (11.4)

$$\text{Prob } (7) = \binom{50}{7}(.01)^7(.99)^{43}$$

$$= (99,884,400)(.00000000000001)(.64910)$$

$$= .0000006.$$

If we should compute the probability of obtaining 8 defectives it would be so small that we could neglect it. This would be true also for any number of defectives greater than 8. Since the probability of 7 or more defectives is less than one in one million, it is unreasonable to suppose that the lot is only one per cent defective. It is much more reasonable to think that it is more than one per cent defective. The lot should therefore be rejected.

Continuous Probability Distributions

The illustrations we have been considering, number of heads when coins are tossed, number of spots showing on dice, number of red balls or defective pieces, are all of a *discrete* nature. Thus, the number of defectives in a sample can take only integral values; we cannot have 2.3667 defectives in a sample. When dealing with things that we measure, rather than count, it is theoretically possible for any value to occur within the range of our data, and we say that the *distribution* is continuous.

It is often useful to consider the graph of a continuous probability distribution. This type of graph, which can also be expressed as a mathematical equation, shows measurements (comparable to number of defectives) on the horizontal scale, and probability densities on the vertical scale. For example, the heights of adult males of the same generation might look like Chart 11.5.

Chart 11.5—Probability Distribution of Heights of Adult Males

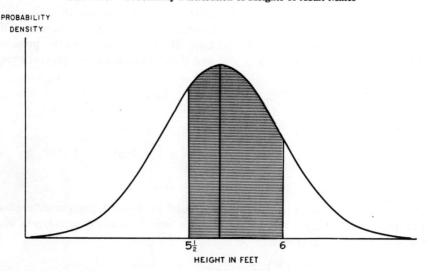

The probability of selecting by random choice a man between 5½ feet and 6 feet in height is indicated by the *ratio* of the shaded area to the total area. Now the probability that a man will be within the range of 5½ feet to 6 feet in height, plus the probability that he will be outside the range, is 1. So if the chart is drawn in such a way that the total area under the curve is equal to 1, the probability that a man selected at random will be between $5\frac{1}{2}$ feet and 6 feet in height *is* the shaded area.

Notice the "bell-shape" of Chart 11.5. This is the general shape that some events governed by chance tend to assume. Distributions with this shape[4] are called *normal* distributions. It is worth while to note that the binomial distribution becomes more and more like the normal distribution as *n* gets larger and larger.

---

[4] Technically the shape is described by the equation $Y = Y_0 e^{-z^2/2}$, where Y_0 is the maximum height of the curve and z is the distance from 0 on the horizontal axis. See Chapter 19, where the normal distribution is more fully considered.

Chapter 12

STATISTICAL INFERENCE

In Chapter 1 it was pointed out that homogeneous statistical data are characterized both by similarity and variability. There is a tendency for the data to be attracted toward some central value, but also a tendency to spread out in such a way that observations gradually become less frequent as we move away from this central value.

In Chapter 2 we discussed ways in which statistical data are analyzed: by classification into relatively homogeneous classes, and by correlation of paired observations.

Chapter 11 was devoted to an elementary exposition of probability and probability distributions.

The time has come to tie these three chapters together, for they are closely related. In statistical work we deal mainly with samples, but we are not so much interested in the sample as we are in the population from which the sample came. Thus in an examination an instructor asks a sample of questions, for he cannot examine a student on every point included in the course. But the examination is supposed to give the instructor some idea of what the student knows about the course as a whole. When we select a random sample of 46 corporation stocks and compare the average gain in price with that of a sample selected on some other basis by an investment counselor, we are not so much interested in the comparison of these two samples as we are in knowing what we can expect if we follow the counselor's advice. Are his selections really random ones after all, in spite of the ostensibly scientific method of selection? When we take samples of four pieces of cloth at hourly intervals and measure the breaking strength of each sample, we are interested in whether the process is being carried on under uniform conditions.

Thus, what we are mainly interested in is making inferences. We can never be sure that our inferences are correct, but we can avoid being wrong too often and too much if we base our inferences on probability theory.

By statistical inference is meant making a probability judgment concerning a population on the basis of one or more samples.

Statistics is mainly concerned with making statistical inferences as a basis for making decisions. Thus, an instructor decides on the basis of examinations that a student has a satisfactory knowledge of the course, and he records a passing grade. An investor may decide, on the basis of a sample, that an investment analyst makes selections that are better than random, and so he subscribes to the service. A quality control engineer decides, after examining the control chart, that the process is "out of control." Therefore he looks for the source of the trouble.

One point may disturb the reader. If one inspects the entire output of a factory during a given day, how can that be regarded as a sample? We might think of it as a sample of the output on the other days of the current year, but this would not be valid unless the same manufacturing conditions existed throughout the year. On the other hand, it could validly be regarded as a sample from an infinite theoretical population of units that would be produced by the same cause system. What you consider to be the population depends on your purpose. You must decide what the population is concerning which you are interested in making inferences.

Types of Statistical Inferences

Types of statistical inferences are generally classified as follows:

1. Making estimates
   a. Point estimates
   b. Interval estimates
2. Testing hypotheses

We shall discuss each of these briefly, and as simply as we can without robbing the concepts of too much content.

Point Estimates

A few selected statistics. A parameter is a summary measure descriptive of the population. A statistic is a measure computed from a sample, for the purpose of summarizing information contained in the sample. A statistic used as an estimate of a parameter, and presented as a single number, is known as a point estimate. Let us consider the data of Table 12.1, which consists of the warp-breaking strengths, in pounds, of four pieces of cloth.

Table 12.1—A Sample of
Four Items

(Sample 6 of Table 2.1)

$X_4 = $ 62 pounds
$X_3 = $ 59 pounds
$X_2 = $ 59 pounds
$X_1 = $ 56 pounds

$\Sigma X = $ 236 pounds

The mean of the X values is

$$(12.1) \qquad \bar{X} = \frac{\Sigma X}{n} = \frac{236}{4} = 59 \text{ pounds.}$$

But each observation is not of the same magnitude. The range of values is

(12.2)　　　　　$R = X_n - X_1 = 62 - 56 = 6$ pounds.

The range is used some in statistical work, but it is obvious that it would not be very helpful for describing a theoretical population that extends from $-\infty$ to $+\infty$, for then the range would be ∞ also. Therefore we could not distinguish between the values of R for two such populations, even though there was a considerable difference between the ranges of (say) the middle half of the items; so statisticians are more likely to use a measure called the variance, computed by the following procedure:

1. Subtract the mean from each item, obtaining n values of $(X - \bar{X})$.
2. Square each of these differences, obtaining n values of $(X - \bar{X})^2$.
3. Sum these squares, obtaining $\Sigma (X - \bar{X})^2$.
4. Divide the sum of the squares by $n - 1$ obtaining s^2.

Let us apply these steps to our illustrative data.

X	$X - \bar{X} = x$	x^2
62	$62 - 59 = 3$	9
59	$59 - 59 = 0$	0
59	$59 - 59 = 0$	0
56	$62 - 59 = -3$	9

$\Sigma X = 236$, and $\bar{X} = 59$　　　　$\Sigma x^2 = 18$

(12.3)　　　　　$s^2 = \dfrac{\Sigma x^2}{n - 1} = \dfrac{\Sigma (X - \bar{X})^2}{n - 1}$

$$= \frac{18}{3} = 6.0.$$

Even more widely used is the standard deviation s, which is the square root of the variance.[1] Thus:

$$s = \sqrt{6.0} = 2.45.$$

Sometimes we deal with qualitative variables, or attributes, rather than quantitative variables; i.e., with qualities that either exist or do not exist, rather than qualities that exist in varying degrees. Thus a shell that explodes may be said to be effective, and one that does not is defective. If we want to, we can assign the value 0 to an effective item and 1 to a defective item. For

---

[1] For some purposes the variance of the sample is defined as $\mathit{s}^2 = \Sigma x^2/n$, and the sample standard deviation as $\mathit{s} = \sqrt{\Sigma x^2/n}$. The variance s^2 may be regarded as the variance adjusted for sample size. As n becomes larger, s^2 tends to become larger, but s^2 does not tend to become either larger or smaller. Also, s^2 is an unbiased estimate of σ^2, the population variance. See section on qualities of a good estimator of a parameter, pp. 157–160.

example, if the first, second, and fifth shells are effective, and the third and fourth defective, we have

$$
\begin{array}{c}
X \\
0 \\
0 \\
1 \\
1 \\
0 \\
\hline
\Sigma X = 2.
\end{array}
$$

The number of defectives is sometimes given the symbol d.

$$d = \Sigma X = 2.$$

The fraction defective is sometimes given the symbol p.

$$p = \bar{X} = \frac{\Sigma X}{n}, \qquad \text{or}$$

(12.4) $$p = \frac{d}{n} = \frac{2}{5} = 0.4.$$

Parameters. Just as statistics describe a sample, so parameters describe a population. Often a statistic is considered to be an estimate of a parameter. A parameter is usually distinguished symbolically from a statistic by assigning to it a Greek, instead of an italic letter, or by some other method.

Measure	Statistic	Parameter
Mean	$\bar{X}$	μ
Variance	s^2	σ^2
Standard deviation	s	σ
Proportion	p	P
Number of items	n	N

Definition of μ and σ^2. The method of computing μ and σ^2 depends on whether the population is finite or infinite.

Finite population. Let us consider this extremely simple population of four observations,

$$X: \ 1, 2, 2, 3.$$

For computational and expository purposes we shall record these data as a *frequency distribution*.

X	f
1	1
2	2
3	1
Total	4

In Table 12.2 are the computations necessary to obtain μ and σ^2.

$$(12.5) \qquad \mu = \frac{\Sigma (fX)}{N} = \frac{8}{4} = 2.$$

$$(12.6) \qquad \sigma^2 = \frac{\Sigma [f(X - \mu)^2]}{N - 1} = \frac{2}{3} = 0.667.$$

Note that formula (12.5) is analogous to formula (12.1) and formula (12.6) is analogous to formula (12.3).

In computing σ^2 we divide by $N - 1$ instead of N because μ is computed from the X values, which restricts the freedom of the X values to vary about μ. If $N = 1$, there is no opportunity for X to differ from μ; if $N = 2$, each X value has $\frac{1}{2}$ of an opportunity; if $N = 3$, each X value has $\frac{2}{3}$ of an opportunity; and so on.

Table 12.2—Computations for Obtaining μ and σ^2, Finite Population

X	f	fX	$X - \mu$	$(X - \mu)^2$	$f(X - \mu)^2$
1	1	1	-1	1	1
2	2	4	0	0	0
3	1	3	1	1	1
Total	4	8	0	...	2

Infinite population. If the size of the population is infinite, we have probabilities instead of frequencies. If the probabilities are the relative frequencies of our preceding illustration, the *probability distribution* is

X	Prob (X)
1	0.25
2	.50
3	.25
Total	1.00

Computation of μ is analogous to the method already considered. See Table 12.3. However:

1. We multiply the X values by their probabilities rather than their frequencies.

2. We do not need to divide by N since the sum of the probabilities is 1.

3. The weighted average obtained by summing the values of $X \cdot$ Prob (X) is called the expected value. Thus, referring to Table 12.3, we have

$$(12.7) \qquad \mu = E(X) = \Sigma [X \cdot \text{Prob } (X)]$$
$$= 2.$$

Similarly, for the population variance,

(12.8) $\sigma^2 = E[X - E(X)]^2 = E(X - \mu)^2 = \Sigma\,[(X - \mu)^2 \cdot \text{Prob}\,(X)]$
              $= 0.50$

In computing σ^2 from an infinite population we do not (and by definition, cannot) take cognizance of the size of the population by "throwing out" one of the observations. The individual X values are not restricted in their opportunity to vary about μ.

**Table 12.3—Computations for Obtaining μ and σ^2,
Infinite Population**

X	Prob (X)	$X \cdot$ Prob (X)	$X - \mu$	$(X - \mu)^2$	$(X - \mu)^2 \cdot$ Prob (X)
1	0.25	0.25	−1	1	0.25
2	.50	1.00	0	0	.00
3	.25	.75	1	1	.25
Total	1.00	2.00	...	...	0.50

Qualities of a good estimator. There are various qualities that are desirable in a statistic.

1. It should be unbiased.
2. It should be reliable.

Lack of bias. An estimator is unbiased if the expected value of the statistic (the mean of the probability distribution for the statistic) is the parameter. Symbolically, if the symbol θ is used to mean parameter, and $\hat{\theta}$ to mean statistic, then if a statistic is unbiased,

$$E(\hat{\theta}) = \theta.$$

Let us compute the expected value of p for samples of 3 taken from an infinite population that is 40 per cent defective ($P = .4$). The probability distribution was computed in Table 11.4. The computational steps are:

1. Multiply each value of p by its probability, obtaining values of $p \cdot$ Prob (p).
2. Sum these products.

These computations are given in Table 12.4.
    Thus we see that

(12.9) $E(p) = \Sigma\,[p \cdot \text{Prob}\,(p)]$
                          $= 0.4,$

Table 12.4—Computation of Expected Value of
p for Samples of 3 from an Infinite Population
with $P = .4$

p	Prob (p)	$p \cdot$ Prob (p)
0.000	0.216	0.000
0.333	.432	.144
0.667	.288	.192
1.000	.064	.064
Total	1.000	0.400

Source: Table 11.4.

which is the value of P. Note the analogy between formula (12.9) and formula (12.7). We can generalize, and say

$$E(p) = P.$$

Similarly, it is true that[2] $E(d) = nP$, $E(X) = \mu$, $E(\bar{X}) = \mu$, and $E(s^2) = \sigma^2$. Therefore we can say:

p is an unbiased estimate of P;
d is an unbiased estimate of nP;
X is an unbiased estimate of μ;
$\bar{X}$ is an unbiased estimate of μ;
s^2 is an unbiased estimate of σ^2.

Reliability. The word reliable is somewhat vague, for it can have various shades of meaning. A statistic is reliable if the variance of the statistic about its expected value is small or if the mean square deviation of the statistic about the parameter is small. If we use the symbol θ to mean parameter, and $\hat{\theta}$ to mean statistic, the two concepts are:

$$E[\hat{\theta} - E(\hat{\theta})]^2 \text{ is a minimum;}$$

$$E[(\hat{\theta} - \theta)^2] \text{ is a minimum.}$$

The first concept has to do with precision; the second one has to do with accuracy. A good argument can be made for preferring a statistic that has smallest variance, even though it may be biased (providing the bias is known). One can also argue that one should select from unbiased estimates that statistic for which the mean square deviation is the smallest. Since p, d, X, $\bar{X}$, and s^2 are all unbiased, the distinction between variance about the expected

---

[2] That $E(s^2) = \sigma^2$ when the population is infinite is proved in Dudley J. Cowden, *Statistical Methods in Quality Control*, Prentice-Hall, Inc., Englewood Cliffs, N.J., 1957, pp. 75–76.

value and mean square deviation about the parameter disappears for those statistics.[3]

To obtain an understanding of the meaning of the variance of a statistic, let us compute the variance of p from the data of Table 12.4. These computations are performed in Table 12.5. The procedure is as follows:

1. Subtract the expected value of the statistic from the statistic. In this case $P = E(p)$, so we obtain values of $p - P$.
2. Square these differences, obtaining $(p - P)^2$.
3. Multiply each value of $(p - P)^2$ by its probability, obtaining $(p - P)^2 \cdot \text{Prob}(p)$.
4. Sum these products.

Table 12.5—Computation of Variance of p from Samples of 3
from an Infinite Population with $P = .4$

p	$p - P$	$(p - P)^2$	Prob (p)	$(p - P)^2 \cdot$ Prob (p)
0.000	−0.400	0.1600	0.216	0.0346
0.333	−0.067	.0044	.432	.0019
0.666	.267	.0711	.288	.0205
1.000	.600	.3600	.064	.0230
Total	...	...	1.000	0.0800

Source: Table 12.4.

It is not necessary to divide by Σ [Prob (p)] since the sum of the probabilities is 1. From Table 12.5 we see that the variance of p is[4]

$$(12.10) \qquad \sigma_p^2 = E(p - P)^2 = \Sigma[(p - P)^2 \cdot \text{Prob}(p)] = 0.08$$

Note the analogy between formula (12.10) and formula (12.8).

---

[3] Often the word *efficiency* is used in referring to reliability. A statistic is *asymptotically efficient* if, as the sample size approaches ∞, the statistic approaches the parameter, and the distribution of the statistic approaches the normal form with minimum variance. Efficiency is also used as a measure of reliability. When so used it is either the ratio of the mean square deviations of two statistics when the sample sizes are the same, or the ratio of the sample sizes when the mean square deviations are equal.

[4] It is mathematically equivalent, and also easier, to compute

$$\sigma_p^2 = \frac{PQ}{n} = \frac{(.4)(.6)}{3} = 0.08.$$

For proof that $E(p) = P$ and $\sigma_p^2 = PQ/n$ see Dudley J. Cowden, *Statistical Methods in Quality Control*, Prentice-Hall, Inc., New York, 1957, pp. 40–42.

Since in each of the following cases the expected value is the parameter, we may write:

$$\sigma_p^2 = E(p - P)^2;$$
$$\sigma_d^2 = E(d - nP)^2;$$
$$\sigma_X^2 = E(X - \mu)^2;$$
$$\sigma_{\bar{X}}^2 = E(\bar{X} - \mu)^2;$$
$$\sigma_{s^2}^2 = E(s^2 - \sigma^2)^2.$$

The following are minimum variance unbiased estimators:

p, since $E(p)\ = P$, and $\sigma_p^2 =$ minimum;

d, since $E(d)\ = nP$, and $\sigma_d^2 =$ minimum;

X, since $E(X) = \mu$, and $\sigma_X^2 =$ minimum;

$\bar{X}$, since $E(\bar{X}) = \mu$, and $\sigma_{\bar{X}}^2 =$ minimum;

$\sigma_{s^2}^2$, since $E(s^2)\ = \sigma^2$, and $\sigma_{s^2}^2 =$ minimum.

Interval Estimates

Since we can never be sure that an estimate of a parameter is correct, it is desirable that we state not only our best single estimate, or point estimate, but also a pair of estimates, one above our point estimate and the other below it. This pair of estimates is made in such a way that it is a fair bet (at stated odds) that the parameter is between them. These estimates are also called confidence limits. If we wish to be very confident of our stated limits we must make them rather wide, but if we are willing to take a big chance we can put them close together. How close together the limits are depends also on other factors. If there is not much variability in the sample the limits will be closer together than if there is large variability. The limits will be closer together for a large sample than for a small sample. If a reliable statistic is used in determining the limits, they will be closer together than they will be if an unreliable one is used.

For the sake of simplicity we shall, in this chapter, illustrate the determination of confidence limits for the mean only, and shall use the range in setting these limits. An estimate of σ based on the range is not an efficient statistic. It does not utilize all of the information contained in the sample, and partly for that reason, estimates of the variance based on the range are subject to a considerable amount of fluctuation from sample to sample. Therefore a larger sample is required when the range is used as a measure of variability than when s^2 is used. But for small samples (say 15 or smaller) the range is not too bad, and it certainly is easy to compute. Interval estimates using σ^2 or s^2 are explained in Chapter 21.

Consider the sample shown in Table 12.6. We wish to set two limits, μ_1 and μ_2, in such a way that we have 90 per cent confidence that these limits enclose μ, the unknown population mean. A very simple procedure involves use of a statistic known as G_1.

(12.11)
$$G_1 = \frac{\bar{X} - \mu}{R}.$$

**Table 12.6—A Sample of
Four Items**
(Sample 5 of Table 2.1)

X (pounds)

71
68
66
57

$\Sigma X = \overline{262}$
$\bar{X} = 65.50$ pounds.
$R = 71 - 57 = 14$ pounds.

If β is the confidence coefficient, and $\alpha + \beta = 1$, we ascertain the value of $G_{1,\alpha/2}$. For the present illustration, $\beta = .90$ and $\alpha/2 = .05$, so we must find the value of $G_{1,.05}$. Turning to the Appendix 17.1, we find that when[5] $k = 1$ and $n = 4$, the value of G_1 at the 5 per cent probability point is .53. The .90 confidence limits are:

$$\mu_2 = \bar{X} + G_{1,.05}R = 65.50 + (.53)(14)$$
$$= 65.50 + 7.42 = 72.92 \text{ pounds};$$
$$\mu_1 = \bar{X} - G_{1,.05}R = 65.50 - (.53)(14)$$
$$= 65.50 - 7.42 = 58.08 \text{ pounds.}$$

It would be fair to give odds of 9 to 1 that the population mean is between 58.08 pounds and 72.92 pounds; for if we made many bets such as this, we should expect to break even.

Let us now see what happens if the range is smaller. Take the data of Table 12.1; $n = 4$; $\bar{X} = 59.00$ pounds, $R = 6$ pounds. For the 90 per cent confidence limits we have

$$\bar{X} \pm G_{1,.05}R = 59.00 \pm (.53)(6) = 59.00 \pm 3.18.$$

$$= 55.82 \text{ pounds and } 62.18 \text{ pounds.}$$

---

[5] When $n \geq 16$ it is better to divide the sample into k subgroups of 6, 7, 8, 9, or 10 items each, and use the mean range $\bar{R}$ instead of the range R in the expression for G_1. The most efficient procedure is to use subgroups of 8 items each. If this is not possible, subgroups of 7 each or 9 each are nearly as good. If this is not possible, subgroups of 6 each or 10 each should be taken.

The confidence limits are much smaller because the variability, as measured by the range, is only 6 pounds instead of 14 pounds.

Now let us see how much wider the confidence limits become when we want to be 95 per cent confident, instead of only 90 per cent. For $G_{1,\alpha/2}$ we use $G_{1,.025}$, instead of $G_{1,.05}$, since now $\alpha/2 = .025$. In Appendix Table 17.1 we find that when $n = 4$, and $k = 1$, the value of $G_{1,.025} = .72$. For the 95 per cent confidence limits, therefore, we have

$$\bar{X} \pm G_{1,.025}R = 59.00 \pm (.72)(6) = 59.00 \pm 4.32$$

$$= 54.68 \text{ pounds and } 63.32 \text{ pounds.}$$

It is important to realize also that as the sample size gets larger, the confidence limits tend to come closer together. Appendix Tables 17.1 and 17.2 show that as n gets larger G_1 gets smaller. It is true that R gets larger as n increases, and this tends to make the computed value of G_1 smaller, but the value of R does not increase fast enough to offset the decrease in the table value of G_1.

Tests of Hypotheses

A hypothesis is a statement, concerning the population, that is open to doubt. We test the hypothesis, making use of probability theory, and either accept the hypothesis or reject it. Accepting a hypothesis leads to one decision, rejecting it leads to another.

Consider, for example, the use of a control chart for means (Chart 2.4). The hypothesis is that the process is in control. If a sample mean goes outside the control limits, as did sample 6, we reject the hypothesis. The business decision is that we look for the source of trouble and correct it. The reason we reject the hypothesis is that it is difficult to reconcile the facts with the hypothesis. It is highly improbable that we would obtain a sample with a mean as small as sample 6 if the hypothesis were true.

Consider also the question of whether to select stocks at random for price appreciation, or to rely on the judgment of an analyst (Chart 2.3). The hypothesis is that both samples are random selections from the same population. If the difference between the means of the two samples is small, we accept the hypothesis; if it is large enough to be considered significant, we reject it. If we accept the hypothesis, we select our stocks at random from stocks listed on the New York Stock Exchange; if we reject the hypothesis, we subscribe to the services of the analyst. The reason we insist that the difference be significant is that the services of the analyst cost money. Unless we can be reasonably confident that the analyst is giving us considerably better than random advice, it is best that we dispense with his services.

In the quality control illustration the hypothesis was that the process is in control; i.e., that the population mean does not differ from some predetermined standard value. Such a hypothesis is sometimes called a null hypothesis. The alternative hypothesis was that the process is out of control.

We can test the null hypothesis, but not the alternative hypothesis in this case, for to say merely that the process is out of control is not specific enough: such a hypothesis does not specify how far out of control it is. Likewise in the investment illustration, the hypothesis was that the difference between the average gains is zero. The alternative hypothesis was that the average gain is not zero. But "not zero" is ambiguous; it covers a wide range of values. One can test only a specific hypothesis. If we accept the specific hypothesis, we reject all of its alternatives. If we reject the specific hypothesis, we accept the stated alternative.

When the hypothesis being tested is that the numerical value of the parameter is zero, the test is also called a test of significance.

It must be apparent that a large difference is more significant than a small one. But the words *large* and *small* have little meaning unless we have some standard for comparison. A difference of one second between two sprinters running the hundred-yard dash is a large difference; a difference of one second between two runners in a marathon is a small difference. This is because a difference of one second for the hundred-yard dash is large compared with the variability in time that is typical in the hundred-yard dash. In most college track meets the slowest runner is within one-half second of the fastest. But in a marathon the intervals between successive runners is likely to be minutes, rather than seconds.

Similarly, in statistics, one compares the amount of variability being tested with the variability that is unaccounted for. If the former is large in comparison with the latter, we say that the difference is significant. Chart 12.1 contains four diagrams. The difference between the two means is more significant in diagram B than in diagram A. Although the two curves in diagram A have the same amount of variability as in diagram B, the difference between $\bar{X}_2$ and $\bar{X}_1$ is larger for diagram B. The difference between the two means is more significant in diagram C than in diagram D, although the difference between $\bar{X}_2$ and $\bar{X}_1$ is the same; the curves of diagram C have smaller variability than those of diagram D.

Another point that seems so reasonable that it hardly needs proving is that, other things being equal, a difference between means obtained from large samples is more significant than one of the same size obtained from small samples.

All of this discussion leads to the following principle: A significant difference is one that has a small probability of occurring if the hypothesis being tested is true; a nonsignificant difference is one that has a large probability of occurring if the hypothesis being tested is true. Let us summarize.

1. If the hypothesis of no difference being tested is true, a small difference has a large probability, and a large difference has a small probability.

2. If the hypothesis being tested is true, a difference of a given magnitude has a small probability if the unexplained variability is sufficiently small.

Chart 12.1—Comparison of Difference Between Means of Two Distributions with
Random Variability Within Distributions:

A. Small Difference Between Means

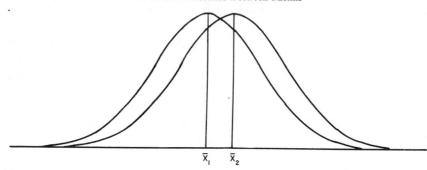

B. Large Difference Between Means;   Random Variability Same as A

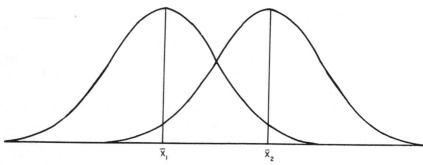

C. Small Random Variability

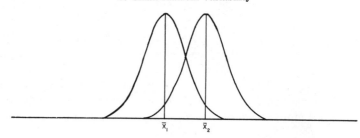

D. Large Random Variability;   Difference Between Means Same as C

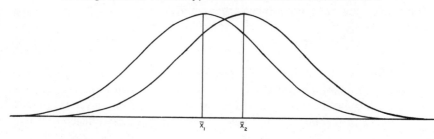

3. If the hypothesis being tested is true, a difference of a given magnitude has a small probability if the sample is sufficiently large.

4. If the probability of obtaining the observed sample(s) is so small that we consider the results of the investigation inconsistent with the hypothesis, we reject the hypothesis and consider the observed difference to be significant. We then accept the alternative hypothesis.

How small does a probability have to be before we consider it small enough to be decisive? This is a difficult question. It should be decided on economic (or perhaps psychological) considerations, but often a conventional value is chosen, such as .05. Decisions of this type are constantly made intuitively. How short must a man be for him to be considered a poor basketball risk? What is the probability of an innocent man being executed as a spy?

It must be obvious that a decision concerning a hypothesis may be correct in either of two ways:

1. We may accept a hypothesis when it is true;
2. We may reject a hypothesis when it is false.

We may also make two kinds of errors:

1. We may reject a hypothesis when it is true;
2. We may accept a hypothesis when it is false.

The probability of making an error of the first kind is given the symbol α. The probability of making an error of the second kind is given the symbol β. It is apparent that a single numerical value can be assigned to α, but β becomes smaller as the discrepancy between the hypothesis and the actuality becomes greater. The smaller the value we assign to α the larger β becomes, and the larger the value we assign to α, the smaller β becomes. We cannot assign a value of 0 to α, for then we could accept all hypotheses, whether they are true or whether they are false. Nor should we assign it a value of 1, for then we would reject all hypotheses, both true and false. The best value to assign to α depends on the seriousness of the consequences of the two kinds of errors. One should, therefore, seek an economical balance between the two kinds of errors.

Most students will agree that it is a minor matter if an ignorant student is passed in a course (the hypothesis of no knowledge being mistakenly rejected), but a more serious matter if a competent one is failed (the hypothesis of no knowledge being mistakenly accepted). On the other hand to convict a man of murder when he is possibly innocent is a decision not to be made lightly; but neither is the decision to acquit a man who is possibly a murderer.

If a major decision is to be made, requiring a considerable investment, one should weigh the loss involved in making the wrong decision against the cost of experimentation or sampling, and computation. One wrong decision may wreck the business. In such a case one should increase the sample size until the probability of deciding in favor of the wrong process is very small.

In devising a test one tries to make β as small as possible for all hypotheses alternative to the null hypothesis, the value of α being given. A test for which β is small is said to be a powerful test. A powerful test has great power of discrimination; the probability of rejecting a false hypothesis is great. To obtain a powerful test one should, among other things,

1. Use a large sample,
2. Use a reliable statistic.

*Use of Range in Tests of Hypotheses

The tests of hypotheses illustrated in this section are "inefficient" tests; they are wasteful of observations. Inefficient tests are not necessarily uneconomical, however. They require a larger sample to obtain the same power of discrimination between a true hypothesis and a false one, but they may require less computation than do efficient tests. If computation is expensive and sampling sufficiently cheap, the inefficient test will be more economical.

It is because of ease of computation that these tests are introduced here. The student can get some idea of the logical procedure for testing hypotheses without having his attention unduly diverted to the mechanics of computation. Efficient tests to accomplish identical purposes are explained in Chapters 21 and 23.

In this section, for the sake of simplicity, we shall always use $\alpha = .05$. A normal population is assumed.

Comparison of a sample mean with a hypothetical population mean. Suppose we wish to decide whether the sample of four items of Table 12.6, which has a mean of 65.50 pounds and a range of 14 pounds, came from a population with a mean of 66.00 pounds. Symbolically the "null" hypothesis H_0 is that $\mu = 66.00$ pounds. The alternative hypothesis (or family of hypotheses) H_a is that $\mu \neq 66.00$ pounds. The test is said to be two-sided, since a large difference (so large that it is highly improbable if H_0 is true), whether positive or negative, will cause us to reject the null hypothesis.

We first compute what is known as the *test statistic*. This is

$$G_1 = \frac{\bar{X} - \mu_0}{R},$$

where μ_0 is the hypothetical population mean, 66.00 pounds in this case. Substituting in this equation, we obtain

$$G_1 = \frac{65.50 - 66.00}{14} = \frac{-0.5}{14} = -0.04.$$

When we look in Appendix Table 17.2 for the entry where $k = 1$ and $n = 4$, we find that $G_1 = 0.72$ at the 2.5 per cent probability point. This means that the probability of obtaining a sample that results in a value of G_1 as large as $+0.72$ or larger is .025. But since G_1 is symmetrically distributed it also means that the probability of obtaining a sample value of G_1 as small as -0.72 or smaller is .025. Finally, it means that the probability of obtaining a sample value as large, numerically (sign neglected), as 0.72 or larger is .05. This is the probability in which we are interested, for this is a two-sided test; we are testing whether $\bar{X}$ is significantly *different* from μ_0, not whether it is significantly smaller. There is not enough evidence for us to reject the null hypothesis, so we must therefore accept it, and conclude that the difference between $\bar{X}$ and μ_0 is not significant. This is because the probability of obtaining a sample that results in a value of G_1 as large, numerically, as the present one or larger is greater than .05, if H_0 is true. We know this to be true because

$$|G_1| < |G_{1,.025}|, \quad \text{i.e.,} \quad 0.04 < 0.72,$$

and the probability gets larger as G_1 gets smaller.

Not only is it true that the probability of our present sample is greater than .05. It is also greater than .10. Appendix Table 17.1 indicates that the probability of obtaining a value of G_1 as large, numerically, as 0.53 or larger is .10. So,

$$|G_1| < |G_{1,.05}|, \quad \text{i.e.,} \quad 0.04 < 0.53.$$

As a second illustration, consider the sample of Table 12.1: $n = 4$; $\bar{X} = 59$ pounds; $R = 6$ pounds. The null hypothesis H_0 is the same; $\mu = 66$ pounds. H_a: $\mu \neq 66$ pounds. The test statistic is

$$G_1 = \frac{59 - 66}{6} = \frac{-7}{6} = -1.17.$$

At the .025 probability point, $G = 0.72$. Since the observed value of G_1 is larger, numerically, than $G_{1,.025}$, we reject the null hypothesis, and conclude that the difference between $\bar{X}$ and μ_0 is significant.

There are two differences between this pair of illustrations. In the second one, the difference between $\bar{X}$ and μ_0 is greater, and R is smaller. Both of these facts contribute to the significance of the difference in the second illustration.

Comparison of two independent sample means. Table 12.7 shows the results obtained from tests on two preparations for killing house flies. Is the mortality from preparation 1 (the new preparation) significantly larger than that of preparation 2 (the old preparation)? The hypothesis we are testing is that $\mu_1 = \mu_2$, the alternative hypothesis being that $\mu_1 > \mu_2$. The test statistic is

(12.12)
$$G_2 = \frac{\bar{X}_1 - \bar{X}_2}{\bar{R}},$$

where $\bar{R}$ is the average of the two ranges, i.e.,

$$\bar{R} = \frac{R_1 + R_2}{2} = \frac{15 + 11}{2} = 13.$$

Therefore, $$G_2 = \frac{67.75 - 61.75}{13} = \frac{6}{13} = 0.46.$$

**Table 12.7—Per Cent of House
Flies Killed by Two
Preparations**

X_1	X_2
68	60
68	67 (high)
59 (low)	61
72	62
64	67
67	63
70	56 (low)
74 (high)	58
$\Sigma\ X_1 = 542$	$\Sigma\ X_2 = 494$
$\bar{X}_1 = \ \ 67.75$	$\bar{X}_2 = \ \ 61.75$
$R_1 = \ \ 15$	$R_2 = \ \ 11$

Source: Frank Wilcoxen, *Some Rapid
Approximate Statistical Procedures,* American
Cyanamid Company, New York, 1949, p. 4.

Since there are 8 observations in each sample, we turn to $n = 8$ in Appendix Table 18.1. Here we find that when $n = 8$, $G_{2,.05} = 0.31$. The probability of obtaining a value of G_2 as large as 0.31 or larger is .05, if $\mu_1 = \mu_2$. Since the computed value of G_2 is 0.46, which is larger than 0.31, it follows that the probability of obtaining a value of G_2 as large as 0.46 or larger is less than .05. We therefore reject the hypothesis that $\mu_1 = \mu_2$ in favor of the alternative hypothesis that $\mu_1 > \mu_2$, and conclude that $\bar{X}_1$ is significantly larger than $\bar{X}_2$.

Comparison of two paired-sample means. In Table 12.8 are recorded data on the compressive strength of 20 concrete cubes. There are 10 batches of concrete, and a pair of cubes was made from each batch, cube number one in each case being given special treatment. This experiment is distinctive in that each observation is paired with another one from the same batch. We take advantage of this pairing by considering the individual differences in compressive strength; i.e., we test the significance of the mean of the differences, rather than the differences between means. It is assumed that there is an inherent difference among the 10 batches; otherwise we would proceed as with the data of Table 12.7, where there is no basis for pairing.

Table 12.8—Compressive Strength of 10 Pairs of Test Cubes of
Concrete, and Computations for Testing of Significances
(Kilograms per square centimeter)

Batch	X_1 (Treated)	X_2 (Untreated)	$X_1 - X_2$ D
1	309	293	16
2	318 (high)	311 (high)	7
3	317	284	33 (high)
4	302	310	−8 (low)
5	315	305	10
6	296	291	5
7	319	301	18
8	285 (low)	279 (low)	6
9	303	295	8
10	290	289	1
Sum	3,054	2,958	96
Mean	305.4	295.8	9.6
Range	33	32	41

Source: Ralph Allen Bradley, "Some notes on the Theory and Application of Rank Order Statistics, Part I," *Industrial Quality Control*, Vol. XI, February, 1955, p. 15.

The hypothesis is that $\mu = 0$, the alternative hypothesis being that $\mu > 0$. The reason we use this alternative hypothesis is that we are interested in discovering whether the treatment is an improvement; we know that the treatment could not weaken the concrete. The test statistic, using (12.11), but substituting $\bar{D}$ for $\bar{X}$, is

$$G_1 = \frac{\bar{D} - \mu_0}{R} = \frac{9.6 - 0}{41} = 0.23.$$

Note that in computing $\bar{D}$, we do it algebraically, subtracting the D-value for batch 4 from the sum of the other D-values. Note also that $3,054 - 2,958 = 96$. This provides a check. Using $k = 1$ and $n = 10$, Appendix Table 17.1 indicates that $G_{1,.05}$ is 0.19. Therefore we reject the hypothesis that the treatment does not affect the compressive strength of concrete in favor of the alternative hypothesis that the treatment improves it.

Chapter 13

SAMPLING DESIGN

Some Basic Ideas

The methods of this chapter apply to all types of investigations requiring the use of samples, such as industrial experiments or surveys of populations. A large proportion of the discussion, however, is directed toward survey sampling.

Factors affecting sampling design. In deciding upon the method of sampling and the design of a sample survey, several factors should be considered.

1. *Whether the population is homogeneous.* Data are said to be homogeneous (alike qualitatively) if all the units in it are governed by the same set of causes. Often it is possible to divide the population into rational groups, among which different sets of causes are at work, but within each of which a constant set of causes is operating. In other words, a heterogeneous population can often be classified into homogeneous subgroups.

2. *The degree of precision required.* Precision refers to the uniformity of results that are to be expected from repeated samples of the same size and type from the same population. As stated in Chapter 12, reliability of an unbiased statistical measure, such as the arithmetic mean, is measured by its variance

$$\sigma_{\overline{X}}^2 = E(\overline{X} - \mu)^2$$

or its standard deviation $\sigma_{\overline{X}}$, which is the square root of the variance. If the standard deviation (usually called the standard error of the mean) is used as the measure of reliability, then the reliability of arithmetic means computed from random samples of size n from a large population varies with the square root of n. Thus, the arithmetic mean of a sample of 10,000 items is 10 times as reliable as the arithmetic mean of a sample of 100 items. Large size alone, however, is no guarantee that a sample is reliable; reliability depends also on the method of sampling and the sampling design used (as well as on the accuracy of the observations). In most cases it is important that an "error-formula" exist for determining the reliability of the results of a sample. Chapters 20–23 will further discuss the errors arising from *random* sampling. Formulas for other types of sampling are beyond the scope of this book.

3. *The cost of the sampling plan.* Although it is possible to increase the reliability of a sample by increasing its size, this may not be economical.

170

The cost may increase more or less proportionately with the sample size, whereas the reliability of the measures we are interested in computing from the sample increases much less rapidly. Other points, also, should be considered. A sample of 500 items comprised of 5 observations from each of 100 small areas taken at random will cost more to collect than will a sample of 500 items comprised of 100 observations from each of 5 large areas taken at random. The cost of sampling, including the cost of administering the plan, as compared with the cost of measurement, is sometimes the decisive consideration in testing materials. It should be noted that measurement may be destructive. If this is the case, design of the entire experiment, including the choice of the test statistic, should be such that the number of units measured be at a minimum.

Definition of population to be sampled. If one is sampling the farm population of a state, he must be able to distinguish between a farm, a garden, and a rural residence. Or, in an enumeration of industrial establishments, one might have to decide whether to try to include, for instance, a college student who strings tennis racquets occasionally in the evenings. The 1921–1939 Biennial Census of Manufacturing followed the procedure of including only those firms making goods worth more than $5,000 during the year, while the more complete enumerations in 1919 and earlier included firms making goods valued at $500 or more during the year. The use of an incomplete list enables one to omit many small firms, thus saving time and money. Obviously, it is dangerous to extend conclusions beyond the population sampled.

Choice of sampling units. In a survey of buying habits, should the ultimate sampling unit be the individual or the family? In the soap study illustrated earlier in Chapter 10, the family was selected as the sampling unit because it is impossible to measure the separate consumption of the different members of a family. Often, however, the choice of sampling units hinges on the reliability that will be obtained from different units compared with the cost of collecting the data.

The place for exercise of judgment. Sampling may be either (1) probability sampling or (2) judgment sampling. This chapter is concerned with probability sampling. Although judgment is exercised in designing a probability sampling plan, the enumerator does not exercise judgment with respect to the units included in his sample. The chief advantages of probability sampling are twofold:

1. The operation of chance is more likely to result in a representative sample than is the exercise of judgment.
2. Random sampling methods result in a probability distribution, and make it possible to estimate the magnitude of the sampling error.

If the sampler is permitted to decide which items to include in his sample, we have judgment sampling. Although it is possible by the exercise of good judgment to obtain a representative sample, usually this will not result. In an endeavor to obtain a reasonable average, some samplers will select only items that they consider typical. This will result in a sample that is more nearly uniform than the population. Other samplers may select small, medium, and large items in an endeavor to obtain representatives of all magnitudes; but such a procedure rarely results in the different sizes being represented in the correct proportion. In interviewing people, there is the danger than the interviewer will select for his sample mainly those who are easily accessible, or those who are pleasant to interview. Such procedures are usually even less likely to result in representative samples than is a conscious effort to select the best sample.

Nonreplacement of items. Consider the following finite population with $N = 6$, the units being identified by letters:

$$A\ B\ C\ D\ E\ F.$$

If n is the sample size, the number of samples that can be taken without replacement is $\binom{N}{n}$. Thus, if $n = 2$, the number of samples is $\binom{6}{2} = 15$. They are

```
            AB
            AC   BC
            AD   BD   CD
            AE   BE   CE   DE
            AF   BF   CF   DF   EF
```

There would be $\binom{6}{3} = 20$ samples of 3 items each.

If we take samples with replacement, however, we replace each item before drawing the next one, and the number of samples is N^n. If $N = 6$ and $n = 2$, there are 36 such samples.

```
        AA   BA   CA   DA   EA   FA
        AB   BB   CB   DB   EB   FB
        AC   BC   CC   DC   EC   FC
        AD   BD   CD   DD   ED   FD
        AE   BE   CE   DE   EE   FE
        AF   BF   CF   DF   EF   FF
```

There would be $6^3 = 216$ samples of 3 items each.

In survey sampling of human beings, the population is finite, and sampling is done without replacement.

About the only case where sampling is done with replacement is where we have the data for a discrete finite population and we wish to simulate the results that would be obtained from sampling an infinite population for which the probabilities are the same as the relative frequencies of the finite population. Suppose we have this discrete, finite population:

X	f
3	1
4	2
5	2
6	1
Total	6

If we sample this population, with replacement, we obtain the same samples with the same relative frequency that we would have if we had the following discrete, infinite population.

X	Prob (X)
3	0.167
4	.333
5	.333
6	.167
Total	1.000

The distinction between sampling without replacement and sampling with replacement is meaningless for an infinite population.

Absolute and relative sample size. The question is often asked whether a sample that is 10 per cent of the population is satisfactory: Such a question cannot be answered. The standard error of a mean depends on both the absolute sample size and the relative sample size n/N.

$$(13.1) \qquad \sigma_{\bar{X}} = \frac{\sigma}{\sqrt{n}} \sqrt{1 - \frac{n}{N}}.$$

Suppose the standard deviation of the population is $\sigma = 100$. Let us see what happens to $\sigma_{\bar{X}}$ as we vary n and N.

$n = 25$
$N = 2500$
$\dfrac{n}{N} = .01$
$\sigma_{\bar{X}} = \dfrac{100}{5} \sqrt{.99} = 19.9$

$n = 25$
$N = 500$
$\dfrac{n}{N} = .05$
$\sigma_{\bar{X}} = \dfrac{100}{5} \sqrt{.95} = 19.5$

$n = 100$
$N = 2000$
$\dfrac{n}{N} = .05$
$\sigma_{\bar{X}} = \dfrac{100}{10} \sqrt{.95} = 9.8$

$n = 100$
$N = 1000$
$\dfrac{n}{N} = .10$
$\sigma_{\bar{X}} = \dfrac{100}{10} \sqrt{.90} = 9.5$

It is apparent that when the sample size is not more than 10 per cent of the population, it doesn't make much difference what the relative size of the sample is. But the absolute sample size greatly affects the reliability of the sample.

Methods of Sampling

There are two types of sampling: random and systematic. All sampling designs utilize one or both of these methods.

Random sampling. *Sampling is said to be random if each possible sample (combination of a given number of items) has the same probability of being drawn.* Suppose we have the presumably homogeneous population shown below, and we wish to obtain a random sample of three units from this population. What are the different combinations of three items, each of which has the same chance of being drawn?

Unit	Diameter (millimeters)
A	3
B	4
C	4
D	5
E	5
F	6

The student should not conclude that these data are necessarily heterogeneous because the different units are of a different size; it must be remembered that the distinction between homogeneity and heterogeneity is a qualitative, not a quantitative, distinction. Also, the student should not conclude that one is likely to want to take a sample of 3 from a population of 6. He is more likely to require a sample of 500 from a population of 100,000. But the above data provide an illustration of manageable proportions.

There are $\binom{6}{3} = 20$ different samples of 3 that can be drawn from the above population of 6, together with the mean value of each sample, rounded to two decimal points.

Sample	Mean	Sample	Mean
ABC	3.67	BCD	4.33
ABD	4.00	BCE	4.33
ABE	4.00	BCF	4.67
ABF	4.33	BDE	4.67
ACD	4.00	BDF	5.00
ACE	4.00	BEF	5.00
ACF	4.33	CDE	4.67
ADE	4.33	CDF	5.00
ADF	4.67	CEF	5.00
AEF	4.67	DEF	5.33

A random sample is an appropriate type of sample for a homogeneous population. Samples of cord to be used in tires and to be tested for flex life and elongation may be selected at random, as may bolts (all of which are of the same material and made by the same or similar machines) to be tested for tensile strength, and likewise many other manufactured items.

When a random sample seems appropriate, the problem of achieving randomness must be solved. Two procedures are available.

Thorough mixing. One method is to mix the units together thoroughly and then draw the units for the sample in some unbiased manner. Sometimes the product being sampled is of such a character that it is very difficult to mix thoroughly. For instance, the heavy units may gravitate to the bottom, and a random sample will not be obtained by ordinary mixing methods. In other cases, the object under consideration is so bulky, fragile, or immobile that physical mixing is out of the question. Even under the most favorable circumstances, it is difficult to know when the units have been mixed *thoroughly enough.*

Use of random numbers. A method of overcoming this difficulty is to number the items and then select the desired number of units by use of a table of random numbers.[1] Assume that the following is a partial table of random numbers:

$$
\begin{array}{ccccc}
4 & 1 & 9 & 2 & 0 \\
9 & 6 & 9 & 7 & 4 \\
2 & 0 & 0 & 7 & 9 \\
4 & 5 & 8 & 4 & 7 \\
3 & 8 & 4 & 0 & 1 \\
\end{array}
$$

If we number the units of our previous illustration consecutively from $A = 1$ to $F = 6$, and proceed with our random numbers from left to right, beginning with the first row, the random sampling numbers used are 4, 1, 2, and the sample is DAB. If we proceed from top to bottom, beginning with the column on the left, the random sampling numbers (ignoring duplicates) are 4, 2, 3, and the sample is DBC. Random numbers may be used in any methodical manner decided upon before noticing the arrangement of items being sampled.

Variance of sample means. The list of sample means of 20 random samples given above may be put in the form of a probability distribution.

$\bar{X}$	Prob $(\bar{X})$
3.67	.05
4.00	.20
4.33	.25
4.67	.25
5.00	.20
5.33	.05

---

[1] A table of random numbers is given as Appendix 28.

The mean $\bar{X}$ of this probability distribution is of course the same as the mean μ of the 6 values comprising the population. $\bar{\bar{X}} = \mu = 4.5$. The variance of these means is[2]

$$\sigma_{\bar{X}}^2 = E(\bar{X} - \mu)^2 = \Sigma\,[(\bar{X} - \mu)^2 \text{ Prob } (\bar{X})]$$
$$= (3.67 - 4.50)^2(.05) + (4.00 - 4.50)^2(.20) + (4.33 - 4.50)^2(.25)$$
$$+ (4.67 - 4.50)^2(.25) + (5.00 - 4.50)^2(.20) + (5.33 - 4.50)^2(.05)$$
$$= 0.183.$$

Systematic sampling. In systematic sampling we select units from the population at uniform intervals of time, space, or order of occurrence. Thus, if we wish to select a systematic sample of 3 from our hypothetical population of 6, there are only two possible samples.

Sample	Mean
ACE	4.0
BDF	5.0

The item number with which to start should be determined at random. Thus, using our abbreviated table of random numbers, and proceeding from left to right with the first row, we encounter digit 1 before we come to digit 2. The sample is therefore ACE.

It may be appropriate to use a systematic sample where the units are arranged in order of magnitude or in some other more or less systematic manner. For instance, it would be convenient, and probably satisfactory, to select names from a telephone directory in this manner (assuming that telephone subscribers constitute the population we wish to sample). Another illustration of a systematic sample is where such items as bolts or rivets are drawn from the production line. For a strictly systematic sample, the units would be selected singly and spaced at equal intervals of time or order of production.

---

[2] The same result can be obtained in another way. The variance of the 6 observations in the population is

$$\sigma_X^2 = \frac{\Sigma\,(X - \mu)^2}{N - 1} = \frac{5.5}{5} = 1.1.$$

If the population were infinite, we could obtain the variance of the means by the expression

$$\sigma_{\bar{X}}^2 = \frac{\sigma_X^2}{n}.$$

But because each sample contains an appreciable proportion n/N of the population, we must multiply σ_X^2/n by the correction factor $(1 - n/N)$. Thus

$$\sigma_{\bar{X}}^2 = \frac{\sigma_X^2}{n}\left(1 - \frac{n}{N}\right)$$
$$= \frac{1.1}{3}\left(1 - \frac{3}{6}\right) = 0.183.$$

A substantial advantage of systematic sampling is its low cost. A list of persons to be interviewed need not be obtained, and a sample of persons laboriously drawn. The interviewer need only to ring the bell at, say, every twentieth household as he follows a predetermined path. It is usually best to take a serpentine route, rather than working one street the full length from east to west, and then starting the next street at the east end.

Often a systematic sample is more reliable than a random sample. For instance, if the population is arranged according to magnitude, a systematic sample would insure that items of different magnitudes be included in approximately the correct proportion, while with a random sample this would be a matter of chance. On the other hand, if the items in the population tend to come in approximately periodic waves, so that every twentieth item is large, then a 5 per cent systematic sample might contain only the largest items, or only the smallest ones. For such a situation, systematic sampling such as that mentioned would be less efficient than would random sampling. The variance of the means of the above systematic samples, computed in the same manner as for the random sample, is 0.25, which is somewhat larger than for the random sample.

$$\sigma_{\bar{X}}^2 = E(\bar{X} - \mu)^2 = \Sigma \left[(\bar{X} - \mu)^2 \, \mathrm{Prob} \, (\bar{X}) \right]$$

$$= (4 - 4.5)^2(.5) + (5 - 4.5)^2(.5) = 0.25.$$

Sampling Designs

Simple sampling. The sampling designs that we have considered are *simple* designs: simple random sampling, and simple systematic sampling. Many other designs are available. In each case the object is to obtain results of a given degree of reliability: (1) with the minimum sample size, or (2) with the minimum expenditure of money. Or stated conversely, with a given sample size or a given expenditure, we want to obtain results that are as reliable as possible (minimum variance among the means or other statistical measures).

Stratified sampling. When heterogeneity is present in a population it is usually desirable to classify the population into strata and select a random or systematic sample from each stratum. Often a proportionately stratified sample is used. This means that each sample stratum has the same proportion[3] of that stratum in the population. Referring again to our hypothetical data, and assuming that items A, B, C, and D constitute a product from the day shift, while E and F constitute a product from the night shift, we shall

---

[3] Sometimes the proportion varies from stratum to stratum, depending on the variability of the data within each stratum. Such a procedure, properly done, yields more reliable information for a given sample size; but computations based on sample data become more complicated.

enumerate the twelve possible stratified random samples of 3, each of which includes 2 items from the day shift and 1 from the night shift.

Sample	Mean	Sample	Mean
ABE	4.00	ABF	4.33
ACE	4.00	ACF	4.33
ADE	4.33	ADF	4.67
BCE	4.33	BCF	4.67
BDE	4.67	BDF	5.00
CDE	4.67	CDF	5.00

Notice that each of these samples has the same chance of being drawn, but that there are 8 random samples that cannot be included among our stratified samples. Also notice that the means of the different samples tend to cluster more closely together for our stratified sampling method than for our random sampling method. This can be seen more clearly if we form a probability distribution of the means.

$\bar{X}$	Prob $(\bar{X})$
4.00	.167
4.33	.333
4.67	.333
5.00	.167
Total	1.000

The variance of the means is

$$\sigma_{\bar{X}}^2 = (4.00 - 4.50)^2(.167) + (4.33 - 4.50)^2(.333)$$
$$+ (4.67 - 4.50)^2(.333) + (5.00 - 4.50)^2(.167)$$
$$= 0.102.$$

This value is much smaller than variance of the simple random sample means, which was 0.183.

It should be obvious that the strata selected should be germane to the problem, otherwise there will be no increase in the reliability of the sample as compared with a simple random sample. For example, a study of expenditures of male white college seniors might not be improved by using as two strata those with light hair and those with dark hair, but it doubtless would be helpful to separate fraternity and nonfraternity men. If the college seniors were to be stratified according to whether or not they are members of a fraternity and also according to academic standing (such as A, B, C, and D average grade), cross-classification is involved, and there are eight strata. If many strata, substrata, and sub-substrata are used, stratification becomes unwieldy.

Ordinarily the sample within each stratum should be taken at random, though occasionally a systematic sample may be appropriate. If enumerators are allowed to exercise their own initiative in selecting the items (sometimes called the "quota" method) within a stratum, they often select the most readily available cases, fail to check back on "not at home" calls, and do other things that result in a sample that is not representative.

Pilot study. One difficulty with stratified sampling is that at least some knowledge of the population must be available before strata can be properly selected. When a study is first undertaken, one's notion of what may constitute pertinent bases of classification may be based on meager information. It is therefore frequently advisable to conduct a pilot study, using a relatively small sample. Such a study is helpful in various ways.

1. It provides an estimate of the means of the different strata, thus giving an indication of what classifications are worth using.

2. It provides an estimate of the variances of the different strata, thus helping one to decide the optimum allocation of the sample among the different strata (See footnote 3.)

3. It provides an estimate of the response rates for the different strata, thus providing a basis for correction of the bias that arises from the differential response rate (especially when the questionnaire method is used).

4. It indicates the effectiveness of the different questions on the schedule.

Cluster sampling. In sampling a manufacturing process there are at least three possible procedures.

1. Inspect every ith item or one item every j minutes. This is systematic sampling.

2. Inspect a random sample of n items from the output during each hour. This is stratified random sampling.

3. Inspect n consecutive items at intervals of approximately one hour. This is cluster sampling, and is the method usually followed in process control.

Cluster sampling usually requires a larger sample, to attain the same degree of reliability, than does simple random sampling, because the different observations in the same cluster usually have about the same values.

An example of cluster sampling is an investigation where the ultimate sampling units are restaurants. It would be theoretically possible to study the operation of a random sample of restaurants covering the entire United States. If one were to spend a month investigating each restaurant, this might be the best way to do. If, however, the investigation involves only a 5-minute interview with each restaurant manager, such a procedure would quite likely involve prohibitive costs. Too much time would be devoted to traveling from place to place, and too little time would be spent in interviewing. It would be cheaper to make a random selection of *cities*, and study each restaurant in the cities selected. We could perhaps reduce the proportion of the total cost devoted to traveling by selecting a sample of *states* at random and investigating each restaurant in the states selected. But although this might be cheaper per sampling unit, it might increase the sampling error too much.

The size of the individual clusters relative to the number of clusters selected, obviously depends on:

1. The cost of alternative sampling plans. When the sampling is spread over a geographical area, the decisive factor is the cost of measurement or interviewing relative to the cost of traveling. In general, for a given sample size, it is cheaper to use a small number of large clusters than a large number of small clusters.

2. The reliability of the results obtained by the alternative plans. In general, for a given sample size, more reliable results are obtained from a large number of small clusters than from a small number of large clusters.

*Multistage sampling. If the units being studied are scattered over a geographical area, it is often economical to divide the territory into regions called *primary sampling units*, a number of which are selected either systematically or at random. Then from each of the regions that were selected by the sampling process, a number of subregions are selected systematically or at random. If each of the *ultimate sampling units* (which may be persons, households, farms, etc.) in a subregion is investigated, we have two-stage sampling, and the ultimate sampling units in a subregion constitute a cluster. If we select systematically or at random a sample from each subregion, we have three-stage sampling.

If human populations are being sampled, it is desirable that each of the regions and subregions have the same population, or that this be taken into consideration in selecting the sample.

Multistage sampling can be applied in other fields also. For example, every hundredth box can be taken from the production line, and samples taken of the contents of the boxes selected.

The advantage of multistage sampling is that a larger number of units can be sampled than by use of a simple sampling design, at the same cost.

*Area sampling. This is not really a separate type of design, but is a term used to refer to sampling designs where the primary sampling units are land areas. Usually area sampling utilizes both multistage sampling and cluster sampling.

*Sampling with probability proportional to size. In Table 13.1 is listed, in rank order, the cities in the United States with population of 500,000 or more in 1950. We wish to select a sample of ten department stores from these eighteen cities, for an intensive investigation.

First, we notice that the total population (in thousands) of these eighteen cities is 26,592. Since $26,592 \div 10 = 2,659$, a sampling interval of 2,659 is appropriate.

Next we select at random, some 4-digit number between 1 and 2,659. The first number in Appendix 28 table of random numbers is 1,581.

Table 13.1—Cities in the United States with Population of 500,000 or More, and Sample of Ten with Probability Proportional to Size

City	Population	Cumulative total	Sample
1. New York	7,892	7,892	1,581; 4,240; 6,899
2. Chicago	3,621	11,513	9,558
3. Philadelphia	2,072	13,585	12,217
4. Los Angeles	1,971	15,556	14,876
5. Detroit	1,850	17,406	
6. Baltimore	950	18,356	17,535
7. Cleveland	915	19,271	
8. St. Louis	857	20,128	
9. Washington, D. C. .	802	20,930	20,194
10. Boston	801	21,731	
11. San Francisco	775	22,506	
12. Pittsburgh	677	23,183	22,853
13. Milwaukee	637	23,820	
14. Houston	596	24,416	
15. Buffalo	580	24,996	
16. New Orleans	570	25,566	25,512
17. Minneapolis	522	26,088	
18. Cincinnati	504	26,592	

Source of data: U.S. Department of Commerce, *Statistical Abstract of the United States*, 1956, pp. 16–18.

Starting with 1,581 we add successive increments of 2,659 until we have obtained 10 numbers. These are shown in the last column of Table 13.1, and indicate that three stores should be selected in New York, and one each in seven other cities.

Note that this method of sampling does not assure that New York will be represented by three stores; nor does it preclude Chicago from having two stores; nor does it preclude Cincinnati from having one store. How it works depends on our random start.

It would be just as satisfactory if the cities were arranged alphabetically, or at random, providing we used a random start.

*Random-point sampling. This method consists first of locating many points at random on a map. A cluster consisting of a given number of items nearest to each point are then included to form the sample. Such a procedure cannot usually be recommended for selecting a sample of farms, for example, since the random points are more likely to fall on or near large farms than small farms. This method, obviously, can be used only for geographical series. It might be worth considering for selecting a sample of land areas classified by use or erosion status where the unit is not a farm but an acre or square mile, and for other similar purposes.

*Sequential sampling. It is sometimes expensive, and occasionally destructive, to test a raw material or manufactured product. In such instances it is desirable to draw inferences by testing a relatively small number of items. With double sampling, a small sample is first tested. If the sample is very good the lot is accepted; if the sample is very bad the lot is rejected; if it is intermediate, a second sample is taken and the product accepted or rejected on the basis of the two samples combined. Multiple sequential sampling employs the same principle, but the decision to accept or reject will not necessarily be made until some predetermined number of samples is taken. With item-by-item sequential sampling, additional items are tested, one at a time, until the desired degree of assurance is obtained. Item-by-item sequential sampling generally minimizes the number of items to be tested, but it may necessitate selecting a relatively large sample from which subsamples are taken. It is also rather expensive to administer because of the clerical work involved.

*Latin square. In agricultural work it is costly to perform an experiment, and it is important to have an efficient experimental design. Suppose we are considering the application of four types of treatment to four varieties of plant with four different types of soil. If we used a *factorial* design, which considers all of the possible combinations of factors, we would need a minimum of 64 observations.

By using a *Latin square* design we can get along with 16 observations. Let us arrange the varieties in columns and the treatments in rows; and designate the soil conditions by the letters A, B, C, D. Then one Latin square is

Treat-	Varieties			
ments	1	2	3	4
1	A	B	C	D
2	B	A	D	C
3	C	D	A	B
4	D	C	B	A

Thus the third row of the second column shows the result of treatment 3 applied to variety 2, planted in soil D. In a Latin square each letter occurs once and only once in each column and in each row. Obviously there is more than one Latin square with 4 columns and 4 rows,[4] and the square or squares to be used can be selected at random. By averaging the values in a given column one obtains an unbiased estimate of that variety mean; by averaging the values in a given row one obtains an unbiased estimate of that treatment mean; by averaging the values of a given letter one obtains an unbiased estimate of the soil mean.

---

[4] For a Tabulation of Latin squares see R. A. Fisher and F. Yates, *Statistical Tables for Biological, Agricultural and Medical Research*, Oliver and Boyd, Ltd., Edinburgh, 1949, Table XV.

This type of design is applicable to industrial experimentation. For example, the factors may be machines, materials, and men. Or it can be used in sampling human populations. For example, cities could be selected for study of buying habits of wage earners after classifying the cities on the basis of size of city, mean temperature, and per capita income.

The Latin square is only one of many designs, some very complex, devised for the purpose of obtaining the maximum information at the least expense.

Chapter 14

EQUATIONS AND CURVES

Straight Line

A straight line equation is of the following form:

$$Y = a + bX.$$

For example, we may have

$$Y = 8 + 0.5X.$$

This equation permits us to find the value of Y that corresponds to any desired value of X. Thus:

$$
\begin{aligned}
\text{If } X &= 0, & Y &= 8 + (0.5)(0) &= 8.0; \\
\text{If } X &= 1, & Y &= 8 + (0.5)(1) &= 8.5; \\
\text{If } X &= 2, & Y &= 8 + (0.5)(2) &= 9.0; \\
\text{If } X &= 3, & Y &= 8 + (0.5)(3) &= 9.5;
\end{aligned}
$$

....

$$\text{If } X = 10, \ Y = 8 + (0.5)(10) = 13.0.$$

This equation is plotted as Chart 14.1. It is apparent that the curve is a straight line. It is also apparent that a, which is 8 for this equation, is the value of Y when $X = 0$. The other constant, b, which is 0.5 in this case, is the slope; i.e., the change in Y that is associated with a unit change in X. We may define the slope as follows:

$$b = \frac{\Delta Y}{\Delta X} = \frac{Y_2 - Y_1}{X_2 - X_1}.$$

For example, consider the two points: $X_1 = 2$, $Y_1 = 9$; $X_2 = 10$, $Y_2 = 13$. Then

$$b = \frac{13 - 9}{10 - 2} = \frac{4}{8} = 0.5.$$

See Chart 14.1. Any two points selected would give the same result.

When we take the first differences of the Y values, we find that they have a constant value b.

X	Y	$\Delta^1 Y$
0	8.0	
		0.5
1	8.5	
		0.5
2	9.0	
		0.5
3	9.5	

Chart 14.1—Graph of Equation $Y = 8 + .05X$

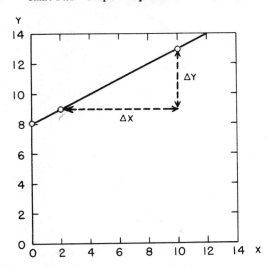

If the value of a, for our equation, were greater than 8, the curve would have the same slope, but it would be at a higher level; it would be parallel to the line plotted, but higher on the chart. If a were smaller than 8, it would be parallel to but lower than the one plotted. If b were greater than 0.5, but $a = 8$, the line would pass through the point $X = 0$, $Y = 8$, but it would be steeper; if b were less than 0.5 the curve would be less steep; if b were -0.5, the line would pass through the point $X = 0$, $Y = 8$, but it would slope downward to the right. Chart 14.2 shows a number of straight line equations and curves.

Exponential Curve

This curve, sometimes called a compound interest curve, has the equation type

$$Y = AB^X.$$

For example, we may have

$$Y = (100)1.5^X.$$

Selected points on this curve are:

$$X = 0, \quad Y = (100)1.5^0 = (100)1 \qquad = 100;$$

$$X = 1, \quad Y = (100)1.5^1 = (100)(1.5) \qquad = 150;$$

$$X = 2, \quad Y = (100)1.5^2 = (100)(2.25) \qquad = 225;$$

$$X = 3, \quad Y = (100)1.5^3 = (100)(3.375) \ = 337.5;$$

$$X = 4, \quad Y = (100)1.5^4 = (100)(5.0625) = 506.25.$$

Chart 14.2—Straight Line Equations and Curves

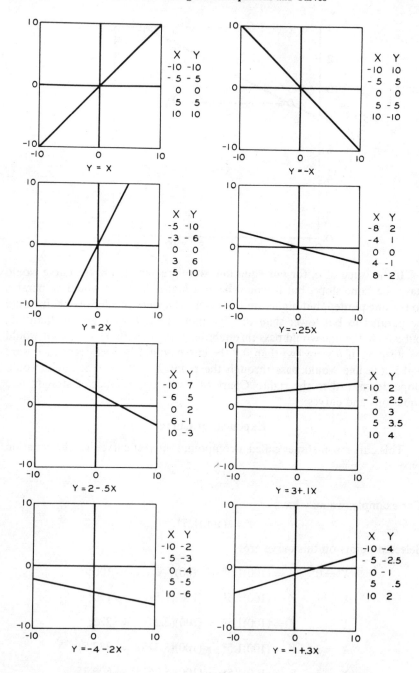

This equation is plotted as Chart 14.3A. It is apparent that A is the value of Y when $X = 0$. Notice also that the percentage growth is constant, each value being 50 per cent larger than the preceding. The slope is obviously not constant in an absolute sense, but is getting larger as X increases. It is, however constant relative[1] to Y.

Chart 14.3—Curves Formed by Y Value and Log Y Values
for the Exponential Equation $Y = (100)1.5^X$

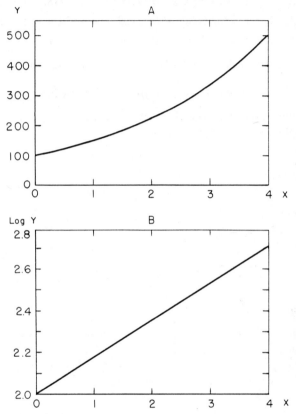

One interesting characteristic of this curve is that the logarithms of the Y values lie on a straight line. See Chart 14.3B. Taking logarithms of both sides of the exponential equation,

$$\text{Log } Y = \log A + (\log B)X.$$

If we let $a = \log A$ and $b = \log B$,

$$\text{Log } Y = a + bX.$$

[1] Although the average slope *between* any two points X_1, Y_1, and X_2, Y_2 that are *one unit apart* is $0.5 Y_1$, the slope at any point is $Y \log_e B = Y(2.302585)(\log_{10} B) = Y(2.302585)(0.1760913) = 0.40546 Y$.

In numerical form,

$$\text{Log } Y = 2 + 0.17609X.$$

Let us verify by substituting different values of X and taking the antilog of the results.

$$X = 0, \quad \log Y = 2.00000 + (0.17609)0 = 2.00000, \quad Y = 100;$$
$$X = 1, \quad \log Y = 2.00000 + (0.17609)1 = 2.17609; \quad Y = 150;$$
$$X = 2, \quad \log Y = 2.00000 + (0.17609)2 = 2.35218, \quad Y = 225;$$
$$X = 3, \quad \log Y = 2.00000 + (0.17609)3 = 2.52827, \quad Y = 337.5;$$
$$X = 4, \quad \log Y = 2.00000 + (0.17609)4 = 2.70426, \quad Y = 506.35.$$

This agrees with the value of Y obtained by use of the equation $Y = (100)1.5X$.

Second-degree Polynomial Equation

A second-degree polynomial equation in one variable, also referred to as a quadratic, or a parabola, is of the type

$$Y = a + bX + cX^2.$$

For example, we may have

$$Y = 10 + 5X + 2X^2.$$

Selected points are:

$$X = 0, \quad Y = 10 + 5(0) + 2(0) = 10;$$
$$X = 1, \quad Y = 10 + 5(1) + 2(1) = 17;$$
$$X = 2, \quad Y = 10 + 5(2) + 2(4) = 28;$$
$$X = 3, \quad Y = 10 + 5(3) + 2(9) = 43;$$
$$X = 4, \quad Y = 10 + 5(4) + 2(16) = 62.$$

This equation is plotted as Chart 14.4A. Again a is the value of Y when $X = 0$. When $X = 0$ the slope is b (which is 5 for this equation), but gets steeper as X gets larger.[2] See Chart 14.4B. When we take the first and second differences of this equation, we obtain,

X	Y	$\Delta^1 Y$	$\Delta^2 Y$
0	10		
		7	
1	17		4
		11	
2	28		4
		15	
3	43		4
		19	
4	62		

[2] If the sign of c is negative, the slope gets smaller as X gets larger.

Chart 14.4—Graph of Equation $Y = 10 + 5X + 2X^2$ and Slope of Curve

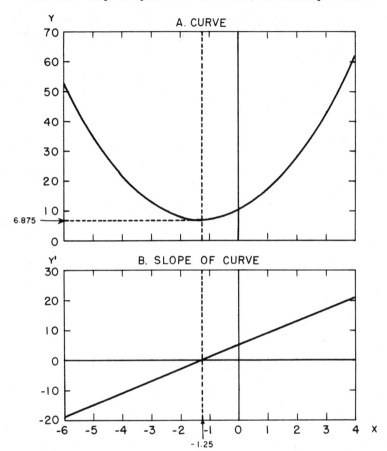

The first differences represent the *average slope* between two points. The second differences have a constant value $2b$, which is 4 for our equation.

This curve has a minimum value of 6.875, which is reached $X = -1.25$. Chart 14.5 shows a number of second-degree equations and curves.

Third-degree Polynomial Equation

A third-degree polynomial equation in X, also referred to as a cubic, is of the type

$$Y = a + bX + cX^2 + dX^3.$$

For example, we may have

$$Y = 3 + 1X + 0.1X^2 - 0.05X^3.$$

Chart 14.5—Second-Degree Equations and Curves

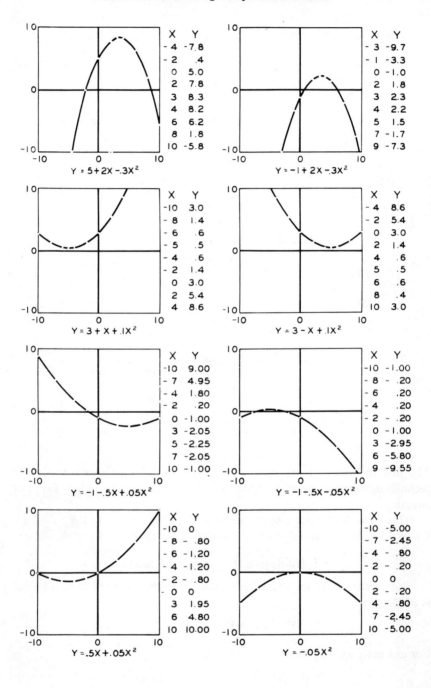

X	Y
- 4	-7.8
- 2	.4
0	5.0
2	7.8
3	8.3
4	8.2
6	6.2
8	1.8
10	-5.8

$Y = 5 + 2X - .3X^2$

X	Y
- 3	-9.7
- 1	-3.3
0	-1.0
2	1.8
3	2.3
4	2.2
5	1.5
7	-1.7
9	-7.3

$Y = -1 + 2X - .3X^2$

X	Y
-10	3.0
- 8	1.4
- 6	.6
- 5	.5
- 4	.6
- 2	1.4
0	3.0
2	5.4
4	8.6

$Y = 3 + X + .1X^2$

X	Y
- 4	8.6
- 2	5.4
0	3.0
2	1.4
4	.6
5	.5
6	.6
8	.4
10	3.0

$Y = 3 - X + .1X^2$

X	Y
-10	9.00
- 7	4.95
- 4	1.80
- 2	.20
0	-1.00
3	-2.05
5	-2.25
7	-2.05
10	-1.00

$Y = -1 - .5X + .05X^2$

X	Y
-10	-1.00
- 8	- .20
- 6	.20
- 4	.20
- 2	- .20
0	-1.00
3	-2.95
6	-5.80
9	-9.55

$Y = -1 - .5X - .05X^2$

X	Y
-10	0
- 8	- .80
- 6	-1.20
- 4	-1.20
- 2	- .80
0	0
3	1.95
6	4.80
10	10.00

$Y = .5X + .05X^2$

X	Y
-10	-5.00
- 7	-2.45
- 4	- .80
- 2	- .20
0	0
2	- .20
4	- .80
7	-2.45
10	-5.00

$Y = -.05X^2$

Chart 14.6—Third-Degree Equations and Curves

A. $Y = 3 + 1X + 0.1X^2 - 0.05X^3$

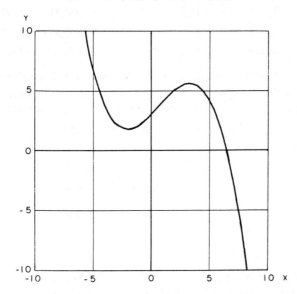

B. $Y = 1 + 1X - 0.4X^2 + 0.05X^3$

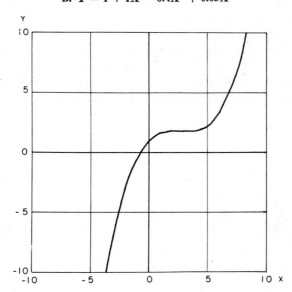

Selected points are:

$$X = 0, \quad Y = 3 + 1(0) + (0.1)(0) \; - (0.05)(0) \;\; = 3.00;$$
$$X = 1, \quad Y = 3 + 1(1) + (0.1)(1) \; - (0.05)(0) \;\; = 4.05;$$
$$X = 2, \quad Y = 3 + 1(2) + (0.1)(4) \; - (0.05)(8) \;\; = 5.00;$$
$$X = 3, \quad Y = 3 + 1(3) + (0.1)(9) \; - (0.05)(27) = 5.55;$$
$$X = 4, \quad Y = 3 + 1(4) + (0.1)(16) - (0.05)(64) = 5.40.$$

This equation is plotted as Chart 14.6A. As usual, a is the value of Y when $X = 0$, and the slope where $X = 0$ is b. Computation of first, second, and third differences show that the third differences have a constant value $6d$.

X	Y	$\Delta^1 Y$	$D^2 Y$	$\Delta^3 Y$
0	3.00			
		1.05		
1	4.05		−0.10	
		0.95		−0.30
2	5.00		−0.40	
		0.55		−0.30
3	5.55		−0.70	
		−0.15		
4	5.40			

This curve has a minimum value of 1.96, which is reached when $X = -4/3$; and a maximum value of 5.55, which is reached when $X = 3$. It also has a *point of inflection*, where the curve changes from concave upward to concave downward. The point of inflection is reached when $X = 2/3$ and $Y = 3.70$. At this point the slope is the steepest for that portion of the curve where the slope is positively inclined.

In order to see the effect of changes in the signs of b and c, the equation $Y = 1 + 1X - 0.4X^2 + 0.05X^3$ is plotted as Chart 14.6B.

Polynomial equations are very flexible, since they can be expanded indefinitely by adding more terms: eX^4, fX^5, and so on.

Chapter 15

THE FREQUENCY DISTRIBUTION

In this chapter we consider first the technique of forming and plotting a frequency distribution. Then we consider the ways in which frequency curves may differ, and what these differences indicate. Finally, we consider some special types of charts that are useful for interpreting frequency distributions.

In this chapter and the three following we confine our discussion almost exclusively to continuous variables. Following is a summary, in outline form, of types of variables.

Qualitative variable, or attribute: objects classified as defective or effective; persons classified as rich or poor; persons classified as single, married, widowed, or divorced. The categories must be exhaustive and mutually exclusive.

Quantitative variable:

Discrete or discontinuous: number of defects per unit; number of defectives in samples of n items each; number of rich people in different random samples of n each. The unit of measurement can have only integral values.

Continuous: weights of lumps of coal; people classified as to degree of wealth. Units of measurement can be divided into arbitrarily small pieces.

Note that an arbitrary boundary must be drawn between rich and poor if that essentially quantitative variable is treated as an attribute. Note also that wealth is usually measured in dollars and cents, but the cent is so small, relatively, that it is unimportant whether the wealth of persons is considered a discrete or continuous variable.

Raw Data

Statistical data may originally appear in a form such as that of Table 1.2. In this table are listed the kilowatt-hours of electricity used by each of 75 residential consumers. The figures are arranged more or less at random. When data are in raw form as here, little information can be obtained by an inspection of them. To obtain such simple information as the greatest and smallest amount of electricity sold to a consumer, a careful examination involving every one of the 75 items is necessary.

The Array

A rearrangement of the data according to the amount of electricity used gives the array shown in Table 15.1. The array may be from the smallest to the largest, or vice versa.

It has certain distinct advantages over the data in the raw form. First, a good idea can be obtained of the range of consumption shown by the 75 readings, since the lowest and highest values can readily be seen; second, the tendency of the items to concentrate somewhere near 75 kilowatt-hours may be observed; third, something can be seen of the distribution of the items between the lower and upper limits—notably that most of the items are

Table 15.1—Array of Kilowatt-Hours of Electricity Used in One Month by 75 Residential Consumers

(Data of Table 1.2)

8	56	73	84	105
9	57	74	86	114
10	58	75	87	115
19	58	75	88	118
28	59	75	89	121
36	60	76	90	125
37	61	77	90	126
38	62	78	91	128
40	64	79	92	131
41	66	80	93	135
50	67	81	94	136
51	68	82	94	144
52	70	83	95	148
53	71	83	96	157
54	72	84	98	158

between 36 and 136 kilowatt-hours, and very few below 36 or above 136 kilowatt-hours. In spite of these advantages, however, the array is cumbersome because there are still 75 separate items to be dealt with. This would be even more apparent if we were dealing with several hundred items.

The Frequency Distribution

Construction of the frequency distribution. Although some of the details shown by the array of the individual items will be sacrificed, there is much to be gained by summarizing the data into the frequency distribution of Table 15.2. In this table the data are grouped into eight classes, each having an interval of 20 kilowatt-hours between the upper and lower limit. While it is desirable, for computational purposes, to have more than eight classes in a frequency distribution, if the number of classes were materially increased in this instance, there would be so few items in the various classes that irregularities due solely to the smallness of the sample would appear. These irregularities, which would tend to disappear if the size of the sample were increased, would be undesirable for graphic presentation.

The frequency distribution no longer gives us the exact value of each individual reading; we cannot obtain from it the exact value of even the highest and lowest items. It does tell us, however, that the lowest value is more than 4.5 kilowatt-hours and the highest value is 164.5 or fewer kilowatt-hours.[1] Compressing the 75 items into a frequency distribution enables us to see at a glance the tendency to concentrate around some central value of the series.

**Table 15.2—Kilowatt-Hours of
Electricity Used in One
Month by 75 Residen-
tial Consumers**

Consumption in kilowatt-hours	Number of consumers
5–24	4
25–44	6
45–64	14
65–84	22
85–104	14
105–124	5
125–144	7
145–164	3
Total	75

Source: Table 1.2.

The frequency distribution is a more useful device than the array especially for dealing with series of many items. It is easy to see how cumbersome the array would be if we had 300 items instead of 75. The frequency distribution may be constructed directly from the original data without the use of the array. However, if an array of the figures is available, the frequency distribution may be made by merely counting, from the array, the number of items in each class. The array may also help one to decide not only how many classes, but also what class limits, to use.

If a frequency distribution is to be made directly from the raw data, it may be done by use of a tallying procedure similar to that shown on page 139. An alternative method which has certain advantages consists of using an entry form such as that of Table 15.3. The kilowatt-hour figures are written in the entry form one after the other as they occur in Table 1.2. By glancing down any column it is easy to see if a misplaced item is present. If, after completing the entry form, it is decided to use different classes, this may be done readily; if a tally sheet is used, there is less flexibility in this respect.

It will be noticed that the class intervals of Table 15.2 are equal. Usually frequency distributions should be constructed with uniform class intervals.

---

[1] While not strictly accurate, we are assuming, for purposes of illustration, that each observation is rounded to the nearest kilowatt-hour.

Table 15.3—Entry Form for Construction of Frequency Distribution of Kilowatt-Hours of Electricity Used in One Month by 75 Residential Consumers

5–24	25–44	45–64	65–84	85–104	105–124	125–144	145–164
19	38	58	82	86	114	131	148
10	28	58	75	90	105	144	158
8	36	57	83	94	118	125	157
9	40	50	74	94	121	126	
	37	52	75	92	115	136	
	41	64	78	96		128	
		62	66	90		135	
		60	81	89			
		59	72	95			
		61	73	88			
		56	76	91			
		54	84	98			
		53	80	93			
		51	71	87			
			70				
			68				
			75				
			84				
			83				
			77				
			79				
			67				

Source: Table 1.2.

This procedure will facilitate the calculations to be described in the following chapters. Also, distributions with unequal class intervals are sometimes misinterpreted, especially when presented graphically.

Graphic Representation

Technique. Chart 15.1 shows how the data of electric consumption of Table 15.2 appear graphically. The horizontal dimension of each bar represents the class; the vertical dimension represents the number of occurrences in the class. The bars are, of course, all of the same width. This method of graphically portraying a frequency distribution is variously referred to as a *column diagram*, or *histogram*.

Instead of using a bar for each class, we may locate a point so that it is at mid-value of the class and opposite the appropriate frequency. The light line on Chart 15.1 shows the result of plotting and connecting the eight points for the frequency distribution. This *frequency polygon* has been extended, by means of broken lines, to meet the base line at distances of one-half a class interval beyond the two end bars. These arguments are in favor of such a procedure: (1) There are no observations for these classes, and therefore points should be plotted to so indicate. (2) The straight lines connecting the points have no validity; they are only for the convenience of the reader. (3) The chart is easier to understand if it is so plotted. (4) If so plotted, the area under the curve is equal to the area of the rectangles. However, there are two arguments against such extensions: (1) The extensions suggest the presence of items that were not found in the sample, but the

Chart 15.1—Kilowatt Hours of Electricity Used in One Month by 75 Residential Consumers, Shown by Column Diagram and Frequency Polygon

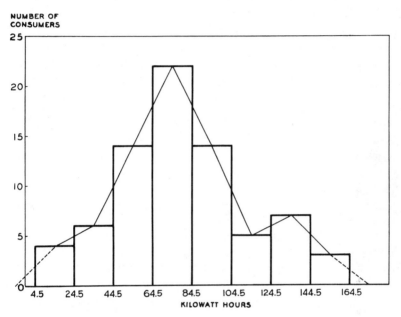

Source of data: Table 15.1

curve is not an estimate of the population from which the sample was drawn. (2) The extension at the left occasionally runs into negative values, which are usually impossible. This is the case with Chart 15.1.

Some statisticians use the column diagram for showing discrete data, the curve for showing continuous data. Certainly the column diagram is more appropriate than the frequency curve when one wishes to show such data as a distribution of the number of families having 1, 2, 3, 4, or more members. For data of this sort the bars may be slightly separated to suggest the discreteness of the data. See the charts in Chapter 11. For popular presentation the column diagram is often used in preference to the frequency polygon. It is more striking and causes the values for the individual classes to stand out more clearly. For the purpose of comparing two sample frequency distributions, however, frequency curves are more effective than are column diagrams. In Chapter 19 the data of a sample will be shown by a column diagram, while the fitted data will be shown by a curve.

Chart 15.1 shows the graphic appearance of the data of electric consumption. This distribution, like many business and economic series, is roughly "bell-shaped" but not symmetrical. It is unusual to encounter an economic or business series that is exactly symmetrical, though occasionally series are found that are nearly so.

Technical Considerations

Determining the number of classes. It is important that a frequency distribution be made with a suitable number of classes. If too few classes are used, the original data will be so compressed that little information will be available. If too many classes are used, there will be too few items in some of the classes, and the frequency polygon will be irregular in appearance.[2] See Charts 18.5 and 18.6.

The number of classes varies inversely with the class interval. To increase the number of classes, we make the class interval smaller. For computational purposes, 12 or more classes are usually desirable.[3]

Selecting the class limits. There are several considerations to bear in mind when selecting the class limits.

Have a representative mid-value. As will be seen later, the *mid-value* of each class is generally used to represent the class. The mid-value of a class is the average of its upper and lower limits. Thus we must select the class limits so that the mid-values of the classes will coincide, so far as possible, with concentrations that may be present. For example, in studying the meals sold by a cafeteria, it was found that a great many checks were multiples of 5 cents—that is, ended in 5 or 0. Consequently, the class intervals for a frequency distribution of the meals checks of this cafeteria

---

[2] For purposes of graphic representation, Kelley suggests the following:

Number of items	Number of classes	Number of items	Number of classes
5	2	100	10
10	4	200	12
25	6	500	15
50	8	1,000	15

See Truman L. Kelley, "The Grouping of Data for Graphic Portrayal," lecture at Cowles Commission Conference at Colorado Springs, Colo., July 25, 1939.

[3] George W. Snedecor (*Statistical Methods*, 4th ed. Collegiate Press, Ames, Iowa, 1946, p. 170) suggests that the class interval should not be more than one fourth of the estimated population standard deviation. The standard deviation is explained in Chapter 16 of the present text.

read 8–12 cents, 13–17 cents, 18–22 cents, and so on, thus making the mid-values 10, 15, 20, and so on. On the other hand, if measurements are made of heights of many thousand men, the data would be graduated smoothly from, say, 4 feet 10 inches to 6 feet 10 inches. Not only would there be men 5 feet 1 inch tall and others 5 feet 2 inches tall, but there would be a great number falling between these two measurements; and if a large enough number of men were measured, the minute variations between 5 feet 1 inch and 5 feet 2 inches would be limited only by the accuracy of the measuring instrument used.

For the purpose of selecting the class limits, important considerations are not only whether the variable is inherently discrete, but also whether there are significant points of concentration in the actual data. Thus, although ages are inherently a continuous variable, ages as reported to the census enumerator show concentrations at years ending in 0 or 5. Likewise salary data are inherently discrete, because annual salaries never end in fractions of a cent. However, the important consideration is that there are apt to be concentrations at such salaries as $4,800, $5,000, $6,000, $7,000, $7,200, $7,500, and so on.

Even though there are no points of concentration, class limits must be selected that are appropriate to the data. For example, if weights of castings are reported to the nearest pound, it is correct to write classes:

Weight in pounds	Mid-value
442–444	443
445–447	446
448–450	449
etc.	etc.

The *stated* class limits are not, of course, the actual class limits, since there is a gap between 444 and 445, and between 447 and 448. The actual boundaries for these classes are 444.5 and 447.5. It is therefore correct to state the actual class limits in writing the classes. Thus:

Weight in pounds	Mid-value
441.5–444.5	443
444.5–447.5	446
447.5–450.5	449
etc.	etc.

If, however, the weights are given to the last full pound, the above is incorrect. We should write

Weight in pounds	Mid-value
442 but less than 445	443.5
445 but less than 448	446.5
448 but less than 451	449.5
etc.	etc.

If several castings were weighted with the results shown in the first column below, the values would be recorded as shown in the two columns to the right.

Actual weight	Rounded to nearest pound	Rounded to last pound
443.500	444	443
443.674	444	443
444.500	444	444
444.730	445	444
449.427	449	449

Observe that the fourth item, above, would fall in the class "445–447" if rounded to the nearest pound,[4] but in the class "442 but under 445" if rounded to the last pound.

Avoid open-end classes. An open-end class is one that includes all items smaller than some specified upper limit, or larger than some specified lower limit. Consider the distribution of Table 15.4.

Table 15.4—Socony Mobile Oil Company Stockholders Classified by Size of Shareholding

Number of shares owned	Shareholders (thousands)
1–9	15
10–49	64
50–100	45
101–999	47
1,000 or more	2
Total	173

Source: Read from Chart on page 25 of Socony Mobile Oil Company, *Annual Report*, 1955.

Since we do not know whether the average shareholding of the 2,000 shareholders who held 1,000 or more shares was close to 1,000 shares or some much larger number,[5] we cannot use the table accurately for computational purposes. For example, one could not estimate accurately the average number of shares per shareholder.

Class interval should usually be uniform. Table 15.4 is unorthodox in

---

[4] Whenever a measurement falls on a class boundary or whenever it is impossible to determine on which side of a class boundary a measurement falls, a more accurate procedure is to split the frequency and place a half frequency in the class on each side. See Table 15.6. For a continuous variable, the probability that an observation will fall exactly on a class boundary is negligible (technically it is zero).

[5] Other information in the report suggests that the average holdings of these 2,000 persons was about 3,000 shares.

two other respects also. It would have been better to have written classes
as follows:

1–9

10–49

50–99

100–999

1,000 or more

The other unusual feature of this table is that the class intervals are not
equal. The result is that the table is possibly misleading. To some people
it may give the impression that the typical shareholding is approximately 40
shares. If the data were classified into intervals of uniform width, the
impression might be considerably different. Certainly such a classification
would show a very skewed distribution, with most of the shareholdings
rather small but a few very large.

Skewed distributions. If a frequency distribution is greatly skewed it
becomes unwieldy if equal class intervals are used. (This is sometimes true
of extremely leptokurtic distributions also. See page 205 for meaning of
the adjective leptokurtic.) During June, 1956, the Iowa State Traveling
Men's Association paid 290 accident claims ranging from $3.00 to $872.71.
These are listed in order of magnitude in Table 15.5.[6]

A frequency distribution of these claims, using $20.00 class intervals,
would require 44 classes, and even such a fine grouping would fail to disclose
the proper detail for the smaller claims. It would, for example, fail to show
that the typical size of claim was between $10.00 and $20.00. In order to
avoid excessive irregularities, and yet show such detail as seems desirable,
the data are grouped in Table 15.6, using class intervals that become progressively larger, each interval being twice the preceding. In tabulating these
data, frequencies at the class limits ($5.00, $10.00, $20.00, and $40.00) have
been apportioned equally between the two classes. For example, 3 of the
$5.00 claims are put in the first class and 3 in the second.

Chart 15.2 shows the actual frequencies of Table 15.6. The typical size of
claim is not obvious from inspection of this chart. Although there are more
frequencies in the $40.00–$80.00 class, one would expect more frequencies
than in the $10.00–$20.00 class because it is four times as wide.

A better, or at least a different, idea of the structure of the distribution
is obtained if the frequencies in each class are adjusted for the relative size of
the class interval.[7] Such an adjustment is made in the last column of Table

---

[6] This array illustrates difficulties, other than those associated with skewness, in forming
a frequency distribution. Note, for example, significant tendencies to cluster around these
values: $5.00; $10.00; $20.00; $37.50; $50.00; $62.50; $75.00; $100.00. It would be
difficult to form a frequency distribution in which each of these would be a mid-value.

[7] In one way the unadjusted frequencies are more informative. The distribution is not
far from normal when the ratio, rather than the distance, between the class limits is uniform.
Thus an orderliness is revealed that is not apparent from the adjusted frequencies.

Table 15.5—Distribution of Accident Claims Paid by Iowa State Traveling Men's Association, During June 1956

(There were 290 accident claims paid, totaling $29,061.00)

$3.00	$12.00	$20.00	$35.71	$50.00	$57.14	$70.71	$100.00	$138.07	$262.50
3.00	12.50	20.00	35.71	50.00	57.14	71.00	100.00	142.85	264.28
3.00	13.00	20.00	35.71	50.00	58.57	72.13	100.00	142.85	275.00
4.28	14.00	20.00	35.71	50.00	58.93	73.21	100.00	144.00	275.00
5.00	14.00	21.00	37.50	50.00	60.00	75.00	100.00	150.00	289.28
5.00	14.00	21.00	37.50	50.00	60.71	75.00	100.00	151.78	289.28
5.00	14.28	21.42	37.50	50.00	60.71	75.00	100.00	153.57	292.85
5.00	14.85	21.42	37.50	50.00	62.20	75.00	100.00	160.50	302.00
5.00	15.00	21.42	38.00	50.00	62.50	75.00	100.00	162.50	316.14
5.00	15.00	23.00	39.80	50.00	62.50	75.00	100.00	175.00	325.00
6.00	15.00	23.50	40.00	50.00	62.50	75.00	100.00	175.00	326.00
7.00	15.00	24.00	40.00	50.00	62.50	76.50	100.00	175.00	328.50
7.75	16.07	25.00	40.17	50.00	62.50	80.35	107.50	175.00	330.00
8.00	16.08	25.00	41.07	50.00	62.50	80.35	112.50	179.28	336.13
8.00	16.15	25.06	41.07	50.00	62.50	82.00	116.07	183.93	362.50
8.00	16.28	25.50	42.50	50.00	62.50	82.28	117.85	189.28	410.00
8.25	16.95	26.00	42.50	50.00	62.50	83.50	117.85	189.85	414.50
9.00	17.00	26.50	42.85	50.00	62.50	83.64	118.50	200.00	421.42
9.50	17.60	26.50	43.00	50.00	62.50	84.28	121.42	200.00	424.00
10.00	17.85	27.00	44.00	50.00	62.50	85.71	125.00	214.28	443.00
10.00	17.85	28.00	44.64	50.00	63.13	92.71	125.00	221.42	464.00
10.00	17.85	28.57	44.64	50.00	64.28	92.85	125.00	229.64	475.00
10.00	18.00	28.57	46.42	50.00	64.90	92.85	125.00	225.00	500.00
10.00	18.00	30.35	45.00	50.00	67.85	94.42	125.00	225.00	524.57
10.00	18.00	31.25	45.00	50.00	67.85	96.64	126.85	240.00	533.64
10.00	18.36	32.14	46.85	50.00	67.94	97.50	128.50	240.35	561.43
10.00	19.00	33.03	48.00	53.57	68.20	100.00	129.64	250.00	606.14
10.50	19.00	35.00	48.21	53.57	69.50	100.00	137.50	250.00	657.14
10.71	19.00	35.21	50.00	53.57	69.63	100.00	137.50	253.57	872.71

Source: Iowa State Traveling Men's Association, Des Moines, Iowa.

Table 15.6—Distribution of Accident Claims Paid by Iowa State Traveling Men's Association, by Size, During June, 1956, and Computation of Frequency Densities

Size of claim	Mid-value (X)	Frequency (f)	Class interval (c)	Adjustment factor (a)	Adjusted frequency ($f \div a$)
$2.50–$5.00	$3.75	7	$2.50	0.0625	112
5.00–10.00	7.50	16	5.00	0.125	128
10.00–20.00	15.00	37	10.00	0.25	148
20.00–40.00	30.00	38	20.00	0.50	76
40.00–80.00	60.00	88	40.00	1.00	88
80.00–160.00	120.00	53	80.00	2.00	26.5
160.00–320.00	240.00	31	160.00	4.00	7.75
320.00–640.00	480.00	18	320.00	8.00	2.25
640.00–1,280.00	960.00	2	640.00	16.00	0.125

Source: Table 15.5.

15.6, which shows the frequencies per interval of $40.00. The adjustment is made by dividing the actual frequencies by correction factors that are proportional to the class intervals. The adjusted frequencies are sometimes called *frequency densities*.

Chart 15.2—Histogram Using Unequal Class Intervals

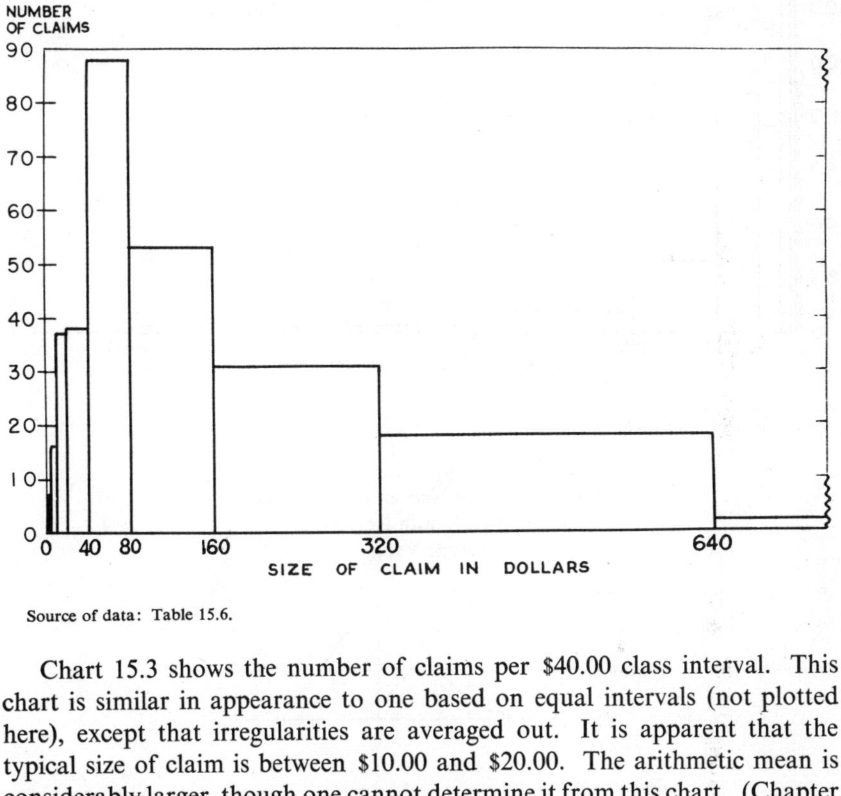

Source of data: Table 15.6.

Chart 15.3 shows the number of claims per $40.00 class interval. This chart is similar in appearance to one based on equal intervals (not plotted here), except that irregularities are averaged out. It is apparent that the typical size of claim is between $10.00 and $20.00. The arithmetic mean is considerably larger, though one cannot determine it from this chart. (Chapter 16 explains how to estimate the arithmetic mean from a frequency distribution.) The bimodality of the curve, which shows a primary mode between $10.00 and $20.00 and a secondary mode between $40.00 and $80.00, should not be assumed to be a sampling irregularity. Presumably it results from policy provisions which tend to give large frequencies to claims of certain sizes; smaller class intervals would reveal other such minor peaks.

One should not think that when unequal class intervals are used they must increase in geometric progression. An interesting exercise would be to obtain frequency densities for the frequencies of Table 15.5, where the intervals of the successive classes are approximately 10, 40, 50, 400, 500.

Interpretation of frequency curves. Frequency distributions may differ in several respects: (1) average value; (2) dispersion; (3) shape.

Chart 15.3—Histogram Using Unequal Class Intervals and Adjusted Frequencies

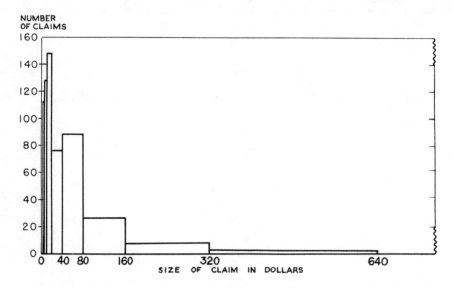

Source of data: Table 15.6.

**Chart 15.4—Two Normal Distributions
Differing Only with Respect to
Average Value**

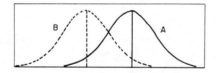

**Chart 15.5—Two Normal Distributions
Having Same Arithmetic Mean but
Different Dispersions**

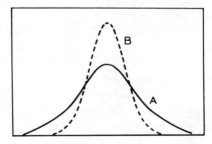

Chart 15.4 compares two distributions that differ only with respect to average value. Distribution A is located farther to the right than distribution B, and therefore has a larger average value. The location of the two means is shown by a vertical line.

Chart 15.5 compares two distributions that differ only with respect to dispersion. Distribution A exhibits more dispersion; it is more spread out. Conversely the values of distribution B are more uniform.

**Chart 15.6—A Positively Skewed Frequency
Curve and a Normal Curve**

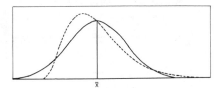

Chart 15.6 compares two distributions that have the same average value and the same degree of dispersion, but differ with respect to shape. Distribution B is normal, while distribution A is skewed to the right. This is spoken of as positive skewness. It indicates fewer than normal extremely small values, but more than normal extremely large values.

**Chart 15.7—A Negatively Skewed Frequency
Curve and a Normal Curve**

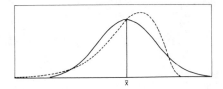

**Chart 15.8—A Leptokurtic Frequency
Curve and a Normal Curve**

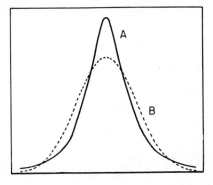

Chart 15.7 is like Chart 15.6, except that the skewness of A is negative, toward the left.

Chart 15.8 compares two distributions that have the same average value and the same amount of dispersion, but differ in another respect. Distribution A has a smaller proportion than normal of medium-sized deviations from the mean, but a larger proportion of deviations that are extremely small or extremely large. Such a distribution is referred to as being *leptokurtic*. Literally leptokurtic means "with sharp curvature," but this is a misnomer. Leptokurtic curves are usually, but not always, peaked.

**Chart 15.9—A Platykurtic Frequency
Curve and a Normal Curve**

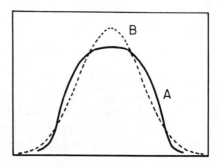

**Table 15.7—Distribution and Percentage Distribution of Hourly Wage
Rates of Union Motortruck Drivers and Helpers, July 1, 1944**

Hourly rate	Number		Per cent of total	
	Drivers	Helpers	Drivers	Helpers
$0.30 but under $0.40	8	38	*	0.1
0.40 but under 0.50	152	610	0.1	2.0
0.50 but under 0.60	1,397	1,867	0.8	6.3
0.60 but under 0.70	6,210	2,808	3.3	9.4
0.70 but under 0.80	10,377	7,258	5.6	24.3
0.80 but under 0.90	37,518	8,720	20.2	29.3
0.90 but under 1.00	44,227	4,601	23.8	15.4
1.00 but under 1.10	38,982	3,175	21.0	10.7
1.10 but under 1.20	24,439	315	13.2	1.1
1.20 but under 1.30	16,520	416	8.9	1.4
1.30 but under 1.40	4,419		2.4	
1.40 but under 1.50	233		0.1	
1.50 but under 1.60	1,340		0.7	
Total	185,822	29,808	100.0	100.0

*Less than one-tenth of one per cent.
Based on data from "Union Wages and Hours of Motortruck Drivers and Helpers, July 1, 1944," *Monthly Labor Review*, December, 1944, p. 1247, and supplementary data from United States Bureau of Labor Statistics. Two helpers at less than $0.30 and 30 drivers at $1.60 or more are omitted from the above table.

Chart 15.9 compares a normal curve and a *platykurtic* curve. Distribution A, which is platykurtic, has a larger proportion than normal of medium-sized deviations, but a smaller proportion than normal of deviations that are extremely small or extremely large. Literally platykurtic means "with wide curvature," but this is a misnomer. Platykurtic curves are usually, but not always, flat-topped.

Chart 15.10—Distribution of Hourly Wage Rates of Union Motortruck Drivers and Helpers, July 1, 1944

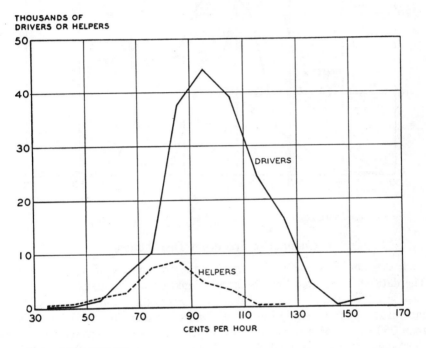

Source of data: Table 15.7.

Percentage Frequency Distribution

The first three columns of Table 15.7 show a frequency distribution of the wage rates of 185,822 motortruck drivers and another of the wage rates of 29,808 helpers. If these two series are plotted on the same axis, as in Chart 15.10, no satisfactory comparison can be made because the series, being based on different numbers of cases, result in curves having different areas. In the last two columns of Table 15.7 the frequencies for each series have been expressed as percentages of the total. These are referred to as *percentage frequencies*, and Chart 15.11 shows the curves resulting from them. From these two curves it is apparent not only that the helpers have a lower wage rate than the drivers, but also that the concentration around a central value is more pronounced for helpers than for drivers.

**Chart 15.11—Percentage Distribution of Hourly Wage Rates of Union
Motortruck Drivers and Helpers, July 1, 1944**

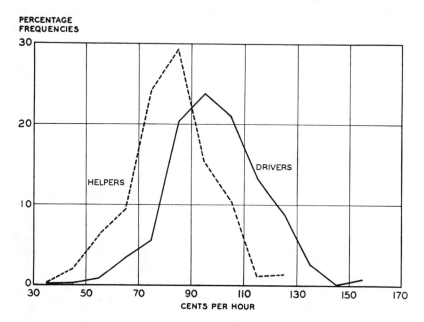

Source of data: Table 15.7.

Cumulative Frequency Distribution

It is sometimes useful to cumulate the frequencies of a distribution. The data of Table 15.8 have been cumulated on an "or more" basis, and also on a "less than" basis, in Table 15.9. From the second column of this table it is easy to ascertain how many lamps lasted less than 650 hours, less than 750 hours, or any other figure which may be of interest. From the third column one may read the number of lamps burning 1,050 hours or more, 1,150 hours or more, and so on.

Occasionally a cumulative curve, or *ogive*, is of assistance in the study of a frequency distribution. The solid line of Chart 15.12 is on an "or more" basis and shows the number of lamps burning the indicated number of hours or more. In drawing this chart, the "or more" cumulative frequencies of Table 15.9 are plotted at the lower limits of the classes. The broken line on Chart 15.12 shows an ogive of the "less than" data of Table 15.9. For the "less than" cumulative data the frequencies are plotted at the upper limits of the classes. Notice that the two curves cross at 60 lamps, which is half of the number of lamps, and that the two curves are symmetrical with respect to each other around the horizontal line at 60 lamps.

An ogive may be used to estimate the cumulative frequencies for values other than those shown. Suppose we wish to know how many lamps burned

**Chart 15.12—60-Watt Incandescent Lamps Burning Specified Hours
or More, and Burning Less than Specified Hours**

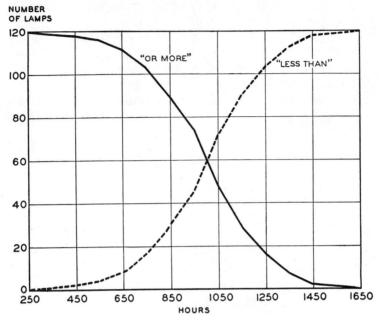

Source of data: Table 15.8.

**Table 15.8—Distribution of Length of Life of
120 60-Watt Incandescent Lamps**

Life in hours	Number of lamps
250 but less than 350	1
350 but less than 450	1
450 but less than 550	2
550 but less than 650	4
650 but less than 750	9
750 but less than 850	14
850 but less than 950	15
950 but less than 1,050	26
1,050 but less than 1,150	19
1,150 but less than 1,250	13
1,250 but less than 1,350	9
1,350 but less than 1,450	5
1,450 but less than 1,550	1
1,550 but less than 1,650	1
Total	120

Based on data from Electrical Testing Laboratories,
New York City.

less than 1,000 hours. We do this by: (1) erecting an ordinate at 1,000 on the X axis until it intersects the curve, (2) drawing an abscissa from this intersection until it meets the Y axis, and (3) reading the estimate, 59, at the point of intersection with the X axis.

While Chart 15.12 is based on cumulative frequencies, ogives may also be made using cumulative percentage frequencies. In fact, if two ogives are to be compared, and they are based on different numbers of items, it is essential that percentage frequencies be used.

If a frequency distribution has classes of unequal intervals, no special problem is involved. The frequencies are merely cumulated and plotted with reference to the class limits.

Table 15.9—60-Watt Incandescent Lamps
Burning Specified Hours or More and
Burning Less Than Specified Hours

Life in hours	Number of lamps burning:	
	Less than indicated hours	Indicated hours or more
250	0	120
350	1	119
450	2	118
550	4	116
650	8	112
750	17	103
850	31	89
950	46	74
1,050	72	48
1,150	91	29
1,250	104	16
1,350	113	7
1,450	118	2
1,550	119	1
1,650	120	0

Source: Data of Table 15.8.
Note that the entries add to 120 for each line.

Lorenz Curve

The Lorenz curve is a device for showing concentration, or inequality, of income, wealth, etc. In Table 15.10 the number of depositors in a rural bank and the amount of their deposits is cumulated. For example, 1,313 of the depositors have deposits of less than $500, and the total amount of money in their deposits is $100,279. The last two columns of the table convert this information into percentages. Thus, 93.2 per cent of the

Table 15.10—Cumulative Number of Depositors and Cumulative
Amount of Deposits of a Rural Bank

Deposit balance	Number of depositors	Amount of deposits	Per cent of total	
			Depositors	Deposits
Less than $50	766	$10,215	54.4	3.4
Less than 100	980	25,512	69.6	8.6
Less than 150	1,089	38,839	77.3	13.0
Less than 200	1,157	50,515	82.1	17.0
Less than 250	1,203	60,896	85.4	20.5
Less than 500	1,313	100,279	93.2	33.7
Less than 1,000	1,378	146,503	97.8	49.2
$1,000 or more	1,409	297,623	100.0	100.0

Source: Confidential.

Chart 15.13—Concentration of Demand Deposits of a Rural Bank
as Shown by a Lorenz Curve

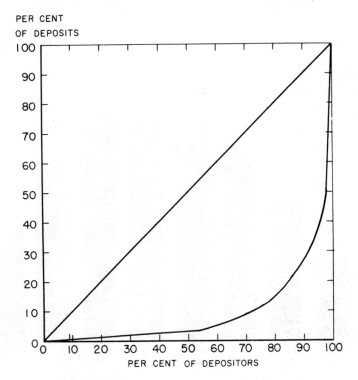

Source of data: Table 15.9.

depositors have deposit balances smaller than $500, and these depositors constitute 33.7 per cent of the total deposits of the bank. The data of these two columns is plotted as Chart 15.13.

The diagonal line of the chart indicates complete equality. This is the way the Lorenz curve would look if everybody's deposit were of the same size. The farther the curve is from the diagonal line, the greater is the inequality. In the present case, reading from the curve, the 50 per cent of the depositors that have the smallest deposits account for only 3 per cent of the total deposits. On the other hand, the 2 per cent of the depositors that have the largest deposits account for nearly 50 per cent of the total deposits. This is indeed extreme inequality. The bank is dependent on a few large accounts, and is burdened with many small ones.

If two curves are plotted on the same chart, the curve that is farthest from the line represents the greatest inequality. It is possible for one curve to be closer in some places and farther away in others. In that case one could compare the two curves with respect to area between the curve and the diagonal line.

As with the ordinary cumulative frequency distribution, class intervals need not be equal. Nor do open-end classes occasion any difficulty.

Chart 15.14—Per Cent of Families Using Installment Credit, by Income Groups

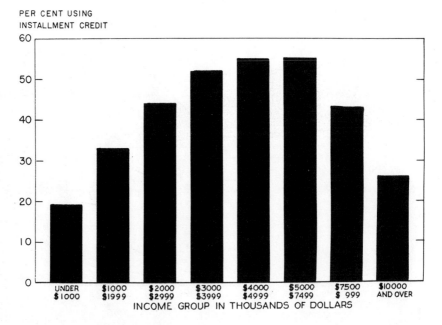

Source of data: Federal Reserve Board, *1955 Survey of Consumer Finances,* as presented graphically by Clyde William Phelps in *Using Instalment Credit* (Studies in Consumer Credit No. 4) Educational Division, Commercial Credit Co., Baltimore, 1955, p. 79.

Look Carefully

One should always look carefully, or not at all, at a chart that looks like a histogram, for maybe that is not what it is. Chart 15.14 looks like a histogram for discrete data. Along the horizontal axis are classes with intervals of $1,000 or more, and percentages are shown for the heights of the different bars.

But it is not a column diagram representing a percentage frequency distribution. This appears obvious if we note that the percentages do not add up to 100 per cent.[8] They represent, not the per cent of installment accounts that are in each income size group, but the per cent of families in each income size group that use installment credit.

From the data it would be impossible to estimate the average income of installment credit users. The chart indicates, not that families with income between $4,000 and $7,500 are most numerous among installment credit users, but that the proportion of families that use installment credit is greatest in these brackets.

---

[8] Note also that the bars are separated, although the variable is substantially continuous. Also notice that the class interval is not uniform. The omission of a column for $8,000–$9,999 is presumably an error.

Chapter 16

AVERAGES

An average is a single value within the range of the data that is used to represent all of the values in the series. Since an average is somewhere within the range of the data, it is sometimes called a measure of central value. Because the different values tend (in some sense) to cluster around this central value, an average is often called a measure of central tendency. Thus in Chart 15.1 we can see a tendency for the items to concentrate most thickly around some value between 65 and 84 kilowatt-hours. Because an average tells us how far to the right a frequency polygon is located on the horizontal scale, an average is sometimes called a measure of location. Thus, it is apparent from inspection of Chart 15.10 that the solid curve is located farther to the right than the dotted curve, and therefore the average wage of drivers is larger than the average wage of helpers.

In this chapter, we shall consider the following averages: arithmetic mean, mid-range, median, mode, geometric mean, harmonic mean, and quadratic mean, giving relatively brief attention to the last three mentioned.

We shall consider the concepts of these averages, how to compute them, and techniques for their computation when the data are in the form of a frequency distribution.

Arithmetic Mean

Because it is used so frequently, the arithmetic mean is the most familiar average. It is the "average" of common parlance.

(16.1)
$$\bar{X} = \frac{\Sigma X}{n}.$$

Suppose that, in a small factory, drill press operators are receiving $0.78, $0.80, $0.83, $0.89, and $0.95 per hour. The arithmetic mean would be

$$\bar{X} = \frac{\$0.78 + \$0.80 + \$0.83 + \$0.89 + \$0.95}{5} = \$0.85 \text{ per hour.}$$

Sometimes a distinction is made between a "weighted" and an "unweighted" mean. The adjective "unweighted" is to be avoided, however, as all arithmetic means are weighted in some manner. A "simple" mean is one in which all the weights are the same. To obtain a weighted mean, one

214

multiplies each observation by its weight, sums these products, and divides this quantity by the sum of the weights. Symbolically,

$$(16.2) \qquad \bar{X} = \frac{\Sigma\, WX}{\Sigma\, W}$$

$$= \frac{W_1 X_1 + W_2 X_2 + \dots + W_n X_n}{W_1 + W_2 + \dots + W_n}.$$

An instructor often assigns different weights to different parts of a course according to his opinion of their importance, for example: Mid-term quiz, 1 point; laboratory, 1 point; final examination, 2 points. If the grades of a particular student are as follows: mid-term quiz, 67; laboratory, 89; final examination, 81, the average grade is

$$\bar{X} = \frac{1(67) + 1(89) + 2(81)}{1 + 1 + 2}$$

$$= \frac{67 + 89 + 162}{4} = \frac{318}{4} = 79.5.$$

If the weights are relative weights, so that their sum is 1, computation of the arithmetic mean is simplified

$$(16.3) \qquad \bar{X} = \Sigma\, VX \qquad (\Sigma\, V = 1).$$

Thus we could write the weights: mid-term quiz, 0.25; laboratory, 0.25; final examination, 0.50. The computations are as follows.

Part of course	Relative weight V	Grade X	VX
Mid-term quiz	0.25	67	16.75
Laboratory	0.25	89	22.25
Final examination	0.50	81	40.50
Total	1.00	...	79.50

The arithmetic mean is the total of the last column.

The sum of the deviations from the mean is zero. Consider the five hourly wage rates used at the beginning of this chapter, and let $x = X - \bar{X}$. Then[1] $\Sigma\, x = 0$. Thus we have

X (cents)	x $(X - \bar{X})$
78	−7
80	−5
83	−2
89	+4
95	+10
$\Sigma\, X = 425$, and $\bar{X} = 85$	$\Sigma\, x = 0$

[1] That $\Sigma\, x = 0$ is easily proved.

$$\Sigma\, x = \Sigma\, (X - \bar{X}) = \Sigma\, X - n\bar{X} = \Sigma\, X - n\frac{\Sigma\, X}{n} = \Sigma\, X - \Sigma\, X = 0.$$

A useful computational technique. Because $\Sigma(X - \bar{X}) = 0$, we can assume some value X_0, called the arbitrary origin, to be the mean, find out how much this value is in error, and correct it, thus obtaining the correct value for $\bar{X}$. If we let $d = X - X_0$, then[2]

(16.4) $\bar{X} = X_0 + d,$

where $\bar{d}$ is the mean of the d values.

As an illustration, let us use the same 5 figures, and take $X_0 = 80$. Then we have the following:

X (cents)	d
78	-2
80	0
83	3
89	9
95	15
Σd	25
$\bar{d}$	5

From (16.4), $\bar{X} = 80 + 5 = 85$ cents.

The sum of the squares of the deviations from the mean is a minimum. This means that when M is defined as $\Sigma X/n$, the quantity $\Sigma(X - M)^2$ is at least as small as when M is defined in any other way.

Consider our wage rate figures. Let us find the sum of the squares of the deviations from the mean.

X (cents)	$X - 85$	$(X - 85)^2$
78	-7	49
80	-5	25
83	-2	4
89	-4	16
95	-10	100
Total	0	194

Next, consider the sum of the squares of the deviations from the median.

X (cents)	$X - 83$	$(X - 83)^2$
78	-5	25
80	-3	9
83	0	0
89	6	36
95	12	144
	10	214

---

[2] The derivation of this expression is very simple. By definition, $d = X - X_0$ and $X = X_0 + d$. Therefore

$$\bar{X} = \frac{\Sigma X}{n} = \frac{\Sigma(X_0 + d)}{n} = \frac{nX_0}{n} + \frac{\Sigma d}{n} = X_0 + \bar{d}.$$

The results of these and other similar computations are plotted on Chart 16.1. It is apparent that when $M = \bar{X} = 85$ cents, the sum of the squared deviations is smallest. Therefore we say that $\Sigma\, x^2 = \Sigma\, (X - \bar{X})^2$ is a minimum.

As will be explained, the arithmetic mean is a measure of central tendency in the sense that it may be thought of as the "center of gravity" of the data.

Chart 16.1—Relationship between M and $\Sigma(X - M)^2$ for the Sample Values: 78; 80; 83; 89; 95

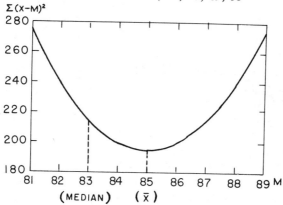

The arithmetic mean should always be used when making an estimate of the mean of a normal population, for it is then the most reliable estimate of the population mean. Also a given sample is more likely when the population mean has the same value as the sample mean than it is when it has any other value.

Mid-range

The mid-range or center is the arithmetic mean of the smallest item and the largest item. Thus if X_1 is the smallest item and X_n is the largest

(16.5) $$C = \frac{X_1 + X_n}{2}.$$

For our 5 drill press operators,

$$C = \frac{78 + 95}{2} = \frac{173}{2} = 86.5 \text{ cents.}$$

The mid-range is often used to compute average temperature or average price of a corporation stock. This is chiefly because maximum and minimum temperature, or high and low price are of special interest.

It is hard to see how the mid-range can be thought of as a measure of central tendency, for there is no implication that the values in a sample tend toward the mid-range.

The mid-range is to be commended chiefly for its computational simplicity, though for extremely platykurtic distributions, it is the best estimate of the population mean.

Median

The median is defined as a value which divides a series so that at least one half of the items are as large as or larger than it, and at least one half the items are as small as or smaller than it. For a series of values such as $1.15, $1.17, $1.19, $1.23, and $1.29 it is clear that the median is $1.19. If, however, we have an even number of items, for example $8.25, $8.37, $8.42, $8.46, $8.51, and $8.52, our definition is satisfied by any value greater than $8.42 but less than $8.46. In such a case we take the median to be the average of the two central values, in this instance $8.44.

The median is sometimes referred to as a *position average*. (Certain other position values, not measures of central value, are mentioned on pages 218–221.) It must be obvious that the median cannot readily be determined for a series of figures unless they have been arrayed or organized into a frequency distribution. If an array is to be used, a little time may be saved by arraying merely the central part of a series. We must know how many smaller and how many larger items are present, but they need not be arrayed.

The median is a measure of central tendency in the sense that an item larger than the median has the same probability as an item smaller than the median, provided there are no other items that have the same value as the median.

For large samples from extremely leptokurtic distributions the median is the best estimate of the population mean.[3]

Quantiles. Several measures are akin to the median in that they are position measures; but they are not measures of central value. The median divides a distribution into 2 parts. We may divide a distribution into 4 parts by using quartiles, into 5 parts with quintiles, into 10 parts by the use of deciles, and into 100 parts by employing percentiles. Beginning at the lower-valued end of a series, we have in order: the first quartile Q_1, the second quartile Q_2, which is the median, and the third quartile Q_3. Thus the value of Q_3 is always greater than the value of Q_1. Similarly, other position measures proceed from the lower-valued end to the higher-valued end of a series as follows:

Deciles: $D_1, D_2, ..., D_9$;

Percentiles: $P_1, P_2, ..., P_{98}, P_{99}$.

It would, of course, be possible to have measures dividing a series into 6, 8,

---

[3] Occasionally, when some of the extreme values are considered to be of doubtful validity, a specified number of the extreme values at each end is discarded, and the arithmetic mean of the remaining central values computed. Such a measure may appropriately be called a *modified mean* if only a few items are excluded, or a *modified median* if only a few items are averaged.

or any other number of parts. Such measures, however, are rarely needed. It was seen above that there are 99 percentiles. In practice only a few of these are ever useful. Percentiles should not be used at all unless a series contains a large number of items. Reference will be made in the following chapter to the possible use of some of these position measures for evaluating dispersion. They may also be used to measure the skewness of a series.

When other data have been arrayed from smallest to largest it is perhaps easiest to compute the quantiles by means of the following formula:

$$(16.6) \qquad \text{Quantile item number} = \frac{p}{q} n + \tfrac{1}{2},$$

where n is the number of items in the sample, p is the quantile number, and q is the number of parts into which the items are to be divided. If this formula results in a number that is not an integer, the fraction indicates the method of interpolating between two X-values, or the method of taking a weighted average of them. For example $5\tfrac{3}{4}$ means that the quantile is computed as $\tfrac{1}{4}X_5 + \tfrac{3}{4}X_6$.

For the quartiles, (16.6) becomes

$$Q_1 \text{ item number} = \tfrac{1}{4}n + \tfrac{1}{2},$$
$$Q_2 \text{ item number} = \tfrac{2}{4}n + \tfrac{1}{2} = (n + 1)/2,$$
$$Q_3 \text{ item number} = \tfrac{3}{4}n + \tfrac{1}{2}.$$

Let us take a simple numerical illustration with these X values:

$$X_1 = 3 \qquad X_5 = 8 \qquad X_8 = 11$$
$$X_2 = 4 \qquad X_6 = 10 \qquad X_9 = 13$$
$$X_3 = 6 \qquad X_7 = 10 \qquad X_{10} = 14$$
$$X_4 = 7 \qquad \qquad X_{11} = 15$$

From (16.5):

$$Q_1 \text{ item number} = (\tfrac{1}{4})11 + \tfrac{1}{2} = 3\tfrac{1}{4};$$
$$Q_2 \text{ item number} = (\tfrac{2}{4})11 + \tfrac{1}{2} = 6;$$
$$Q_3 \text{ item number} = (\tfrac{3}{4})11 + \tfrac{1}{2} = 8\tfrac{3}{4}.$$

Therefore:

$$Q_1 = (\tfrac{3}{4})6 + (\tfrac{1}{4})7 = 6.25;$$
$$Q_2 = 10;$$
$$Q_3 = (\tfrac{1}{4})11 + (\tfrac{3}{4})13 = 12.5.$$

Possibly Chart 16.2 will facilitate understanding the concept used in this method of computing quartiles. Each X value is thought of as having boundaries, located half way between the specified numbers and the adjacent numbers. Note that these are $2\tfrac{3}{4}$ rectangles between consecutive quartiles. Thus, when $n = 11$, the quartiles divide the items in the array into 4 equal parts, $2\tfrac{3}{4}$ items in each part.

Chart 16.2—Location of Quartiles

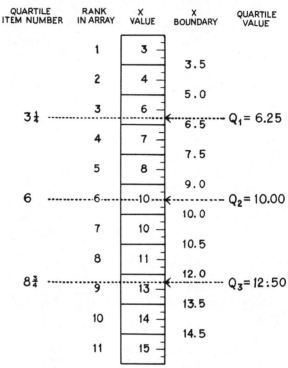

Graphic method of estimating median and quartiles. Chart 15.12 shows two cumulative frequency curves based on Tables 15.8 and 15.9. From the same data Chart 16.3 gives cumulative percentage frequency curves. The three quartiles are estimated by drawing horizontal lines at the 25, 50, and 75 per cent points and dropping perpendiculars at the intersections of these lines with the "less than" curve. The readings appear to be:[4]

$$Q_1 = 843 \text{ hours;}$$
$$\text{Median} = Q_2 = 1{,}004 \text{ hours;}$$
$$Q_3 = 1{,}145 \text{ hours.}$$

It should be realized that since the points on the curve are connected by straight lines, these estimates imply that the items are distributed evenly within classes. A more realistic, but subjective, assumption would involve connecting the plotted points by a smoother curve. Such a procedure is to be preferred when carried out by someone who has acquired judgment in such matters.

---

[4] When the student reaches the section on computation of the median and quartiles from grouped data (pp. 229–230), it will be worthwhile to check the accuracy of these graphic estimates.

Chart 16.3—Graphic Estimation of Median and Quartiles

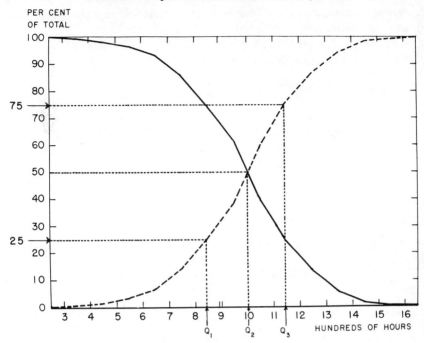

Source of data: Table 15.8.

Mode

The mode is the value around which the items tend to concentrate. It is therefore the most typical value. An item selected at random from some population has a greater likelihood of being the mode than any other single value.

As an example, consider the number of typing errors per day made on different days by a stenographer:

10, 10, 8, 9, 10, 10, 10, 11, 10, 9.

It is almost imperative that data be arrayed in order to locate the mode, and preferably it should also be graphed. From the array,

8, 9, 9, 10, 10, 10, 10, 10, 10, 11,

we see that 10 occurs most frequently and other values occur with decreasing frequency the more they differ from 10. The mode is therefore 10.

The variable is discrete, since there cannot be a fraction of an error. If it were continuous, we could say only that the mode is approximately 10, without further computation.

When one stops to consider that with a continuous variable there would not usually be two items of exactly the same size (if measurements are made with sufficient precision), it is apparent that our definition of the mode of a sample is somewhat vague. Because of this vagueness of concept, the best method of computing the mode of a sample is not obvious.

The mode of a probability distribution offers no conceptual difficulty. It is the value of X that has the maximum ordinate.

Chart 16.4—Graphic Estimation of Mode

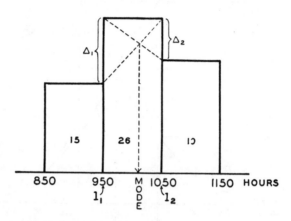

Source of data: Table 15.8.

Graphic method of estimating the mode. Before trying to estimate the mode, one ordinarily groups the data. Consider Table 15.8, which shows the length of life of 60-watt incandescent lamps. Reference to that table reveals that the modal class, which is "950 but under 1,050 hours," has 26 frequencies. The next lower-valued class contains 15 frequencies, while the next higher-valued class has 19 frequencies. A diagram of these three classes only is shown as Chart 16.4. The mode is determined by the intersection of the two dotted lines. A perpendicular line from this point intersects the X axis at the mode. It appears to be about 1,010 hours.

In grouping the data one should make the class interval large enough so that the frequencies on each side of the mode get progressively smaller, at least for the two classes on each side of the modal class. Another problem is the location of the class limits. There are several alternative sets of classes for frequency distributions formed from the same data and with the same class intervals. The particular way in which one groups the data has considerable effect on the estimate of the mode.

Sometimes one encounters a distribution that seems to have two modes. See for example Chart 2.1. Such data are usually heterogeneous; they are the result of mixing together two separate distributions. For such data, no average is meaningful. It is better to compute an average for each distribution.

Characteristics of the Mean, Median, and Mode

Sometimes the question is raised as to which of the three already described measures of central tendency is the "best." There is no simple answer to such a question. However, after considering the differing nature and behavior of the three measures, the student should know which measure or measures to use in a specific instance.

Definitions. It will be remembered that the three measures are based upon different concepts. The arithmetic mean is the sum of the values divided by the number of items. The median is the value which divides the series so that at least half of the items are equal to or greater than it, and at least half are equal to or smaller than it. The mode is the value around which the items tend to concentrate.

Chart 16.5—**Diagramatic Representation of Arithmetic Mean,
Median, and Mode**

(Distributions A and B are different, but have the same $\bar{X}$. Sections
B, C, and D show respectively $\bar{X}$, median, and mode for the same
distribution.)

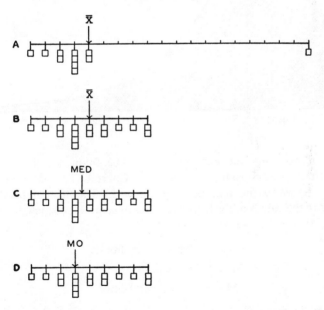

Mechanical concepts. The arithmetic mean is similar in concept to the idea of "center of gravity" as used in physics. Parts A and B of Chart 16.5 show two arrangements, each of which has the same mean. In part A the eight items to the left of the mean are offset by one item far to the right so that the point of balance is at $\bar{X}$. In part B the same eight items to the left of the mean are offset by six items not so far removed as in part A. Parts

B, C, and D show the same arrangement of items, but B shows the mean, C shows the median, and D shows the mode.

In terms of the frequency curve, the "center of gravity" idea of the arithmetic mean may not be easy for everyone to visualize. The median, however, divides the curve into two equal areas and the mode is below the highest point of the smooth frequency curve. These are shown in Chart 16.6.

Chart 16.6—Location of Arithmetic Mean, Median, and Mode for a Positively Skewed Distribution

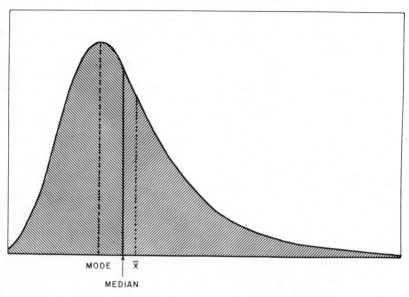

Effect of skewness and extreme values. The frequency distribution of residential electrical consumption shown in Chart 15.1 is not symmetrical. It is slightly skewed to the right (positively skewed.) The effect of this skewness is reflected in the values of the three measures of central tendency that we have discussed. It was found that

$$\overline{X} = 79.6 \text{ kilowatt-hours,}$$
$$\text{Med} = 76.8 \text{ kilowatt-hours,}$$
$$\text{Mo} = 74.5 \text{ kilowatt-hours.}$$

The arithmetic mean is the largest of the three values; the mode is the smallest. The reason for this lies in the fact that the arithmetic mean is influenced by the *value* of every item in the series, and the presence of a few large items increases the value of the arithmetic mean. These same items, however, have no more effect on the median than have the same number of items of *any* value greater than the median. The median is sensitive to the position of the values but not to their size. The mode, as computed in this text,[5] is not at all affected by the extreme values in the series. When the skewness is to the left (negatively skewed) the mean is the smallest and the mode is the largest.

Because the arithmetic mean is sensitive to extremely large or extremely small values in a series, it may occasionally not be a typical value and may therefore be misleading. Suppose the five annual salaries are:

$$
\begin{array}{r}
\$2,000 \\
2,300 \\
2,400 \\
2,400 \\
2,500 \\
10,000 \\
\hline
\Sigma\,X = \$21,600 \\
n = 6 \\
\bar{X} = \$\ 3,600
\end{array}
$$

The value of $3,600 as the arithmetic mean does not give us a useful measure.

Effect of kurtosis. Occasionally a set of data may be found which has no mode. This is true for a rectangular distribution, which is a type of platykurtic distribution. A rectangular distribution is one in which the values are spaced at equal intervals, with each item occurring the same number of times. Consider the series: $4, $6, $8, $10, $12. These data have no mode. The mean, median, and mid-range, however, are $8. An extremely platykurtic distribution may be U-shaped. Such a distribution has a mean, median, and mid-range, but no mode.

The mid-range is recommended for distributions that are extremely platykurtic. The median is preferable if the population is extremely leptokurtic.

Algebraic manipulation. If we know any two of the three quantities $\Sigma\,X$, N, and $\bar{X}$, the third quantity may be computed. If the arithmetic means of several series are to be averaged, this may be accomplished by using appropriate weights for each. The resulting mean of the means is also the mean of the combined distribution. Similar algebraic treatment for the median and mode is not possible.

Mathematical properties. There are two important properties of the arithmetic mean: First, as was noted earlier, $\Sigma\,x = 0$. This property was made use of in developing a short method for computing $\bar{X}$. Second, $\Sigma\,x^2$ = a minimum. This means that the sum of the squared deviations of the items of a series about $\bar{X}$ yields a smaller total than the sum of the squared deviations of the same items about any other value. The standard

---

[5] Another method consists of determining the value below the highest point of a fitted curve. With such a procedure extreme values would have a slight effect on the value of the mode.

deviation, a measure of dispersion described in Chapter 17, is based upon $\Sigma\, x^2$.

The absolute sum (signs neglected) of the deviations of the items is a minimum about the median.

Reliability. The arithmetic mean is a more reliable estimate of the central tendency in the population than the median or the mode for a wide variety of populations. That is, there is less variability among arithmetic means computed from different random samples than among medians or modes. While this is not true for all types of populations, it is true for a normal population and for many others. This is an extremely important characteristic of the arithmetic mean; if the population is normal the arithmetic mean is to be preferred to all other measures as an estimate of the population mean. For extremely leptokurtic distributions the median is the most reliable, while for extremely platykurtic distributions the mid-range is the most reliable.

Necessity for organizing data. It is not necessary to rearrange or group the raw figures to compute $\overline{X}$. In fact, it is not even necessary to have the individual items. All that is necessary is to know the total, $\Sigma\, X$, and the number of items, n. The median and mode cannot easily be computed unless the data have been arrayed or made into a frequency distribution.

Effect of open-end classes. Frequency distribution sometimes have open-end classes "Less than ..." or "... or more." Because the mid-value of such a class is not apparent, the value of $\overline{X}$ cannot be accurately determined for the series unless a note is appended to the table giving the total value of the items in the open-end class or classes. Open-end classes do not cause any difficulty in the location of the median and the mode. Computations for grouped data are explained in the next section.

Computations Using Grouped Data

Arithmetic mean. In Table 15.3 data were shown of the consumption of electricity by 75 residential consumers. To obtain the arithmetic mean we may add the 75 values and divide by 75. The result is 79.7 kilowatt-hours.

When the data are in frequency distribution form, as in Table 16.1, we are unable to sum the 75 individual items but must consider the distribution class by class. This we do by considering each class to be represented by its mid-value. These mid-values are then averaged, each being first multiplied by its respective frequency. The mid-values are our X_1, X_2, X_3, ..., values, and we use the following expression:

$$(16.7) \qquad \overline{X} = \frac{\Sigma f X}{n},$$

which is a special case of equation (16.2), where the weights are frequencies, and therefore $\Sigma f = n$. Table 16.1 shows the procedure for computing the arithmetic mean for the frequency distribution of sales of electric current.

The value of $\bar{X}$ is found to be 79.6 kilowatt-hours. The slight difference between this value and the more exact figure (79.7 kilowatt-hours) obtained from summing the 75 original items indicates that there was negligible loss of accuracy due to grouping the items into eight classes. The reason for this close agreement lies in the fact that although each mid-value may be inaccurate as the representative value for a class, these inaccuracies *tend* to offset.

Table 16.1—Calculation of Arithmetic Mean of Grouped Data by Long Method: Kilowatt-Hours of Electricity Used in One Month by 75 Residential Consumers

Consumption in kilowatt-hours	Number of consumers f	Mid-value of class X	fX
5–24	4	14.5	58.0
25–44	6	34.5	207.0
45–64	14	54.5	763.0
65–84	22	74.5	1,639.0
85–104	14	94.5	1,323.0
105–124	5	114.5	572.5
125–144	7	134.5	941.5
145–164	2	154.5	463.5
Total	75	...	5,967.5

$$\bar{X} = \frac{\Sigma fX}{n} = \frac{5,967.5}{75} = 79.6 \text{ kilowatt-hours.}$$

Because of the central tendency within the distribution as a whole, the average of the values in a class below the class of greatest frequency will be usually greater than the mid-value of the class in question, while the average of a class above the class of greatest frequency will usually be smaller than the mid-value of that class. Take, for instance, the 14 items in the class "45–64 kilowatt-hours." These 14 items may be identified in Table 15.1 and are found to average 56.8, which is *larger* than the mid-value 54.5. The 14 items in the class "85–104 kilowatt-hours" average 91.6, which is *smaller* than the mid-value 94.5. See also Chart 16.7, which shows the distribution of items within each class, as well as the number of items that each class contains. The tendency of the errors in the mid-value to offset each other will virtually never be perfect, but it will usually result in a value for the arithmetic mean of the frequency distribution which will closely agree with the arithmetic mean of the ungrouped data. The agreement will generally be closer for series showing continuous variation than for series showing gaps and concentrations, and it will usually be closer for symmetrical series than for skewed series. For very irregular or greatly skewed series the error due to grouping may be large.

Chart 16.7—Central Tendency Within a Frequency Distribution

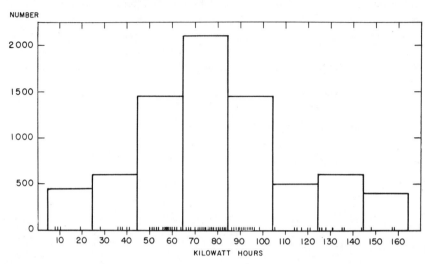

Source of data: Table 15.3.

The method just described for computing the value of $\bar{X}$ of a frequency distribution is the most obvious and straightforward procedure. However, a method is available which yields the identical result and saves appreciable time, especially for a distribution of many classes and large numbers of cases.

Table 16.2—Calculation of Arithmetic Mean of Grouped Data by Short Method: Kilowatt-hours of Electricity Used in One Month by 75 Residential Consumers

Consumption in kilowatt-hours	Number of consumers f	Mid-value of class X	Deviation from assumed mean d'	fd'	
5–24	4	14.5	−3	−12	
25–44	6	34.5	−2	−12	
45–64	14	54.5	−1	−14	−38
65–84	22	74.5	0		
85–104	14	94.5	+1	+14	
105–124	5	114.5	+2	+10	
125–144	7	134:5	+3	+21	
145–164	3	154.5	+4	+12	+57
Total	75	...	...	...	+19

$$\bar{X} = X_0 + \left(\frac{\Sigma fd'}{n}\right)c = 74.5 + \left(\frac{19}{75}\right)20 = 74.5 + 5.07 = 79.6 \text{ kilowatt-hours.}$$

Let

$$d' = \frac{X - X_0}{c},$$

where c is the class interval. Then

(16.8) $$\bar{X} = X_0 + \frac{\Sigma f d'}{n} c.$$

The use of this expression is shown in Table 16.2, and the value of $\bar{X}$ is found to be 79.6 kilowatt-hours the same as in Table 16.1. Two observations concerning this short method and its use are in order: (1) The answer is not affected by the value selected for X_0. (2) To avoid fractional values of d', the value of X_0 must be the mid-value of a class and the class intervals must be uniform.

When the classes are not uniform the procedure in Table 16.1 is simpler. It must be clearly understood, however, that the computation of $\bar{X}$ from grouped data when the distribution has classes of varying width may yield a value differing markedly from the mean of the raw data. This is because the offsetting of errors in the mid-values is not fully realized.

*__Median.__ In computing the median from a frequency distribution we must interpolate between the lower and upper limits of the class that contains the median.

(16.9) $$\mathrm{Med} = l_1 + \frac{\frac{n}{2} - \Sigma f_1}{f\ \mathrm{med}} c,$$

where l_1 is the lower limit of the class containing the median, Σf_1 is the sum of the frequencies in all classes below l_1, and f med is the frequency of the class in which the median falls. This method of computation does not require a uniform class interval. For the data of electric consumption the median falls in the class 65–84, since Table 16.2 shows that there are 46 observations that are 84.5 or smaller and 24 observations that are smaller than 64.5 while $n/2 = 37.5$. Therefore

$$\mathrm{Med} = 64.5 + \frac{\frac{75}{2} - 24}{22} 20$$

$$= 76.8 \text{ kilowatt-hours.}$$

Beginning from the upper end of the distribution,

(16.10) $$\mathrm{Med} = l_2 - \frac{\frac{n}{2} - \Sigma f_2}{f\ \mathrm{med}} c,$$

where l_2 is the upper limit of the class containing the median and Σf_2 is the sum of the frequencies in all classes above l_2. For our present data,

$$\text{Med} = 84.5 - \frac{\frac{75}{2} - 29}{22} \, 20$$

$$= 76.8 \text{ kilowatt-hours.}$$

When values have been rounded to the nearest unit as in Table 16.1, there is a discrepancy between the stated and actual limits, since the actual limits are 4.5, 24.5, 44.5, 64.5, etc. The mid-values of the classes are 14.5, 34.5, 54.5, etc., whether computed from stated limits or the actual limits. However, when computing the median, mode, or other measures based upon a class limit, the actual limits must be used.

Equations (16.9) and (16.10) assume that the items are distributed evenly within each class, rather than being more dense on the side toward the center of the distribution. This is, of course, a minor source of inaccuracy in the computation of the median from grouped data.

*Quartiles. The method of interpolation to locate the quartiles is essentially the same as for the median (which is the second quartile). Thus:

$$Q_1 = 44.5 + \frac{\frac{75}{4} - 10}{14} \, 20 = 57.0 \text{ kilowatt-hours;}$$

$$Q_2 = 104.5 - \frac{\frac{75}{4} - 15}{14} \, 20 = 99.1 \text{ kilowatt-hours.}$$

*Mode. Reference to the electric consumption data of Table 16.2 shows that the modal class is "65–84." Furthermore, there are 14 frequencies in each of the classes on either side of this class. Therefore we take the mid-value of the class as the mode and write

$$\text{Mo} = 74.5 \text{ kilowatt-hours.}$$

Now let us consider a frequency distribution which does not have balanced frequencies in the classes adjacent to the modal class. Table 15.8 shows such a distribution.

Let Δ_1 be the difference between the frequencies in the modal class and those in the next class below; and let Δ_2 be the difference between the frequencies in the modal class and those in the next class above. See Chart

16.4. Thus for our incandescent lamp data $\Delta_1 = 26 - 15 = 11$ and $\Delta_2 = 26 - 19 = 7$. We then locate the mode so that[6]

$$\frac{\Delta_1}{\Delta_2} = \frac{Mo - l_1}{l_2 - Mo},$$

where l_1 is the lower limit of the modal group and l_2 is the upper limit. This provides us with a method of interpolating between the lower and upper limits of the modal class. Therefore the expression for determining the mode is

(16.11) $$Mo = l_1 + \frac{\Delta_1}{\Delta_1 + \Delta_2} c.$$

We may also use

(16.12) $$Mo = l_2 - \frac{\Delta_2}{\Delta_1 + \Delta_2} c.$$

The results are, of course, identical. Using the first expression for the incandescent lamp data, we have

$$Mo = 950 + \frac{11}{11 + 7} \, 100$$

$$= 950 + 61.1 = 1{,}011.1 \text{ hours.}$$

For this method of computing the mode, it is necessary that the width of the class on each side of the mode be the same.

------

[6] It is interesting to note that this method of estimating the mode is equivalent to dropping a perpendicular from the maximum point of a parabola that passes through the mid-point of the modal class and the class on each side. The three points are

X	f
900	15
1000	26
1100	19

and the parabola is $f = -894 + 1.82X - 0.0009X^2$. To find the slope of f take the first derivative:

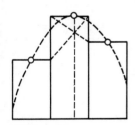

$$\frac{df}{dX} = 1.82 - 0.0018X.$$

The maximum value of f is at that value of X for which the slope is 0 (See accompanying chart.)

$$1.82 - 0.0018X = 0; \qquad X = 1{,}011.1.$$

This is an estimate of the mode.

Needless to say, this method of obtaining the mode is too laborious for practical use. It is of interest, however, because for a *probability distribution* the mode is the value of X that has the maximum ordinate. In estimating the mode, therefore, it is theoretically best to fit a curve to all the data, not merely 3 centrally located classes.

The value of the mode of a frequency distribution may be considerably affected by the grouping chosen in making the distribution. In the first edition of this book a frequency series was set up with five different arrangements, all using the same class interval. An estimate of the mode was made from each of the five arrangements. These estimates, arranged from smallest to largest were: $7.54, $7.75, $8.00, $8.00, $8.28. This is a considerable amount of variability. From the same groupings the estimates of the median varied much less: $8.01, $8.08, $8.21, $8.25, $8.40.

A frequency distribution may occasionally be found which has two modes. It is bimodal, and the curve would show two "humps" or concentrations. Such a condition may occur through chance, but it is more likely to be due to the fact that two really different series have been combined, for example, wages of unskilled and skilled employees, weights of minors and adults, batting records of substitutes and regular players, and so on.

Other Means

A few other means are sometimes used: geometric; harmonic; quadratic. All of these means belong to the same family:

The geometric mean is the antilog of the arithmetic mean of the logs.

The harmonic mean is the reciprocal of the arithmetic mean of the reciprocals.

The quadratic mean is the square root of the arithmetic mean of the squares.

Actually there is an infinite number of types of means, but others are rarely, if ever, used. Of these, the geometric merits the most attention at this point.

Geometric mean. The geometric mean is the nth root of the product of the values. Thus, while the arithmetic mean of 4, 9, and 15 is

$$\bar{X} = \frac{4 + 9 + 15}{3} = 9.3,$$

the geometric mean is

$$G = \sqrt[3]{4 \times 9 \times 15} = \sqrt[3]{540} = 8.1.$$

Symbolically the geometric mean is

$$(16.13) \qquad G = \sqrt[n]{X_1 \times X_2 \times \dots \times X_n}.$$

We may also write

$$\text{Log } G = \bar{X}_{\log} = \frac{\log X_1 + \log X_2 + \dots + X_n}{n};$$

$$(16.14) \qquad G = \text{antilog } \frac{\log X_1 + \log X_2 + \dots + \log X_n}{n}$$

If frequencies are present the expression becomes

$$G = \text{antilog} \frac{f_1 \log X_1 + f_2 \log X_2 + \ldots + f_n \bar{X}_n}{n},$$

and this form is used for computing the geometric mean of a frequency distribution.

Referring to the numerical illustration above, we find that G is smaller than $\bar{X}$. For any series of different positive values this is always true. If one or more zeroes are present, $G = 0$. If any of the values are negative, the geometric mean has no useful meaning.

The essential difference between the arithmetic mean and the geometric mean may be made clear if we compare their mathematical characteristics.

(1) While the sum of the deviations from $\bar{X}$ is zero, the product of the ratios of the items to G is one. Thus if the X values are 2 and 18, $\bar{X} = 10$ and $G = 6$, and we find:

$$(2 - 10) + (18 - 10) = 0;$$

$$\frac{2}{6} \times \frac{18}{6} = 1.$$

(2) Series of the same number of items and having the same *total value* have the same arithmetic mean, while series of the same number of items and having the same *product* have the same geometric mean. Thus:

$$\frac{4 + 6}{2} = \frac{1 + 9}{2} = \frac{10}{2} = 5;$$

$$\sqrt{8 \times 12.5} = \sqrt{2 \times 50} = \sqrt{100} = 10.$$

(3) The greater the difference among the original values, the greater the difference between $\bar{X}$ and G. For example, consider two examples with numbers not differing greatly:

$$\frac{8 + 12.5}{2} = 10.25 \quad \text{and} \quad \sqrt{8 \times 12.5} = 10;$$

$$\frac{8 + 12}{2} = 10 \quad \text{and} \quad \sqrt{8 \times 12} = 9.8.$$

Now consider two examples with numbers that differ greatly:

$$\frac{2 + 50}{2} = 26 \quad \text{and} \quad \sqrt{2 \times 50} = 10;$$

$$\frac{2 + 18}{2} = 10 \quad \text{and} \quad \sqrt{2 \times 18} = 6.$$

Applications of the geometric mean. Three applications will be mentioned. (1) Averaging rates. Consider the following data:

Company	Net worth	Debt	Ratio of net worth to debt	Ratio of debt to net worth
A	$2,500	$1,000	2.5	0.4
B	$1,000	$2,000	0.5	2.0
	$3,500	$3,000		

The arithmetic mean of the two ratios of net worth to debt is 1.5. But the arithmetic mean of the ratios of debt to net worth is 1.2, and $1.5 \times 1.2 > 1$. This apparent absurdity arises because we failed properly to weight the ratios when we averaged them. Properly weighting the net-worth-to-debt ratios gives

$$\frac{(2.5 \times \$1,000) + (0.5 \times \$2,000)}{\$1,000 + \$2,000} = 1.167$$

which is, of course, the same as dividing total net worth by total debt,

$$\$3,500 \div \$3,000 = 1.167.$$

Similarly we may average the debt-to-net-worth ratios and obtain

$$\frac{(0.4 \times \$2,500) + (2.0 \times \$1,000)}{\$2,500 + \$1,000} = 0.8571,$$

or, using totals,

$$\$3,000 \div \$3,500 = 0.8571.$$

These two figures are consistent with each other in that $1.167 \times 0.8571 = 1.000$. However, these averages did not assign equal weights to the two ratios. If we wish to assign equal weight to each of the ratios being averaged and at the same time obtain consistent results, we may use the geometric mean. For the net-worth-to-debt ratios

$$G = \sqrt{2.5 \times 0.5} = \sqrt{1.25} = 1.118,$$

and for the debt-to-net-worth ratios

$$G = \sqrt{0.4 \times 2.0} = \sqrt{0.8} = 0.8944.$$

The product is $1.118 \times 0.8944 = 1$.

The reader should not infer from the preceding discussion that the geometric mean of the ratios is the correct measure to use and that the ratio of total values is incorrect, nor vice versa. The measure to use depends upon the purpose. If, for a number of firms, it is desired to establish a typical net-worth-to-debt ratio, which will be independent of the amount of debt or of net worth of the different firms, the geometric mean may be used. If it is desired to ascertain what the net-worth-to-debt ratio of a number of firms would be after consolidation, then the proper figure is obtained by taking the ratio of total net worth to total debt.

Other cases in which the geometric mean is used for averaging ratios will be considered in connection with correlation (Chapter 26) and index numbers (Chapter 32).

(2) Occasionally a frequency distribution is encountered which is skewed to the right, but if logarithms of the X-values are used, with the class interval of the logs constant, the curve becomes symmetrical. In such a situation the geometric mean may be appropriate. In such a case the mode of the logarithms is also the geometric mean. One type of data which often falls into this category is ratios.

(3) Averaging rates of change. For example: If a man invests $400 in the stock market, and at the end of one year it has grown to $500, he has had a 25 per cent profit. If at the end of the next year his principal has grown to $676, the rate of increase is 35.2 per cent for the year. What is the average rate of increase of his principal during the two years? This rate may be obtained by the geometric mean. The average ratio is

$$\sqrt{1.25 \times 1.352} = 1.30,$$

and the average rate of increase is therefore 30 per cent.

The geometric mean may be used if more than two years are involved. Suppose we have the principle at 5 instants of time one year apart: X_0, X_1, X_2, X_3, X_4, then

$$G = \sqrt[4]{\frac{X_1}{X_0} \cdot \frac{X_2}{X_1} \cdot \frac{X_3}{X_2} \cdot \frac{X_4}{X_3}}$$

$$= \sqrt[4]{\frac{X_4}{X_0}}.$$

From this formula we can see that we need to know only the principle at the beginning and the end of time under consideration. If the X-values do not form a geometric progression, it is often better to fit an exponential curve to the data, as explained in Chapter 38.

*Harmonic mean. The harmonic mean is defined as the reciprocal of the arithmetic mean of the reciprocals. Thus, for a simple harmonic mean,

(16.15)
$$H = \frac{n}{\dfrac{1}{X_1} + \dfrac{1}{X_2} + \cdots + \dfrac{1}{X_n}}.$$

For a weighted harmonic mean

(16.16)
$$H = \frac{\Sigma W}{W_1 \left(\dfrac{1}{X_1}\right) + W_2 \left(\dfrac{1}{X_2}\right) + \cdots + W_n \left(\dfrac{1}{X_n}\right)}.$$

Although the harmonic mean is of relatively limited usefulness, one illustration where it can be used will be given. Suppose the following:

You spend $12.00 on $3.00 shirts;
You spend $10.00 on $5.00 shirts.

What is the average price per shirt? The X-values are the prices per shirt and the weights are the amounts spent on the shirts. Therefore

$$H = \frac{12 + 10}{(12)(\frac{1}{3}) + (10)(\frac{1}{5})} = \$3.67.$$

This problem could obviously be stated, and solved, differently:

You buy 4 shirts at $3.00 per shirt;
You buy 2 shirts at $5.00 per shirt.

The X-values are still the prices per shirt, but the weights are now the numbers of shirts bought.

$$\bar{X} = \frac{(4 \times 3) + (2 \times 5)}{4 + 2} = \$3.67.$$

Although the example is far-fetched, the principle is simple. You are averaging rates, in this case, dollars per shirt. The numerator of each ratio is dollars spent, while the denominator is shirts bought. When denominator weights are employed, use the arithmetic mean; when numerator weights are employed, use the harmonic mean. Another illustration where either the arithmetic or the harmonic mean could be used is in averaging miles per hour. If the weights are miles covered, use H; if the weights are hours consumed, use $\bar{X}$.

*Quadratic mean. It will be remembered that the geometric mean is the antilogarithm of the arithmetic mean of the logarithms and the harmonic mean is the reciprocal of the arithmetic mean of the reciprocals. Similarly the quadratic mean is the square root of the arithmetic mean of the squares. Thus

(16.17)
$$Q = \sqrt{\frac{X_1^2 + X_2^2 + \dots + X_n^2}{n}}.$$

Use will be made of the quadratic mean in averaging deviations, rather than original values, when computing the standard deviation. See Chapter 17 for meaning of the standard deviation.

*Averages of means. If several means are to be averaged, one should use the same method of averaging that was employed in computing the original averages. Thus one takes the arithmetic mean of several values of $\bar{X}$, the geometric mean of several values of G, the harmonic mean of several values of H, and the quadratic mean of several values of Q.

*Relative magnitude of different means. Provided all the X values are positive, and all of them are not the same, this relationship will always obtain:

$$Q > \bar{X} > G > H.$$

Chapter 17

DISPERSION

Chapter 1 pointed out that in nature chaos is as pervasive as order, and in statistical data, variability is as characteristic as similarity. It is only because of variability that we compute averages. We no not, for example, speak of the average number of days in a week. On the other hand, if there is too much variability among the data, an average is so unreliable that it is almost useless. When asked the average number of fish he caught during the day, the fisherman replied: "There ain't no average; it varies."

To characterize a sample merely by stating its average value is to give an inadequate description. Samples differ also as to their variability, or dispersion. Consider the data of Table 17.1, which shows the strength of the slotted end of valve caps made by the National Equipment Company and by a competitor. The mean strength of the National Equipment valve caps is 152.5 pounds; for the competitor the mean is 147.1 pounds. Therefore the National Equipment product is stronger. Looking more closely at the data, which are in arrays, it may be seen that the tensile strength of the National Equipment product varies from 130.1 pounds to 180.7 pounds, while the competing product varies from 65.7 pounds to 204.8 pounds. Thus the National Equipment valve caps seem to be more uniform in quality, or we may say that those of the competing company are more variable.

Usually a high degree of uniformity (small amount of dispersion) is a desirable quality. Mass production would usually be uneconomical if there were a large amount of variability in materials or manufactured parts, for interchangeability of parts is essential. On the other hand, while a uniformly mediocre athlete may never win a point in a track meet, an inconsistent performer of mediocre average ability will probably pick up several points during a season.

In this chapter we consider several measures of dispersion. But there are only two that are used much: the range and the standard deviation.

Range

The range is the difference between the largest value and the smallest value.

$$(17.1) \qquad R = X_n - X_1.$$

For the illustration under consideration, the range of the National Equipment Company data is

$$R = 180.7 - 1301 = 50.6 \text{ pounds,}$$

Table 17.1—Tensile Strength of Valve Caps Made by Two Companies
(Tensile Strength is in pounds; data adapted from confidential source)

National Equipment Company   Competitor

Item number	Tensile strength X		Item number	Tensile strength X
1	130.1		1	65.7
2	132.3		2	101.3
3	133.4		3	103.0
4	135.5		4	103.6
5	137.7		5	107.2
6	139.3		6	115.9
7	140.4		7	117.4
8	144.2		8	122.6
9	145.0		9	126.5
10	146.7		10	129.1
11	147.4		11	132.1
12	148.3		12	134.6
13	149.7		13	135.2
14	150.6		14	136.7
15	151.1		15	138.3
16	151.8		16	142.1
17	152.1		17	143.4
18	152.7		18	147.2
19	153.5		19	148.2
20	154.1		20	149.4
21	154.7		21	151.0
22	155.4		22	153.3
23	156.7		23	155.2
24	157.5		24	157.6
25	158.4		25	160.7
26	159.4		26	164.3
27	160.7		27	166.1
28	161.9		28	168.8
29	163.1		29	170.4
30	164.8		30	180.6
31	169.3		31	184.6
32	171.2		32	188.8
33	174.0		33	192.9
34	180.7		34	196.0
			35	200.4
Total	5,183.7		36	204.8
Mean	152.5		Total	5,295.2
			Mean	147.1

whereas for the competitor's data it is 139.1 pounds. This indicates that National Equipment Company produces a more uniform product that its competitor.

Although it is the simplest measure of dispersion, the range has certain shortcomings. All of these shortcomings are attributable to the fact that the range does not utilize all of the information contained in the sample.

First, since it is based on the smallest and largest values of a sample, it may be unduly influenced by one unusual value. Such a situation actually occurs in the case of the competitor's data. The smallest reading was 65.7 pounds, almost 35 pounds less than the next larger value. Because of this shortcoming, the range would not ordinarily be used to describe a sample having one, or a few, unusual values at the other end.

Second, the range is insensitive to the behavior of the values between the extremes. In the case of the National Equipment data, we might have had one test of 130.1 pounds, 16 of 132 pounds, 16 of 180 pounds, and 1 of 180.7 pounds. The range would still be 50.6 pounds.

Third, the range is extremely sensitive to the size of the sample. As the sample size is increased, the range tends to increase, though not proportionately. Thus the range of the sample is a *biased* estimate of the variability in the population, as measured by the *standard deviation* σ. Obviously the range cannot be computed for a normal population, for the values vary from $-\infty$ to $+\infty$.

The bias of the range can be corrected by multiplying it by a correction factor c_3, which varies with the sample size. Values of c_3 are given in Appendix 10.

Fourth, the range is less reliable than some of the other measures of dispersion explained in this chapter, notably the standard deviation. It varies too much from sample to sample, taken at random from the same population.

In spite of its shortcomings, there are special situations where the range is satisfactory. When sampling from a normal population with sample size small (say 12 or smaller), the quantity c_3R, which is an unbiased estimate of σ, is nearly as reliable as the more laboriously computed standard deviation. When $n = 2$, they are equally reliable. In quality control, the range is customarily used for control charts, since the sample size is usually 4 or 5.

There are also certain types of data and certain purposes for which use of the range is appropriate. Among these are the range in temperature during the day or year, and the range in stock prices during some period of time. In the latter case we learn the maximum profit that could have been made over the period by one purchase and one sale.

It is always desirable to state the average for a set of data, as well as a measure of its dispersion. In the case of the range it is convenient and often desirable to state also the two values, X_1 and X_n, from which the range was computed.

Quartile Deviation

The quartile deviation, sometimes called the *semi-interquartile range*, is a measure of dispersion based upon the quartiles. It is the average difference between the median and the two quartiles, and is most easily obtained by subtracting the lower quartile (Q_1) from the upper quartile (Q_3), and dividing by 2.

$$(17.2) \qquad\qquad QD = \frac{Q_3 - Q_1}{2}.$$

A charateristic of the quartile deviation is the fact that within $\pm QD$ of the median, approximately 50 per cent of the items are found. It must be obvious, if a series is symmetrical, that QD measured in either direction from the median must coincide exactly with Q_1 and Q_3, and thus include the central 50 per cent of the frequencies. However, when a series is skewed, as is usually the case, QD laid off on either side of the median coincides with neither Q_1 not Q_3. But even though a series is somewhat skewed, approximately 50 per cent of the total frequencies are included from (Med $-$ Q) to (Med $+$ Q). For the National Equipment Company data, $Q_1 = 145.0$ pounds, Med $= 152.4$ pounds, and $Q_3 = 159.4$ pounds.

$$QD = \frac{159.4 - 145.0}{2} = \frac{14.4}{2} = 7.2 \text{ pounds.}$$

$$\text{Med} \pm QD = 152.4 \pm 7.2 = 145.2 \text{ and } 159.6 \text{ pounds}$$

In this case 17 items, or exactly 50 per cent, are included between these two values.

The quartile deviation is easy to compute and is a relatively simple concept. It is not affected by the magnitude of extremely large or extremely small values. It is therefore useful chiefly when the data include extreme values that are thought to be unrepresentative. It has, however, an important defect. Being based upon the quartiles, it is completely insensitive to the distribution of the items smaller than Q_1, between Q_1 and Q_3, and larger than Q_3.

Mean Deviation

Mean deviation, known also as the *average deviation*, is the mean of the *numerical* amounts by which the individual items deviate from the mean. It is computed by the following procedure.

1. Obtain the numerical deviations from the mean;[1] i.e., $|x| = |X - \bar{X}|$. The vertical bars indicate that the sign of the deviations is disregarded; each of the n deviations is treated as if it were positive. See Table 17.2.

---

[1] Occasionally the deviations are measured from the median since $\Sigma |X - M|$ is minimized when M is the median.

Table 17.2—Computation of $\Sigma |x|$ for Obtaining Mean Deviation of National Equipment Company Data

(X = tensile strength in pounds; $\bar{X}$ = 152.46 pounds; data of Table 17.1.)

X	$\|X - \bar{X}\|$ $\|x\|$	X	$\|X - \bar{X}\|$ $\|x\|$
130.1	22.36	152.7	0.24
132.3	20.16	153.5	1.04
133.4	19.06	154.1	1.64
135.5	16.96	154.7	2.24
137.7	14.76	155.4	2.94
139.3	13.16	156.7	4.24
140.4	12.06	157.5	5.04
144.2	8.26	158.4	5.94
145.0	7.46	159.4	6.94
146.7	5.76	160.7	8.24
147.4	5.06	161.9	9.44
148.3	4.16	163.1	10.64
149.7	2.76	164.8	12.34
150.6	1.86	169.3	16.84
151.1	1.36	171.2	18.74
151.8	0.66	174.0	21.54
152.1	0.36	180.7	28.24
		5,183.7	312.50

2. Sum the n deviations. Although $\Sigma x = 0$, $\Sigma |x| \neq 0$. Table 17.2 shows that $\Sigma |x| = 312.50$ pounds for the National Equipment data.

3. Divide the sum of the deviations by n.

Symbolically, these steps may be summarized as follows:

$$(17.3) \qquad MD = \frac{\Sigma |x|}{n}$$

For the National Equipment Company data,

$$MD = \frac{312.50}{34} = 9.2 \text{ pounds.}$$

The mean deviation is a simple and easily understood measure of dispersion. Unlike QD, it is affected by the value of each item. While MD gives a reasonably good statement of the dispersion of a sample, it is not as frequently employed as is the standard deviation, which will be described in the next section.

One objection to the mean deviation is that the signs of the deviations are all taken to be positive, though in fact, some are positive and some are negative. The standard deviation does not offend in this respect. Also, the standard deviation is more reliable. Finally, the standard deviation has been found to be better suited to a wide variety of other uses. Among these should be mentioned correlation, and the description of probability distributions. Both of these are described in later chapters.

Standard Deviation

The standard deviation s is similar to the mean deviation in that it considers the deviation of each X-value from $\bar{X}$. However, instead of using the numerical values of the deviations, it uses the squares of the deviations. These are summed, divided by n, and the square root extracted.

Sometimes it is convenient to think of the computations as involving 3 stages, each of which has a name, a symbol, and a formula.[2]

$$(17.4) \qquad \text{Variation:} \qquad \Sigma\, x^2.$$

$$(17.5) \qquad \text{Variance:} \qquad s^2 = \frac{\Sigma\, x^2}{n}.$$

$$(17.6) \qquad \text{Standard deviation:} \qquad s = \sqrt{\frac{\Sigma\, x^2}{n}}.$$

We can state the above expression more fully as follows:

$$(17.7) \qquad \text{Variation:} \quad \Sigma\, x^2 = \Sigma\, (X - \bar{X})^2.$$

$$(17.8) \qquad \text{Variance:} \qquad s^2 = \frac{\Sigma\, (X - \bar{X})^2}{n}.$$

$$(17.9) \qquad \text{Standard deviation:} \qquad s = \sqrt{\frac{\Sigma\, (X - \bar{X})^2}{n}}.$$

Basic computations for the National Equipment Company data are shown in Table 17.3. From these we obtain, by stages:

$$\text{Variation:} \quad \Sigma\, x^2 = 4{,}770;$$

$$\text{Variance:} \quad s^2 = \frac{4{,}770}{34} = 140.3;$$

$$\text{Standard deviation:} \quad s = \sqrt{140.3} = 11.8 \text{ pounds.}$$

Or using (17.9) directly,

$$s = \sqrt{\frac{4{,}770}{34}} = \sqrt{140.3} = 11.8 \text{ pounds.}$$

---

[2] In Chapter 12 the standard deviation was defined as $s = \sqrt{\dfrac{\Sigma\, x^2}{n-1}}$. We shall return to that concept on page 253.

Table 17.3—Computations of Σx^2 for Obtaining Standard Deviation of National Equipment Company Data

(X = tensile strength in pounds; $\bar{X}$ = 152.46 pounds; data of Table 17.1.)

X	$X - \bar{X}$ x	x^2	X	$X - \bar{X}$ x	x^2
130.1	−22.36	499.97	152.7	+0.24	0.06
132.3	−20.16	406.43	153.5	+1.04	1.08
133.4	−19.06	363.28	154.1	+1.64	2.69
135.5	−16.96	287.64	154.7	+2.24	5.02
137.7	−14.76	217.86	155.4	+2.94	8.64
139.3	−13.16	173.19	156.7	+4.24	17.98
140.4	−12.06	145.44	157.5	+5.04	25.40
144.2	−8.26	68.23	158.4	+5.94	35.28
145.0	−7.46	55.65	159.4	+6.94	48.16
146.7	−5.76	33.18	160.7	+8.24	67.90
147.4	−5.06	25.60	161.9	+9.44	89.11
148.3	−4.16	17.31	163.1	+10.64	113.21
149.7	−2.76	7.62	164.8	+12.34	152.28
150.6	−1.86	3.46	169.3	+16.84	283.59
151.1	−1.36	1.85	171.2	+18.74	351.19
151.8	−0.66	0.44	174.0	+21.54	463.97
152.1	−0.36	0.13	180.7	+28.24	797.50
			5,183.7	−0.06*	4,770.34

* The total should be zero. The discrepancy does not indicate a mistake; it is the result of rounding.

When using (17.7) to compute variation, care must be taken to carry $\bar{X}$ to a sufficient number of decimal places. If this is not done, the results will not only be inaccurate, but will also have an upward bias.

Because of the method of computation, the standard deviation is sometimes called the *root mean square deviation*. Most concisely of all it may be defined as the quadratic mean of the x-values. See page 236.

Often a subscript is attached to s. For example, s_X means the standard deviation of the X-values, and s_Y means the standard deviation of the Y-values.

The standard deviation is the most important of the measures of dispersion. In later chapters frequent use will be made of variation, variance, and standard deviation. In Chapter 19 the standard deviation will be used in fitting a normal curve to a frequency distribution. In Chapter 26 all three measures will be used in explaining the correlation coefficient.

The standard deviation is also the most reliable of any of the measures of dispersion (except when $n = 2$, in which case $s = R/2$). It is usually true that a measure which utilizes all the information in a sample is more reliable than one which utilizes only part of it. Of the measures considered so far in this chapter, only MD and s make use of each X-value.

Although s is reliable, both s and s^2 are biased estimators of σ and σ^2, respectively. $E(\mathit{s}) < \sigma$, and $E(\mathit{s}^2) < \sigma^2$. As n increases, so does s, though the increase is not so rapid as it is for the range R. Furthermore, as n approaches infinity, s approaches σ, so s is a *consistent* estimator of σ. The bias of s can be corrected by multiplying it by a correction factor a_1, which varies with the sample size, and is given in this text as Appendix 8.

Chart 17.1—The Standard Deviation and the Normal Curve

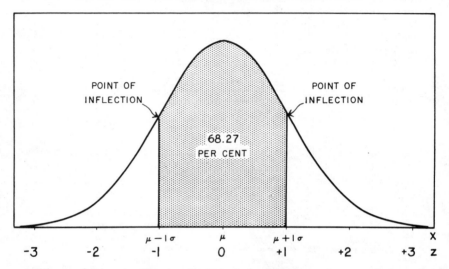

When referring to the standard deviation of the entire population, the symbol σ is used. A graphical characteristic[3] of the standard deviation σ is that it is the distance between the mean μ and a point of inflection on the normal curve. See Chart 17.1. A point of inflection is a point where the curve ceases to be concave upward and becomes concave downward. On a normal curve it is the point on the curve where the slope is steepest.

If a distribution is normal, slightly more than 68 per cent of the items are included within the limits of one standard deviation on either side of the arithmetic mean. More precisely, the area between $(\mu - \sigma)$ and $(\mu + \sigma)$, shaded in Chart 17.1, is 68.27 per cent of the entire area under the curve, and the probability that an item selected at random will be between $(\mu - \sigma)$ and $(\mu + \sigma)$ is .6827. For a skewed distribution the proportion would not necessarily be 68.27 per cent, and for a leptokurtic or platykurtic distribution the discrepancy might be quite large.

For the data of Table 17.3, $\overline{X} \pm \mathit{s} = 152.5 \pm 11.8 = 140.7$ and 164.3 pounds. These two values include 22/34 or 65 per cent of the items. For a sample containing so few items exact agreement is not to be expected.

---

[3] It may be of interest to students of mechanics to note that σ is analogous to the radius of gyration.

Efficient computational methods. Use of formula (17.4) is unnecessarily laborious because $\bar{X}$ must be subtracted from each value of X. The labor is especially great if $\bar{X}$ contains a large number of digits or decimal places. If $\bar{X}$ is rounded before being subtracted, the standard deviation loses in accuracy.

Use of correction term. Instead of computing $\Sigma (X - \bar{X})^2$, which requires n subtractions, it is usually easier to compute ΣX^2 and then subtract a correction term[4] which can be written in various ways: $(\Sigma X)^2/n$; $n\bar{X}^2$; $\bar{X}\Sigma X$. Thus

$$(17.10) \qquad \text{Variation:} \quad \Sigma x^2 = \Sigma X^2 - \frac{(\Sigma X)^2}{n}.$$

The variance and standard deviation are now computed by formulas (17.5) and (17.6), using the value of Σx^2 obtained from formula (17.10). Nevertheless it may be helpful to indicate the procedure explicitly.

$$(17.11) \qquad \text{Variance:}[5] \quad \sigma^2 = \frac{\Sigma X^2 - (\Sigma X)^2/n}{n};$$

$$(17.12) \qquad \text{Standard deviation:} \quad \sigma = \sqrt{\frac{\Sigma X^2 - (\Sigma X)^2/n}{n}}.$$

The computation of σ that follows, using formulas (17.10), (17.11), and (17.12), are based on Table 17.4.

$$\text{Variation:} \quad \Sigma x^2 = 795{,}086 - \frac{(5{,}183.7)^2}{34}$$

$$= 795{,}086 - 796{,}316 = 4{,}770.$$

$$\text{Variance:} \quad \sigma^2 = \frac{4{,}770}{34} = 140.3$$

$$\text{Standard deviation:} \quad \sigma = \sqrt{140.3} = 11.8 \text{ pounds.}$$

---

[4] A proof that $\Sigma x^2 = \Sigma X^2 - (\Sigma X)^2/n$ is as follows. By definition,

$$\Sigma x^2 = \Sigma (X - \bar{X})^2.$$

Therefore,

$$\Sigma x^2 = \Sigma (X^2 - 2\bar{X}X + \bar{X}^2)$$
$$= \Sigma X^2 - 2\bar{X}\Sigma X + n\bar{X}^2$$
$$= \Sigma X^2 - 2\bar{X}\Sigma X + \bar{X}\Sigma X$$
$$= \Sigma X^2 - \bar{X}\Sigma X$$
$$= \Sigma X^2 - n\bar{X}^2$$
$$= \Sigma X^2 - \frac{(\Sigma X)^2}{n}.$$

If $\bar{X}\Sigma X$ or $n\bar{X}^2$ is used as the correction term, one must be sure to compute $\bar{X}$ to a sufficient number of digits.

[5] Some persons prefer to write

$$\sigma^2 = \frac{\Sigma X^2}{n} - \left(\frac{\Sigma X}{n}\right)^2 = \frac{\Sigma X^2}{n} - \bar{X}^2.$$

Then one can say: variance is the mean of the squares minus the square of the mean.

Table 17.4—Computation of ΣX^2 for Obtaining Standard Deviation of National Equipment Company Data

(X = tensile strength in pounds; data of Table 17.1.)

X	X^2	X	X^2
130.1	16,926.01	152.7	23,317.29
132.3	17,503.29	153.5	23,562.25
133.4	17,795.56	154.1	23,746.81
135.5	18,360.25	154.7	23,932.09
137.7	18,961.29	155.4	24,149.16
139.3	19,404.49	156.7	24,554.89
140.4	19,712.16	157.5	24,806.25
144.2	20,793.64	158.4	25,090.56
145.0	21,025.00	159.4	25,408.36
146.7	21,520.89	160.7	25,824.49
147.4	21,726.76	161.9	26,211.61
148.3	21,992.89	163.1	26,601.61
149.7	22,410.09	164.8	27,159.04
150.6	22,680.36	169.3	28,662.49
151.1	22,831.21	171.2	29,309.44
151.8	23,043.24	174.0	30,276.00
152.1	23,134.41	180.7	32,652.49
		5,183.7	795,086.37

The results are, of course, the same as those obtained before, using more laborious methods of computation.

Use of arbitrary origin. Subtracting a constant X_0 from each value has no effect on the standard deviation. If $d = X - X_0$, it follows that $d - \bar{d} = X - \bar{X}$ for each value[6] of X, and so $\sigma_d = \sigma_X$. Therefore:

$$(17.13) \quad \text{Variation:} \quad \Sigma x^2 = \Sigma d^2 - \frac{(\Sigma d)^2}{n};$$

$$(17.14) \quad \text{Variance:} \quad \sigma^2 = \frac{\Sigma d^2 - (\Sigma d)^2/n}{n};$$

$$(17.15) \quad \text{Standard deviation:} \quad \sigma = \sqrt{\frac{\Sigma d^2 - (\Sigma d)^2/n}{n}}.$$

[6] $d - \bar{d} = (X - X_0) - \dfrac{\Sigma(X - X_0)}{n}$

$= (X - X_0) - \dfrac{\Sigma X - nX_0}{n}$

$= (X - X_0) - (\bar{X} - X_0)$

$= X - \bar{X}$

Computation of $\Sigma\, d^2$ for the National Equipment Company data are given in Table 17.5. The arbitrary origin is $X_0 = 130.0$. Any other value for X_0 leads to the same results.

$$\text{Variation:} \quad \Sigma\, x^2 = 21{,}924 - \frac{(763.7)^2}{34}$$

$$= 21{,}924 - 17{,}154 = 4{,}770;$$

$$\text{Variance:} \quad s^2 = 140.3;$$

$$\text{Standard deviation:} \quad s = 11.8 \text{ pounds.}$$

Table 17.5—Computation of $\Sigma\, d^2$ for Obtaining Standard Deviation of National Equipment Company Data
$(X_0 = 130.0;\ \text{data of Table 17.1.})$

X	d $X - X_0$	d^2	X	d $X - X_0$	d^2
130.1	0.1	0.01	152.7	22.7	515.29
132.3	2.3	5.29	153.5	23.5	552.25
133.4	3.4	11.56	154.1	24.1	580.81
135.5	5.5	30.25	154.7	24.7	610.09
137.7	7.7	59.29	155.4	25.4	645.16
139.3	9.3	86.49	156.7	26.7	712.89
140.4	10.4	108.16	157.5	27.5	756.25
144.2	14.2	201.64	158.4	28.4	806.56
145.0	15.0	225.00	159.4	29.4	864.36
146.7	16.7	278.89	160.7	30.7	942.49
147.4	17.4	302.76	161.9	31.9	1,017.61
148.3	18.3	334.89	163.1	33.1	1,095.61
149.7	19.7	388.09	164.8	34.8	1,211.04
150.6	20.6	424.36	169.3	39.3	1,544.49
151.1	21.1	445.21	171.2	41.2	1,697.44
151.8	21.8	475.24	174.0	44.0	1,936.00
152.1	22.1	488.41	180.7	50.7	2,570.49
			5,183.7	763.7	21,924.37

The advantage of this method of computation is that the values of d and d^2 are somewhat smaller than the values of X and X^2 used in formula (17.10).

   *Computations for grouped data. One may use the formula

$$(17.16) \qquad s = \sqrt{\frac{\Sigma\, fx^2}{n}},$$

where the x-values are deviations from mid-values of their classes. This formula is analogous to (17.6). More fully we can write

$$(17.17) \qquad s = \sqrt{\frac{\Sigma\, f(X - \bar{X})^2}{n}},$$

where the X-values are mid-values of the different classes. This formula is analogous to (17.9). It is usually easier, however, to use a formula that is analogous to (17.12).

(17.18)
$$\sigma = \sqrt{\frac{\Sigma f X^2 - (\Sigma f X)^2/n}{n}}.$$

When the classes are of uniform width, it is still easier to use a formula analogous to (17.15).

(17.19)
$$\sigma = \sqrt{\frac{\Sigma f d^2 - (\Sigma f d)^2/n}{n}}.$$

But easiest of all is to work with deviations in class interval units. The formula is exactly the same as (17.19) with two exceptions:

(1) Instead of d we use d', where

$$d' = \frac{X - X_0}{c} = \frac{d}{c},$$

c is the class interval, and X_0 is an arbitrary origin.

(2) Since we have divided the d-values by c, obtaining $d' = d/c$, we must multiply[7] $\sigma_{d'} = \sigma_{d/c}$ by c in order to obtain σ_d, which is the same as σ_X. Thus we have[8]

(17.20)
$$\sigma = c\sqrt{\frac{\Sigma f(d')^2 - (\Sigma f d')^2/n}{n}}.$$

Table 17.6 shows the computation of $\Sigma f d'$ and $\Sigma f (d')^2$ needed for computing the standard deviation of the National Equipment Company data of Table 17.1. Ordinarily one would not group 34 items for the purpose of computing σ, but this will permit us to compare the results with computations using ungrouped data. The reason for the fractional frequencies in the second and third classes is that one item is recorded in Table 17.1 as 145.0

---

[7] It is always true that if the original data are coded by dividing by a constant c, the standard deviation of the coded data is the standard deviation of the original data divided by c. This is easily proved. We know that

$$\Sigma \left(\frac{x}{c}\right)^2 = \frac{\Sigma x^2}{c^2}.$$

Dividing by n, we have

$$\sigma_{x/c}^2 = \frac{\sigma_x^2}{c^2}.$$

Extracting the square root

$$\sigma_{x/c} = \frac{\sigma_x}{c}.$$

[8] It is correct, also, to write

$$\sigma^2 = c^2 \left[\frac{\Sigma f(d')^2}{n} - \left(\frac{\Sigma f d'}{n}\right)^2\right].$$

Compare with footnote 5.

Table 17.6—Computation of Values for Obtaining Standard Deviation of
National Equipment Company Data, Using Frequency Distribution
(Tensile strength in pounds; data of Table 17.1.)

Tensile strength	f	d'	fd'	$f(d')^2$
125–135	3	−2	−6	12
135–145	5.5	−1	−5.5	5.5
145–155	12.5	0	0	0
155–165	9	1	9	9
165–175	3	2	6	12
175–185	1	3	3	9
Total	34	...	6.5	47.5

pounds. We have no way of telling whether it is slightly more or slightly
less than 145 pounds. Actually, it makes little difference whether the item is
placed in the second class, the third class, or split between them. Note that
the deviations are in class interval units; if formula (17.19) were used, the
column labeled d' would be labeled d, and the values would be 10 times as
large, since $c = 10$. The fd' column is obtained by multiplying the d'-values
by the f-values. The $f(d')^2$ column is obtained by multiplying the fd'-values
by the d'-values. Substituting in formula (17.20) we have

$$\mathit{s} = 10\sqrt{\frac{47.5 - (6.5)^2/34}{34}} = 10\sqrt{\frac{47.5 - 1.24}{34}}$$

$$= 10\sqrt{\frac{46.26}{34}} = 10\sqrt{1.361} = 10(1.167) = 11.7 \text{ pounds.}$$

Although there are only 6 classes in Table 17.6, the results differ only
slightly from those obtained from the ungrouped data.

Correction for grouping. It was pointed out on page 227 that the arithmetic mean of a symmetrical frequency distribution closely approximates
the arithmetic mean of the raw data from which the frequency distribution
was constructed, because errors in the mid-values tend to offset. In the case of
the standard deviation, however, the mid-value errors are not offsetting;
the value of s for the frequency distribution tends to be a little too large.
Sheppard's corrections are designed to eliminate this bias under certain
conditions: the variable must be continuous and must approach zero
asymptotically at each end of the distribution. The formula for the standard
deviation with Sheppard's correction is

(17.21) $$\tilde{\mathit{s}} = c\sqrt{\frac{\Sigma f(d')^2 - (\Sigma fd')^2/n}{n} - \frac{1}{12}}.$$

It is better not to use Sheppard's corrections unless one is confident that the conditions are fulfilled.

The Standard Deviation as a Unit of Measurement

We have noted that the standard deviation is the distance between the mean and a point of inflection of a normal curve. It may therefore be thought of as a unit of measurement. Thus, we may think of an X-value as being z standard deviations above (or below) the mean, or that $x = z$ standard deviations.

For the entire population,

$$(17.22) \qquad z = \frac{X - \mu}{\sigma};$$

while for a sample,

$$(17.23) \qquad z = \frac{X - \bar{X}}{\measuredangle}.$$

It might be thought adequate to divide an x-value by the mean of the distribution, and express this ratio as per cent of average. This leaves out of the picture, however, the tendency of some sets of data to vary more than others. If an instructor gives C's to nearly all of his students, a student who obtains an A has made a remarkable achievement. However, if the instructor gives many A's and many F's, but an average of C, an A grade is not very noteworthy.

A z-value is sometimes referred to as a *standard measure*, or a *standardized value*. By means of z-values we can compare *individual* items, even though they are from different distributions. Suppose that an individual accomplishes a score of 125 on an achievement test based on volume of output, the mean for all employees being 92 and the standard deviation 24.5. Then

$$z = \frac{125 - 92}{24.5} = +1.35.$$

Suppose also that he is given a score of 84 by his supervisor, this score being based on considerations other than volume of output. Now if for all employees $\bar{X} = 70$ and $\measuredangle = 21$,

$$z = \frac{84 - 70}{21} = +0.67.$$

Apparently the person being investigated is more satisfactory with respect to output than with respect to other qualifications.

The standard measure is used a great deal in subsequent chapters to determine the probability of obtaining a value of a specified magnitude, when sampling from a normal distribution. It is, therefore, a very important concept. It is interesting at this point to turn back to Chart 17.1 and observe that the proportion of the total area beyond $|z| = 3$ in a normal curve is almost negligible.

Relative Dispersion

It will be recalled that the data on strength of valve caps made by the National Equipment Company showed $\bar{X} = 152.5$ pounds and $\Delta = 11.8$ pounds. Similar test data of 36 valve caps made by a competitor had $\bar{X} = 147.1$ pounds and $\Delta = 31.3$ pounds. If we wish to compare the dispersions of these two sets of data, it is not incorrect to compare the two Δ-values. The arithmetic means of the two series are not greatly different, and it is clear that the dispersion of the competitor's test data is greater than that of the National Equipment Company data.

In other instances the comparison takes on a different aspect. The Goodyear Tire and Rubber Company developed a type of cord for use in automobile tires known as "Supertwist"—a cord that not only will stretch more than ordinary cord but that also has a longer flex life. The mean flex life, as tested by an apparatus for bending the cord, was 138.64 minutes for Supertwist and 87.66 minutes for regular cord. These tests were made on cord as received from the cotton mill but prior to fabrication in tires. Now, what concerns us at this point of the discussion is the *dispersion* in flex life of the two types of cords. If the two Δ-values are compared, there seems to be little difference between the two, since the standard deviation for Supertwist is 15.27 minutes while for regular cord it is 14.12 minutes. It must be remembered, however, that the standard deviation of Supertwist is 15.27 minutes in relation to a rather high mean flex life, while the standard deviation of regular cord is 14.12 minutes in relation to a rather low mean flex life. Hence we have the concept of relative dispersion V in which Δ is compared to the arithmetic mean. For the population,

$$(17.24) \qquad\qquad V = \frac{\sigma}{\mu},$$

while for a sample,

$$(17.25) \qquad\qquad V = \frac{\Delta}{\bar{X}}.$$

For Supertwist: $V = \dfrac{15.27}{138.64} = 0.1101$, or 11.0 per cent.

For regular cord: $V = \dfrac{14.12}{87.66} = 0.1611$, or 16.1 per cent.

From a comparison of the two V's it is apparent that the relative variation is much less for Supertwist than for regular cord.

It may help to think of the coefficient of variation as the standard deviation of the percentages of average. Consider this simple example.

X	x	x^2
2	-2	4
3	-1	1
7	3	9
$\Sigma X = 12$	$\Sigma x = 0$	$\Sigma x^2 = 14$
$\bar{X} = 4$		$\vartheta_x^2 = 4.667$
		$\vartheta_x = 2.16$

$$V = \frac{\vartheta_x}{\bar{X}} = \frac{2.16}{4} = 0.54 = 54 \text{ per cent.}$$

Now let $Y = X/\bar{X}$. Then $V = \vartheta_Y$. Thus, expressing Y as a percentage, we obtain these results,

Y (per cent)	y	y^2
50	-50	2500
75	-25	625
175	75	5625
$\Sigma Y = 300$	$\Sigma y = 0$	$\Sigma y^2 = 8800$
$\bar{Y} = 100$		$\vartheta_Y^2 = 2933$
		$\vartheta_Y = 54 \text{ per cent}$

At times it is necessary to compare the dispersions of two series expressed in different units. As was noted above, the mean *flex life* of Supertwist was 138.64 minutes, and ϑ was 15.27 minutes. The mean *tensile strength* of Supertwist was 18.3 pounds, while ϑ was 0.73 pounds. If it is desired to know whether Supertwist shows greater dispersion of tensile strength or of flex life, it is not possible to compare the two ϑ-values, 15.27 minutes and 0.73 pounds. It is absolutely necessary to resort to use of the V's. Relative variability in respect to tensile strength is

$$V = \frac{0.73}{18.3} = 0.0399, \text{ or } 4.0 \text{ per cent.}$$

The V for flex life was shown above to be 11.0 per cent, and it is thus seen that Supertwist is less variable in respect to tensile strength than in respect to flex life.

When comparing dispersions, three types of situations may be found present, each of which has been illustrated:

1. The series may be expressed in the same units, and the arithmetic means may be the same or nearly the same in size. Here the ϑ-values may validly be compared, and no additional information is obtained by use of the V's.

2. The series may be expressed in the same units, but the arithmetic means may be of different size. A comparison of absolute dispersion may be had by considering the δ-values, but a more meaningful comparison results from comparing relative dispersion through a consideration of the V's.

3. The series may be expressed in different units. In this case it is not possible to compare the δ-values, but comparison may be made of the V's.

Unbiased Estimates of σ^2

The sample variance $\delta^2 = \Sigma (X - \bar{X})^2/n$ is a biased estimate of $\sigma^2 = E[(X - \mu)^2]$. The arithmetic mean of all possible values of δ^2, for a given sample size, called the expected value of δ^2, is smaller than σ^2. Symbolically, $E(\delta^2) < \sigma^2$. This will seem plausible when we remember that for any particular sample the sum of the squares of the deviations is at a minimum when the deviations are measured around the mean of the sample. Therefore, *for any particular sample,*

$$\frac{\sum_{1}^{n} (X - \bar{X})^2}{n} \quad \text{is smaller than} \quad \frac{\sum_{1}^{n} (X - \mu)^2}{n}.$$

We can also rationalize as follows: As a random sample becomes larger and larger we tend to get a larger range of values, and so δ^2 tends to become larger and larger, and as n approaches infinity δ^2 approaches σ^2 in value. Thus δ^2 is a consistent estimator of σ^2, although it is a biased estimator.

The quantity

(17.26) $$s^2 = \frac{\Sigma x^2}{n - 1}$$

is an unbiased estimate[9] of σ^2.

$$E(s^2) = \sigma^2.$$

When we compute s^2 by formula (17.26) we are dividing the variation, not by the sample size n, but by the number of degrees of freedom v. The number of degrees of freedom is $n - 1$ because the mean $\bar{X}$, around which the deviations x are measured, is independent of all but one of the items in the sample. Of the n items, $n - 1$ can be selected arbitrarily, but having done that, the remaining X-value determines the value of $\bar{X}$. If we knew the value of μ we could obtain an unbiased estimate of σ^2 as follows:

$$\hat{\sigma}^2 = \frac{\Sigma (X - \mu)^2}{n}.$$

When we take the square root of s^2 we obtain s. All of the formulas for δ that we have recorded can be converted into formulas for s merely by

---

[9] This is proved for an infinite population in Dudley J. Cowden, *Statistical Methods in Quality Control,* Prentice-Hall, Inc., Englewood Cliffs, N.J., 1957, pp. 75–76,

substituting $n - 1$ for n in the denominator of the expression for variance. These formulas are summarized for ease of reference.

$$(17.27) \qquad s = \sqrt{\frac{\Sigma x^2}{n - 1}}$$

$$(17.28) \qquad s = \sqrt{\frac{\Sigma X^2 - (\Sigma X)^2/n}{n - 1}}$$

$$(17.29) \qquad s = \sqrt{\frac{\Sigma d^2 - (\Sigma d)^2/n}{n - 1}}$$

$$(17.30) \qquad s = \sqrt{\frac{\Sigma f x^2}{n - 1}}$$

$$(17.31) \qquad s = \sqrt{\frac{\Sigma f X^2 - (\Sigma f X)^2/n}{n - 1}}$$

$$(17.32) \qquad s = \sqrt{\frac{\Sigma f d^2 - (\Sigma f d)^2/n}{n - 1}}$$

$$(17.33) \qquad s = c\sqrt{\frac{\Sigma f(d')^2 - (\Sigma f d')^2/n}{n - 1}}$$

Although s is not (in the technical sense) an unbiased estimate of σ, it is widely used in statistical work. Generally speaking, s is preferable to Δ, but there are uses for which Δ is the correct measure.

*Unbiased Estimates of σ

Various methods of obtaining unbiased estimates of σ are available, using factors given in appendix tables of this text.

Using Appendix 8 compute

$$(17.34) \qquad \hat{\sigma}_1 = a_1 \Delta \quad \text{or} \quad a_1 \bar{\Delta}.$$

If the sample is large it is more efficient to divide it at random into k subsamples of 6 to 10 items each, and compute $a_1 \bar{\Delta}$. The variance of $\hat{\sigma}_1$ is at least as small as that of any other unbiased estimator of σ.

Using Appendix 9 compute

$$(17.35) \qquad \hat{\sigma}_2 = \Sigma b_i X_i,$$

where the X-values have been ranked in ascending order. $\hat{\sigma}_2$ is the most efficient unbiased *linear* estimator of σ. The efficiency of $\hat{\sigma}_2$ is about 99 per cent.

Using Appendix 10 compute

$$(17.36) \qquad \hat{\sigma}_3 = c_3 R \quad \text{or} \quad c_3 \bar{R}.$$

If the sample is large it is more efficient to divide it at random into k sub-samples of 6 to 10 items each, and compute $c_3\bar{R}$. As the sample size and the number of subsamples increase, the efficiency of $\hat{\sigma}_3$ declines asymptotically to about 75 per cent.

Using Appendix 11 compute

$$(17.37) \qquad\qquad \hat{\sigma}_4 = c_4 R_q,$$

where R_q is the quasi-range, the range of the array after excluding q items at each end. $\hat{\sigma}_4$ is the most efficient unbiased estimator of σ when only two values of X are used. The asymptotic efficiency of $\hat{\sigma}_4$ is approximately 65 per cent.

Summary

There are two important measures of dispersion, the range and the standard deviation. The standard deviation is the most reliable of all measures of dispersion. It is greatly to be preferred to the range, except when the sample size is very small.

The standard deviation is the square root of the variance, and the variance is the variation (Σx^2) divided either by the number of observations (n) or the number of degrees of freedom ($n-1$).

$$\Delta^2 = \frac{\Sigma x^2}{n} \text{ is a biased estimator of } \sigma^2.$$

$$s^2 = \frac{\Sigma x^2}{n-1} \text{ is an unbiased estimator of } \sigma^2.$$

Although there are many ways of computing Δ, one needs to remember only these:

$$\Delta = \sqrt{\frac{\Sigma(X-\bar{X})^2}{n}} \text{, a definitional formula;}$$

$$\Delta = \sqrt{\frac{\Sigma X^2 - (\Sigma X)^2/n}{n}} \text{, for ungrouped data;}$$

$$\Delta = \sqrt{\frac{\Sigma d^2 - (\Sigma d)^2/n}{n}} \text{, for ungrouped data;}$$

$$\Delta = c\sqrt{\frac{\Sigma f(d')^2 - (\Sigma f d')^2/n}{n}} \text{, for grouped data.}$$

The others are in the text either for expository purposes, or for purposes of reference.

The standard deviation is not only a measure of dispersion, but also a unit of measurement. By means of z one can compare individual items in different distributions.

$$\text{For the population:} \quad z = \frac{X - \mu}{\sigma}.$$

$$\text{For the sample:} \quad z = \frac{X - \bar{X}}{s}.$$

In order to measure the variability of a set of items considered as percentages of their mean, one uses the coefficient of variation.

$$\text{For the population:} \quad V = \frac{\sigma}{\mu}.$$

$$\text{For the sample:} \quad V = \frac{s}{\bar{X}}.$$

Chapter 18

SHAPES OF FREQUENCY DISTRIBUTIONS

As pointed out in Chapter 15, frequency distributions differ not only with respect to average value and variability, but also with respect to shape. The most important characteristics of shape are: (1) skewness and (2) kurtosis. This chapter is concerned mainly with the measurement of skewness and kurtosis. We also consider, however, how a skewed distribution can be transformed into one that is more nearly normal.

Skewness

A distribution is skewed if the mean, median, and mode do not all have the same value.

If $\bar{X} >$ Median $>$ Mode, the skewness is positive (Chart 18.1).
If $\bar{X} <$ Median $<$ Mode, the skewness is negative (Chart 18.2).

Chart 18.1—A Positively Skewed Frequency Curve,
Showing Location of Mean, Median, and Mode

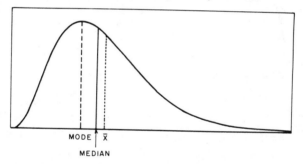

Chart 18.2—A Negatively Skewed Frequency Curve,
Showing Location of Mean, Median, and Mode

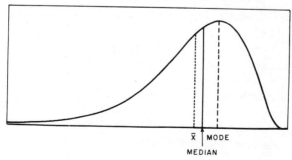

257

A symmetrical distribution is not skewed, and a skewed distribution is always unsymmetrical. (But an unsymmetrical distribution is not necessarily skewed, for the lack of symmetry may be due to various kinds of irregularities.) A positively skewed distribution is stretched out from its mode farther to the right than to the left, so a positively skewed distribution is often said to be skewed to the right. Similarly, a negatively skewed distribution is said to be

Chart 18.3—Straight-Time Average Hourly Earnings, Exclusive of Overtime and Night Work, of Plant Workers in Metal Furnishings Establishments in the United States, January 1947

$(a_3 = 0.43)$

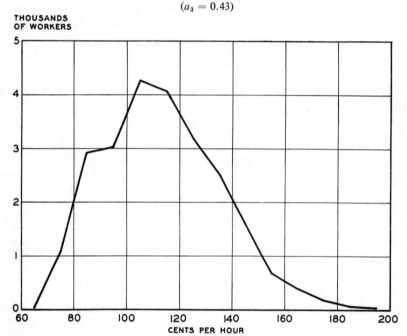

Source of data: "Wages in Metal Furniture Industry, January 1947," *Monthly Labor Review*, October 1947, p. 447. Twenty-four workers whose earnings were less than $0.60 per hour and 73 who earned $2.00 or more per hour are not shown on this chart.

skewed to the left. Chart 18.3 shows a positively skewed distribution, while the distribution of Chart 18.4 is negatively skewed.

Distributions of ratios are often positively skewed. This seems reasonable when we consider that a ratio can only be as small as zero, but may be as large as infinity. Also, characteristics that consist of several *multiplicative* factors may be positively skewed. Thus, although heights of a homogeneous group of people tend to be normally distributed, their weights (the product of height, breadth, and other factors) tends to be positively skewed. Negative skewness is not common, and it is not easy to rationalize concerning its cause.

Chart 18.4—Tensile Strength of 1,000 Cap Screws

$(a_3 = -0.45)$

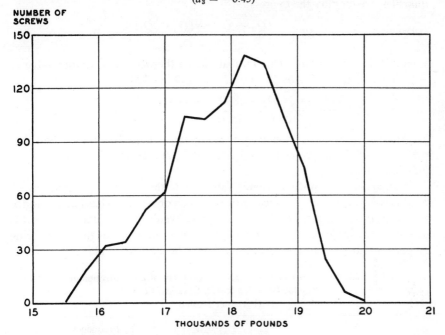

NUMBER OF
SCREWS

THOUSANDS OF POUNDS

Source of data: H. B. Pulsifer, "Physical Properties of Fine Bolts," *Automotive Industry*, 1930, as quoted by H. A. Freeman in *Industrial Statistics*, John Wiley and Sons, New York, 1942, p. 30.

Pearson's measure of skewness. A frequently used measure of skewness, suggested by Karl Pearson, is computed from the expression

$$(18.1) \qquad \text{Sk} = \frac{3(\overline{X} - \text{Med})}{s}.$$

It was pointed out in Chapter 16 that the arithmetic mean is affected more by extreme values than is the median. Therefore this measure yields a positive value for a distribution skewed to the right and a negative value for a distribution skewed to the left. If no skewness is present, the numerical value is zero. The measure has a theoretical maximum value of ± 3, but curves having a skewness greater than ± 1 are not often encountered. Thus if $\overline{X} = 92.0$, Med $= 88.57$, and $s = 24.5$, use of formula (18.1) suggests that the mean is larger than the mode by an amount equal to 42 per cent of the standard deviation.[1]

$$\text{Sk} = \frac{3(92.0 - 88.57)}{24.5}$$

$$= +0.42.$$

---

[1] The numerator is an estimate of the value $\overline{X} - \text{Mo}$. For some types of moderately skewed distributions it has been found that Mo $\doteq \overline{X} - 3(\overline{X} - \text{Med})$.

Quartile measure of skewness. To measure skewness by use of the quartiles, we employ the expression

$$(18.2) \qquad Sk_Q = \frac{(Q_3 - Q_2) - (Q_2 - Q_1)}{Q_3 - Q_1},$$

where Q_2 is the median. This measure has a theroetical maximum value of ± 1. Thus, if $Q_1 = 74.16$, $Q_2 = 88.57$, and $Q_3 = 104.61$,

$$Sk_Q = \frac{(104.61 - 88.57) - (88.57 - 74.16)}{104.61 - 74.16} = \frac{+1.63}{30.45} = +0.54.$$

Although this measure is easy to compute, it must be remembered that the values of the quartiles are not affected by the exact values of all of the individual items.

*Logarithmic transformation.[2] Table 18.1 shows 150 observations of residue resulting from a chemical process. Each observation has been rounded to the nearest integer. For the sake of convenience in later analysis the class interval increases geometrically, each class interval, in this case, being 50 per cent larger than the preceding. Since the class interval is not uniform,

Table 18.1—Distribution of 150 Observations of Concentration of Residue Resulting from a Chemical Process

(Parts per 10,000)

Class	Class interval	f	Frequency density per class interval of 1
1.0000–1.5000	0.5	1	2.00
1.5000–2.2500	0.75	2	2.67
2.2500–3.3750	1.125	9	8.00
3.3750–5.0625	1.6875	18	10.67
5.0625–7.5938	2.5313	20	7.90
7.5938–11.391	3.797	26	6.85
11.391–17.086	5.695	24	4.21
17.086–25.629	8.543	18	2.13
25.629–38.443	12.814	17	1.33
38.443–57.665	19.222	7	0.36
57.665–86.498	28.833	5	0.17
86.498–129.75	43.25	2	0.05
129.75–194.62	64.87	1	0.01
Total	...	150	...

Source: Adapted from "Control Charts for Nonsymmetrical Distribution," *Industrial Quality Control*, Vol. I, November, 1944, pp. 9–12. The data are from Table 2. Observations for individual items were estimated, conforming to that table, and a random sample of 150 items was taken.

[2] This section is taken, with minor changes, from Dudley J. Cowden, *Statistical Methods in Quality Control*, Prentice-Hall, Inc., Englewood Cliffs, N.J., 1957, pp. 315–329.

frequency densities per class interval of 1, as well as actual frequencies, are recorded. The frequency densities are plotted in Chart 18.5. Plotting frequency densities gives some idea of the way the distribution would look if the class intervals were all the same size, but the number of observations increased enough to reduce the sampling irregularities. (Because of considerations of space, the last three classes are not plotted.) It is obvious from inspection of the chart that the skewness is tremendous.

Chart 18.5—Histogram of Concentration of Residue Resulting from a Chemical Process

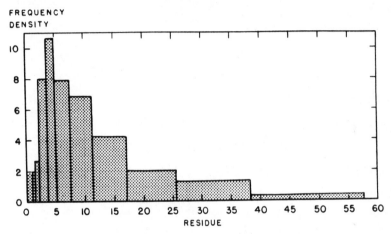

Source of data: Table 18.1.

Sometimes the difficulties presented by extreme asymmetry can be overcome by transforming the data into logarithms (or some other function). Although this procedure involves an extra amount of labor, once the logarithms are ascertained the method of analysis is identical with that using data in arithmetic form.

A theoretical case can be made for a logarithmic transformation in some cases. Whenever the effect of simultaneous variation in several factors affecting the variable is multiplicative, rather than additive, and the number of factors is limited, the logarithms of the observations tend to be normally distributed. The logarithms of ratios, also, are often distributed normally.[3] For example, if diameters of ball bearings are distributed normally, the logarithms of their weights should be distributed normally. Bacterial count in samples of milk subject to normal random variation in temperature is another illustration, provided the original contamination is also distributed normally.

---

[3] Sometimes the scale of measurement is such as to result in normal distribution. For example, volume response, amplitude gain, transmission loss, etc., are measured in units of the decibel, the logarithm of a ratio.

On the other hand, the reciprocals of some data may be distributed normally. Take the case of a simple electric circuit containing a battery of fixed voltage and resistance with random variations normally distributed. Since the current is proportional to the reciprocal of the resistance, the reciprocals of the measurement of the current would tend to be distributed normally.[4]

Table 18.2 contains the same distribution as Table 18.1, but the class limits recorded are the logarithms of the class limits of Table 18.1. The logarithmic class interval is uniform, each interval being .17609 ($= \log 1.5$) and each logarithmic mid-value is .17609 larger than the preceding. Columns for computation of the mean and standard deviation are also provided in Table 18.2. The mean is

$$\bar{X}_{\log} = 1.1446 - (.17609)\left(\frac{63}{150}\right) = 1.07064.$$

The geometric mean is

$$G = \text{antilog } \bar{X}_{\log} = \text{antilog } 1.07064 = 11.766.$$

The variance is

$$\Delta^2_{\log} = (.17609)^2 \left[\frac{813 - \dfrac{(63)^2}{150}}{150} \right] = .16261;$$

$$\Delta_{\log} = .40325.$$

The antilog of $\Delta_{\log}$ gives us $\Delta_{X/G}$, the standard deviation of the X-values relative to their geometric mean. Thus

$$\Delta_{X/G} = \text{antilog } .40325 = 2.5308.$$

Now $G\Delta_{X/G} = (11.766)(2.5308) = 29.78$. This is the same as antilog $(\bar{X}_{\log} + \Delta_{\log}) = \text{antilog } (1.07064 + .40325) = \text{antilog } 1.47389 = 29.78$.

The logarithmic frequency distribution of Table 18.2 is plotted as Chart 18.6. By inspection, the distribution appears to have lost most of its skewness. The broken line is a normal curve fitted[5] to the data, using the values of $\bar{X}_{\log}$ and $\Delta_{\log}$ computed from Table 18.2. Fitting a normal curve is described in Chapter 19.

---

[4] The above discussion of skewed distributions is based largely on G. Rupert Gause, ed., "Problems Department," *Industrial Quality Control*, Vol. 7, September, 1950, pp. 18–20.

[5] If the logarithms of the data form a distribution that is skewed, either positively or negatively, the fit will be improved by adding to the original observations, and therefore to the class limits, the quantity $(Q_2^2 - Q_1 Q_3)/(Q_1 + Q_3 - 2Q_2)$. See F. E. Croxton and D. J. Cowden, *Applied General Statistics*, Prentice-Hall, Inc., Englewood Cliffs, N.J., 1955, p. 619.

Table 18.2—Logarithmic Frequency Distribution of Concentration of Residue Resulting from a Chemical Process, and Values for Computation of Mean and Standard Deviation of Logarithms

Logarithm of class limits	Mid-value of logs $X_{\log}$	d	f	fd'	$f(d')^2$
0.00000–0.17609	0.08804	−6	1	−6	36
0.17609–0.35218	0.26414	−5	2	−10	50
0.35218–0.52827	0.44022	−4	9	−36	144
0.52827–0.70437	0.61632	−3	18	−54	162
0.70437–0.88046	0.79242	−2	20	−40	80
0.88046–1.05655	0.96850	−1	26	−26	26
1.05655–1.23264	1.14460	0	24	0	0
1.23264–1.40873	1.32068	1	18	18	18
1.40873–1.58482	1.49678	2	17	34	68
1.58482–1.76091	1.67286	3	7	21	63
1.76091–1.93700	1.84896	4	5	20	80
1.93700–2.11310	2.02505	5	2	10	50
2.11310–2.28919	2.20114	6	1	6	36
Total	...	...	150	−63	813

Source: Table 18.1.

Chart 18.6—Histogram of Logarithms of Concentration of Residue Resulting from a Chemical Process

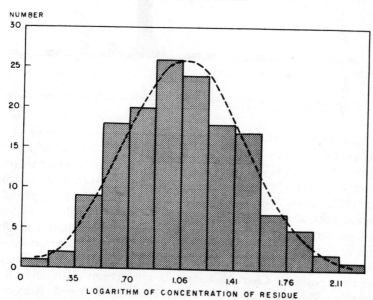

Source of data: Table 18.2.

Kurtosis

As was pointed out in Chapter 15, a distribution is *leptokurtic* if it has more small deviations, and also more large deviations, than normal, but fewer medium-sized ones. It is *platykurtic* if it has more medium-sized deviations than normal, but fewer small ones or large ones. In each case the comparison is with a normal curve with the same standard deviation. A leptokurtic curve is usually, though not always, peaked; a platykurtic curve is usually, though not always, flat-topped. These typical characteristics account for the perhaps strange-sounding adjectives.

Chart 18.7—Distribution of Prices of Foods in May 1956 Relative to April 1956: Class Interval of One Per Cent
$$(a_4 = 13.21)$$

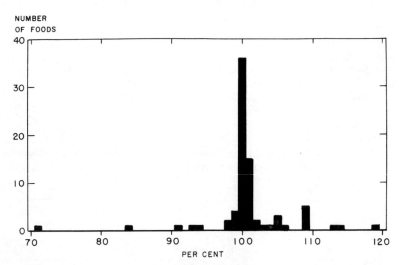

Source of data: U.S. Department of Labor, Bureau of Labor Statistics, "Consumer Price Index for May, 1956," a news release issued June 26, 1956, Table 6, p. 6.

Charts 18.7 and 18.8 show a leptokurtic distribution. Both of these charts are for the same data. Chart 18.7 uses a class interval of 1 in order to show detail; Chart 18.8 uses a class interval of 10 in order to smooth out irregularities. These data are prices of food in May, 1956, relative to April, 1956. There were 22 foods, mostly packaged foods, that did not change in price at all, and 13 more were so sluggish that they changed less than 1 per cent. This tendency for most foods to show either virtually no change or else a very large change accounts for the leptokurtic nature of the curve. The behavior of one food, strawberries, makes the skewness negative rather than positive. Chart 18.9 shows a symmetrical distribution that is platykurtic. The curve of Chart 18.10, which is U-shaped, is extremely platykurtic.

Chart 18.8—Distribution of Prices of Foods in May 1956 Relative to April 1956: Class Interval of 10 Per Cent

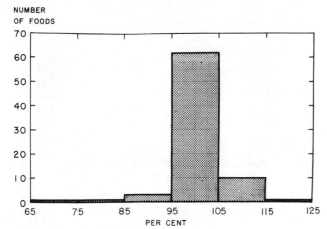

Source of data: See Chart 18.6.

Chart 18.9—Mortality of Electric Lamps
$(a_4 = 2.22)$

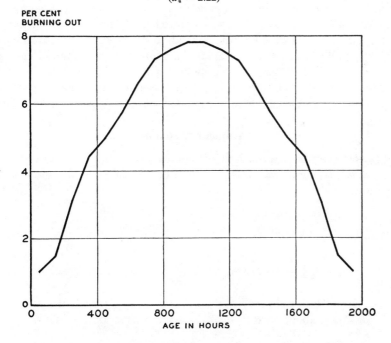

Source of data: Robley Winfrey and Edwin B. Kurtz, *Life Characteristics of Physical Property,* Bulletin 103, Iowa Engineering Experiment Station, p. 58, Property Group 28–2.

**Chart 18.10—Rough Running Beams Classified by
Per Cent Loaded when Doffed**
$(a_4 = 1.28)$

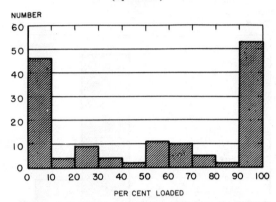

Source of data: James Armstrong Jr., "Some Uses of Statistics
in Plant Maintenance," *Industrial Quality Control*, Vol. XII, January
1956, pp. 12–17.

One reason why we are interested in kurtosis is that the kurtosis of the
population influences the type of average to use for a sample. It was pointed
out in Chapter 16 that: if the population is very platykurtic, the mid-range
is appropriate; if the population is approximately normal, the arithmetic
mean should always be used; if the population is very leptokurtic, the median
is slightly preferable. Also, the area of a probability distribution enclosed
by specified values of z are affected by kurtosis.

Both skewness and kurtosis are best measured by moment statistics,
which utilize the exact value of each observation. We now turn briefly to
that topic.

*Moment Statistics

A sample can be described almost completely by the first four moments
(M_1, m_2, m_3, m_4) and two measures based on the moments (a_3 and a_4). By
definition:

(18.3)

First moment
about zero: $M_1 = \dfrac{\Sigma X}{n} = \bar{X}$, or mean;

Second moment
about mean: $m_2 = \dfrac{\Sigma x^2}{n} = \varDelta^2$, or variance;

Third moment
about mean: $m_3 = \dfrac{\Sigma x^3}{n}$, a measure of absolute skewness;

Fourth moment
about mean: $m_4 = \dfrac{\Sigma x^4}{n}$, a measure of absolute kurtosis.

Note that while the first moment is taken about zero, the second, third, and fourth moments are taken about the mean.

From the moments are derived measures of relative skewness and kurtosis:

(18.4) $$a_3 = \frac{m_3}{s^3} = \frac{m_3}{m_2^{3/2}}, \text{ a measure of relative skewness;}$$

(18.5) $$a_4 = \frac{m_4}{s^4} = \frac{m_4}{m_2^2}, \text{ a measure of relative kurtosis.}$$

The corresponding values for the population are:

First moment about zero: μ;

Second moment about mean: $\mu_2 = \sigma^2$;

Third moment mean: about μ_3;

Fourth moment about mean: μ_4;

(18.6) $$\alpha_3 = \frac{\mu_3}{\sigma^3} = \frac{\mu_3}{\mu_2^{3/2}};$$

(18.7) $$\alpha_4 = \frac{\mu_4}{\sigma^4} = \frac{\mu_4}{\mu_2^2}.$$

For a normal distribution, $\alpha_3 = 0$. A good idea of the relationship between the magnitude of α_3 and the degree of skewness can be obtained by examining Chart 18.11. It appears that if the absolute value of α_3 is greater than 0.5, there is considerable skewness. For a normal distribution $\alpha_4 = 3$; for a leptokurtic distribution $\alpha_4 > 3$; for a platykurtic distribution $\alpha_4 < 3$. Because of these relationships, $\alpha_4 - 3$ is sometimes taken as a

Chart 18.11—Pearsonian Type III Curves for Varying Degrees of Skewness:
$$\alpha_3 = 0; \quad \alpha_3 = 0.5; \quad \alpha_3 = 1.0$$

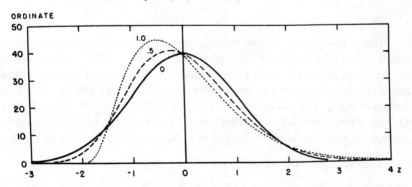

Source: Dudley J. Cowden, *Statistical Methods in Quality Control*, Prentice-Hall, Inc., Englewood Cliffs, New Jersey, 1957, Figure 2.7, p. 19.

measure of skewness.[2] A good idea of the relationship between the value of $\alpha_4 - 3$, and the degree of kurtosis can be obtained by examining Chart 18.12. For a rectangular distribution $\alpha_4 = 1.8$ and $\alpha_4 - 3 = -1.2$.

Chart 18.12—Pearsonian Type Curves with $\alpha_3 = 0$ for Varying Degrees of Kurtosis:

$$\alpha_4 = 1.8; \quad \alpha_4 = 2.2; \quad \alpha_4 = 3; \quad \alpha_4 = 5$$

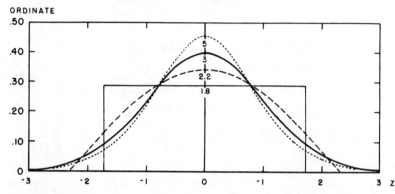

Source: Dudley J. Cowden, *Statistical Methods in Quality Control*, Prentice-Hall, Inc., Englewood Cliffs, New Jersey, 1957, Figure 2.8, p. 21.

Computations using deviations from mean. As an illustration of computations let us return to an example used in Chapter 1. The data are the lengths of time taken by an operator to pick up a bolt and put it in a chuck. Table 18.3 gives these results:

$$\overline{X} - M_1 = 9.7;$$

$$s^2 = m_2 = 0.610;$$

$$m_3 = -0.3240;$$

$$m_4 = 1.17370.$$

From these computations we can see that the skewness is negative, which agrees with the visual impression of Chart 18.13. It is easy to see why m_3 measures skewness. When a deviation is cubed, its sign is not changed, but large deviations are increased more, numerically, by cubing them than are small ones. For example, $4 = 3 + 1$, but $4^3 > 3^3 + 1^3$; $64 > 27 + 1$. On the other hand, we cannot tell whether the distribution is leptokurtic, normal, or platykurtic by looking at m_4. Nevertheless, it is easy to see why

---

[2] Alternative systems of notation are sometimes used:

$$\gamma_1 = \alpha_3 \quad \text{and} \quad \gamma_2 = \alpha_4 - 3;$$

$$\sqrt{\beta_1} = \alpha_3 \quad \text{and} \quad \beta_2 = \alpha_4.$$

m_4 measures kurtosis. Large deviations are greatly magnified by raising them to the fourth power. So if there is an excess of large deviations the distribution will be leptokurtic.

Table 18.3—Computation of Moments About Mean Using Deviations from Mean, Ungrouped Data
(Time in hundredths of minute taken to pick up a bolt and insert it in a chuck.)

X	$X - \bar{X}$ x	x^2	x^3	x^4
8	−1.7	2.89	−4.913	8.3521
9	−0.7	.49	−0.343	.2401
9	−0.7	.49	−0.343	.2401
10	.3	.09	.027	.0081
10	.3	.09	.027	.0081
10	.3	.09	.027	.0081
10	.3	.09	.027	.0081
10	.3	.09	.027	.0081
10	.3	.09	.027	.0081
11	1.3	1.69	2.197	2.8561
Sum: 97	0.0	6.10	−3.240	11.7370
Mean: 9.7	0.0	0.610	−0.3240	1.17370

Data of p. 2.

Chart 18.13—Distribution of Lengths of Time Taken to Pick Up a Bolt and Insert it in a Clutch
($a_3 = -0.68$; $a_4 = 3.15$)

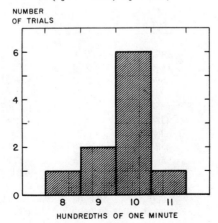

Source of data: Table 18.3.

Let us now compute our measures of relative skewness and relative kurtosis.

$$\measuredangle = \sqrt{0.610} = 0.7810.$$
$$\measuredangle^2 = 0.610.$$
$$\measuredangle^3 = 0.4764.$$
$$\measuredangle^4 = 0.3721.$$
$$a_3 = -\frac{0.3240}{0.4764} = -0.68.$$
$$a_4 = \frac{1.1737}{0.3721} = 3.15.$$

Thus the distribution has considerable negative skewness, but it is only slightly leptokurtic.

Computations using standardized values. It is helpful to understand the meaning of both the z-values and the a-values in computing moments of the z-values. The following relationship exists.

(18.8)
$$\begin{cases} \dfrac{\Sigma z}{n} = 0 \\[2mm] \dfrac{\Sigma z^2}{n} = 1 \\[2mm] \dfrac{\Sigma z^3}{n} = a^3 \\[2mm] \dfrac{\Sigma z^4}{n} = a_4 \end{cases}$$

Table 18.4—Computation of Moments About Mean, Using Standardized Values
(Data of Table 18.3, $\measuredangle = 0.7810$.)

X	x $X - \bar{X}$	z $x/\measuredangle$	z^2	z^3	z^4
8	−1.7	−2.1767	4.7380	−10.3132	22.4486
9	−0.7	−0.8963	.8034	−0.7201	.6455
9	−0.7	−0.8963	.8034	−0.7201	.6455
10	.3	.3841	.1475	.0567	.0218
10	.3	.3841	.1475	.0567	.0218
10	.3	.3841	.1475	.0567	.0218
10	.3	.3841	.1475	.0567	.0218
10	.3	.3841	.1475	.0567	.0218
10	.3	.3841	.1475	.0567	.0218
11	1.3	1.6645	2.7706	4.6117	7.6762
Sum: 97	0.0	−0.0002	10.0004	−6.8015	31.5466
Mean: 9.7	0.0	0.0000	1.0000	−0.68	3.15

Thus the variance and standard deviation of the standardized values is 1, a_3 is their third moment, and a_4 is their fourth moment.

Computations using the data of Table 18.3 are given in Table 18.4.

Computations using X-values. If data are not grouped into a frequency distribution, one would not ordinarily compute the moments by use of formula (18.3), which employs x-values, or (18.8), which employs z-values. Those moments of computation were given solely to explain the concepts. The following procedure is much more expeditious. The moments about zero are:[3]

$$(18.9) \quad \begin{cases} M_1 = \dfrac{\Sigma\,X}{n}\,, \\[2ex] M_2 = \dfrac{\Sigma\,X^2}{n}\,, \\[2ex] M_3 = \dfrac{\Sigma\,X^3}{n}\,, \\[2ex] M_4 = \dfrac{\Sigma\,X^4}{n}\,. \end{cases}$$

From these we compute the moments about the mean.

$$(18.10) \quad \begin{cases} m_2 = M_2 - M_1^2, \\ m_3 = M_3 - 3M_2M_1 + 2M_1^3, \\ m_4 = M_4 - 4M_3M_1 + 6M_2M_1^2 - 3M_1^4. \end{cases}$$

Computation of the M_r values is given in Table 18.5.

Table 18.5—Computation of Moments About Zero
(Data of Table 18.3.)

	X	X^2	X^3	X^4
	8	64	512	4,096
	9	81	729	6,561
	9	81	729	6,561
	10	100	1,000	10,000
	10	100	1,000	10,000
	10	100	1,000	10,000
	10	100	1,000	10,000
	10	100	1,000	10,000
	10	100	1,000	10,000
	11	121	1,331	14,641
Sum:	97	947	9,301	91,859
M_r:	9.7	94.7	930.1	9,185.9

---

[3] If we wish, we can define the M_r as being the means of the rth powers of the deviations about an arbitrary origin X_0. Then: $M_1 = \Sigma\,d/n$; $M_2 = \Sigma\,d^2/n$; $M_3 = \Sigma\,d^3/n$; $M_4 = \Sigma\,d^4/n$. If we do this we can still use equations (18.10) without change to obtain the m_r.

We now proceed to compute the moments about the mean.

$$m_2 = 94.7 - (9.7)^2 = 0.61,$$

$$m_3 = 930.1 - 3(94.7)(9.7) + 2(9.7)^3 = -0.324,$$

$$m_4 = 9,185.9 - 4(930.1)(9.7) + 6(94.7)(9.7)^2 - 3(9.7)^4 = 1.1737.$$

These results of course agree with the m_r computed from the x-values, so a_3 and a_4 will not be recomputed.

Computations using grouped data. Usually when one computes a_3 and a_4 the sample size is large enough to justify the use of grouped data. If we let M_r' denote the rth moment about an arbitrary origin in class interval units, we have:

(18.11)

$$\begin{cases} M_1' = \dfrac{\Sigma f d}{n}\ ; \\[2mm] M_2' = \dfrac{\Sigma f(d')^2}{n}\ ; \\[2mm] M_3' = \dfrac{\Sigma f(d')^3}{n}\ ; \\[2mm] M_4' = \dfrac{\Sigma f(d')^4}{n}\ . \end{cases}$$

Then:[4]

(18.12)

$$\begin{cases} \bar{X} = X_0 + cM_1'; \\ m_2 = c^2 m_2' = c^2[M_2' - (M_1')^2]; \\ m_3 = c^3 m_3' = c^3[M_3' - 3M_1'M_2' + 2(M_1')^3]; \\ m_4 = c^4 m_4' = c^4[M_4' - 4M_3'M_1' + 6M_2'(M_1')^2 - 3(M_1')^4]. \end{cases}$$

The similarity of these formulas to (18.9) and (18.10) is obvious.

Computation of the M_r' values for the data of Chart 18.3 is given in Table 18.6. The moments about the mean and the $\varDelta^r$ values are as follows.

$$m_2' = 6.33333 - (-1.15000)^2 = 5.01083;$$

$$m_3' = -13.9750 - 3(6.3333)(-1.15000) + 2(-1.15000)^3 = 4.833;$$

$$m_4' = 91.0833 - 4(-13.9750)(-1.15000) + 6(6.3333)(1.3225)$$

$$- 3(-1.15000)^4 = 71.806;$$

$$\varDelta' = 2.2385;\quad (\varDelta')^2 = 5.0108;\quad (\varDelta')^3 = 11,217;\quad (\varDelta')^4 = 25.108;$$

$$m_2 = 501.08;\qquad m_3 = 4,833;\qquad m_4 = 718,060;$$

$$\varDelta = 22.385;\qquad \varDelta^2 = 501.08;\qquad \varDelta^3 = 11,217;\qquad \varDelta^4 = 251,080.$$

---

[4] If Sheppard's corrections are applied,

$$\tilde{m}_2' = m_2' - \frac{1}{12} \quad \text{and} \quad \tilde{m}_4' = m_4' - \frac{1}{2}m_2' + \frac{7}{240},$$

where $\tilde{m}_r'$ refers to moments about the mean in class interval units after applying Sheppard's corrections. In computing a_3 and a_4, the $\tilde{m}_r$ replace the m_r.

In computing a_3 and a_4 one can use the m_r values of equations (18.12), or one can use the m_r' values [enclosed by brackets in equations (18.12)], which are m_2/c^2, m_3/c^3, and m_4/c^4. That is,[5] it is not necessary to multiply the m_r' values by c^r.

Table 18.6—Computation of Moments about an Arbitrary Origin, in Class Interval Units, Using Grouped Data
(Data of Chart 18.3.)

Class (cents per hour)	X	f (hundreds of workers)	d'	f(d')	f(d')²	f(d')³	f(d')⁴
70–80	75	11	−5	−55	275	−1,375	6,875
80–90	85	29	−4	−116	464	−1,856	7,424
90–100	95	30	−3	−90	270	−810	2,430
100–110	105	42	−2	−84	168	−336	672
110–120	115	41	−1	−41	41	−41	41
120–130	125	32	0	0	0	0	0
130–140	135	25	1	25	25	25	25
140–150	145	16	2	32	64	128	256
150–160	155	7	3	21	63	189	567
160–170	165	4	4	16	64	256	1,024
170–180	175	2	5	10	50	250	1,250
180–190	185	1	6	6	36	216	1,296
Sum	...	240	...	−276	1,520	−3,354	21,860
M_r'	...	...	...	−1.15000	6.33333	−13.9750	91.0833

[5] This is because

$$\frac{m_3'}{(m_2')^{3/2}} = \frac{\dfrac{m_3}{c^3}}{\left(\dfrac{m_2}{c^2}\right)^{3/2}} = \frac{\dfrac{m_3}{c^3}}{\dfrac{m_2^{3/2}}{c^3}} = \frac{m_3}{m_2^{3/2}}, \quad \text{and} \quad \frac{m_4'}{(m_2')^2} = \frac{\dfrac{m_4}{c^4}}{\left(\dfrac{m_2}{c^2}\right)^2} = \frac{\dfrac{m_4}{c^4}}{\dfrac{m_2^2}{c^4}} = \frac{m_4}{m_2^2}.$$

Chapter 19

THE NORMAL PROBABILITY DISTRIBUTION

Probability distributions are of interest to statisticians chiefly because they permit us to make inferences concerning the population on the basis of a particular sample.

1. We can test a hypothesis concerning the population.
2. We can state the degree of confidence that we have that the parameter (such as P or μ or σ) is between two specified limits.

In Chapter 11 (pages 149-150) we tested the hypothesis that a sample of 50 items containing 7 defectives came from a large lot that was 1 per cent defective. We rejected the hypothesis, and decided that the lot should be rejected. In testing this hypothesis we used the binomial probability distribution. Types of discrete probability distributions that are appropriate under particular circumstances are:

1. The hypergeometric;
2. The binomial;
3. The Poisson.

These will be defined but not extensively treated in this text.[1]

Continuous probability distributions are even more widely used in making statistical inferences. Among the more important continuous probability distributions used in this text are:

1. Normal;
2. "Student's" t;
3. Chi-square;
4. Variance ratio, F.

Of these, the normal probability distribution is by far the most important. Under certain conditions, as the sample size increases, each of the six types of nonnormal probability distributions mentioned above approaches the normal form. But most important, means of random samples are distributed almost normally if the sample size is large enough, almost regardless of the shape of the population.

In the following chapters we shall constantly be making use of the normal and other probability distributions. In this chapter, however, we shall devote much of our attention to fitting a normal curve to observed data.

---

[1] They are extensively treated in Dudley J. Cowden, *Statistical Methods in Quality Control*, Prentice-Hall, Inc., Englewood Cliffs, N.J., 1957, especially Ch. 4, 25, 32.

In Chapter 18 charts were shown which illustrated some of the forms that a frequency distribution may assume. These curves were based upon data of a few score or a few hundred cases; each was a sample from a much larger, possibly infinite, group called the *population*. Being a sample, a given curve would not necessarily have exactly the same shape as the curve for the population, but if the sample is properly selected, the curve for the sample will tend to be of the same general shape as the curve for the population. A curve based upon sample data will show certain irregularities but we may fit a curve to the data obtained and thus smooth out those irregularities presumably due to sampling. Such a fitted curve is a generalization, believed to represent the actual situation underlying the sample.

Many types of curves may be fitted to frequency distributions. For example, when dealing with data representing a continuous variable, we may fit a symmetrical or an asymmetrical curve of the Pearsonian group or of the Gram-Charlier series,[2] while for data representing a discrete variable, we may use a hypergeometric, a binomial, or a Poisson distribution. For the purposes of this text we will discuss only one of the symmetrical curves of the Pearsonian group, known as the "normal curve," or the Gaussian curve. This is also a "generating function" for the Gram-Charlier series.

We may be interested in fitting a curve to a set of data in order to generalize concerning the fundamental shape of the distribution. Such a purpose is served when a normal curve is used to describe errors made in repeated measurements. This use also permits us to estimate the proportion of measurements that will fall within a certain range above, below, or between selected values.

If we are studying the life expectancy of physical property, such as telephone poles, it may be important to know what proportion of the poles will need to be replaced during each year after installation. An example of this sort will be considered later. A curve may also be fitted to one set of data in order to generalize concerning an associated variable. Thus a curve may be fitted to the circumferences of boys' heads, enabling a reasonable conclusion to be drawn as to the number of caps of each size which should be made for such a group of boys.

Normal Curve as Limiting Form of Other Distributions

The normal curve represents a distribution of values that may occur, under certain conditions, when chance is given full play. In every case the necessary conditions include the existence of a large number of causes, each operating independently in a random manner.

Symmetrical binomial. The operation of chance may be illustrated by coin tossing. For coin-tossing experiments, the coin should be so

---

[2] For a discussion of the Pearsonian and Gram-Charlier systems, as well as illustrations of fitting, see Dudley J. Cowden, *Statistical Methods in Quality Control*, Prentice-Hall, Inc., Englewood Cliffs, N.J., 1957, Ch. 20.

constructed that it is incapable of standing on edge, and is perfectly balanced, so that a head or a tail is equally probable. Thus, if one coin is tossed the probability of throwing a tail or a head is indicated by

$$\tfrac{1}{2}T + \tfrac{1}{2}H = .5T + .5H.$$

The probability distribution is rectangular, the probability of 0 heads or 1 head each being 0.5.

If two coins are tossed the probabilities are represented by

$$(\tfrac{1}{2}T + \tfrac{1}{2}H)^2 = \tfrac{1}{4}T^2 + \tfrac{2}{4}TH + \tfrac{1}{4}H^2$$
$$= .25T^2 + .50TH + .25H^2.$$

The exponent of T and H indicates the number of tails of heads. Thus, the probability is .25 of obtaining two tails, .50 of obtaining a tail and a head, and .25 of obtaining two heads. Or, we may say the probability of 0 heads is .25, of 1 head is .50, of 2 heads is .25. The probability distribution is thus triangular in shape. If 2 coins are thrown 1,000 times, our expectation would be 0 heads 250 times, 1 head 500 times, and 2 heads 250 times.

If four coins are tossed the probabilities are

$$(\tfrac{1}{2}T + \tfrac{1}{2}H)^4 = \tfrac{1}{16}T^4 + \tfrac{4}{16}T^3H + \tfrac{6}{16}T^2H^2 + \tfrac{4}{16}TH^3 + \tfrac{1}{16}H^4.$$
$$= .0625T^4 + .25T^3H + .375T^2H^2 + .25TH^3 + .0625H^4.$$

These binomial probabilities are of course obtained by use of formula (11.4), which is Prob $(d) = \dbinom{n}{d}P^d Q^{n-d}$, or by formula (11.3), which is the simple form that (11.4) takes when $P = Q = .5$. Formula (11.3) is Prob $(d) = \dbinom{n}{d}.5^n$. In these expressions d refers to the number of heads. The results are recorded in Table 19.1.

Table 19.1—Binomial Probability Distribution
$n = 4, p = .5$

Number of heads	Probability
0	.0625
1	.2500
2	.37500
3	.2500
4	.0625
Total	1.0000

As n approaches infinity the binomial distribution approaches normal form. Chart 19.1 illustrates the gradual approach of the binomial $(.5T + .5H)^n$ to the normal form as n is in turn 4, 16, and 64. In each case the horizontal scale is so selected that the different histograms will exhibit the same amount

Chart 19.1—Binomial Probability Distribution, $P = .5$

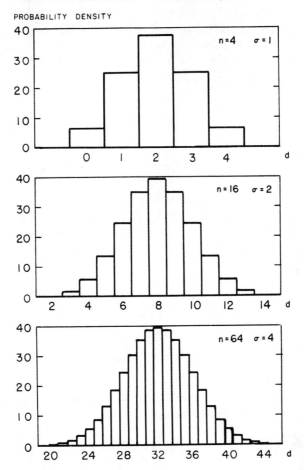

of dispersion, and the height of the bars is such that each histogram has the same area;[3] technically, the area of each histogram is 1. The three column

---

[3] Technically, the space alloted to the base of a rectangle on the horizontal axis is in inverse proportion to the standard deviation. Thus:

when $n = 4$, $\sigma = 1$, and the width of one bar is 1.0σ;

when $n = 16$, $\sigma = 2$, and the width of one bar is 0.5σ;

when $n = 64$, $\sigma = 4$, and the width of one bar is 0.25σ.

The height of each bar is σ Prob (d); i.e., the height that is appropriate for a bar one standard deviation wide. It is for this reason that the vertical scale is labeled *probability density*, instead of simply *probability*. Only for the case where $n = 4$ and $\sigma = 1$ is the probability and the probability density the same.

The standard deviation is computed in the usual manner, using probabilities as weights (see p. 159), or by use of formula (20.16), which is $\sigma_d = \sqrt{nPQ}$.

diagrams exhibit considerable similarity in appearance. The chief difference is that n becomes larger, the bars become narrower and more numerous. If n were to be continually increased, the bars would become narrower and narrower until the steps would finally disappear, and we would have a continuous curve that is normal in form. See Chart 19.4.

It can be shown[4] that as n approaches ∞, the expression

$$\binom{n}{d} P^d Q^{n-d}$$

approaches

(19.1) $$f(X) = \frac{1}{\sigma\sqrt{2\pi}} e^{-(X-\mu)^2/2\sigma^2}.$$

The symbol $f(X)$ is read "function of X," or simply "f of X." The mean of the normal probability distribution, or $E(X)$, is μ, and the standard deviation is σ. The two points of inflection are one standard deviation removed from the mean. See Chart 19.5. The maximum ordinate, which is at the mean, is

(19.2) $$f(0) = \frac{1}{\sigma\sqrt{2\pi}}.$$

The symbol $f(0)$ means value of $f(X)$ when $X = 0$. It is read "f of zero." The height of an ordinate relative to the maximum ordinate is

(19.3) $$\frac{f(X)}{f(0)} = e^{-(X-\mu)^2/2\sigma^2}.$$

Expression (19.1) can be simplified if we consider the normal distribution as a function of z, the standard measure, where $z = (X - \mu)/\sigma$.

(19.4) $$f(z) = \frac{1}{\sqrt{2\pi}} e^{-z^2/2}.$$

In this form, the standard deviation is 1. The maximum ordinate, which is at $z = 0$, is

(19.5) $$f(0) = \frac{1}{\sqrt{2\pi}},$$

and the height of an ordinate relative to the maximum ordinate is

(19.6) $$\frac{f(z)}{f(0)} = e^{-z^2/2}.$$

Values of $f(z)$, and also of $e^{-z^2/2}$, which is the height of an ordinate relative to the maximum ordinate, are given in Appendix 13 at intervals of 0.1.

---

[4] See Dudley J. Cowden, *Statistical Methods in Quality Control*, Prentice-Hall, Inc., Englewood Cliffs, N.J., 1957, pp. 54–56.

Some readers may find the expression for the normal curve easier if the symbols are replaced by numbers. Since $\pi \doteq 3.14159$, $\sqrt{2\pi} \doteq 2.50663$, $1/\sqrt{2\pi} \doteq 0.39894$, and $e \doteq 2.71828$, we may write[5]

(19.7) $f(z) = (0.39894)2.71828^{-z^2/2}.$

Chart 19.2—Binomial Probability Distribution, $P = .1$

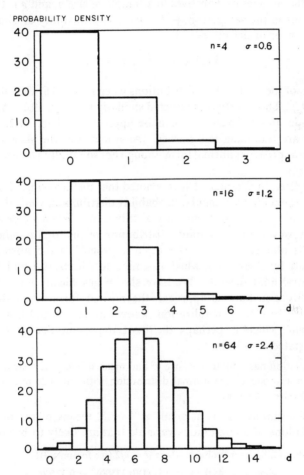

When stated as a function of z, the maximum ordinate, which is at $z = 0$, is 0.39894. If the reader will again turn to Chart 19.1, he will notice that as n increases the height of the tallest bar is gradually increasing.

---

[5] π is the ratio of the circumference to the diameter of a circle, while e is the base of the natural, or Naperian, system of logarithms.

$$e = \lim_{x \to \infty}\left(1 + \frac{1}{x}\right)^x.$$

It is approaching[6] the value of 0.39894, and when $n = 64$ it has reached 0.39739.

Skewed binomial. If we select samples from an infinite population that is (say) 10 per cent defective, we have the binomial

$$(0.9g + 0.1d)^n,$$

where d is the number of defectives in a sample of size n, and g is the number of good items in the sample; $g + d = n$. The probability of obtaining any specified number of defectives is

$$\text{Prob } (d) = \binom{n}{d} . 1^d . 9^{n-d}.$$

Histograms of the probability distributions when $n = 4$, 16, and 64 are shown in Chart 19.2. This chart is constructed similarly to Chart 19.1. All generalizations made about Chart 19.1 can be applied to Chart 19.2. Also, the histograms are becoming less skewed. As n increases the skewed binomial distribution approaches normal form, though not so rapidly as the symmetrical binomial.

Tossing dice. In Chapter 11 it was noted that the throwing of one 6-sided die is represented by a rectangular probability distribution, while the throwing of 2 dice gives a triangular probability distribution.[7] When 4 dice are thrown at a time, however, the probability distribution of the total number of spots per throw is almost normal. The rapid approach to the normal form is shown vividly by Chart 19.3, which is similar to Charts 19.1 and 19.2.

The central limit theorem. We have shown graphically how three kinds of probability distributions approach the normal form. Actually we can make a much broader generalization, known as the central limit theorem. This theorem, which is perhaps the most important one in statistics, is sometimes stated as follows.[8]

If a population has a finite variance σ^2 and mean μ, then the distribution of the sample mean approaches the normal distribution with variance σ^2/n and mean μ as the sample size increases.

When the sample size is as small as 4 or 5, means of random samples from populations of a continuous variable that are likely to be encountered

---

[6] The height of a bar is σ Prob (d), where $d = n/2$ (see footnote 3):

when $n = 4$, the height is (1)(0.37500) $= 0.37500$;

when $n = 16$, the height is (2)(0.19638) $= 0.39276$;

when $n = 64$, the height is (4)(0.099347) $= 0.39739$;

when $n = \infty$, the height is $1/\sqrt{2\pi}$ $= 0.39894$.

[7] The probabilities are obtained by expanding the multinomial $[\frac{1}{6}(\text{I}) + \frac{1}{6}(\text{II}) + \frac{1}{6}(\text{III}) + \frac{1}{6}(\text{IV}) + \frac{1}{6}(\text{V}) + \frac{1}{6}(\text{VI})]^4$, remembering that an expression like (II)(III)^2(V), for example, means $2 + 3 + 3 + 5 = 13$ spots.

[8] A. M. Mood, *Introduction to the Theory of Statistics*, McGraw-Hill Book Co., Inc., New York, 1950, p. 136.

Chart 19.3—Dice Throwing Probability Distribution

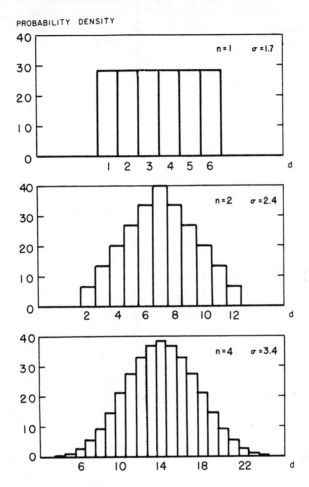

PROBABILITY DENSITY

by the business statistician will be distributed almost normally. We can thus use normal probabilities in making statements concerning the arithmetic mean.

Probability and the Normal Curve

The mathematical properties of the normal distribution function are well known. For example:

beyond μ is 50 per cent of the area;

beyond $\mu + 1\sigma$ is 15.866 per cent of the area;

beyond $\mu + 2\sigma$ is 2.275 per cent of the area;

beyond $\mu + 3\sigma$ is 0.135 per cent of the area.

These statements can be visualized by inspection of Chart 19.4. If we prefer we can make probability statements. The probability that an item taken at random will be equal to or:[9]

larger than μ is .5;

larger than $\mu + 1\sigma$ is .15866;

larger than $\mu + 2\sigma$ is .02275;

larger than $\mu + 3\sigma$ is .00135.

When the normal distribution is considered as a function of z, we may use the symbol $P(z)$ to refer to the probability of obtaining a value of z that is equal to or larger than the one specified.[10]

When $z = 0$, $P(z) = .5$.

When $z = 1$, $P(z) = .15866$.

When $z = 2$, $P(z) = .02275$.

When $z = 3$, $P(z) = .00135$.

Even more simply we may write:

$$P(0) = .5;$$
$$P(1) = .15866;$$
$$P(2) = .02275;$$
$$P(3) = .00135.$$

Normal curve probabilities have been tabulated in various ways, but in Appendix 14.1 they are arranged so that knowing z, we read $P(z)$, the probability of obtaining a value of z equal to or greater than the one specified. Only positive values of z are given, since it is apparent that

$$P(-z) = 1 - P(z).$$

For example,

$$P(-2) = 1 - P(2) = 1 - .02275 = .97725.$$

If we define $Q(z)$ as the probability of obtaining a value of z smaller than the one specified, $P(z) + Q(z) = 1$, and $Q(z) = 1 - P(z)$. Therefore:

$$Q(0) = 1 - P(0) = 1 - .5 = .5;$$
$$Q(1) = 1 - P(1) = 1 - .15866 = .84134;$$
$$Q(2) = 1 - P(2) = 1 - .02275 = .97725;$$
$$Q(3) = 1 - P(3) = 1 - .00135 = .99865.$$

---

[9] Technically, the probability of obtaining any specified value of X is zero.

[10] In general, P is the probability of obtaining a statistic (such as x, z, or χ^2) equal or greater than the one specified. Where no confusion can arise concerning the statistic to which we refer we sometimes omit the parentheses and identifying statistic. Thus, for simplicity, we sometimes write P instead of $P(z)$.

Chart 19.4—Normal Curve and Values of $P(z)$ for Selected Values of z

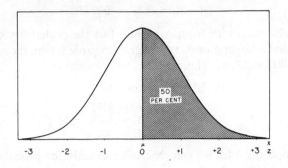

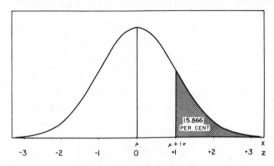

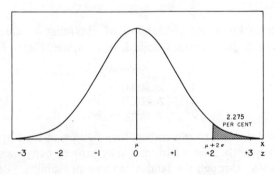

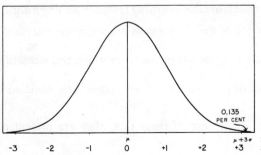

Since the normal curve is symmetrical and $P(z) + Q(z) = 1$, it follows that $Q(-z) = 1 - Q(z) = P(z)$. For example,

$$Q(-2) = P(2) = .02275.$$

We can also determine from Appendix 14.1 the probability of obtaining a value of z that is larger numerically (sign disregarded) than the one specified. This probability is $2P(z)$. Thus:

$|z|$	Probability
1	2(.15866) = .3173
2	2(.02275) = .0455
3	2(.00135) = .0027

From Appendix 14.2 we can determine directly the probability $F(z)$ of obtaining a value of z that is between 0 and the one specified.

z	Probability
1	.34134
2	.47725
3	.49865

Note that $F(z) = P(0) - P(z)$, and also that $F(z) = F(-z)$.
Also $P(-z) = P(0) + F(-z) = P(0) + F(z) = .5 + F(z)$.

z	$P(0) + F(z) = P(-z)$
1	.5 + .34134 = .84134
2	.5 + .47725 = .97725
3	.5 + .49865 = .99865

If we wish to know the probability of obtaining a value of z that is smaller numerically than the one specified, we compute $2F(z) = F(z) + F(-z)$.

$|z|$	Probability
1	2(.34134) = .6827
2	2(.47725) = .9545
3	2(.49865) = .9973

The student will do well to remember these figures, at least approximately, for they are frequently referred to, and they provide convenient landmarks to guide one's way through the land of normal probability. Perhaps it will be sufficient to remember the following facts concerning a normal distribution.

Approximately $\frac{2}{3}$ of the observations are within one standard deviation from the mean.

Approximately $\frac{19}{20}$ of the observations are within two standard deviations from the mean.

Practically all of the observations are within three standard deviations from the mean.

Because of the importance of these facts they are presented graphically in Chart 19.5.

Finally, suppose we wish to know the probability of obtaining a value of z between -1 and $+2$.

$$\text{Prob } (-1 > z > 2) = P(-1) - P(2)$$
$$= .84134 - .02275$$
$$= .81859.$$

Chart 19.5—Normal Curve and Values of $F(z)$ for Selected Values of z

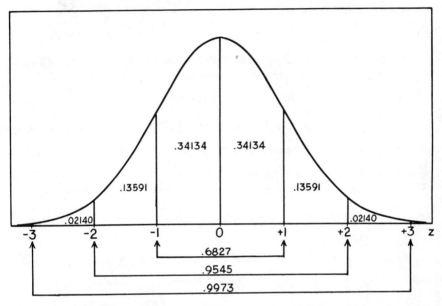

For purposes of testing hypotheses it is usually helpful to know the value of z corresponding to specified probabilities. For example:

$$\text{Prob } (z \geq 1.645) = P(1.645) = .05;$$
$$\text{Prob } (z \geq 1.96) = P(1.96) = .025;$$
$$\text{Prob } (|z| \geq 1.96) = 2P(1.96) = .05;$$
$$\text{Prob } (|z| \geq 2.576) = 2P(2.576) = .01.$$

These and other values of z for specified values of $P(z)$ are given in Appendix 14.3.

Some illustrations. Suppose we are manufacturing cotton cloth and it is known that the process turns out items that are normally distributed with respect to breaking strength, with $\mu = 66$ pounds and $\sigma = 3$ pounds.

What is the probability of obtaining an item stronger than 73.628 pounds?

Since $z = \dfrac{73.628 - 66}{3} = 2.576$, the probability is $P(2.576) = .005$.

What is the probability of obtaining an item stronger than 61.5 pounds?
Since $z = \dfrac{61.5 - 66}{3} = -1.5$, the probability is $P(-1.5) = P(0) + F(1.5) =$
$.5 + .4339 = .93319$.

What is the probability of obtaining an item weaker than 71.588 pounds?
Since $z = \dfrac{71.588 - 66}{3} = 1.96$, the probability is $Q(1.96) = 1 - P(1.96) =$
$1 - .025 = .975$.

What is the probability of obtaining an item weaker than 54 pounds?
Since $z = \dfrac{54 - 66}{3} = -4$, the probability is $Q(-4) = P(4) = .00003$.

What is the probability of obtaining an item with breaking strength *differing* (in either direction) from average more than 6 pounds? Since $z = \dfrac{6}{3} = 2$, the probability is $2P(2) = 2(.02275) = .0455$.

What is the probability of obtaining an item with breaking strength *differing* from average not more than 9 pounds? Since $z = \dfrac{9}{3} = 3$, the probability is $2F(3) = 2(.49865) = .9973$.

What is the probability of obtaining an item with breaking strength between 66 pounds and 72 pounds? Since $z = \dfrac{72 - 66}{3} = 2$, the probability is $P(0) - P(2) = .50000 - .02275 = .47725$.

What is the probability of obtaining an item with breaking strength between 66.5 pounds and 72 pounds? Since $z_1 = \dfrac{66.5 - 66}{3} = 0.5$ and $z_2 = \dfrac{72 - 66}{3} = 2.0$, the probability is $P(0.5) - P(2.0) = .30854 - .02275 = .28579$.

What is the probability of obtaining an item with breaking strength between 65.5 pounds and 72 pounds? Since $z_1 = \dfrac{65.5 - 66}{3} = -0.5$ and $z_2 = \dfrac{72 - 66}{3} = 2.0$, the probability is $P(-0.5) - P(2.0) = .69146 - .02275 = .66871$. Also, $F(-0.5) + F(2.0) = .19146 + .47725 = .66871$.

*Fitting a Normal Curve to Observed Data

We have already noted that the normal probability function may be written in various forms. Expression (19.4) is

$$f(z) = \frac{1}{\sqrt{2\pi}} e^{-z^2/2}.$$

This describes a normal curve with mean of 0, standard deviation of 1, and area of 1. $f(z)$ is the probability density per class with interval of 1. On the other hand, expression (19.1) is

$$f(X) = \frac{1}{\sigma} \frac{1}{\sqrt{2\pi}} e^{-(X-\mu)^2/2\sigma^2}$$

This describes a normal curve the mean of which is μ, and the standard deviation of which is σ. $f(X)$ is the probability density per class with interval of 1σ. If we have n observations, we wish the area to be n, and since the frequency densities of any distribution vary directly with the class interval, we must substitute nc for 1 in the expression (19.1) when fitting a curve to sample data. Furthermore we must substitute $\bar{X}$ for μ, and s for σ, in the above expression, since $\bar{X}$ and s are our best joint estimates of μ and σ. We then have

$$(19.8) \qquad Y_X = \frac{nc}{s} \frac{1}{\sqrt{2\pi}} e^{-(X-\bar{X})^2/2s^2}$$

Y_X is used instead of $f(X)$ in order to indicate that we are referring to a curve fitted to a sample, rather than the curve of the population. The maximum ordinate is at the mean. When $X = \bar{X}$,

$$e^{-(X-\bar{X})^2/2s^2} = e^{-0} = 1,$$

since any number raised to the zero power is 1, and the maximum ordinate is

$$(19.9) \qquad Y_0 = \frac{nc}{s} \frac{1}{\sqrt{2\pi}}.$$

Y_0 means the value of Y when $Z = 0$. Therefore we may rewrite equation (19.8) in a somewhat simpler form,

$$(19.10) \qquad Y_X = Y_0 e^{-(X-\bar{X})^2/2s^2}.$$

It is of course true that the items in a sample cannot be distributed normally, since n is a finite number and an actual sample cannot extend to $\pm\infty$. But Y_X refers to the expected frequency densities of a sample of size n taken from a normal population with the same mean and standard deviation as the sample.

Computation of ordinates. Table 19.1 shows the life experience of wooden telephone poles. If a suitable curve can be fitted to the data, it will be possible to state the expected proportion or number of poles to be replaced each year. Chart 19.6 includes a histogram of the data that shows an approximately symmetrical outline. From the appearance of the chart is seems that the fitting of a normal curve might not be inappropriate.

**Table 19.1—Life Experience of Wooden
Telephone Poles**
(Years)

Class limits	Mid-value	Number replaced
0.5–2.5	1.5	11
2.5–4.5	3.5	47
4.5–6.5	5.5	87
6.5–8.5	7.5	134
8.5–10.5	9.5	200
10.5–12.5	11.5	198
12.5–14.5	13.5	164
14.5–16.5	15.5	102
16.5–18.5	17.5	48
18.5–20.5	19.5	6
20.5–22.5	21.5	3
Total	...	1,000

Source: Adapted from Roble Winfrey and
Edwin B. Kurtz, *Life Characteristics of Physical
Property*, Bulletin 103, Iowa Engineering Experiment
Station, p. 57, property group 24–5.

**Chart 19.6—Normal Curve Fitted to Life Experience of 1,000
Wooden Telephone Poles**

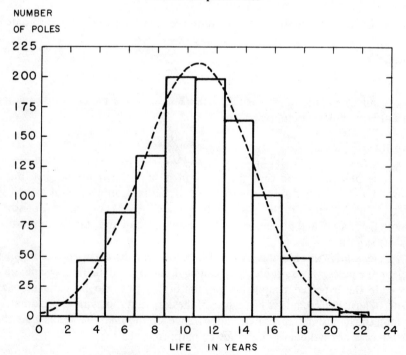

Source of data: Tables 19.1 and 19.3.

Fitting a normal curve consists of determining the height of a number of ordinates from the equation, plotting these ordinates, and connecting them with a smooth curve.

The values needed for fitting the curve to the life experience of telephone poles are:

$$\bar{X} = 10.658 \text{ years}; \quad s = 3.765 \text{ years}; \quad c = 2 \text{ years}; \quad n = 1{,}000.$$

Substituting these values in equation (19.9), we find that the maximum ordinate is

$$Y_0 = \frac{(1{,}000)(2)}{3{,}765}(0.39894) = 211.92,$$

while (19.10) becomes

$$Y_X = 211.92e^{-(X-10.658)^2/2(3.765)^2}.$$

It simplifies the appearance of the equation to consider Y as a function of z.

$$Y_z = 211.92e^{-z^2/2}.$$

It will be convenient to find the values of ordinates at intervals of one half of a standard deviation from the mean; i.e., at values for z of -3, $-2\frac{1}{2}$, -2, $-1\frac{1}{2}$, $-\frac{1}{2}$, 0, $\frac{1}{2}$, 1, $1\frac{1}{2}$, 2, $2\frac{1}{2}$, 3. This gives us enough ordinates to plot a reasonably smooth curve. These ordinates can be computed by use of the last equation without great difficulty. For example,[11] when $z = 3$, $e^{-z^2/2} = e^{-4.5} = 0.01111$, and $Y_z = (211.92)(0.01111) = 2.35$. This gives us the ordinate for $X = 21.95$, since when $\dfrac{X - 10.658}{3.765} = 3$, $X - 10.658 = 11.295$, and $X = 21.953$.

Computation of the different values of $e^{-z^2/2}$, however, is not necessary. It is easier to follow the procedure of Table 19.2. In that table we proceed as indicated concisely by the symbolic statements at the top of the successive columns, and by the verbal directions that follow.

1. Record convenient values of z.
2. Multiply these z-values by the standard deviation (which is 3.765), obtaining deviations from the mean.
3. Add $\bar{X}$ (which is 10.658) to each deviation, obtaining X-values.
4. Look up in Appendix 13 the values of $e^{-z^2/2}$ for the different values of z, thus obtaining ordinates expressed as a fraction of the maximum ordinate.
5. Multiply each of these proportionate heights by the height of the maximum ordinate, which is $Y_0 = 211.92$.

---

[11] $e^{-4.5}$ is easily computed by use of logarithms. Log $e^{-4.5} = -4.5 \log e = -(4.5)(.43429) = -1.9543 = \bar{1}.0457$, and $e^{-4.5} = 0.01111$. The value of $e^{-z^2/2}$ can also be determined directly from Appendix 13.

**Table 19.2—Computation of Ordinates of Normal Curve Fitted to
Life Experience of 1,000 Wooden Telephone Poles**
($\bar{X} = 10.658$ years;　$\lambda = 3.765$ years;　$Y_0 = 211.92$.)

Standard measure $\dfrac{X - \bar{X}}{\lambda}$	Deviation from mean x	Life in years X	Height of ordinate	
			Relative $\dfrac{Y_x}{Y_0}$	Absolute Y_x
z	$z\lambda$	$x + \bar{X}$	$e^{-z^2/2}$	$Y_0 e^{-z^2/2}$
−3.0	−11.2950	−0.64	0.01111	2.4
−2.5	−9.4125	1.25	.04394	9.3
−2.0	−7.5300	3.13	.13534	28.7
−1.5	−5.6475	5.01	.32465	68.8
−1.0	−3.7650	6.89	.60653	128.5
−0.5	−1.8825	8.78	.88250	187.0
0.0	0.0000	10.66	1.00000	211.9
0.5	1.8825	12.54	.88250	187.0
1.0	3.7650	14.42	.60653	128.5
1.5	5.6475	16.31	.32465	68.8
2.0	7.5300	18.19	.13534	28.7
2.5	9.4125	20.07	.04394	9.3
3.0	11.2950	21.95	.01111	2.4

Source: Table 19.1.

Since the curve is symmetrical, the ordinates in the upper half and lower half are identical. The ordinates obtained from the table have been plotted as a frequency curve in Chart 19.6, and show a rather close agreement with the original curve. The fitted curve smooths out the irregularities of the original data and shows the expected life distribution of the telephone poles, assuming that length of life is distributed normally. It is perhaps a little disturbing that $\bar{X} - 3\lambda$ gives a negative value for X, suggesting the possibility that the curve should be adjusted for skewness or kurtosis.

Computation of expected frequencies. The procedure just described serves no useful purpose other than for giving a visual basis for judging whether or not the normal curve is a good fit. The practical use of the normal curve is to enable us to estimate the proportion of poles that will wear out during specified intervals of time.

The computation of theoretical frequencies in each class interval consists essentially of integrating[12] the curve. The process of integration is avoided,

---

[12] If the student wishes to verify the probabilities given in Appendix 14, he can use the simple, though somewhat laborious, method of equation (6) on p. 57 of Dudley J. Cowden, *Statistical Methods in Quality Control*, Prentice-Hall, Inc., Englewood Cliffs, N.J., 1957. In that equation $F(z)$ has the meaning of $.5 - P(z)$.

however, by making use of a table of normal curve probabilities, such as Appendix 14. The procedure, as illustrated in Table 19.3, and indicated symbolically at the top of the different columns, is as follows:

1. Record the class limits. Each of the X-values except $-\infty$ and $+\infty$ is both an upper limit of one class and a lower limit of the next.

Table 19.3—Computation of Expected Frequencies in Each Class for Life of Wooden Telephone Poles
$(\bar{X} = 10.658 \text{ years}; \ \varDelta = 3.765 \text{ years}; \ n = 1,000.)$

Class limits (years)	Deviation from mean x	Standard measure z	Probability of lasting at least X years*	Probability of wearing out between stated time limits f/n	Expected number wearing out between stated time limits f
X	$X - \bar{X}$	$\dfrac{x}{\varDelta}$	$P(z)$	$P(z_1) - P(z_2)$	$n\left(\dfrac{f}{n}\right)$
$-\infty$	$-\infty$	$-\infty$	1.00000	....	....
...	....	....	....	0.00336	3.36†
0.5	−10.185	−2.71	0.99664	....	....
...	....	....	....	.01164	11.64
2.5	−8.185	−2.17	.98500	....	....
...	....	....	....	.03550	35.50
4.5	−6.185	−1.64	.94950	....	....
...	....	....	....	.08300	83.00
6.5	−4.185	−1.11	.86650	....	....
...	....	....	....	.14746	147.46
8.5	−2.185	−0.58	.71904	....	....
...	....	....	....	.19910	199.10
10.5	−0.185	−0.05	.51994	....	....
...	....	....	....	.20433	204.33
12.5	1.815	0.48	.31561	....	....
...	....	....	....	.15936	159.36
14.5	3.815	1.01	.15625	....	....
...	....	....	....	.09447	94.47
16.5	5.815	1.54	.06178	....	....
...	....	....	...	.04302	43.02
18.5	7.815	2.08	.01876	....	....
...	....	....	....	.01423	14.23
20.5	9.815	2.61	.00453	....	....
...	....	....	....	.00369	3.69
22.5	11.815	3.14	.00084	....	....
...	....	....	....	.00084	0.84
∞	∞	∞	00000	....	....
Total				1.00000	1,000.00

* From Appendix 14.
† Although 2.33 of these 3.36 expected frequencies are for values of X that are below zero, this is a physical impossibility, and they are considered as falling between 0.0 and 0.5 year.
Source: Table 19.1.

2. Subtract the mean (which is 10.658) from each class limit, obtaining deviations from the mean.

3. Divide each of these deviations by the standard deviation (which is 3.765), thus converting the class limits into standard measures.

4. To estimate the probability of a pole lasting at least X years, ascertain from Appendix 14 the value of $P(z)$.

5. Subtract each $P(z)$ value from the one immediately above it, and record the difference in the space between the class limits. Thus, the probability is .99664 that a pole will last more than 0.5 year, and .98500 that a pole will last more than 2.5 years; so the probability is $.99664 - .98500 = .01164$ that a pole will last between 0.5 year and 2.5 years. In the column for f/n, subscript 1 is used to refer to the lower limit of any class and the subscript 2 is used to refer to the upper limit of that class.

6. The total of the f/n column is 100 per cent. Since there were 1,000 poles in the original distribution, the probabilities of the f/n column are multiplied by n (which is 1,000) to give the expected frequencies of the last column.

From data of this nature a telephone company may budget in advance the cost of replacements of its poles and may purchase or contract for purchase upon the basis of these figures. A lumber dealer, long engaged in the sale of such poles, commented upon the possibility of using these fitted data as an indication of what might be expected of his salesmen.

The method given for the determination of the computed frequencies in the various classes is not confined to the use of the classes of the original distribution. For simplicity and clarity of explanation, Table 19.3 retained the original class limits, though class limits of 0, 1, 2, etc., years might have been more useful from a business standpoint. For instance, if it is desired to estimate the number of poles that will wear out between the end of the first year and the end of the second year, we compute as follows:

$$z_1 = \frac{1 - \bar{X}}{\Delta} = \frac{-9.658}{3.765} = -2.57, \quad P(z_1) = .99492;$$

$$z_2 = \frac{2 - \bar{X}}{\Delta} = \frac{-8.658}{3.765} = -2.30, \quad P(z_2) = .98928;$$

$$P(z_1) - P(z_2) = .99492 - .98928 = .00564;$$

$$\hat{f} = (1,000)(.00564) = 5.64.$$

Fitting curves to body measurements. Data are available[13] for body measurements of persons classified by age, sex, and place of residence. By fitting normal, or other types of curves to such body measurements, the number of garments of different sizes can be estimated. When manufacturing for a national market, good results can often be obtained from such a procedure. But if the market is a local one, estimates based on national data are likely to be inapplicable. It is better to fit a curve to actual sales data, though body measurements can be used as a temporary expedient until sales data have been accumulated.

---

[13] For example, *Body Measurements of American Boys and Girls for Garment and Pattern Construction*, U.S. Department of Agriculture Miscellaneous Publication No. 366, and *Women's Measurements for Garment and Pattern Construction*, U.S. Department of Agriculture Miscellaneous Publication No. 454.

*Determining the Suitability of the Normal Curve

Whether or not a normal curve is an appropriate type of function to fit to a frequency distribution may be ascertained in advance of the fit.

1. The appearance of a histogram of the data gives us a clue to the suitability of the normal curve. While this is a crude guide, nevertheless it is possible to observe the presence of marked skewness or kurtosis. It has already been remarked that the appearance of the histogram of Chart 19.6 gives us little reason to doubt the suitability of the normal curve.

**Chart 19.7—Life Experience of Wooden Telephone Poles
Shown on Probability Paper**

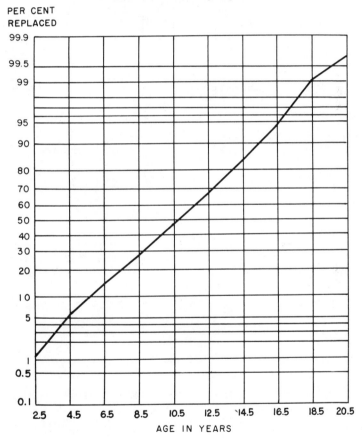

Source of data: Table 19.1.

2. The data may be cumulated, as in Table 19.4, and percentage frequencies may then be calculated and plotted on probability paper, as in Chart 19.7. An idea of the shape of a frequency distribution can often be obtained by examining the graph.

**Table 19.4—Cumulative Frequency
Distribution of Life in Years of
1,000 Wooden Telephone Poles**

Class limit X	Number less than X	Per cent less than X
2.5	11	1.1
4.5	58	5.8
6.5	145	14.5
8.5	279	27.9
10.5	479	47.9
12.5	677	67.7
14.5	841	84.1
16.5	943	94.3
18.5	991	99.1
20.5	997	99.7
22.5	1,000	100.0

Source: Table 19.1.

If the distribution is normal, the curve is a straight line.

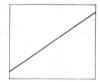

If the distribution is positively skewed, the curve tends to be concave downward at the lower end.

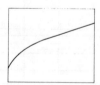

If the distribution is negatively skewed, the curve tends to be concave upward at the upper end.

If the distribution is leptokurtic, the curve tends to be S-shaped, flattening out at the ends.

If the distribution is platykurtic, the curve tends to become steeper at the ends.

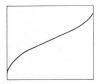

In the present case the line is approximately straight, except at the ends, suggesting that the distribution may be platykurtic. It should be recognized, however, that the paucity of cases at the tails of a distribution makes those frequencies subject to considerable sampling error.

Note that the percentage for $X = 22.5$ is not plotted, since normal probability paper cannot extend to 100 per cent. It is worth noting, also, that unequal class intervals do not invalidate the use of normal probability paper.

3. Measures of skewness and kurtosis may be computed, and tested to ascertain if the amount of skewness and kurtosis present is significant. For the telephone data:

$$a_3 = -0.063; \quad a_4 = 2.618; \quad a_4 - 3 = -0.382.$$

Thus the frequency distribution is slightly skewed in a negative direction, and is platykurtic, since α_3 and $\alpha_4 - 3 = 0$ for a normal population.

If we should take a large number of samples of n items each from a normal population, and compute the value of a_3 and a_4, we could form a frequency distribution of a_3 values and another of a_4 values. We could then compute the standard deviation of the a_3 values and the a_4 values. If the number of samples was sufficiently large we would tend to get these results:

$$\sigma_{a_3} \doteq \sqrt{\frac{6}{n}}; \quad \sigma_{a_4} \doteq \sqrt{\frac{24}{n}}.$$

Although a_3 is distributed symmetrically but not quite normally, and the distribution of a_4 has considerable positive skewness, it is nevertheless true that, if the population is normal, sample values of a_3 and $a_4 - 3$ are twice as large as their standard errors or larger only (very roughly) about one time in twenty. Therefore if $|a_3| \div \sigma_{a_3} \geq 2$, we conclude that the sample is significantly skewed; if $(a_4 - 3) \div \sigma_a \leq 2$, we conclude that the sample is significantly platykurtic; and if $(a_4 - 3) \div \sigma_{a_4} \geq 2$, we conclude that it is significantly leptokurtic.

In the present instance,

$$\sigma_{a_3} \doteq \sqrt{\frac{6}{1000}} = 0.077, \quad \text{and} \quad \frac{a_3}{\sigma_{a_3}} = -\frac{0.063}{0.077} = -0.82;$$

so we accept the hypothesis that $\alpha_3 = 0$, and conclude that the sample is not significantly skewed. However,

$$\sigma_{a_4} \doteq \sqrt{\frac{24}{1000}} = 0.155, \quad \text{and} \quad \frac{a_4 - 3}{\sigma_{a_4}} = -\frac{0.382}{0.155} = -2.46;$$

so we reject the hypothesis that $\alpha_4 = 3$, and conclude that the sample is significantly platykurtic.[14]

4. Whether or not a normal curve is an appropriate type of curve for use in describing a frequency distribution can also be decided after the expected frequencies have been computed. This is done by the χ^2 (chi-square) test of "goodness of fit" described in the next section.

*Chi-square Test of Goodness of Fit

The chi-square test involves a comparison of the expected frequencies with the observed frequencies in order to ascertain whether the discrepancy is greater than might be expected to occur by chance. If the discrepancy is so great that it could hardly have occurred accidentally, we conclude that the discrepancy is significant and reject the hypothesis that the sample was taken at random from a normal population. On the other hand, if there is considerable probability of obtaining a discrepancy as large as that obtained or larger, we accept the hypothesis that the population is normal, for there is not enough evidence for us to reject it. Thus chi-square really tests "badness" of fit; we conclude either that the fit is bad or that we are not convinced that it is bad.

Chi-square is computed from the expression[15]

(19.11)
$$\chi^2 = \sum \frac{(f - \hat{f})^2}{\hat{f}},$$

---

[14] More exact tests of significance of a_3 and a_4 can be made by use of Tables 34B and C of E. S. Pearson and H. O. Hartley (editors), *Biometrika Tables for Statisticians*, Vol. I, Cambridge University Press, Cambridge, pp. 183–184. On page 63, Pearson and Hartley give an illustration of the use of these tables. In the Biometrika tables, the symbol $\sqrt{b_1}$ is used instead of a_3, and b_2 is used instead of a_4.

[15] When $\Sigma f = \Sigma \hat{f}$, which is the case for the type of problem we are discussing, the labor of computation can be reduced by use of the formula

$$\chi^2 = \Sigma \frac{f^2}{\hat{f}} - n.$$

where f represents the observed frequency in a class, and $\hat{f}$ the corresponding expected frequency.

Table 19.5 illustrates the method of computing χ^2. First the observed and expected frequencies for each class are recorded. For the test to be substantially accurate it is desirable that n be at least 50, and that there be at least 1 expected frequency in each class.[16] We have therefore grouped the

Table 19.5—Computation of Chi-square for Test of Goodness of Fit for
Normal Curve Fitted to Life Experience of Wooden Telephone Poles

Life in years	Observed frequency f	Expected frequency $\hat{f}$	$f - \hat{f}$	$(f - \hat{f})^2$	$\dfrac{(f - \hat{f})^2}{\hat{f}}$
Less than 0.5	0	3.36	−3.36	11.29	3.36
0.5–2.5	11	11.64	−0.64	0.41	0.04
2.5–4.5	47	35.50	11.50	132.25	3.73
4.5–6.5	87	83.00	4.00	16.00	0.19
6.5–8.5	134	147.46	−13.46	181.17	1.23
8.5–10.5	200	199.10	0.90	0.81	0.00
10.5–12.5	198	204.33	−6.33	40.07	0.20
12.5–14.5	164	159.36	4.64	21.53	0.14
14.5–16.5	102	94.47	7.53	56.70	0.60
16.5–18.5	48	43.02	4.98	24.80	0.47
18.5–20.5	6	14.23	−8.23	67.73	4.76
20.5 or more	3	4.53	−1.53	2.34	0.52
Total	1,000	1,000	0.00	$\chi^2 \quad = \quad$	15.24

Source: Tables 19.1 and 19.3.

last two classes of Table 19.5. Both the observed and expected frequencies have the same total, which is 1,000 in this case. Next, the difference between the observed and expected frequencies is computed. The total of these differences is of course zero, since $\Sigma f = \Sigma \hat{f}$. Now the differences are squared. Finally the squared difference for each class is divided by the expected frequency for that class. The sum of these ratios is χ^2.

It is now necessary to ascertain whether the value of χ^2 is so unusual as to suggest that the fit is unsatisfactory. Suppose that a population is known to be normal and that we select a random sample of 1,000 items from that population. We fit a normal curve to the sample and compute the value of χ^2 based upon 12 classes. As a result we have a *single value* of χ^2. If we

[16] See William G. Cochran, "The χ^2 Test of Goodness of Fit," *Annals of Mathematical Statistics*, Vol. 23, September, 1952, pp. 315–345. See especially p. 329. The reason why n and each $\hat{f}$ should not be too small is that the probability distribution of χ^2 assumes a normal distribution of f about $\hat{f}$ for each class. But f is distributed binomially and approaches a symmetrical form as $\hat{f}/n$ approaches 0.5, and approaches a normal form as n approaches ∞.

should repeat the procedure many times, we would get *many values* of χ^2. These values of χ^2 could be formed into a frequency distribution and a curve could be drawn of them. The curve would look like Chart 19.8. It has its mode at $\chi^2 = 7$. This is the χ^2 distribution for 9 degrees of freedom, $v = 9$. The mode is always at $\chi^2 = v - 2$, which is 7 for our illustration. We will explain the concept of degrees of freedom more fully in the following

Chart 19.8—Probability Distribution of χ^2 with 9 Degrees of Freedom

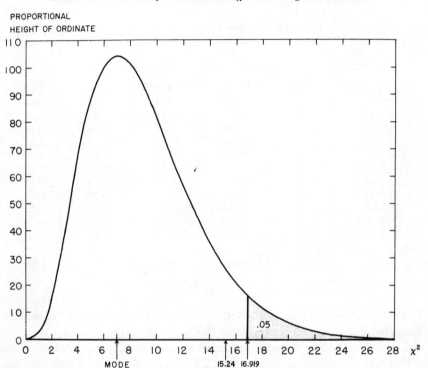

chapters. For the present it will suffice to point out that the observed and expected frequencies were forced by the procedure of Table 19.3 to agree in three respects: $\bar{X}$, Δ, and n. Therefore three degrees of freedom were lost, and since our fit was to 12 classes, we have $12 - 3 = 9$ degrees of freedom remaining. The chi-square curve changes shape as v changes, approaching the normal form as v approaches infinity.

The value of χ^2 in Table 19.5 was found to be 15.24. It will be seen from Chart 19.8 that a χ^2 value of 15.24 falls a little to the left of the shaded part of the curve which represents 5 per cent of the entire area. Referring to Appendix 22 we see that when $v = 9$, a value of χ^2 that is 16.919 or greater has a probability of 0.05, but that a value of χ^2 that is 15.24 or greater will occur for about 9 per cent of the samples; i.e., $P(\chi^2) = .09$, or more simply we may say "$P = .09$." If the population is normal, the probability of a fit this bad or worse is .09. The usual convention is to consider any fit yielding $P \leq .05$ as unsatisfactory. Technically we say that the criterion of significance[17] is $\alpha = .05$. Therefore, since $P > \alpha$ (i.e., $.09 > .05$) the chi-square fit does not discredit our hypothesis that the life of telephone poles is distributed normally. Note that if we had considered $P = .10$ to be the dividing line between a good fit and a bad one, we would have considered our present fit to be unsatisfactory.

Whether a fit is considered a bad fit depends not only on α, the criterion of significance, and the magnitude of the observed frequencies relative to the expected frequencies, but also on n, the sample size. If n and each value of f were doubled, χ^2 would also be doubled. The appearance of a chart such as 19.6, however, would be unaltered, and visually the normal curve would appear to fit just as well. But with the value of χ^2 doubled, P would be much smaller, and the apparent departure from normality more significant. This is merely another way of saying that if the sample size is increased we ought to get a better looking fit, if indeed the population is normal.

Even a high value of P may not be indicative of a good fit, for these reasons.

1. The test can only indicate that the discrepancy between the observed and expected values is too large to be attributed to chance. It cannot, on the other hand, show that the fit is good. As far as it can go is to indicate that there is not enough evidence to reject the hypothesis that the sample came from a normal population.

2. The chi-square test is a general test, and shows whether the discrepancies, taken together, are unreasonably large. It does not consider specific patterns of deviations. But too many consecutive $f - \hat{f}$ values of the same sign indicate that the population is not normal. In the present case the discrepancies at the two ends of the distribution are negative, and among them they contribute more than half of the value of χ^2. This is not surprising when we recall that the frequency distribution was found to be significantly platykurtic.

We should remember that χ^2 and other tests of normality do not tell us whether a normal curve fits the data well enough for practical use, but only whether the sample appears to have been taken at random from a normal population. Perhaps we can summarize with respect to the telephone data by saying that the normal curve provides a satisfactory basis for planning telephone pole replacements, but that some curve (such as a Gram-Charlier curve or a Pearsonian type II curve) adjusted for kurtosis would be better.

The versatility of chi-square. Chi-square is a very versatile statistic. It can be used for testing the fit of types of curves other than the normal curve, for example Gram-Charlier curves, Pearsonian curves, the binomial,

---

[17] Not to be confused with α_3 and α_4, which are parameters describing skewness and kurtosis.

the Poisson, and the hypergeometric. The procedure is the same that we have illustrated, but the degrees of freedom are different.[18]

Chi-square is used to test independence. For example, it can be used to test whether preferences of people with respect to television programs are independent of their place of residence. Tests of this type are often considered under the heading of "contingency tables."

Chi-square is used to test hypotheses concerning the standard deviation, and to establish "confidence limits" for the standard deviation.

Some of these uses of chi-square are considered in later chapters of this text.

-----

[18] In Dudley J. Cowden, *Statistical Methods in Quality Control*, Prentice-Hall, Inc., Englewood Cliffs, N.J., 1957, pp. 376–377, is a detailed illustration of the application of the χ^2 test to a binomial distribution. In that book also the χ^2 test is applied to the distribution of means for: the normal distribution (p. 167); the Gram-Charlier curve adjusted for skewness, and also for skewness and kurtosis (pp. 306–307); the Pearsonian type III curve (p. 314); the logarithmic normal distribution (p. 330). In these cases only 2 degrees of freedom were lost, because the observed and theoretical distributions of the means were made to agree only with respect to the number of means and the mean of the means.

Chapter 20

PROBABILITY DISTRIBUTIONS AND QUALITY CONTROL

The purposes of this chapter are threefold. First, the concept of the fluctuation of various statistics around a central value is made vivid by a consideration of control charts. Second, some of the various types of fundamental probability distributions encountered in statistical work are brought together and relationships among them pointed out. Third, formulas for standard errors of various statistics are given. These standard errors are used in Chapters 21 and 22.

Parameters of Selected Distributions

Arithmetic mean. In Chapter 17 reference was made to the data of flex life of Supertwist cord made by the Goodyear Tire and Rubber Company. The 50 pieces of Supertwist cord showed a mean flex life of 138.64 minutes. This was the result obtained for one sample of 50 pieces. If other samples of 50 pieces each were selected from the same roll of cord (that is, the same population), the means of the samples would not be exactly the same. They would tend to cluster around a central value with many of them being slightly above or below that value and few of them markedly above or below it. To be more explicit: The sample means would tend to form a normal curve around the mean of the population. If the population is normal, means based on samples of any size, large or small, can be expected to yield a normal distribution. If the population shows marked skewness or kurtosis, then the distribution of means of small samples will show the same characteristic as the population, though to a less degree. However, if we consider larger samples from such populations, we find that the distribution of their means becomes more nearly normal.[1]

Suppose that we have not one but many samples of the same size, n, and that for each of these the value of $\bar{X}$ has been ascertained. Suppose, also, that we know the value of the mean of the population, μ, from which the samples were drawn. If the number of samples is designated by k, we can ascertain the mean of the sample means.

$$\bar{\bar{X}} = \frac{\bar{X}_1 + \bar{X}_2 + \bar{X}_3 + \dots + \bar{X}_k}{k},$$

---

[1] The limiting form, as n approaches ∞, is the normal distribution. This is a special application of the central limit theorem, stated in Chapter 19.

and $\bar{X}$ may be expected to approximate μ, becoming a better approximation as k increases. The expected value, or mean of the entire probability distribution of $\bar{X}$-values, is μ.

$$(20.1) \qquad\qquad E(\bar{X}) = \mu.$$

With a large number of sample means it is also possible to ascertain their standard deviation in the same manner as for any other series of values. Thus we have

$$\sigma_{\bar{X}} = \sqrt{\frac{(\bar{X}_1 - \mu)^2 + (\bar{X}_2 - \mu)^2 + (\bar{X}_3 - \mu)^2 + \ldots + (\bar{X}_k - \mu)^2}{k}}$$

$$= \sqrt{\frac{\Sigma\,(\bar{X} - \mu)^2}{k}}.$$

The above expression for the *standard error* of a sample mean may be reduced to[2]

$$(20.2) \qquad\qquad \sigma_{\bar{X}} = \frac{\sigma}{\sqrt{n}}.$$

To illustrate the use of the expression just given, let us assume that the value of μ for the flex life of Supertwist cord is 137.50 minutes, and that $\sigma = 15.0$ minutes. From these figures we may ascertain the reliability of sample means from samples of any desired size. For samples of $n = 50$,

$$\sigma_{\bar{X}} = \frac{15}{\sqrt{50}} = \frac{15}{7.071} = 2.12 \text{ minutes.}$$

Since the distribution of sample means follows the normal curve, we may expect about 68.27 per cent of the means computed from samples of 50 to fall within $\mu \pm \sigma_{\bar{X}}$, which is 137.50 ± 2.12 minutes, or between 135.38 and 139.62 minutes. Also, 16 per cent would fall above 139.62 minutes and 16 per cent below 135.38 minutes. If we consider the range of $\pm 2\sigma_{\bar{X}}$ around μ, which runs from 133.26 minutes to 141.74 minutes, we would expect to include 95.45 per cent of the sample means within those limits and 4.55 per cent would be excluded. Within the limits $\mu \pm 3\sigma_{\bar{X}}$ (131.14 minutes and 143.86 minutes), 99.73 per cent of the sample means would be expected to

---

[2] The derivation of this formula, when the population is infinite, is given in Dudley J. Cowden, *Statistical Methods in Quality Control*, Prentice-Hall, Inc., Englewood Cliffs, N.J., 1957, p. 76. If the population is finite, then the above expression must be multiplied by a correction factor, and we have

$$\sigma_{\bar{X}} = \frac{\sigma}{\sqrt{n}} \sqrt{1 - \frac{n}{N}},$$

where N is the number of items in the population.

occur and 0.27 of 1 per cent would be beyond those limits. Chart 20.1 shows a graphic representation of these statements. On this chart the lower scale is for

$$(20.3) \qquad z = \frac{\bar{X} - \mu}{\sigma_{\bar{X}}}.$$

Chart 20.1—Expected Distribution of Sample Means of Flex Life of Supertwist Cord, showing $z = 1$, $z = 2$, and $z = 3$

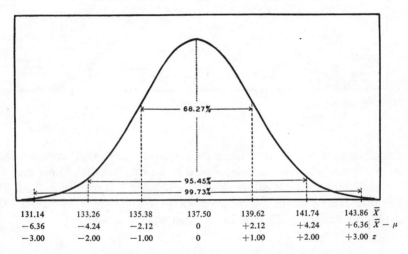

$\bar{X}$	131.14	133.26	135.38	137.50	139.62	141.74	143.86
$\bar{X} - \mu$	−6.36	−4.24	−2.12	0	+2.12	+4.24	+6.36
z	−3.00	−2.00	−1.00	0	+1.00	+2.00	+3.00

Instead of considering the proportions of means occurring within values of z of ± 1, ± 2, ± 3, we may ascertain the multiple of $\sigma_{\bar{X}}$ which, measured off on either side of μ, will include, say, 95 per cent and exclude 5 per cent of the sample means. Referring to Appendix 14.3 we may see that the value is $1.96\sigma_{\bar{X}}$. In our illustration, 95 per cent of the sample means would be expected to fall within $137.50 \pm 1.96(2.12)$ minutes or between 133.34 and 141.66 minutes. Further, 2.5 per cent would be above 141.66 minutes and 2.5 per cent below 133.34 minutes. Chart 20.2 illustrates what has just been said. The combined areas of the two tails of the curve comprise 5 per cent of the entire area.

We are also often interested in the ".01 level of significance," and it appears that $\mu \pm 2.576\sigma_{\bar{X}}$ will include 99 per cent of the area and exclude 0.5 of 1 per cent in each tail. For our illustration, 99 per cent of sample means would be expected to fall within $137.5 \pm 2.576(2.12)$ minutes, or within 132.04 and 142.96 minutes. One half of 1 per cent would occur above 142.96 minutes and one half of 1 per cent below 132.04 minutes. This is shown in Chart 20.2.

Occasionally it is important to know the size of a sample which should be drawn in order to yield a certain degree of reliability in our results. For

Chart 20.2—Expected Distribution of Sample Means of Flex Life of Supertwist Cord, Showing $z = 1.96$ and $z = 2.576$

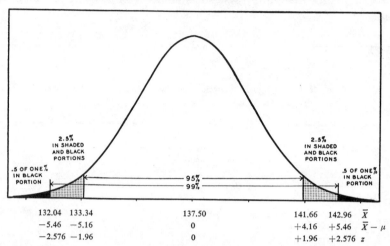

	132.04	133.34	137.50	141.66	142.96	$\overline{X}$
	-5.46	-5.16	0	$+4.16$	$+5.46$	$\overline{X} - \mu$
	-2.576	-1.96	0	$+1.96$	$+2.576$	z

example, using the preceding population figures, $\mu = 137.50$ minutes and $\sigma = 15$ minutes, what size samples should be drawn if we wish 95 per cent of our sample means to fall within the limits 135 and 140 minutes? Since 95 per cent of sample means are included within $\pm 1.96\sigma_{\overline{X}}$ of μ, and since 135 and 140 minutes are ± 2.5 minutes on either side of μ, we have

$$2.5 = 1.96\sigma_{\overline{X}} = 1.96 \frac{\sigma}{\sqrt{n}} = 1.96 \frac{15}{\sqrt{n}};$$

$$2.5\sqrt{n} = 29.40,$$

$$6.25n = 864.36,$$

$$n = 138.$$

If our requirement were that 99 per cent of sample means be included within the range of 135 and 140 minutes, the samples would, of course, need to be larger. The procedure is the same, using $2.576\sigma_{\overline{X}}$.

$$2.5 = 2.576\sigma_{\overline{X}} = 2.576 \frac{\sigma}{\sqrt{n}} = 2.576 \frac{15}{\sqrt{n}},$$

$$2.5\sqrt{n} = 38.640,$$

$$6.25n = 1,493.05,$$

$$n = 239.$$

The skewness of the distribution of arithmetic means is

(20.4) $$\alpha_3(\overline{X}) = \frac{\alpha_3}{\sqrt{n}}.$$

As n approaches infinity, $\alpha_3(\bar{X})$ approaches 0. It should be recalled that the skewness is zero for a normal curve. Usually, if $n = 4$, the distribution of means is close enough to normal to justify use of the normal curve tables.

Standard deviation. Standard deviations computed from random samples have a probability distribution just as do arithmetic means. This distribution is positively skewed, but becomes more nearly symmetrical as n increases. The expected value of the standard deviation is

$$(20.5) \qquad\qquad E(s) = \frac{\sigma}{a_1},$$

and

$$(20.6) \qquad\qquad E(a_1 s) = \sigma.$$

a_1 is a factor that depends on the sample size. It is tabulated here as Appendix 8. From (20.6) we obtain

$$(20.7) \qquad\qquad \sigma = a_1 E(s).$$

We can estimate σ by computing the standard deviation of a number of random subsamples, taking their mean, and multiplying by a_1. Thus

$$(20.8) \qquad\qquad \hat{\sigma}_1 = a_1 \bar{s}.$$

The standard error of the standard deviation, for samples taken from a normal population is

$$(20.9) \qquad\qquad \sigma_s = \frac{\sigma}{\sqrt{2n}}\sqrt{2(n-1) - \frac{2n}{a_1^2}}.$$

For large samples it is satisfactory to use the approximation

$$(20.10) \qquad\qquad \sigma_s \doteq \frac{\sigma}{\sqrt{2n}}.$$

In Chapter 22 we shall use the distribution of s/σ, rather than s. Values of s/σ at various probability points are tabulated as Appendix 23.

Range. The expected value of the range is

$$(20.11) \qquad\qquad E(R) = \frac{\sigma}{c_3},$$

and

$$(20.12) \qquad\qquad E(c_3 R) = \sigma.$$

c_3 is a factor that depends on the sample size. It is tabulated here as Appendix 10. From (20.12) we obtain

$$(20.13) \qquad\qquad \sigma = c_3 E(R).$$

We can estimate σ from the mean range as follows:

$$(20.14) \qquad\qquad \hat{\sigma}_3 = c_3 \bar{R}.$$

The expression for the standard error of the range is too complicated to be considered here, but Appendix 25 gives factors for use in constructing control charts for ranges.

The distribution of R/σ, rather than R, is sometimes used in statistical work. Values of R/σ at various probability points are tabulated as Appendix 24.

Number of defectives. Often data are composed of two different kinds, such as defective and effective, or persons preferring Camel cigarettes to other brands and persons not preferring Camel cigarettes. In such cases the number of items of a given kind in a sample of n items from an infinite[3] population is usually distributed binomially. In Chapter 11 the binomial distribution obtained by expanding the expression $(P + Q)^n$ was explained. P is the proportion of items in the population having the attribute in question, and Q is the proportion not having it. $P + Q = 1$. The expression for the probability that d items in a sample of n will possess the attribute was also given in Chapter 11.

$$\text{Prob } (d) = \binom{n}{d} P^d Q^{n-d}.$$

As pointed out in earlier chapters, the binomial is positively skewed if $P < .5$, and negatively skewed if $P > .5$. The skewness diminishes as P gets closer to .5. The normal distribution is the limit of the binomial as n approaches infinity, with P constant.

Various tables of the binomial probability distribution are available, including the following:

Dudley J. Cowden, *Statistical Methods in Quality Control*, Prentice-Hall, Inc., Englewood Cliffs, N.J, 1957, pp. 659-663. This gives selected values of P from 0.001 through 0.20, for selected sample sizes from 5 through 50.

National Bureau of Standards, *Tables of the Binomial Probability Distribution*, 1950. This gives values of P from .01 through .50, at intervals of 0.01, for sample sizes through $n = 49$.

Harry G. Romig, *50–100 Binomial Tables*, John Wiley & Sons, Inc., New York 1953. This gives values of P from .01 through .50, at intervals of .01 for sample sizes 50 through 100, at intervals of 5.

U.S. Army Ordnance Corps, Tables of the *Cumulative Binomial Probabilities*, Office of Technical Services, U.S. Department of Commerce, 1952. This table gives sample sizes through 150.

For tests of hypotheses, power functions, and tests of significance, where accuracy is important, these tables should be used, or formula (11.4) employed. Where n is large, so that nP or nQ (whichever is smaller) ≥ 25,

---

[3] If the population is finite, the distribution becomes the hypergeometric. See equation (39.18) of this text. The hypergeometric distribution is more fully treated in Dudley J. Cowden, *Statistical Methods in Quality Control*, Prentice-Hall, Inc., Englewood Cliffs, N.J., 1957, Chapter 32.

it is usually satisfactory to proceed as if the distribution were normal, and use the standard error of d or p.

The expected value of the number of items in a sample of size n that possess a given attribute is

(20.15) $$E(d) = nP,$$

and the standard deviation is

(20.16) $$\sigma_d = \sqrt{nPQ}; \quad \text{or} \quad \sqrt{n(P - P^2)}, \qquad \text{since } Q = 1 - P.$$

These formulas give the mean and standard deviation of the binomial probability distribution: the values we would obtain if we computed the mean and standard deviation of the d's of all possible samples.

Proportion defective. If we are interested in the *proportion* of items having a given attribute, we divide $E(d)$ and σ_d by n, obtaining

(20.17) $$E(p) = P;$$

(20.18) $$\sigma_p = \sqrt{\frac{PQ}{n}}; \quad \text{or} \quad \sqrt{\frac{P - P^2}{n}}, \qquad \text{since } Q = 1 - P.$$

It is apparent from formulas (20.16) and (20.18) that the maximum values of σ_d and σ_p are reached when $P = Q = .5$.

The skewness of the binomial distribution is

(20.19) $$\alpha_3(d) = \alpha_3(p) = \frac{Q - P}{\sqrt{nPQ}}.$$

This equation clearly shows that as P gets closer to .5 and n gets larger, the skewness gets smaller.

***Number of defects.** Number of defects per unit, such as the number of blemishes on a sheet of paper, usually has the Poisson distribution,

(20.20) $$\text{Prob}(c) = \frac{a^c}{c!} e^{-a},$$

where c is the number of defects per sample, and a is the expected number of defects per sample.[4]

(20.21) $$E(c) = a.$$

The standard deviation is

(20.22) $$\sigma_c = \sqrt{a}.$$

---

[4] The symbol e is used to mean the base of the Napierian, or natural, logarithmic system,

$$e = \lim_{X \to \infty} \left(1 + \frac{1}{X}\right)^X = 2.71828,$$

to six significant digits.

The Poisson distribution is positively skewed, but the skewness diminishes as a increases.

$$(20.23) \qquad \alpha_3(c) = \frac{1}{\sqrt{a}}.$$

The Poisson distribution is the limit of the binomial as n approaches infinity with nP constant.[5] When so considered the formula may be written

$$(20.24) \qquad \text{Prob } (d) = \frac{(nP)^d}{d!} e^{-nP}.$$

The expected value is

$$(20.25) \qquad E(d) = nP,$$

while the standard deviation is

$$(20.26) \qquad \sigma_d = \sqrt{nP}.$$

It is apparent that Poisson $\sigma_d = nP$ is the limit of binomial $\sigma_d = \sqrt{nPQ}$, as n approaches infinity, with nP constant.

The Poisson distribution is easier to compute than the binomial, and may be substituted for the binomial with very little loss in accuracy when $n \geq 20$ and $P \leq .05$. (A less conservative rule often advocated is $n > 10$ and $P \leq 0.10$.) Tables of the Poisson distribution are readily available, the best known one being E. C. Molina, *Poisson's Exponential Binomial Limit*, D. Van Nostrand Company, Inc., Princeton, N.J., 1942.

Probability, Statistics, and Quality Control[6]

Purposes of quality control. As stated in Chapter 1, variability is inherent in nature, and therefore in all manufactured products. No two objects are exactly alike, though the difference between them may be too small to be detected by the naked eye. Recognizing that variability is bound to occur, manufacturers, or buyers of manufactured goods, often set standards to which their products must conform if they are to be considered satisfactory. These standards generally specify not only a desirable norm, but limits above and below this norm, within which a satisfactory item must lie. These upper and lower limits are called tolerances, or specification limits.

It is apparent that a manufacturer is faced with two quality control problems. (1) His manufacturing *process* should be so controlled that the proportion of unsatisfactory or defective units is not excessive. (2) He

---

[5] Think of the defects as being distributed over the area of a surface, any unit being defective if it contains a defect. If the surface area is divided into very small units, so that no unit of area has more than one defect, the distinction between defect c and defective d disappears. As the number of units n increases, nP remaining constant, P gets smaller and smaller, and the binomial distribution gradually approaches the Poisson.

[6] This section is essentially Chapter 1 of Dudley J. Cowden, *Statistical Methods in Quality Control*, Prentice-Hall, Inc., Englewood Cliffs, N.J., 1957.

should not ship out *lots* that contain an excessive proportion of defective pieces. We shall refer to these two aspects of quality control as: (1) process control; and (2) product or lot control. It might, at first glance, be thought that if the process is properly controlled there would be no need to worry about whether to accept the product for shipment or purchase. To some extent this is true; the better the process is controlled the smaller the expense involved in product control. But, although the process may be in satisfactory control, so that the number of defective items will not be excessive for the entire output over a long period of time, individual lots occasionally may not be satisfactory.

The meaning of control. Variability is of two types: (1) systematic, which is attributable to differences in cause systems, and (2) random, which is due to a large number of small independent causes within a system of causes. For instance, the quality of output of the night shift may differ from that of the day shift, and the quality of the product made in the Los Angeles plant may differ from that of the Baltimore plant. But though we may account for the variability between shifts, and between plants, there will still be variability of a random nature within shifts and within plants.

This classification of types of variability is for purposes of convenience. It seems reasonable to suppose that with sufficient information all variability could be accounted for. But when we have eliminated all assignable causes of variation which it is economical to eliminate, there still remains a type of variability which may behave statistically in a way that we call random.

When manufacturing process is governed by a constant system of causes, operating in a random manner, it is said to be in control. Thus if all non-random types of variation have been eliminated, or taken into consideration quantitatively, and we have discovered the probability distribution of the random variations, we know that the process is in control. This is another way of saying that when a process is in control we can state the probability of an item's falling within specified quality limits. The writer is of the opinion that a process is rarely in a state of complete control; nevertheless, it can be brought into a sufficiently close state of control that predictions can be made accurately enough for practical purposes.

Although quality is usually controlled partly by methods not involving statistical techniques, we shall limit ourselves mainly to a consideration of statistical methods which are useful as an aid to controlling quality. All these methods involve the use of sampling, and an inference from the sample concerning the population.

A state of controlled quality is desirable for several reasons. (1) We can determine whether the quality of manufacturing is satisfactory. A process may be in control, and yet may produce too many defective items, either because the average value is too large or too small, or because there is too much variability in the process. (2) We have a sound basis for making specifications. There is no point in making specifications so tight that they cannot be economically enforced. On the other hand, if it appears that the natural tolerances are far inside the upper or lower specification limits, these limits usually should be changed. (3) Lot acceptance sampling is more economical if the process is in control. Smaller samples can be used, and the most economical sampling plan of a given type can be determined.

The meaning of quality. There are several ways of assessing quality of a product by statistical methods.

Variables. Many quality characteristics are measurable, such as: diameter of a shell; tensile strength of yarn; torque of a motor; resistance of a relay; flash point of oil; chemical composition of steel; life of an electric lamp; blowing time of a fuse.

Usually such variables are continuous; any value, within some range of values, is possible. A frequency distribution of one of these quality characteristics, when the process is in control, is often approximately normal, though sometimes moderately skewed.

Sometimes a quality characteristic is discrete. An example is the thread count of a piece of cloth; another is the number of surface defects on a metal disk. Obviously, there will be no defects or one or more defects; but the number of defects per disk will be an integer. A distribution of disks according to the number of surface defects per disk usually tends to follow the *Poisson* law if the process is in control.

Attribute. Often a unit of product must be classified as either good (effective) or bad (defective). Thus a cigarette lighter that will not light is defective. A unit of product may also be classified as defective if it contains a defect. Sometimes the defects are classified as to major defects and minor defects. For instance, a missing screw on a piece of machinery might be a major defect, while a streak in the paint finish might be a minor defect. In such cases a unit of product with one major defect, or more than one major or minor defect, might be classified as defective. Finally, though the quality characteristic is measurable, as a matter of economy it may be decided to treat it as an attribute. Thus, instead of recording the blowing time of a fuse, it may be classified as defective if the blowing time is too long or too short. Although individual items are thus classified into two classes—good and bad, or effective and defective—random samples of a given size may be classified according to the number of defectives per sample. Such distributions generally approximate the binomial distribution if the lot size N is large relative to the sample size n. If the sample size is large relative to the lot size, however, the type of distribution appropriate is known as the *hypergeometric*.

Process control. The primary object of process control is to keep the process in control. The characteristic tool is the control chart, a graphic method of presenting a sequence of samples. Chart 20.3 is fairly typical. On this chart are shown the mean warp-breaking strengths ($\bar{X}$-values) of 50 successive samples of 4 units each of cotton cloth. The samples were taken at intervals of approximately one hour. It will be noticed that the means fluctuate around a central line, and for the most part inside of two broken lines known as control limits. Whenever a point goes outside the control limits (samples 30–35 and 48 in this case) trouble is indicated; the foreman is immediately notified to look for the source of the trouble. The trouble will, of course, be corrected if it is found.

Chart 20.3—Control Chart for Means: Warp-Breaking Strength in Pounds of 50 Samples of 4 Items Each of Cotton Cloth

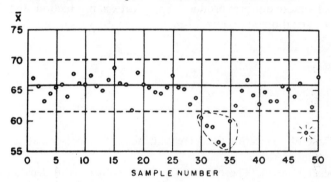

Source of data: Dudley J. Cowden and William S. Connor, "The Use of Statistical Methods for Economic Control in Industry", *Southern Economic Journal*, Vol. XII, October 1945, pp. 115–129.

The control limits are located statistically, in such a way that the process engineer will usually look for serious trouble, but not waste his time on wild goose chases. The control limits are supposed to strike an economical balance between two kinds of errors: (1) looking for trouble that does not exist; and (2) failing to look for trouble that does exist. Neither of these kinds of error should be unduly large, yet neither should be reduced to such as extent that it unduly increases the other.

The control chart is a valuable tool because: (1) it gives early warnings of trouble; (2) it is flexible. Referring to Chart 20.3, we see that sample 30 is the first to go outside the control limits. Yet an alert person might suspect impending trouble earlier by noticing the downward trend in the plotted points. Another type of warning may be too long a run of items above (or below) the central line. In fact, any unusual arrangement of plotted points may cause suspicion, in some cases strong enough to lead to action.

Control charts similar in appearance to Chart 20.3 are used not only for variables (means, ranges, number of defects, etc.) but also for attributes (number of defectives or per cent defective).

Benefits obtained from process control. The following are among the objects accomplished in actual practice by quality control:

1. Trouble is caught, and corrected in its early stages.

2. One avoids "correcting" the process when a random fluctuation occurs which is mistakenly considered a process change, and thus avoids introducing trouble where none previously existed.

3. Rejections by the manufacturer's inspectors or by the purchaser are reduced. This not only reduces expense, but it also builds up good will.

4. Specifications may be changed on the basis of what the control chart shows to be feasible. This may mean raising the average quality; or it may mean lowering it if this can be done at a saving of cost without violating specification limits. It often means narrowing specifications, and the manufacture of a more uniform product. Specification, production, and inspection under statistical quality control becomes a continuous chain:

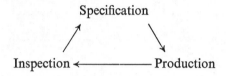

Specification

Inspection ← —————— Production

5. Cost of inspection is decreased, since a process that is in control needs less inspection.

Product Control. The object of product control is to decide whether to accept or reject a lot on the basis of evidence afforded by one or more samples drawn at random from the lot in question. If the lot is always either accepted or rejected on the basis of one sample, we have *single sampling*. Sometimes a relatively small sample is taken, and if the quality of the sample is very good or very bad, the lot is then either accepted or rejected; otherwise a second sample is taken, and the lot is accepted or rejected on the basis of the two samples combined. This is known as *double sampling*. Sometimes a very small sample is first drawn, and then its size is gradually increased until the evidence is clear whether to accept or reject the lot. This is known as *multiple sequential* sampling. The purpose of double and multiple sampling is to reduce the amount of inspection.

Lot acceptance sampling plans are often designed so as to accomplish at least two of the following objectives: (1) the probability of rejecting a good lot shall be some specified value (producer's risk); (2) the probability of accepting a bad lot shall be some specified value (consumer's risk);[7] (3) the average quality of goods shipped out AOQL shall not be worse than some specified standard; (4) the amount of inspection (consistent with the conditions imposed) shall be minimized.

The reader should notice the analogy between the conditions for locating control limits on a control chart and the first two objectives mentioned for

---

[7] Producer and consumer may be thought of as seller and buyer, respectively, or as manufacturing and inspection department, respectively, in the selling firm. Sometimes the buyer inspects the product at the seller's plant.

acceptance sampling plans. The most widely held theory of statistical inference has as its core the judicious balancing of these two kinds of errors, which may be stated more generally as (1) the error of rejecting a true hypothesis, and (2) the error of accepting a false hypothesis.

In practice, lot acceptance sampling plans are used more widely in connection with attributes than with variables. This is mainly because it is easier to classify objects as good or defective than it is to measure them accurately, and because counting the number of defectives is easier than making measurements and averaging a set of values. These advantages may be offset, however, by the fact that a larger sample is required to reach a decision on a lot when attributes, rather than variables, are used.

Although the objectives of process control and product control are distinct, the basic statistical methods are the same. Also, as previously noted, if the process is kept in control, acceptance sampling is made more economical. If the process is in control one can make a valid estimate of the quality being manufactured. Knowledge of the process quality, in turn, may enable one to select the most economical lot acceptance sampling plan. Some acceptance sampling plans call for varying size or frequency of samples according to evidence provided by the control chart.

Control Charts for Variables

Analysis of historical data. Chart 20.4 includes three control charts: an X chart, an $\bar{X}$ chart, and an R chart. The first 25 samples are for the purpose of determining whether the process is in control, and for establishing standard values. The last 25 samples are for analysis during current production, in order to *keep* the process in control.

Each of the 25 samples contains 4 items each: $n = 4$, $k = 25$, $N = nk = 100$. It is desirable that $N \geq 100$ in order to obtain good estimates of μ and σ. It is desirable that $n \geq 4$ so that the distribution of the means will not be too greatly skewed. On the other hand, samples should be taken at relatively frequent intervals, so that trouble, if it develops, will be discovered quickly. For the sake of economy, if there are to be frequent samples, each will have to be relatively small.

The central lines are obtained from the first 25 samples as follows. For items and means:

$$\bar{\bar{X}} = \frac{\Sigma \bar{X}}{k}, \quad \text{where there are } k \text{ samples of } n \text{ items each, or}$$

$$\bar{X} = \frac{\Sigma X}{N}, \quad \text{where } N = nk.$$

For ranges:
$$\bar{R} = \frac{\Sigma R}{k}.$$

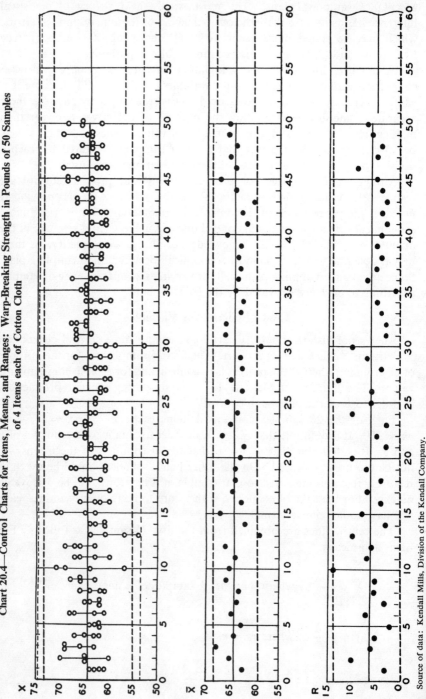

Chart 20.4—Control Charts for Items, Means, and Ranges: Warp-Breaking Strength in Pounds of 50 Samples of 4 Items each of Cotton Cloth

Source of data: Kendall Mills, Division of the Kendall Company.

The control limits are located in each case at 3 standard errors from the central line.

For items: $\qquad \bar{X} \pm 3\hat{\sigma}$,   where $\hat{\sigma} = c_3 \bar{R}$.

For means: $\qquad \bar{X} \pm 3\hat{\sigma}_{\bar{X}}$,   where

(20.27) $\qquad\qquad\qquad 3\hat{\sigma}_{\bar{X}} = A\hat{\sigma} = A_2\bar{R}$.

For ranges:

(20.28) $\quad \begin{cases} \text{Upper control limit:} & \bar{R} + 3\hat{\sigma}_R = D_2\hat{\sigma} \quad \text{or} \quad D_4\bar{R}. \\ \text{Lower control limit:} & \bar{R} - 3\hat{\sigma}_R = D_1\hat{\sigma} \quad \text{or} \quad D_3\bar{R}. \end{cases}$

Values of A, A_2, D_1, D_2, D_3, and D_4 are given in Appendix 25. All of these factors vary with the sample size. If $n \leq 6$, the last four are zero.

Setting tentative standards. Examination of the historical data reveals that the range for sample 10 is slightly above its upper control limit, while the mean of sample 13 is slightly below its lower control limit, and one of the items in that sample is below its lower control limit.

Since there were only a few points marginally beyond the control limits, and since it is usually difficult to locate a cause for trouble that occurred far in the past, one would not ordinarily waste time looking for trouble in connection with samples 10 and 13. Bear in mind that the quality control engineer did not know that these points were out of control at the time they were plotted, since the control limits had not yet been computed. If, however, there were a large number of points beyond the control limits, or if some of the points were far beyond the control limits, one would try to locate the cause of the trouble. If this cause were found (or perhaps if one is convinced that an assignable cause existed), the control limits for items, means, and ranges would be recomputed, using only those items drawn from samples considered representative of the process. The revised control limits would then be plotted on the chart, extending to the right, and points from new samples would be plotted currently. Sources of trouble would then be run down immediately whenever a point fell outside the control limits, and these sources of trouble would be eliminated until finally the process would be brought into control. One can conclude that a process is not in control if:

1. There is one point far outside the control limits among the last 25 samples, or
2. There is more than one point outside in the last 35, or
3. There are more than 2 points outside in the last 100.

Since there is one point outside in each of the sections, and only 25 samples have been accumulated, one cannot be confident that a state of control exists from inspection of the control chart. It is not contradictory for one sample mean or range to be smaller than the central value by an amount that could occur accidentally only once in 500 times and yet for the sample means or ranges in general to differ from the central value only to such an extent that tends to occur accidentally, say, 1 time in 10. It must be remembered that there are 25 opportunities for an individual mean to go beyond the control limits, and the probability of some one of the 25 means or ranges going outside the control limits is *much* greater than the probability for any one named in advance.

Tentative standards for central lines on the different charts are therefore set at the central values shown, namely, at $\bar{X} = 64.210$ and $\bar{R} = 6.120$, if it appears that these standard values are satisfactory from an engineering standpoint. On the section of the control chart devoted to items will be found two dotted lines, the upper one at 74.5 and the lower one at 53.5. These lines are specification limits, set by the design engineer, presumably with a view to the utility of salability of the product and the cost of manufacturing. These limits are beyond the control limits. This means that so long as the process remains in control, considerably less than 3 items in 1,000 will be defective because of being outside the specification limits. If the specification limits happen to be $4\hat{\sigma}$ removed from $\bar{X}$, this would mean that only about 6 in 100,000 items would be defective.

If the process is definitely in control, but nevertheless unsatisfactory, as when one or both specification limits fall inside the control limits, one or more of three things may be done.

1. Change the specification limits. It may be that the engineering requirements are more strict than are required for a satisfactory product.

2. Change the process, so as to make it at a higher (or lower) average, or so as to make it more uniform. This may or may not be expensive.

3. Inspect the product thoroughly before shipping it out, so as to weed out defective pieces that are bound to occur. Perhaps even 200 per cent inspection, whereby each piece is inspected by two different inspectors, may be necessary. This is, of course, likely to be expensive.

Use of control chart during production. The central values and control limits computed from the preliminary data have been extended in Chart 20.4 through the next 25 samples (through sample 50). The items, means, and ranges are then plotted as soon after the samples are collected as possible. Ordinarily if the process goes very much out of control, one of the points will soon, though not necessarily immediately, go outside its control limits. When this happens the foreman is notified, the trouble is located if possible, and corrected.

The control chart is a very flexible device for giving warning of actual or impending trouble. Among the danger signals are:

1. A point beyond its control limits.
2. Several points, especially several consecutive points, close to a control limit.

3. A preponderance of points above (or below) a central value, or an unusually long run of consecutive points above (or below) a central value.

4. A trend in points.

In using the control chart during production one may make two kinds of errors:

1. One may look for trouble that does not exist. Errors of this type will occur too frequently if the control limits are made too narrow.

2. One may fail to look for trouble that does exist. Errors of this type will occur too frequently if the control limits are made too wide.

On the other hand, one will be correct if:

1. One does not look for trouble that does not exist.

2. One does look for trouble that does exist.

If control limits are set at 3 sigma above and below the central line one will, in the case of items and means, look for nonexistent trouble only about 3 times in 1,000, and will avoid looking for nonexistent trouble about 997 times in 1,000. One cannot state the probability of looking for or failing to look for trouble that does exist without knowing the magnitude of the trouble in question. However, if the trouble gets very great one is likely to be warned before many samples have been taken. It is said that, in practice, 3-sigma limits have often been found to be economical; though limits including a selected proportion, beyond each control limit (upper and lower), are undoubtedly better.

Chart 20.2 shows that sample 30 is below the control limit for means, and one item of that sample is below the control limit for items. Not only is that item below the lower control limit, but it is also below the lower specification limit. Immediate investigation revealed that there was trouble with the humidifier for a short time, which affected only one lot. Had the trouble still been present it would of course have been corrected.

There are no other points beyond the control limits, though sample 27 looks a little suspicious with respect to one item, and also with respect to the range. On the other hand, there is a tendency for the ranges, beginning with sample 30, to fall below the central line. Since the distribution of ranges is positively skewed, there should be a few more ranges below $\bar{R}$ than above it, but not this great a preponderance. There are also 9 consecutive ranges (37–45) below the central line. It would be appropriate to investigate the cause for this apparent improvement in process, and if located, to make it a permanent feature of the process. In the present instance no investigation was undertaken. Occasionally a more uniform product results from the psychological reaction of the employees to control charts.

Periodically the central values and control limits are revised and extended. Chart 20.4 shows control limits based upon samples 26–50, excluding sample 30, extended through sample 60, ready for plotting as the data are collected. In computing these control limits sample 30 was excluded from computations involving *all three* sections of the control chart, since an assignable cause was found. A sample is not excluded as being unrepresentative merely because the point falls outside a control limit. It is necessary that the cause of the trouble be located. On the other hand, some samples may be discarded even though statistical measures computed from them are inside the control limits. When a process gets out of control, it does not follow that a point will immediately go outside the limits. Consequently, several samples preceding the one that gives the alarm may actually be out of control. If so, these should be excluded when the new central values and control limits are computed.

*Control Chart for Number of Defectives

Sometimes it is difficult to measure quality. For instance, a tank may or may not leak, or the appearance of an article may be either satisfactory

Table 20.1—Number of Defective Items in Twenty Consecutive Lots of Galvanized Hardware

Lot and sample number	Sample size n	Number of defectives d
1	580	9
2	550	7
3	580	3
4	640	9
5	760	11
6	1,120	19
7	510	9
8	550	10
9	640	10
10	640	10
11	640	8
12	640	10
13	580	7
14	580	9
15	550	5
16	430	5
17	640	3
18	280	2
19	510	6
20	580	8
Total	12,000	160

Source: Adapted from American Society for Testing Materials. *A. S. T. M. Manual on Quality Control of Materials*, Philadelphia, 1951, p. 85.

or unsatisfactory. In other cases it may be uneconomical to take measurements, but the article may be considered satisfactory or defective depending on whether or not it meets a "go–no go" gage requirement. Thus, an article may be considered defective if it will not work, or if it contains a defect (or more than a specified number of defects), or if it is too large or too small, or for other reasons. In practice many manufacturers keep track of the percentage defective of daily output even though they do not have a system of statistical quality control. Since the data are readily available, and the chart is easy for the executive to understand, quality control is often started with charts of the number or fraction defective.

Table 20.1 shows the results of 100 per cent sampling for 20 consecutive days. These are plotted as a control chart in Chart 20.5. Nevertheless,

**Chart 20.5—Control Chart for Number of Defectives in 20
Consecutive Lots of Galvanized Hardware**

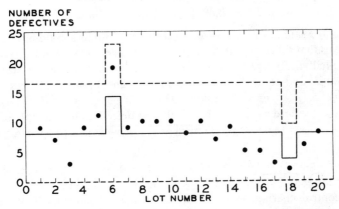

Source of data: Adapted from American Society for Testing Materials, *A.S.T.M. Manual on Presentation of Data*, p. 64.

the observations may be regarded as samples from the (nonexistent) population of results that this particular process would produce.

The central line is obtained as follows:

$$\bar{d} = \frac{\Sigma d}{k} = \frac{160}{20} = 8.00.$$

The control limits are

$$\bar{d} \pm 3\hat{\sigma}_d,$$

where

$$\hat{\sigma}_d = \sqrt{\bar{n}\bar{p}\bar{q}}.$$

This formula is analogous to formula (20.16). Such a procedure is justifiable where the sample size does not vary a great deal. In the present instance, if we exclude samples 6 and 18, the largest sample is less than twice the size of the smallest sample, which is not excessive. The average sample size, excluding these two samples, is

$$\bar{n} = \frac{\Sigma n}{k} = \frac{12,000 - 1,120 - 280}{18} = \frac{10,600}{18} = 588.9.$$

The fraction defective is

$$\bar{p} = \frac{\Sigma d}{\Sigma n} = \frac{160}{12,000} = 0.01333.$$

We include all 20 samples in computing $\bar{p}$, since samples 6 and 18 are unusual in respect to n but presumably not in respect to p. From these values we may compute the estimated standard error:

$$\hat{\sigma}_d = \sqrt{\bar{n}\bar{p}\bar{q}} = \sqrt{(588.9)(0.01333)(0.98667)} = 2.78.$$

The control limits are

$$\bar{d} \pm 3\hat{\sigma}_d = 8.00 \pm 3(2.78) = 16.34 \text{ and } 0.$$

Where the samples vary in size, special control limits should be computed for samples that differ greatly from the average size, say samples that are less than one-half the average size or more than twice the average size. The central values and control limits for samples 6 and 18 are as follows:

Sample 6. $d' = n\bar{p} = (1120)(0.01333) = 14.93$, where d' is used to represent a standard value for the number of defectives in a sample of given size. $d' \pm 3\hat{\sigma}_d = 14.93 \pm 3\sqrt{(1120)(0.01333)(0.98667)} = 14.93 \pm 3(3.84) = 22.9$ and 0.

Sample 18. $d' = n\bar{p} = (280)(0.01333) = 3.73$. $d' \pm 3\hat{\sigma}_d = 3.73 \pm 3\sqrt{(280)(0.01333)(0.98667)} = 3.73 \pm 3(1.92) = 9.49$ and 0.

The control chart gives no evidence of lack of control. If one of the dots (other than 6 or 18) had been outside the upper control limit, and the sample size were above average, a special control limit should have been computed for it; and likewise if it were close to the limit but the sample size were below average.

Instead of number of defectives, a control chart may be run for fraction defective. This involves extra labor, since the fraction defectives must be computed separately for each sample. If such a chart were run for these data, the central line would be $\bar{p} = 0.01333$ and the control limits $\bar{p} \pm 3\hat{\sigma}_p$.

$$\hat{\sigma}_p = \sqrt{\frac{\bar{p}\bar{q}}{\bar{n}}} = \sqrt{\frac{(0.01333)(0.98667)}{588.9}} = 0.0047.$$

The distribution of number or fraction defective follows the binomial distribution $(P + Q)^n$ and is ordinarily skewed. But the binomial distribution approaches normal form as n approaches infinity, and especially rapidly as P approaches 0.5. Consequently, the setting of control limits based upon the standard error is reasonably satisfactory if n is large.

The sample size should be large, say 100 or more, for control charts (with 3-sigma control limits) for number of fraction defective. This is because the binomial distribution is badly skewed when n and p are small. Also the average number of defectives should not be too small, say not less than 6.

Principles governing analysis of preliminary data and use of control chart during production are the same for charts based on number of defectives, percentage defectives, or number of defects (explained in next section) as for charts based on items, means, and ranges.

*Control Chart for Number of Defects

When examining a surface for defects it is impossible to compute $\bar{p}$, since the maximum possible number of defects is not known; theoretically it may be infinity. The data of Table 20.2 and Chart 20.6 represent the

Table 20.2—Number of Breakdowns in Twenty Consecutive Lengths of 10,000 Feet Each of Rubber-Covered Wire

Length number	Number of breakdowns c
1	1
2	1
3	3
4	7
5	8
6	1
7	2
8	6
9	1
10	1
11	10
12	5
13	0
14	19
15	16
16	20
17	1
18	6
19	12
20	4
Total	124

Source: Adapted from American Society for Testing Materials, *A. S. T. M. Manual on Quality Control of Materials*, Philadelphia, 1951, p. 88.

number of breakdowns in rubber-covered wire in successive lengths of 10,000 feet at specified test voltage. The probability of a breakdown at any specified point is very small, the opportunities for breakdown are infinite, and there is at least one breakdown in every 10,000-foot length except one. In running this sort of control chart, the size of each unit, such as area or length examined, should be the same (or very nearly the same) and it should be large enough so that nearly all of the samples should have one defect.

**Chart 20.6—Control Chart for Number of Breakdowns in 20
Consecutive Lots of 10,000 each of Rubber-Covered Wire**

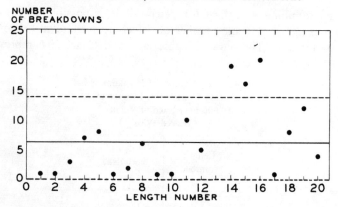

Source of data: Adapted from American Society for Testing Materials, *A.S.T.M. Manual on Presentation of Data*, p. 66.

The central line is

$$\bar{c} = \frac{\Sigma c}{k} = \frac{124}{20} = 6.20.$$

The control limits are set at $\bar{c} \pm 3\hat{\sigma}_c$, where $\hat{\sigma}_c = \sqrt{\bar{c}}$. In this case,

$$\bar{c} \pm 3\hat{\sigma}_c = 6.20 \pm 3\sqrt{6.20} = 6.20 \pm 3(2.490) = 13.67 \text{ and } 0.$$

In this illustration samples 14, 15, and 16 are beyond the control limits.

When using control charts for number of defectives, with $\bar{p} \leq .05$ and $\bar{n} \geq 20$, satisfactory results can be obtained by use of the formula

$$\hat{\sigma}_d = \sqrt{\bar{d}}, \quad \text{rather than } \hat{\sigma}_d = \sqrt{\bar{n}\bar{p}\bar{q}}.$$

Thus, using the data of the preceding section,

$$\bar{d} = \sqrt{8} = 2.83, \quad \text{rather than } \sqrt{\bar{n}\bar{p}\bar{q}} = 2.78.$$

Chapter 21

TESTS OF HYPOTHESES AND CONFIDENCE LIMITS: ARITHMETIC MEAN

It is unusual for a businessman to test every unit of a product that he uses or produces. Doing so would often be unnecessarily expensive. Also, many tests are destructive, as, for example, a test of tensile strength. If every unit were tested for tensile strength, there would be none left to use. Usually, then, a sample involving but a modest portion of the entire lot or population is all that is subject to scrutiny. Even if every unit of a lot were thoroughly tested, one would still find it advantageous to test the significance of the departure of the average quality of that lot from some previously adopted standard.[1]

In Chapter 12, quick and easy tests were used. These test utilized the range as a measure of variability. Because estimates of σ based on the range are not as efficient as estimates based on Σx^2, the tests of hypotheses were inefficient.

In this chapter we shall continue to assume that the population is normal, and we shall use the standard deviation as a measure of dispersion. We shall therefore obtain more powerful tests than those of Chapter 12. For samples of the same size, the tests of the present chapter will have greater power to reject a hypothesis when it is false. Or we can say that they have greater power efficiency; the sample size required to reject a hypothesis, when it is false, is smaller.

It should not be thought that efficient tests are always to be preferred to inefficient ones. The power of a test can always be improved by increasing the sample size. It may be more economical to spend one's money on more extensive sampling, rather than the more laborious computations usually required by efficient tests.

Simple Hypothesis

A sample of 50 pieces of Supertwist cord has a mean flex life of $\bar{X} = 138.64$ minutes. Let us test the hypothesis that the sample is from a population with mean of 137.50 minutes. The standard deviation σ is 15 minutes.

---

[1] Occasionally an alternative procedure to sampling is available. For example, the tensile strength and the hardness of a metal product may be found to be closely associated; in general, the harder the piece the greater is its tensile strength. Under such a condition we may ascertain the hardness of every piece and from this information determine the approximate tensile strength. Such a procedure is discussed in Chapter 24.

Two-sided test. We are going to ascertain if the above sample mean differs more from the population mean than might be expected for a mean of random sample of 50 items. Symbolically, the *null*[2] hypothesis and the *alternative* hypothesis (or family of hypotheses) are:

$$H_0: \quad \mu = 137.50 \text{ minutes};$$
$$H_a: \quad \mu \neq 137.50 \text{ minutes}.$$

The test is said to be two-sided, since we will reject H_0 and consider that $\overline{X}$ is significantly different from μ_0 if the sample mean is either so much larger or so much smaller than the hypothetical population mean that it is unreasonable to attribute the difference to chance.

We must, of course, decide how large a difference is required for significance *before* we apply our test. This decision is to some extent arbitrary. For illustrative purposes, let us say that the required level of significance is .05; we will reject the null hypothesis[3] if the observed difference is so large that the probability of its occurrence is equal to or less than .05. Symbolically, $\alpha = .05$.

First, we must compute the standard error of the mean. From equation (20.2) we compute

$$\sigma_{\overline{X}} = \frac{\sigma}{\sqrt{n}} = \frac{15}{\sqrt{50}} = 2.12 \text{ minutes}.$$

Now, the sample mean differs from the hypothetical population mean by 1.14 minutes ($\overline{X} - \mu_0 = 138.64 - 137.5 = 1.14$ minutes). This deviation is equal to a little more than one half of the standard error and therefore is not a sufficiently great deviation to be considered unusual. To be more explicit, we may evaluate the tails of the normal curve cut off by this deviation. We first compute

$$z = \frac{\overline{X} - \mu_0}{\overline{X}} = \frac{138.64 - 137.50}{2.12} = \frac{1.14}{2.12} = 0.54.$$

Chart 21.1 shows the distribution of sample means about μ_0 and the portion of the curve cut off by the observed $\overline{X}$. Referring to Appendix 14.2 we find

---

[2] This hypothesis is referred to as a "null hypothesis," an "hypothesis of no difference," because we are testing the hypothesis that there is no difference between the mean of the population from which our sample was drawn and the mean of the hypothetical population. It is a simple hypothesis, since it specifies not only μ, but also σ; i.e., it specifies all the parameters.

[3] Sometimes, instead of definitely stating that a hypothesis is accepted or rejected, one states the degree of significance that is attached to an observed difference. An often-used rule is as follows:

Probability	Conclusion
$\leq .01$	Highly significant
$\leq .05$	Significant
$> .05$	Not significant

It seems better, however, to decide upon a definite, but appropriate, value for α for each test.

that there is 0.2054 or 20.54 per cent of a normal curve included between the mean and $z = 0.54$; thus the proportion of the curve shown cross-hatched is $0.5000 - 0.2054 = 0.2946$ or 29.46 per cent. There are 295 chances out of 1,000 that means from samples of this size will *exceed* the population mean by 1.14 minutes or more because of the variability of random

Chart 21.1—Expected Distribution of Sample Means of Flex Life of Supertwist Cord, Showing Probability that $|z|$ will Exceed 0.54

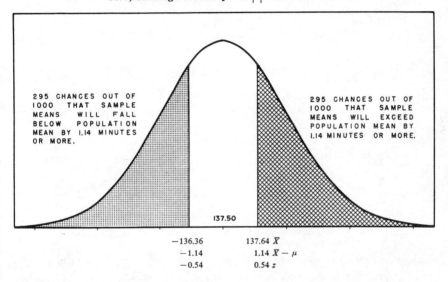

295 CHANCES OUT OF 1000 THAT SAMPLE MEANS WILL FALL BELOW POPULATION MEAN BY 1.14 MINUTES OR MORE.

295 CHANCES OUT OF 1000 THAT SAMPLE MEANS WILL EXCEED POPULATION MEAN BY 1.14 MINUTES OR MORE.

137.50

-136.36	137.64 $\bar{X}$
-1.14	1.14 $\bar{X} - \mu$
-0.54	0.54 z

sampling. (We say that $P = 0.295$.) Since this is a two-sided test, we also evaluate the corresponding tail at the left of the curve. This is the stippled area of Chart 21.1. There are, of course, 295 chances out of 1,000 that sample means will *fall below* the population mean by 1.14 minutes or more.

Combining the two tails of Chart 21.1, we find that the chances are 59 out of 100 that means from samples of $n = 50$ will depart ± 1.14 minutes or more from the population mean. (We say $2P = 0.59$.) Clearly, since $2P > \alpha$, or $P > \alpha/2$, chance is *not* ruled out as an explanation of the difference between $\bar{X}$ and μ_0. We accept H_0, and conclude that there is *not* a significant difference between $\bar{X}$ and μ_0.

If a sample of 50 items yielded $\bar{X} = 144.00$, we would have

$$z = \frac{\bar{X} - \mu_0}{\sigma_{\bar{X}}} = \frac{144.00 - 137.50}{2.12} = \frac{6.50}{2.12} = 3.07.$$

Referring to Appendix 14.2, we find that the proportion of the area of a normal curve included between $\pm 3.07 \sigma_{\bar{X}}$ of the mean is 0.9978, and therefore the proportion of the area in the two tails is 0.0022. This is shown in Chart 21.2. A divergence as great as or greater than ± 6.50 minutes could be expected to arise by chance about 2 times in 1,000. Such a divergence would occur so rarely through the operation of random sampling that we consider the divergence significant.

In declaring such a difference as this to be significant, we know that when H_0 is true we will occasionally be wrong but that we will usually be right.

Chart 21.2—Expected Distribution of Sample Means of Flex Life of Supertwist Cord, Showing Probability that $|z|$ will exceed 3.07

II CHANCES OUT OF 10,000 THAT SAMPLE MEANS WILL FALL BELOW POPULATION MEAN BY 6.50 MINUTES OR MORE.

II CHANCES OUT OF 10,000 THAT SAMPLE MEANS WILL EXCEED POPULATION MEAN BY 6.50 MINUTES OR MORE

131.00	137.50	144.00 $\bar{X}$
-6.50	0	$+6.50$ $\bar{X} - \mu$
-3.07	0	$+3.07$ z

In this instance the observed difference could occur by chance, when H_0 is true, 2 times in 1,000, and in those 2 cases our declaration of significance would have been wrong. A significant difference between a sample and a hypothetical population mean may occur either because the sample was not chosen *at random* from the population, or because it was from some *other population*, or both. If the sample is known to be from the population in question, then it may[4] not have been random. If the sample is known to be a random sample, then it may not have been from the population in question.

Rejection region. It is perhaps a little simpler to establish rejection regions based upon the criterion of significance α, and then reject H_0 if z is in the rejection region. Otherwise H_0 is accepted. This procedure relieves us of the necessity of finding P.

For a two-sided test, when $\alpha = .05$, the rejection region, sometimes called the critical region, is the region beyond $z_{.025}$, which is 1.96. We reject H_0 if the computed value of z is equal to or greater, numerically, than 1.96. Referring to our first illustration, where $\bar{X} = 138.64$, we found that $z = 0.54$, so we accepted H_0. Referring to our second illustration, where $\bar{X} = 144.00$, we found that $z = 3.07$, so we rejected H_0.

---

[4] It is conceivable that the means are not distributed normally; but with $n = 50$, we can ignore this qualification. See statement of the central limit theorem, p. 280.

We can also state our rejection region in units of the original data. If $z_{\alpha/2} = 1.96$, then the critical values for the rejection region are

$$\mu_0 \pm z_{\alpha/2}\sigma_x.$$

For our data

$$137.50 \pm (1.96)(2.12) = 133.34 \text{ and } 141.66.$$

Thus we reject our null hypothesis if $\bar{X}$ is smaller than 133.34 or larger than 141.66. Thus, if $\bar{X} = 138.64$ we accept H_0, but if $\bar{X} = 144.00$ we reject H_0.

Power of test. It should be recalled that α is the probability of rejecting H_0 when H_0 is true, and β is the probability of accepting H_0 when H_0 is false. Therefore $1 - \beta$ is the probability of rejecting H_0 when H_0 is false. In setting up a test procedure, α is determined more or less arbitrarily, depending on the circumstances. We want the probability $(1 - \beta)$ of rejecting the null hypothesis to get larger as the difference between μ and μ_0 gets larger. This is accomplished by establishing a rejection region in the manner we have indicated. We also want the probability $(1 - \beta)$ of rejecting the null hypothesis, given α, to be as large as possible when the null hypothesis is false.

A power function indicates the probability of rejecting the null hypothesis for each possible value of μ, the value of α being fixed. It is $1 - \beta$ as a function of μ. A power curve is the graph of the power function.[5] Referring to our example, the critical values for $\bar{X}$ were 133.34 and 141.66. Now if the null hypothesis is true, i.e., if $\mu = 137.50$,

$$z_1 = \frac{133.34 - 137.50}{2.12} = -\frac{4.16}{2.12} = -1.96, \quad \text{and}^6 \quad Q = .025.$$

$$z_2 = \frac{141.66 - 137.50}{2.12} = \frac{4.16}{2.12} = 1.96, \quad \text{and} \quad P + .025.$$

$$\alpha = P + Q = .050.$$

Suppose, however, that $\mu = 135.00$.

$$z_1 = \frac{133.34 - 135.00}{2.12} = -\frac{1.66}{2.12} = -0.78, \quad \text{and} \quad Q = .718.$$

$$z_2 = \frac{141.66 - 135.00}{2.12} = \frac{6.66}{2.12} = 3.14, \quad \text{and} \quad P = .001.$$

$$1 - \beta = P + Q = .719.$$

Table 21.1 shows the computation of values of $1 - \beta$ for other values of μ, by the formula

$$(21.1) \qquad\qquad 1 - \beta = Q(z) + P(z)$$

---

[5] In quality control it is customary to refer to the operating characteristic of a test, generally abbreviated as OC. The operating characteristic is the probability of accepting a process or lot. If the hypothesis is that the process or lot is good, then $OC = \beta$.

[6] Q is the probability of a value smaller than z, while P is the probability of a value equal to or larger than z.

Table 21.1—Computation of Power Function for a Two-Sided Test of Hypothesis
Concerning μ.
$(\overline{X}_1 = 133.34; \ \overline{X}_2 = 141.66; \ \sigma_{\overline{X}} = 2.12)$

μ	$\overline{X}_1 - \mu$	z_1 $\dfrac{\overline{X}_1 - \mu}{\sigma}$	$Q(z_1)$	$\overline{X}_2 - \mu$	z_2 $\dfrac{\overline{X}_2 - \mu}{\sigma}$	$P(z_2)$	$1 - \beta$ $P + Q$
127.50	5.84	2.75	0.997	14.16	6.68	0.000	0.997
130.00	3.34	1.58	.942	11.66	5.26	.000	.942
132.50	0.84	0.40	.655	9.16	4.32	.000	.655
135.00	−1.66	−0.78	.218	6.66	3.14	.001	.219
136.25	−2.91	−1.37	.085	5.41	2.55	.005	.090
137.50	−4.16	−1.96	.025	4.16	1.96	.025	$\alpha = .050$
138.75	−5.41	−2.55	.005	2.91	1.37	.085	.090
140.00	−6.66	−3.14	.001	1.66	0.78	.218	.219
142.50	−9.16	−4.32	.000	−0.84	−0.40	.655	.655
145.00	−11.66	−5.26	.000	−3.34	−1.58	.942	.942
147.50	−14.16	−6.68	.000	−5.84	−2.75	.997	1.000

Chart 21.3—Probability of Rejecting H_0 for Specified Values of μ,
Two-sided Test

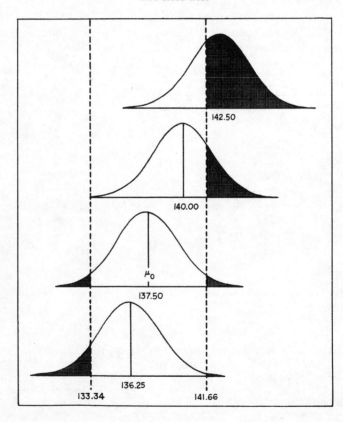

The shaded areas of Chart 21.3 show the probabilities of rejecting H_0 that are associated with selected values of μ. These are the probabilities of Table 21.1. On Chart 21.4 the probabilities associated with these and other values of μ are shown as a continuous solid curve. The important thing to notice is that as μ departs farther from $\mu_0 = 175$, the probability of rejecting the null hypothesis gets larger.

Chart 21.4—Power of a Two-Sided Test

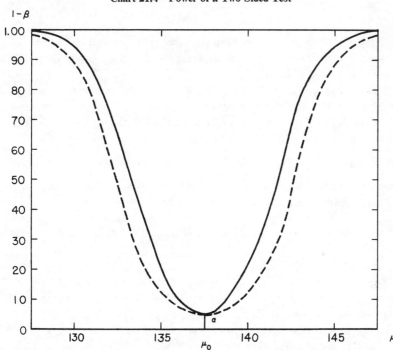

The most powerful test is the one that results in the greatest probability of rejecting a hypothesis when it is false. In comparing the power of the two tests, the value of α must be the same for both. On a graph the most powerful test will be above the less powerful ones at all points except where $\mu = \mu_0$. Thus on Chart 21.4, the solid line represents a more powerful test than the broken line. In order to obtain a powerful test one should select a reliable test statistic. Thus, for hypotheses concerning μ, it is better to use the sample mean than the sample median, and it is better to make use of the standard deviation than the range. Also, increasing the sample size increases the power of the test. Sometimes it is economical to increase the sample size and use a test statistic that is easy to compute, though its power efficiency is low.

One-sided test. In most business situations we are not usually interested in testing whether a set of data comes from a population with a specified mean. Indeed, it is incredible that the population mean could be exactly that which is specified. Usually we are interested in whether the population mean is *at least as large as* some specified value (or perhaps *at least as small as* some specified value). If we wish to be convinced beyond reasonable doubt that the flex life of Supertwist cord is at least as great as 135.00 minutes we should use a one-sided test.

$$H_0: \quad \mu = 135.00 \text{ minutes.}$$

$$H_a: \quad \mu > 135.00 \text{ minutes.}$$

If we reject the hypothesis it is because we believe the cord to have a significantly *larger* flex life than 135.00 minutes, and the business decision will be to adopt that type of cord.

Again let us use $\alpha = .05$. Since 5 per cent of the area in a normal curve is beyond 1.645σ, the rejection region is any value of z equal to or greater than $z_\alpha = z_{.05} = 1.645$. In units of our original data the rejection region is a sample mean equal to or greater than

$$\mu_0 + z_\alpha \sigma_{\bar{X}} = 135.00 + (1.645)(2.12) = 138.487.$$

Since the sample mean is 138.64 we see immediately that it falls in the rejection region. Alternatively, we may compute

$$z = \frac{138.64 - 135.00}{2.12} = \frac{3.64}{2.12} = 1.72.$$

We reject the hypothesis because $z > z_\alpha$; i.e., $1.72 > 1.645$. We arrive at the same conclusion when (using Appendix 14.1) we find that Prob $(z \geq 1.72) = .053$. Since $P > \alpha$, i.e., $.053 > 0.05$, we reject H_0 and say that the flex life is significantly *greater* than 135.00 minutes.

Power of test. We have just seen that the critical value for $\bar{X}$ is 138.487. If the null hypothesis is true, i.e., if $\mu = 135$,

$$z = \frac{138.487 - 135.00}{2.12} = \frac{3.487}{2.12} = 1.645, \quad \text{and} \quad P = .05.$$

Suppose, however, that $\mu = 140$. Then

$$z = \frac{138.49 - 140.00}{2.12} = -\frac{1.51}{2.12} = -0.71, \quad \text{and} \quad P = .761.$$

This is the value of $1 - \beta$ when $\mu = 140.00$. In general,

(21.2) $$\begin{cases} 1 - \beta = P(z), & \text{when } H_a \text{ is } \mu > \mu_0; \\ 1 - \beta = Q(z), & \text{when } H_a \text{ is } \mu < \mu_0. \end{cases}$$

Table 21.2 shows the computation of values of $1 - \beta$ for other values of μ. The shaded areas of Chart 21.5 show the probabilities of rejecting H_0

**Table 21.2—Computation of Power Function for a
One-sided Test of Hypothesis Concerning μ.**
$(\bar{X}_c = 138.487; \ \sigma_{\bar{X}} = 2.12)$

μ	$\bar{X}_c - \mu$	z_c $\dfrac{\bar{X}_c - \mu}{\sigma_{\bar{X}}}$	$1 - \beta$ $P(z)$
132.5	5.99	2.83	0.002
135.0	3.487	1.645	$\alpha = .050$
137.5	0.99	0.47	.319
140.00	−1.51	−0.71	.761
142.50	−4.01	−1.89	.971
145.00	−6.51	−3.07	.999

**Chart 21.5—Probability of Rejection H_0 for Specified
Values of μ, One-Sided Test**

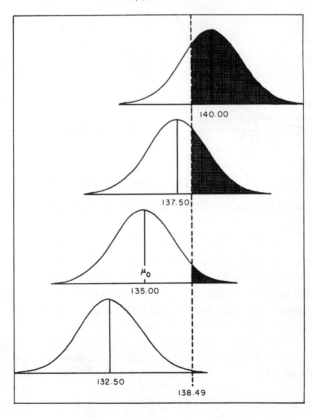

associated with selected values of μ taken from Table 21.2. On Chart 21.6 the probabilities associated with these and other values of μ are shown. The important thing to notice is that as μ gets larger, the probability of rejecting the hypothesis gets larger.

Chart 21.6—Power of a One-Sided Test

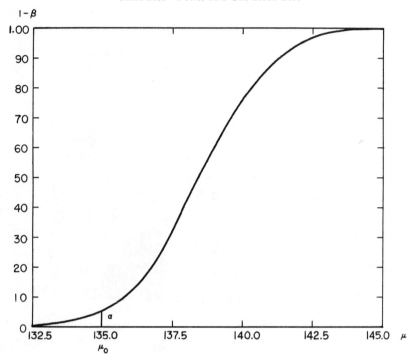

The t Distribution

In the preceding section we made use of the expression (20.2)

$$\sigma_{\bar{X}} = \frac{\sigma}{n},$$

which enables us to determine $\sigma_{\bar{X}}$ if σ is known. The value of σ is occasionally known. In certain instances, special investigations may be made under carefully controlled conditions in order to estimate its value. Such a procedure is sometimes followed by manufacturers in establishing optimum quality standards for a product. More often, however, σ is unknown.

When σ is not known or specified in the hypothesis, we must make an estimate of it from the information available in the sample. Such an estimate of σ is indicated by s. It was stated in Chapters 12 and 17 that

$$s = \sqrt{\frac{\Sigma x^2}{n - 1}}.$$

When estimating $\sigma_{\bar{X}}$, we substitute s for the unknown σ, obtaining[7]

(21.3)
$$s_{\bar{X}} = \frac{s}{\sqrt{n}}.$$

When σ is known, or specified in the null hypothesis, we use z in making tests, where z is expression (20.3),

$$z = \frac{\bar{X} - \mu}{\sigma_{\bar{X}}}.$$

This ratio is normally distributed if the population is normal, or if n is large.

When σ is unknown and not specified in the null hypothesis, we use t in making tests. The ratio

(21.4)
$$t = \frac{\bar{X} - \mu}{s_{\bar{X}}}$$

has its own distribution.

In general, if deviations (such as $\bar{X} - \mu$) are distributed normally around zero when divided by their true standard error, they are distributed according to the t distribution when divided by estimates of the standard error based on degrees of freedom.

The t distribution is symmetrical but is more widely dispersed than the normal distribution for the same values of z and t. For the same value of z and t, there is always a larger proportion of the area in the tail of the t distribution. The fewer the degrees of freedom $v = n = 1$, the more widely dispersed is the t distribution. Chart 21.7 shows the t distribution for $v - 2$ in comparison with the normal distribution, and also the distribution for $v = 20$ compared with the normal distribution. As v increases, the t distribution more closely approximates the normal distribution. Comparison of Appendix Tables 14.3 and 16 shows that when $n = \infty$, the values of z and t are the same for the same values of P. In fact, when the size is 100 or larger there is little difference between z and t, except for very small values of P. Chart 21.7 indicates that the two distributions are about the same when n is as large as 20. Because the difference between z and t is important only when n is small, methods employing the t distribution are often called small-sample methods. The theoretical distinction, however, is not whether n is large or small, but whether σ is given or estimated.

---

[7] An equivalent expression is

$$s_{\bar{X}} = \frac{s}{\sqrt{n-1}}.$$

This follows from the fact that $s = s \sqrt{\dfrac{n}{n-1}}.$

Chart 21.7—Comparison of *t*-Distribution with Normal Distribution for $\nu = 2$ and $\nu = 20$

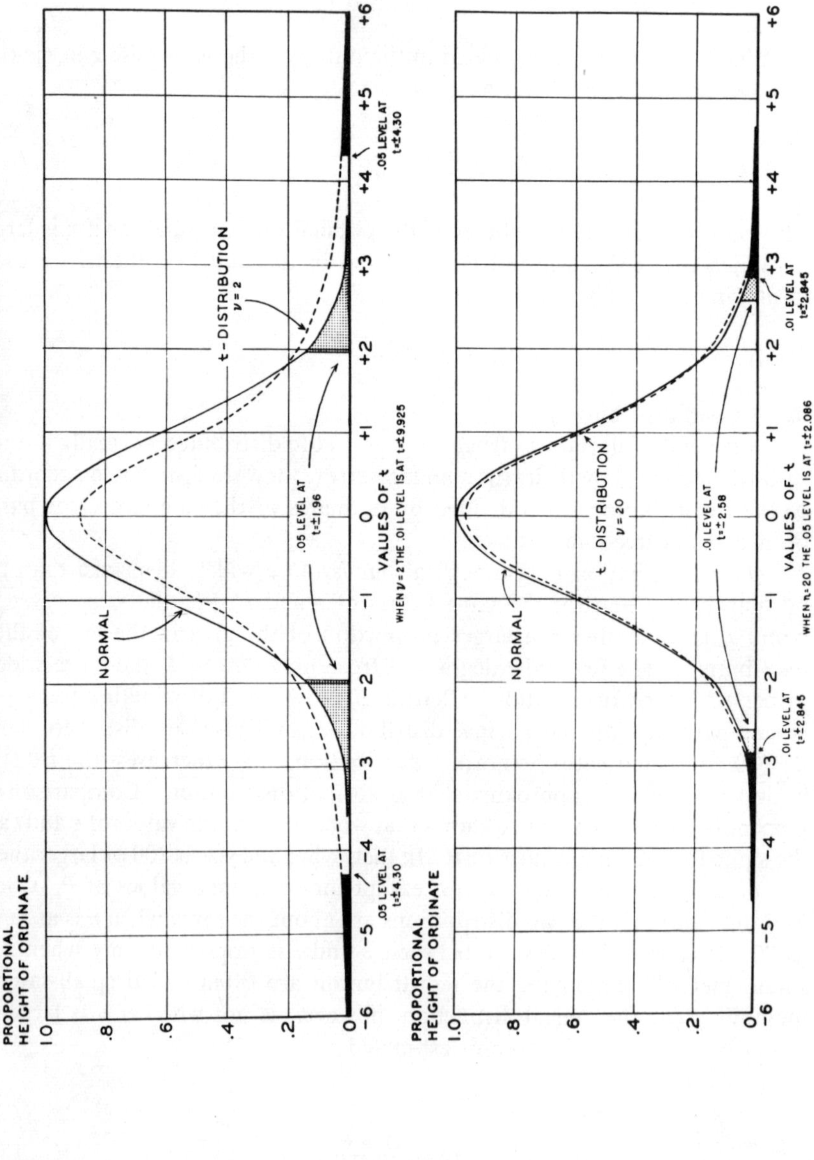

Hypothesis Concerning Mean, Standard Deviation Unspecified[8]

Two-sided test. For the data of flex life of Supertwist cord $\overline{X}$ was found to be 138.64 minutes for a sample of 50 pieces. It is reasonable to believe

Table 21.3—Computation of $\overline{X}$ and $\Sigma\,x^2$ for Flex Life of Supertwist Cord

Flex life in minutes X_1	X_1^2	Flex life in minutes X_1	X_1^2
140	19,600	158	24,964
158	24,964	119	14,161
147	21,609	157	24,649
127	16,129	195	38,025
163	26,569	135	18,225
124	15,376	123	15,129
139	19,321	128	16,384
121	14,641	150	22,500
146	21,316	136	18,496
159	25,281	139	19,321
150	22,500	172	29,584
132	17,424	123	15,129
131	17,161	121	14,641
135	18,225	117	13,689
112	12,544	123	15,129
150	22,500	143	20,449
127	16,129	137	18,769
149	22,201	135	18,225
141	19,881	142	20,164
138	19,044	137	18,769
121	14,641	134	17,956
151	22,801	143	20,449
135	18,225	129	16,641
147	21,609	128	16,384
126	15,876		
139	19,321	6,932	972,720

Source: The Goodyear Tire and Rubber Company.

$$\overline{X}_1 = \frac{\Sigma\,X_1}{n_1} = \frac{6,932}{50} = 138.64 \text{ minutes}$$

$$\Sigma\,x_1^2 = \Sigma\,X_1^2 - \frac{(\Sigma\,X_1)^2}{n}$$

$$= 972,720 - \frac{(6,932)^2}{50} = 11,668.$$

[8] A hypothesis where one or more parameters are unspecified is called a *composite* hypothesis. The power function of a composite hypothesis is beyond the scope of this book. In E. S. Pearson and H. O. Hartley (editors) *Biometrika Tables for Statisticians*, Vol. I, Cambridge University Press, 1954, pp. 24–25, the power function of the *t* test is explained and illustrated. A chart for determining the power function is on page 135.

that this mean may be the mean of a random sample from a population having $\mu = 138.00$ minutes. Our hypothesis is that the population of which our sample is a random sample has $\mu = 138.00$ minutes. We shall proceed to test this hypothesis by determining $s_{\bar{X}}$, and P. From P we shall be in a position to draw our conclusion as to the tenability of the hypothesis. In Table 21.3, the flex life figures give $\Sigma X^2 = 972,720$. $\Sigma X = 6,932$, and $\bar{X} = 138.64$. Using formula (17.28),

$$s = \sqrt{\frac{\Sigma X^2 - (\Sigma X)^2/n}{n-1}}$$

$$= \sqrt{\frac{972,720 - (6,932)^2/50}{49}} = \sqrt{\frac{11,668}{49}} = 15.43 \text{ minutes.}$$

Substituting this value in expression (21.3) gives

$$s_{\bar{X}} = \frac{15.43}{\sqrt{50}} = 2.18 \text{ minutes.}$$

We now compute

$$t = \frac{\bar{X} - \mu}{s_{\bar{X}}} = \frac{138.64 - 138.00}{2.18} = \frac{0.64}{2.18} = 0.29.$$

Since $n = 50$, $v = n - 1 = 49$. Now we are dealing with t-values instead of z-values and we refer to the "t-table" of Appendix 16. This table shows the degrees of freedom, v, in the first column; t is given in the body of the table; the probabilities P and $2P$ are recorded, across the top of the table. In this appendix we find entries for $v = 40$ and $v = 60$. Using the former, we find that $|t| = 0.29$ or greater may be expected to occur by chance slightly fewer than 80 times in a hundred if the hypothesis is true. Chart 21.8 illustrates the preceding, and we conclude that $\bar{X} = 138.64$ minutes does not deviate

Chart 21.8—Distribution of Values of t when $n = 40$, Showing Probability of Obtaining $|t|$ equal to or larger than .29

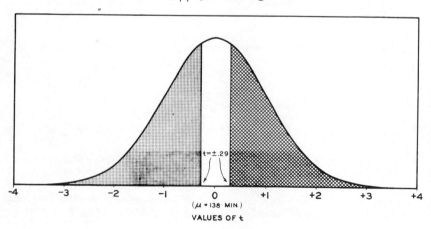

VALUES OF t

significantly from a hypothetical $\mu = 138.00$ minutes and that therefore it is reasonable to believe that this sample mean may have been based on a random sample from a population having $\mu = 138.00$ minutes.

Now let us ask if it is reasonable to believe that our sample mean, $\bar{X} - 138.64$ minutes, may be the mean of a random sample from a population having $\mu = 146.00$ minutes. The procedure given below in outline form may be regarded standard for testing hypotheses.

Hypothesis: Our sample is a random sample from a normal population with mean of 146.00 minutes, or symbolically,

$$H_0: \quad \mu = 146.00 \text{ minutes.}$$

$$H_a: \quad \mu \neq 146.00 \text{ minutes.}$$

Criterion of significance: $\alpha = .05$.

Rejection region: With $\nu = 49$, $t_{.025} = 2.01$, so the rejection region is $|t| \geq 2.01$.

Estimated standard error: $s_{\bar{X}} = 2.18$ (as previously computed).

Test statistic: $t = \dfrac{\bar{X} - \mu}{s_{\bar{X}}} = \dfrac{138.64 - 146.00}{2.18} = -\dfrac{7.36}{2.18} = -3.38.$

Probability: With $\nu = 49$, $2P$ is slightly greater than 0.001. This is the probability of obtaining a value of $|t|$ as large as 3.38 or larger if the hypothesis is true.[9]

Conclusion: The hypothesis is rejected.[10]

$$|t| > t_{\alpha/2}; \quad \text{i.e.,} \quad 3.38 > 2.01,$$

and therefore

$$2P < \alpha; \quad \text{i.e.,} \quad .001 < .05.$$

It is *not* reasonable to believe that this sample is a random sample from a population having $\mu = 146.00$. The difference between 138.64 minutes and 146.00 minutes is *significant*.

One-sided test. Suppose the question asked is whether the flex life is at least as small as 142.00 minutes. If we are convinced that this is the case,

---

[9] We must be careful not to say that this is the probability of obtaining a value of $\bar{X}$ that deviates as much as 7.36 minutes from the hypothetical population mean. The *t*-ratio is affected not only by the difference between $\bar{X}$ and a hypothetical μ, but also by the value of $s_{\bar{X}}$, which may be too large or too small, since s is an estimate of σ. When a value of t is associated with a small value of P, it may be that the deviation of $\bar{X}$ from the hypothetical μ is unusually large, or that the estimate of s is unusually small or both. Conversely, a large value of P may result from an unusually small value of $\bar{X} - \mu$, or an unusually large estimate of s, or both.

[10] It is not necessary to determine the probability of the sample if the rejection region is determined, for the conclusion follows directly from a comparison of the sample t with $t_{\alpha/2}$.

we will consider the cord to be unsatisfactory. This situation clearly calls for a one-sided test.

Hypothesis: H_0: $\mu = 142.00$ minutes.

                       H_a: $\mu < 142.00$ minutes.

Criterion of significance: $\alpha = .05$.

Region of rejection: With $v = 49$, $t_{.05} = 1.68$, so the region of rejection is $t \leq -1.68$.

Estimated standard error: $s_{\bar{X}} = 2.18$ minutes.

Test statistic:

$$t = \frac{\bar{X} - \mu_0}{s_{\bar{X}}} = \frac{138.64 - 142.00}{2.18} = -\frac{3.36}{2.18} = (-1.54).$$

Probability: With $v = 49$, $Q \doteq .07$.

Conclusion: Hypothesis is accepted.

Sample $t > t_\alpha$;   i.e., $-1.54 > -1.68$.

$Q > \alpha$;   i.e., $.07 > .05$.

Confidence Limits

Confidence limits were explained and illustrated in Chapter 13, using short-cut methods of computation involving the range. In this chapter we shall use the standard deviation. By so doing we obtain closer limits for the same degree of confidence, or greater confidence for the same limits.

Standard deviation known. To determine the β per cent confidence limits of μ, we determine: (1) a value of μ_1 *less* than $\bar{X}$, such that $\bar{X}$ cuts off the *upper* $\alpha/2$ per cent tail of the normal distribution ($\alpha + \beta = 1$); (2) a value of μ_2 *greater* than $\bar{X}$, such that $\bar{X}$ cuts off the lower $\alpha/2$ per cent tail of the normal distribution. Thus, if $\beta = .95$, $\alpha/2 = .05$, and μ_1 is so determined that $\bar{X}$ cuts off the upper $2\frac{1}{2}$ per cent tail, while μ_2 is so determined that $\bar{X}$ cuts off the lower $2\frac{1}{2}$ per cent tail.

The two values of μ, the lower and upper confidence limits, are both obtained from the expression

(21.5) $\bar{X} - \mu_1 = \mu_2 - \bar{X} = z_{\alpha/2}\sigma_{\bar{X}}.$

The 95 per cent confidence limits for our Goodyear data are easily obtained.

$$138.64 - \mu_1 = (1.96)(2.12) = 4.16;$$

$$\mu_1 = 138.64 - 4.16 = 134.48.$$

$$\mu_2 - 138.64 = (1.96)(2.12) = 4.16;$$

$$\mu_2 = 138.64 + 4.16 = 142.80.$$

This procedure is a little easier to understand after examination of Chart 21.9. If $\mu = 134.48$, the probability that $\overline{X}$ will be as large as 138.64, or larger, is .025. If $\mu = 142.80$, the probability that $\overline{X}$ will be as small as 138.64, or smaller, is .025.

We have just made an estimate of the 95 per cent confidence limits of μ from *one sample*. The true, but unknown, value of μ may or may not lie

Chart 21.9—Upper and Lower 95 Per Cent Confidence Limits for μ: $n = 50$;
$\overline{X} = 138.64$ minutes; $\sigma = 15$ minutes

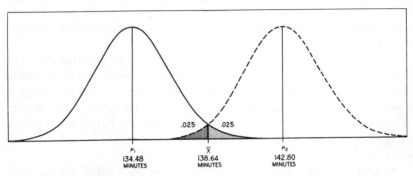

within the limits of 134.48 and 142.80; and it is illogical to say that the probability is 0.95 that μ is within these limits. But if we made *many determinations* of the 95 per cent confidence limits of μ, each from a different sample, we would find that our many sets of limits would include μ about

Chart 21.10—95 Per Cent Confidence Limits for Mean, and 40 Samples,
Standard Deviation Known

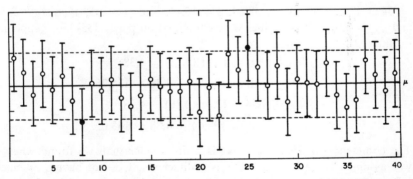

95 times in 100, and fail to include μ about 5 times out of 100. The reason this is so is that the means of 95 out of 100 samples are within $1.96\sigma_{\overline{X}}$ of μ, and the confidence limits are determined by measuring $\pm 1.96\sigma_{\overline{X}}$ from the different sample means. Consider Chart 21.10. The solid line represents μ. The dotted lines are $1.96\sigma_{\overline{X}}$ from μ. Of the 40 samples, shown by circles, 38 (or 95 per cent) are inside the dotted lines; two, shown in black, are

outside the broken lines. μ_1 and μ_2 are shown by horizontal bars. These horizontal bars are at distances of $1.96\sigma_{\bar{x}}$ from $\bar{X}$. Each vertical line of Chart 20.10 corresponds to the base line of Chart 20.9. Only in the case of the two black observations is the line representing μ not enclosed.

A correct probability statement concerning 95 per cent confidence limits is: "Before we select a sample, the probability is 95 per cent that the confidence limits we compute from the sample will enclose the population mean."

If different confidence limits were desired the procedure would be identical, but different z-values would be used. For 99 per cent limits ($\alpha/2 = .005$), $z = 2.576$, and the confidence interval would be wider. For 90 per cent limits ($\alpha/2 = .05$), $z = 1.645$, and the confidence interval would be narrower.

Since the standard error of the mean varies inversely with the square root of the sample size, the confidence interval ($\mu_2 - \mu_1$, given β) becomes narrower as we increase the sample size. Thus, when $n = 100$ the confidence limits are one-half as far apart as when $n = 25$. If we wish to retain the same confidence limits, the confidence coefficient becomes larger as we increase the sample size, though the relationship between n and β, given μ_1 and μ_2, is not so simple.

Stating confidence limits may be thought of as a substitute for testing a hypothesis. If μ_0 is between the confidence limits, H_0 is accepted; if μ_0 is on or outside the confidence limits H_0 is rejected.[11]

Standard deviation unknown. Usually the standard deviation is not known, and t rather than z must be used in determining confidence limits. Otherwise the procedure is the same. The appropriate formula is

$$(21.6) \qquad \bar{X} - \mu_1 = \mu_2 - \bar{X} = t_{\alpha/2}s_{\bar{x}}.$$

Thus if $n = 50$, $\bar{X} = 138.64$, $s = 15.43$, and $\beta = .95$, then $s_{\bar{x}} = 2.18$ and $t_{\alpha/2} = 2.01$. These values were computed on pages 335–336. Applying formula (21.6),

$$138.64 - \mu_1 = (2.01)(2.18) = 4.38;$$

$$\mu_1 = 138.64 - 4.38 = 134.26.$$

$$\mu_2 - 138.64 = (2.01)(2.18) = 4.38;$$

$$\mu_2 = 138.64 - 4.38 = 143.02.$$

The confidence interval ($\mu_2 - \mu_1$) is a little wider than we found when σ was assumed to be known. This is a direct result of not having as much information to work with. When σ was known, we used $z = 1.96$; but with σ unknown, we used $t = 2.01$. Another reason is that σ was 2.12, but s was computed as 2.18. This however was the accident of sampling; sometimes

---

[11] This statement has reference to a two-sided test of hypothesis, and a *central* confidence limit. If the test of hypothesis is one-sided, the confidence limit is also one-sided; μ_1 or μ_2 is stated, but not both.

s would be larger than σ, sometimes s would be smaller than σ. Recall that $E(s^2) = \sigma^2$.

Chart 21.11, which is analogous to Chart 21.10, differs from Chart 21.10 in one important respect. Although $\overline{X} - \mu_1$ always equals $\mu_2 - \overline{X}$, nevertheless $\mu_2 - \mu_1$ varies from sample to sample. This is because s, and therefore $s_{\overline{X}}$, varies from sample to sample. As a consequence: the length of the

Chart 21.11—95 Per Cent Confidence Limits for Mean, and 40 Samples, Standard Deviation Unknown

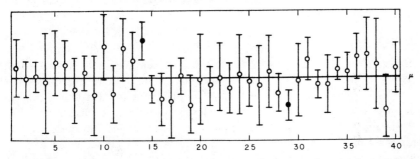

vertical lines varies from sample to sample; there can be no dotted line above the solid line which represents μ, at a uniform distance from that line; it is not necessarily the samples with the means deviating farthest from μ that yield interval estimates failing to enclose μ.

Chapter 22

TEST OF HYPOTHESES AND CONFIDENCE LIMITS: PROPORTIONS AND STANDARD DEVIATIONS

This chapter is essentially a continuation of Chapter 21. One partially new concept, the operating characteristic, which is closely related to the power function of a test, is introduced in connection with hypotheses concerning proportions. In the interest of simplicity, neither the power function nor the operating characteristic is illustrated for the standard deviation. We again make use of relatively quick and easy methods, however, using the range or mean range, as well as the conventional method, when testing a hypothesis concerning the standard deviation.

Hypothesis Concerning a Proportion

Use of normal distribution. There are various "cola" drinks on the market, and the question is often raised as to whether it is possible for a person to identify a given brand by taste. A test was run by one of the authors concerning R C Cola and Coca-Cola. Each of 44 persons was given a drink of R C Cola and a drink of Coca-Cola, and asked to state which was which. Thirty-four answered correctly and 10 answered incorrectly. If the two drinks were identical half of the subjects would be able to distinguish between them.

Now $nP = (44)(0.5) = 22$, which is almost 25, and so use of the normal curve should be reasonably accurate. We proceed in the conventional manner.

Hypothesis: H_0: $P = 0.50$.

H_a: $P > .50$.

Criterion of significance: $\alpha = .05$.

Rejection region: From Appendix 14.3, we obtain $z_\alpha = z_{.05} = 1.645$. The hypothesis will be rejected if, for the sample, $z \geq 1.645$.

Standard error of d:

$$\sigma_d = \sqrt{nPQ} = \sqrt{(44)(.5)(.5)} = \sqrt{(44)(.25)} = \sqrt{11} = 3.317.$$

Significance ratio:[1]

$$z = \frac{d - nP}{\sigma_d} = \frac{34 - 22}{3.317} = \frac{12}{3.317} = 3.62.$$

Conclusion: H_0 is rejected, since the sample z is greater than z_α; i.e., $3.62 > 1.645$. We conclude that more than 50 per cent of the population is able to distinguish between R C Cola and Coca-Cola.

The same results are obtained[2] if we use p instead of d.

$$p = \frac{34}{44} = .773; \qquad q = \frac{10}{44} = .227.$$

$$\sigma_p = \sqrt{\frac{PQ}{n}} = \sqrt{\frac{(.5)(.5)}{44}} = \sqrt{\frac{.25}{44}} = \sqrt{.005682} = .0754.$$

(22.1) $$z = \frac{p - P}{\sigma_p} = \frac{.773 - .50}{.0754} = \frac{.273}{.0754} = 3.62.$$

Use of binomial distribution. A lot (assumed to be very large) is considered to be satisfactory if it is not more than 2 per cent defective. We select a sample of 100 and find 5 defectives. We are willing to subject the *producer* to a 5 per cent risk of rejecting a lot when the lot quality P_1 is good. A sample contains 6 defectives. Should the lot be accepted or rejected?

Hypothesis: $\qquad\qquad\qquad H_0: \ P_1 = .02.$
$\qquad\qquad\qquad\qquad\qquad H_a: \ P_1 > .02.$

Criterion of significance (producer's risk):
$$\alpha_1 = .05.$$

---

[1] With $z = 3.62$, $P(z) = .00015$.

For small sample sizes it is usually better to use a correction for continuity,

$$z = \frac{|d - nP| - .5}{\sigma_d}.$$

In the present case this would result in

$$z = \frac{11.5}{3.317} = 3.47,$$

and $P(z) = .00025$. If the sample is so small that a correction for continuity is required, it is better, and just as easy, to use a table of the binomial probability distribution, and obtain the correct probability. Thus, using formula (11.4) or the National Bureau of Standards *Tables*, with $n = 44$ and $P = .5$, we find that the probability of obtaining a value of d equal to or less than 10 is .00019. In the present case, the sample is not small, and the correction for continuity overcorrects.

[2] Some people find it easier to avoid decimal point trouble if all computations are made in percentages.

$$\sigma_p = \sqrt{\frac{(50)(50)}{44}} = \sqrt{\frac{2500}{44}} = \sqrt{56.82} = 7.54 \text{ per cent.}$$

$$z = \frac{77.3 - 50.0}{7.54} = \frac{27.3}{7.54} = 3.62.$$

Rejection number: Since $nP_1 = (100)(.02) = 2$, it would not be sufficiently accurate to use normal probabilities. Using formula (11.4) or Romig's *Tables* with $n = 100$ and $P_1 = .02$, we find that the probability is .95 that there will be 4 or fewer defectives, and therefore .05 that there will be 5 or more. The rejection number is therefore 5.

Conclusion: Since we found 6 defectives, we reject the lot.

Suppose now we wish to protect the *consumer* against accepting a lot that is as much as 8 per cent defective. More specifically, if the lot is 8 per cent defective, we are willing to assume a risk of 9 per cent of accepting such a lot.

Hypothesis: H_0: $P_2 = .08.$

H_a: $P_2 < .08.$

Criterion of significance (consumer's risk): $\beta_2 = .09$. We are here using β_2 to mean the probability of accepting the *lot* when the lot quality P_2 is bad.

Acceptance number: We are here using acceptance number to mean a value of d, such that if there are fewer defectives, we will accept the *lot*. Since $nP = (100)(.08) = 8$, we again use formula (11.4) or Romig's *Tables*. When $n = 100$ and $P = .08$, Romig's *Tables* show that the probability is .09 that there will be 4 or fewer defectives.

Conclusion: Since we found 6 defectives, which does not fall in the acceptance region, we reject the lot.[3]

Operating characteristic. The operating characteristic OC of an acceptance sampling plan, as the words are used in quality control, is the probability of accepting the lot (or process). These probabilities vary with P, the quality of the lot. If the null hypothesis is that the lot is good, then the probabilities (β) for the OC function are the complements of the probabilities ($1 - \beta$) of the power function.

We already have four points for the OC curve:

When $P = .00$, $\beta = 1.00$ (the sample will contain good items only);

When $P = .02$, $\beta = .95$ (this is $\beta_1 = 1 - \alpha_1$);

When $P = .08$, $\beta = .09$ (this is β_2);

When $P = 1.00$, $\beta = .00$ (the sample will contain defective items only).

Two more points will permit us to plot the OC curve with reasonable accuracy. Romig's *Tables* with $n = 100$, show:

When $P = .05$, Prob $(d \leq 4) \doteq .44$;

When $P = .10$, Prob $(d \leq 4) \doteq .02$.

---

[3] We have been considering a sampling plan in which "producer's risk" and "consumer's risk" is specified. The sample size is a consequence of these specifications. See Dudley J. Cowden, *Statistical Methods in Quality Control*, Prentice-Hall, Inc., Englewood Cliffs, N.J., 1957, Chapter 34, for an analysis of this problem.

Chart 22.1 shows the OC curve for this test. A powerful test is one that discriminates sharply between good and bad lots. The more powerful the test, for given values of α_1 and β_2, the closer together are P_1 and P_2, and the steeper is the OC curve.

Chart 22.1—Operating Characteristic Curve for a Sampling Plan for Defectives

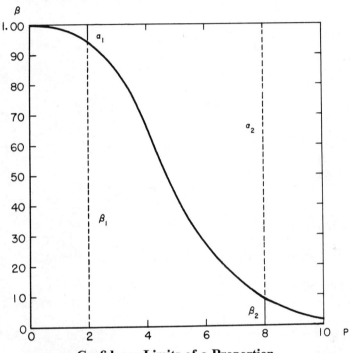

Confidence Limits of a Proportion

When dealing with sample means we found it useful to ascertain the confidence limits of μ from a knowledge of the information given by one sample. Similarly, it is sometimes important to determine the confidence limits of P when only p and n are known.

The Chicago, Milwaukee, and Saint Paul and Pacific Railway tested various sorts of woods and preservatives for railroad ties. One lot of 50 red oak ties treated with 20 per cent creosote and 80 per cent zinc chloride was examined after 19 years of use and 19, or 38 per cent of them, were found to still be good. Our sample values are $n = 50$ and $p = 0.38$. Let us ascertain the 95 per cent confidence limits of P. We want first to ascertain P_1, less than p, so located that p cuts off the upper $2\frac{1}{2}$ per cent tail of the distribution of sample p's around P_1; and, second, to determine P_2, greater than p, so located that p cuts off the lower $2\frac{1}{2}$ per cent tail of the distribution of sample p's around P_2.

Use of normal distribution. Although we do not yet know the value of nP_1 or nP_2, the value of $np = d = 19$, which is sufficiently close to 25 to justify the use of the normal distribution for an approximate solution. The equation for the confidence limits of P parallels equations (21.5) and (21.6)

$$(22.2) \qquad p - P_1 = P_2 - p = z_{\alpha/2}\sigma_p.$$

But since $\sigma_p = \sqrt{(P - P^2)/n}$, this equation can be written in a different form.

$$(22.3) \qquad (np^2) - (z_{\alpha/2}^2 + 2np)P + (z_{\alpha/2}^2 + n)P^2 = 0.$$

Substituting for n, p, and $z_{\alpha/2}$, we have

$$[(50)(.38)^2] - [(1.96)^2 + (2)(50)(.38)]P + [(1.96)^2 + 50]P^2 = 0;$$
$$7.220 - 41.8416P + 53.8416P^2 = 0.$$

This is a quadratic equation of the type

$$a + bX + cX^2 = 0,$$

and it is solved by the expression

$$(22.4) \qquad X = \frac{-b \pm \sqrt{b^2 - 4ac}}{2c}$$

For our problem,

$$P = \frac{41.8416 \pm \sqrt{(41.8416)^2 - 4(7.220)(53.8416)}}{2(53.8416)}.$$

P_1 is 0.259 and P_2 is 0.519. Notice that p is closer to P_1 than P_2.

Use of binomial distribution. Charts for estimating the confidence limits of P, based on the binomial distribution, are shown in Appendix 12. To use these charts, for our problem, erect a perpendicular line at $p = 0.38$. Where it intersects the two curves for $n = 50$, draw a horizontal line.[4] It intersects the perpendicular line at $P_1 \doteq 0.25$ and $P_2 \doteq 0.53$. Notice that these values are farther apart than those based on the approximate normal solution.

A mathematical solution, equivalent to the above graphic one, is as follows.

Find the value of P_1, smaller than p, such that:

$$\text{Prob } (d \geq 19) = .025; \quad \text{i.e.,}$$

$$\sum_{d=19}^{50} P_1^d Q_1^{n-d} = .025.$$

Using Romig's *Tables*, it appears that when $P_1 \doteq 0.246$ this equation is satisfied. This can be verified by use of formula (11.4).

---

[4] The points of intersection must be estimated. There is a curve for $n = 40$, and another for $n = 60$, but none for $n = 50$.

Next, find the value of P_2, larger than p, and such that

Prob $(d \leq 19) = .025$; i.e.,

$$\sum_{d=0}^{19} P_2^d Q_2^{n-d} = .025.$$

When we try to determine P_2 by use of Romig's *Tables*, we run into a slight snag. It soon becomes evident that $P_2 > .50$, but Romig's *Tables* only go to $P = 0.50$. This is not a very serious snag, however. All we need to do is to interchance P and Q, and also d and $n - d$. In our equation for finding P_2 we therefore substitute 31 in place of 19, and interchanging P_2 and Q_2, find

Prob $(d \leq 31) = .025$; i.e.,

$$\sum_{d=31}^{50} Q_2^d P_2^{n-d} = .025.$$

Romig's *Tables* show that when $Q_2 = 0.471$ this equation is satisfied. Therefore $P_2 = 0.529$.

The accuracy of the mathematical solution is limited only by the extent of one's willingness to experiment with trial values of P_1 and P_2.

Chart 22.2, which is similar to Charts 21.10 and 21.11, brings out two additional points of interest :

Chart 22.2—95 Per Cent Confidence Limits for Proportions, and 40 Samples

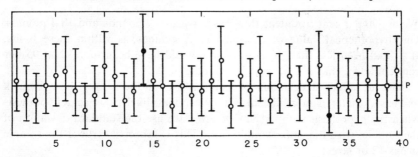

(1) The upper and lower confidence limits are unsymmetrical. When $p < 0.50$, then $P_2 - p > p - P_1$. This can be seen on Chart 22.2 by comparing the lengths of the vertical lines above and below the circles. (Compare with Charts 21.10 and 21.11.) This difference is especially noticeable for values of p that differ greatly from 0.50.

(2) The distance between P_2 and P_1 varies with p. The closer p is to 0.5 the greater the distance between P_2 and P_1. This is easy to understand when one realizes that σ_p is at a maximum when $P = 0.50$.

Tests of Hypotheses and Confidence Limits for Standard Deviation

Use of range. Let us introduce the topic by using one of the simplest *statistics*, the range R.

TEST OF HYPOTHESIS. We wish to assure ourselves that the standard deviation of the population from which the sample of Table 13.4 was taken is less than 10 pounds. The X-values are: 71; 68; 66; 57. We shall make use of the statistic $w = R/\sigma$. Values of w are tabulated in Appendix 24.

Hypothesis: H_0: $\sigma = 10$ pounds.

                              H_a: $\sigma < 10$ pounds.

Criterion of significance: $\alpha = .05$.

Range: $R = 71 - 57 = 14$ pounds.

Rejection region: From Appendix 24, we find that when $n = 4$, the lower .05 probability value for w is 0.759. When $R/10 = 0.759$, $R = 7.59$ pounds. Therefore, if $\sigma = 10$ pounds, we should expect 5 sample values of R out of 100 to be equal to or less than 7.59 pounds.

Conclusion: We accept H_0; there is no convincing evidence that $\sigma < 10$ pounds.

CONFIDENCE LIMITS. Equivalent results are obtained by use of the .9 confidence limits. From Appendix 24 we find that the values of w at the .05 points are 7.59 and 3.63.

Upper confidence limit: $\dfrac{14}{\sigma} = 0.759$,   and $\sigma_2 = 18.4$ pounds.

Lower confidence limit: $\dfrac{14}{\sigma} = 3.63$,   and $\sigma_1 = 3.9$ pounds.

We are 90 per cent confident that σ is between 3.9 pounds and 18.4 pounds. Our hypothetical value of σ, which is 10 pounds, is within these limits. If σ_2 had been less than 10 pounds, we would have been more than 95 per cent confident that σ is at least 10 pounds.

Use of standard deviation of sample. Use of the range, though quick and easy, results in an inefficient test. We are less likely to reject a hypothesis when the hypothesis is false than we are if we use the standard deviation of the sample, with the same sample size. This is especially true if the sample size is 12 or larger.

A manufacturer is making springs which, upon the basis of a carefully controlled run, were shown to have (under working conditions) tensions averaging 60 pounds and showing a standard deviation of 3.50 pounds. These are considered population figures and it is desired to know the limits within which 98 per cent of sample standard deviations might be expected to vary by chance if samples of $n = 15$ are used.

Questions of this type may be answered by use of Appendix 23, which shows values of $v = \measuredangle/\sigma$ at selected probability points. This Appendix shows that when $n = 15$, the value of v at the upper .01 point is 1.394, giving

$$1.394 = \frac{\Delta}{3.50}, \quad \text{and} \quad \Delta = (1.394)(3.50) = 4.9 \text{ pounds.}$$

The value of v at the lower 0.01 point is 0.557, giving

$$0.557 = \frac{\Delta}{3.50}, \quad \text{and} \quad \Delta = (0.557)(3.50) = 1.9.$$

Note that the probability points are unsymmetrical: $1.394 - 1.000 < 1.000 - 0.557$. As n gets larger the distribution of v becomes more nearly symmetrical.[4]

---

[4] Δ/σ is closely related to χ^2, which we used earlier, and to F, which we shall use in Chapter 23 and other places, especially Chapter 39.

By definition,

$$\chi^2 = \frac{vs^2}{\sigma^2} = \frac{\Sigma x^2}{\sigma^2}, \quad \text{with } v \text{ degrees of freedom.}$$

Therefore

$$\frac{\Delta^2}{\sigma^2} = \frac{\chi^2}{n}, \quad \text{and} \quad \frac{\Delta}{\sigma} = \sqrt{\frac{x^2}{n}}.$$

By definition also,

$$F = \frac{s_1^2}{s_2^2}, \quad \text{with } v_1 \text{ degrees of freedom for } s_1^2 \text{ and } v_2 \text{ degrees of}$$

freedom for s_2^2.

Now when $v_2 = \infty$, $\quad s_2^2 = \sigma_2^2, \quad \text{and} \quad F = \dfrac{s^2}{\sigma^2}.$

Therefore

$$\frac{\Delta^2}{\sigma^2} = \frac{n-1}{n} F, \quad \text{and} \quad \frac{\Delta}{\sigma} = \sqrt{\frac{n-1}{n}} \sqrt{F}.$$

If we wish to find, say, the upper 0.05 probability point for Δ/σ when $n = 9$, we may do it in any of these three ways:

Using Appendix 23, $\dfrac{\Delta}{\sigma} = 1.313$, when $n = 9$.

Using Appendix 22, $\chi^2 = 15.507$, when $v = n - 1 = 8$.

Therefore

$$\frac{\Delta}{\sigma} = \sqrt{\frac{15.507}{9}} = \sqrt{1.723} = 1.313.$$

Using Appendix 21, $F = 1.938$, when $v_1 = 8$ and $v_2 = \infty$.

Therefore

$$\frac{\Delta}{\sigma} = \sqrt{\frac{8}{9}} \sqrt{1.938} = \sqrt{0.889} \sqrt{1.938} = (0.9428)(1.392) = 1.312.$$

Thus, the more general distributions of χ^2 or F can be used, instead of the specialized Δ/σ, for testing hypotheses concerning σ or determining confidence limits of σ. The use of Δ/σ is easier, however.

Test of hypothesis. A sample of 25 springs shows $\varDelta = 3.49$ pounds. Does the sample differ significantly from the standard value of 3.55 pounds ?[5] Let us use $\alpha = .20$ for this problem. Appendix 23 shows that when $n = 25$:

The upper .10 probability point for $\varDelta/\sigma$ is 1.152;

The lower .10 probability point for $\varDelta/\sigma$ is 0.791.

Multiplying these values by our hypothetical standard value, we obtain the limits of the acceptance region.

$$\text{Upper limit:}\quad (1.152)(3.55) = 4.09.$$
$$\text{Lower limit:}\quad (0.791)(3.55) = 2.81.$$

Since 3.49 falls within the acceptance region, we accept the hypothesis that the manufacturing process is producing springs with $\sigma = 3.55$ pounds. The difference between 3.55 and 3.49 is not significant.

Confidence limits. Ten pieces of hard drawn copper wire showed a mean breaking strength of 575.2 pounds and $\varDelta = 8.25$ pounds. There is no other information concerning the population except that breaking strength values are believed to be normally distributed. It is desired to compute the 0.95 confidence limits of σ. Referring to Appendix 23, we find that the two values of $v = \varDelta/\sigma$ at the .025 probability points when $n = 10$ are 0.520 and 1.379. We therefore write

$$\frac{8.25}{\sigma} = 0.520, \quad \text{and} \quad \sigma = \frac{8.25}{0.520} = 15.9 \text{ pounds;}$$

$$\frac{8.25}{\sigma} = 1.379, \quad \text{and} \quad \sigma = \frac{8.25}{1.379} = 6.0 \text{ pounds.}$$

The 95 per cent confidence limits are thus 15.9 and 6.0 pounds. If this is too wide a range, the manufacturing process should be revised.

Statistical Decisions

In any applied field one does not usually test hypotheses for the purpose of adding to the store of human knowledge. Rather, statistical tests are conducted for the purpose of arriving at a decision. A business decision is correct if it increases profits. Decision making is therefore of central importance in business statistics.

To make the best decision we must know: 1. the costs of making alternative statistical tests; 2. the costs or losses that will result from various decisions; 3. the probabilities of making various decisions. The best decision rule is that which minimizes the total cost, giving proper consideration to the probabilities involved.

---

[5] It is perhaps of interest to note that if $\varDelta = 3.49$, our best estimate of σ is $s = 3.49\sqrt{\dfrac{25}{24}} = 3.56$ pounds. Note that $\varDelta$ is smaller than σ_0, but s is larger.

1. The cost of conducting each possible type of test, using each possible sample size, includes the cost of sampling and measurement, and the cost of computation. The cost of sampling and measurement will be a function of the sample size, but the cost of computation will depend on the type of test.

2. The cost or loss resulting from a specified business decision, such as to accept a lot rather than to reject it, or to use method of production 1 rather than method of production 2, depends on the value of the parameter involved, such as P, μ, σ, $P_1 - P_2$, $\mu_1 - \mu_2$, or σ_1/σ_2. For example, one loses more by accepting a lot that is 25 per cent defective than by accepting a lot that is 2 per cent defective. The test may, of course, involve more than one parameter; for example it may involve μ and σ.

3. The probability of making a specific decision depends on the nature of the test, the choice of the rejection region, the sample size, and the probability distribution of the parameter, or parameters, involved.

Determination of the probability distribution of the parameter is a difficult problem. One way of solving the problem is to assume that all values of the parameter, within some reasonable range, are equally probable. We would then select the test for which the simple average cost is smallest.

If there is any basis for so doing, one could assume that different values of the parameter occur with different relative frequencies. We could then take a weighted average, obtaining thereby an expected value for each plan, and select the plan with the smallest expected value.[6]

Still another solution is to assume that the worst possible luck will happen. One then selects the plan that has the smallest maximum cost. This is the minimax solution.

It must be apparent to the reader that most of the needed information is either unavailable, or too costly to obtain. Only item 3 is in part obtainable in the form of an OC or power function. Scientific statistical decision making is at present, therefore, primarily of theoretical interest.

---

[6] A numerical illustration following this approach is given as Chapter 29 of Dudley J. Cowden, *Statistical Methods in Quality Control*, Prentice-Hall, Englewood Cliffs, New Jersey, 1957.

*Chapter 23

HYPOTHESES CONCERNING DIFFERENCES
BETWEEN TWO SAMPLES

A comparison between two samples is frequently of greater interest than a comparison between a mean and a hypothetical value. In this chapter we compare two means, two proportions, and two standard deviations. In Chapter 39, these types of comparisons are extended to comparisons among three or more samples. For means, the technique is known as analysis of variance, a method of very wide applicability.

In the present chapter we shall also consider some nonparametric tests. These do not make stringent assumptions concerning the population. Conclusions from nonparametric tests are therefore more general than those resulting from parametric tests, but usually this advantage is obtained by sacrificing efficiency. Nonparametric tests are usually less laborious than parametric tests.

Hypothesis that Two Samples are from Populations with Same Mean

Independent samples. The data of Table 21.3 showed the results of tests of flex life for 50 pieces of Supertwist cord. In Table 23.1 data are shown of the flex life of each 50 pieces of Regular cord. It will be noted that the mean flex life of the 50 pieces of Supertwist cord $(\bar{X}_1)$ is 138.64 minutes and for Regular cord the mean $(\bar{X}_2)$ is 87.66 minutes. We wish to know if there is a significant difference between these two means. Our *hypothesis* is that the two means are computed from random samples from the same population or from two populations having $\mu_1 = \mu_2$, it being assumed that $\sigma_1 = \sigma_2$. If we knew σ, we could test this hypothesis by comparing $\bar{X}_1 - \bar{X}_2$ with the standard error of the difference between the two sample means. Now the variance of a sum or difference is the sum of the variances.[1]

(23.1) $$\sigma_{X_1+X_2}^2 = \sigma_{X_1-X_2}^2 = \sigma_1^2 + \sigma_2^2.$$

Similarly,

(23.2) $$\sigma_{\bar{X}_1-\bar{X}_2}^2 = \sigma_{\bar{X}_1}^2 + \sigma_{\bar{X}_2}^2,$$

and the standard error is the square root of this quantity. But, in such a situation as the above we rarely know σ^2. Since we do not know σ^2, we

---

[1] See Dudley J. Cowden, *Statistical Methods in Quality Control*, Prentice-Hall, Inc., Englewood Cliffs, N.J., 1957, pp. 223–224.

substitute an estimate of σ^2 which is the weighted average of the two separate estimates of the population variance. This estimate of σ^2 is given by[2]

$$(23.3) \quad s_W^2 = \frac{\nu_1 s_1^2 + \nu_2 s_2^2}{\nu_1 + \nu_2} + \frac{\Sigma x_1^2 + \Sigma x_2^2}{\nu_1 + \nu_2} = \frac{\Sigma x_1^2 + \Sigma x_2^2}{(n_1 - 1) + (n_2 - 1)},$$

which allows proper weight for each sample according to its degrees of freedom.

Table 23.1—Computation of $\bar{X}$ and Σx^2 for Flex Life of Regular Cord

Flex life in minutes X_2	X_2^2	Flex life in minutes X_2	X_2^2
116	13,456	107	11,449
70	4,900	77	5,929
77	5,929	80	6,400
97	9,409	77	5,929
124	15,376	74	5,476
95	9,025	113	12,769
75	5,625	89	7,921
92	8,464	114	12,996
76	5,776	93	8,649
88	7,744	106	11,236
88	7,744	80	6,400
118	13,924	62	3,844
81	6,561	73	5,329
87	7,569	96	9,216
95	9,025	77	5,929
91	8,281	84	7,056
81	6,561	95	9,025
78	6,084	78	6,084
91	8,281	83	6,889
83	6,889	68	4,624
93	8,649	72	5,184
83	6,889	64	4,096
103	10,609	80	6,400
84	7,056	90	8,100
105	11,025		
80	6,400	4,383	394,181

Source: The Goodyear Tire and Rubber Company.

$$\bar{X}_2 = \frac{\Sigma X_2}{n_2} = \frac{4,383}{50} = 87.66 \text{ minutes}$$

$$\Sigma x_2^2 = \Sigma X_2^2 - \frac{(\Sigma X_2)^2}{n} = 394,181 - \frac{(4,383)^2}{50} = 9,967.$$

---

[2] The expression shown above is equivalent to the "within columns" variance used in analysis of variance (Chapter 39) when there are only two columns.

The value of Σx^2 may be obtained from the expression

$$\Sigma x^2 = \Sigma X^2 - \frac{(\Sigma X)^2}{n}.$$

If we know s,

$$\Sigma x^2 = ns^2,$$

or, if we know s,

$$\Sigma x^2 = (n-1)s^2.$$

When computing Σx_1^2, the subscript 1 appears in the above expressions; when determining Σx_2^2, the subscript 2 is used.

For the variance of the difference between two sample means we have

(23.4)
$$s_{\bar{X}_1 - \bar{X}_2}^2 = \frac{s_w^2}{n_1} + \frac{s_w^2}{n_2} = s_w^2 \left(\frac{1}{n_1} + \frac{1}{n_2} \right).$$

If $n_1 = n_2$, a mathematically equivalent expression is

(23.5)
$$s_{\bar{X}_1 - \bar{X}_2}^2 = \frac{s_1^2}{n_1} + \frac{s_2^2}{n_2} = s_{\bar{X}_1}^2 + s_{\bar{X}_2}^2.$$

Summarizing the data of Tables 21.3 and 23.1, we have the following:

Supertwist cord	Regular cord
$n_1 = 50$	$n_2 = 50$
$\bar{X}_1 = 138.64$ minutes	$\bar{X}_2 = 87.66$ minutes
$\Sigma x_1^2 = 11{,}668$	$\Sigma x_2^2 = 9{,}967$

From these values we obtain:

$$s_w^2 = \frac{11{,}668 + 9{,}967}{49 + 49} = 220.77;$$

$$s_{\bar{X}_1 - \bar{X}_2}^2 = (220.77)\left(\frac{1}{50} + \frac{1}{50} \right) = 8.831;$$

$$s_{\bar{X}_1 - \bar{X}_2} = 2.97.$$

Using the above data, we are able to compute

(23.6)
$$t = \frac{\bar{X}_1 - \bar{X}_2}{s_{\bar{X}_1 - \bar{X}_2}}$$

$$= \frac{138.64 - 87.66}{2.97} = \frac{50.98}{2.97} = 17.2.$$

Each set of data contributes 49 degrees of freedom, so we refer to the t-table for $t = 17.2$ and $\nu = 98$. This value of t greatly exceeds the value for t at the 0.05 level, and we conclude that there is a significant difference between the two means.

Wilcoxon's nonparametric T_2 test. If we do not know anything about the variances or shapes of the two populations, we can still make a test of the hypothesis that $\mu_1 = \mu_2$. Even if we did not know the exact values of the items in the two samples, but were able to rank them, we could use the following procedure, provided $n_1 = n_2$.

1. Rank the items in ascending order, without respect to sample, as in Table 23.2.

Table 23.2—Per cent of House Flies Killed by Two Preparations, and Rank of Percentages Without Respect to Sample

Preparation 1		Preparation 2	
X_1	Rank	X_2	Rank
68	12.5	60	4
68	12.5	67	10
59	3	61	5
72	15	62	6
64	8	67	10
67	10	63	7
70	14	56	1
74	16	58	2
Total	91	Total	45

Source of data: See Table 12.7.

2. Find the total of the ranks for the sample with the smallest of the two rank totals. In Table 23.2 this is 45, for preparation 2. This is the statistic T_2.

3. Evaluate T_2 by reference to a table of probability points. Appendix Table 20 gives *lower* probability points. If the sample value of T_2 is *smaller* than the value of T_2 at the appropriate probability level, reject the null hypothesis. Using $\alpha = 0.05$, we find that Table 20 gives $T_2 = 49$ when $n = 8$. Since 45 is smaller than 49 we reject the hypothesis that the two preparations are equally potent, and consider that the difference between them is significant.

This test is not so efficient as the (parametric) t test, but it is obviously very easy for small values of n.

Paired samples. If some way can be found of pairing each value of X_1 with a related value of X_2, we can test the significance of the mean difference rather than the significance of the difference between the means. This eliminates one source of random variability in the data, leaving that which results from the lack of perfect correlation between the two variables.[3] It is desirable to plan an investigation in such a way that we can logically pair the samples, for by so doing we are likely to detect a difference when it is significant.

For an illustration we shall use the data of Table 23.3, which are the compressive strength of 10 pairs of test cubes of concrete of Table 12.8.

Table 23.3—Compressive Strength of 10 Pairs of Test Cubes of Concrete, and Computations for Testing Significance of Mean Difference

Batch	Treated X_1	Not treated X_2	D $X_1 - X_2$	D^2
1	309	293	16	256
2	318	311	7	49
3	317	284	33	1,089
4	302	310	−8	64
5	315	305	10	100
6	296	291	5	25
7	319	301	18	324
8	285	279	6	36
9	303	295	8	64
10	290	289	1	1
Total	3,054	2,958	96	2,008

Source of data: Table 12.8.

We use the symbol D to mean values of $X_1 - X_2$ for the sample and Δ to mean the same thing for the population. Since we are interested in discovering only whether the strength of the concrete is significantly increased by the treatment, it seems reasonable to use a one-sided test

$$H_0: \quad \Delta = 0; \qquad H_a: \quad \Delta > 0.$$

---

[3] Formula (23.1) assumes that there is no correlation between X_1 and X_2. If there is correlation, it is not difficult to show that the formula is

$$\sigma^2_{X_1-X_2} = \sigma_1^2 + \sigma_2^2 = 2\rho_{12}\sigma_1\sigma_2.$$

Similarly it can be shown that

$$s_D^2 = s^2_{X_1-X_2} = s_1^2 + s_2^2 - 2r_{12}s_1s_2.$$

Using the data of Table 23.1 we obtain

$$s_1^2 = 149.156; \quad s_2^2 = 115.956; \quad r_{12} = +0.5490.$$
$$s_D^2 = 120.71; \quad s_D = 10.99.$$

This is the same value that we obtain by the simpler method of this section. An equivalent solution can be obtained by the very general method of analysis of variance. See Chapter 39.

We now proceed as if we were dealing with a single variable.

$$\bar{D} = \frac{\Sigma D}{n} = \frac{96}{10} = 9.6 \text{ kilograms.}$$

$$s_D = \sqrt{\frac{\Sigma D^2 - (\Sigma D)^2/n}{n-1}} = \sqrt{\frac{2,008 - (96)^2/10}{9}} = 10.99 \text{ kilograms.}$$

$$s_{\bar{D}} = \frac{s}{\sqrt{n}} = \frac{10.99}{\sqrt{10}} = 3.476 \text{ kilograms.}$$

$$t = \frac{\bar{D}}{s_{\bar{D}}} = \frac{9.6}{3.476} = 2.76.$$

With $\nu = 9$, and $\alpha = .025$, $t_\alpha = t_{.025} = 2.26$. Since the computed value of t is greater than $t_{.025}$, we reject H_0 and conclude that the treatment significantly increases the strength of the concrete.

This method is to be preferred to the methods of Chapter 12 because, though more laborious, it is more efficient.

Wilcoxon's nonparametric T_1 test. This test makes no assumptions concerning the two populations. However, we must know enough about the two samples to be able to rank the differences. The procedure is as follows:

1. Rank in ascending order the differences according to their *numerical* values, as in Table 23.4, which uses the data of Table 23.3. In Table 23.4 batch 4 shows a difference of -8, while batch 9 shows a difference of $+8$. They are tied for ranks 5 and 6, and each is assigned a rank of 5.5.

Table 23.4—Differences in Compressive Strength of 10 Pairs of Test Cubes of Concrete, and Rank of Differences

Batch	Difference	Rank
1	16	8
2	7	4
3	33	10
4	−8	−5.5
5	10	7
6	5	2
7	18	9
8	6	3
9	8	5.5
10	1	1
Smallest rank total		−5.5

Source of data: Table 23.3.

2. Affix the appropriate signs to the ranks. Thus, in Table 23.4, a negative sign is affixed to 5.5 for batch 4.

3. Find the smallest rank total of the ranks of the same sign. This is the statistic T_1. In Table 23.4, the sum of the negative ranks is smaller than the sum of the positive ranks. This total (only one item in this case), is 5.5.

4. Evaluate T_1 by reference to a table of probability points. Appendix Table 19 gives *lower* probability points. If the sample value of T_1 is *smaller* than the table value of T_1, reject the null hypothesis. Thus, for $n = 10$ we find that $T_1 = 8$ when $\alpha = .05$ for a two-sided test, or when $\alpha = .025$ for a one-sided test. Thus, if $\alpha = .025$, using a one-sided test we would reject H_0. The results of this test are in agreement with those of the G_1 test of Chapter 12.

This test is almost as powerful as the (parametric) t test.

Sign test. If all we know is which item is larger for each pair, we can still test the hypothesis that $\mu_1 = \mu_2$.

Table 23.4 shows that out of ten values of $X_1 - X_2$, one difference is negative and nine are positive. Now, what is the probability that for a sample of 10 pairs, the treated blocks will be superior for at least 9 pairs, the untreated blocks being superior for not more than one pair? If $P = .5$ what is the probability that when $n = 10$, $d \leq 1$? Appendix 5 shows values of the binomial coefficients $\binom{N}{n}$, or $\binom{n}{d}$ in terms of our problem. If we sum the binomial coefficients for $N = 10$, we obtain 1,024. The first 2 binomial coefficients are 1 and 10. Therefore,

$$\text{Prob}\,(d \leq 1) = \frac{11}{1,024} = .01.$$

Using $\alpha = .025$, we therefore reject the hypothesis that $\mu_1 - \mu_2 = 0$ in favor of the alternative hypothesis that $\mu_1 - \mu_2 > 0$.

The sign test makes no assumptions concerning the populations, and requires less information concerning the sample, than the t test or the T_1 test. The conclusions are therefore more general, but it is also the least powerful of the three tests.

Hypothesis that Two Samples are from Populations with Same Proportional Favorable

A survey conducted for a tire company, which we will call "Superior" in order not to reveal its actual name, found that of 954 persons (n_1) in a certain rural county who were planning to buy new tires during the coming summer, 259 (d_1) or 27.15 per cent (p_1) were planning to buy Superior tires. In an adjacent county 770 persons (n_2) expected to buy new tires during the summer, and 206 (d_2) or 26.75 per cent (p_2) were planning to purchase the Superior brand. It is desired to know if the difference between these two percentages is significant or if it may have been due to chance arising from sampling variability. If it develops that the difference is significant, it will be advisable to ascertain the reason for the difference. Possibly one county has road conditions which Superior tires do not adequately meet; possibly there is a more aggressive dealer in one county.

The test follows the same general outline as that for testing the difference between two means where the samples are independent.

Null hypothesis: The two samples are random samples from populations with the same proportion favorable.

$$H_0: \quad P_1 = P_2; \qquad H_a: \quad P_1 \neq P_2.$$

The proportion favorable in the population is unknown, and is not specified in the hypothesis.

Estimate of P: This is the weighted mean of p_1 and p_2.

$$(23.7) \qquad \bar{p} = \frac{d_1 + d_2}{n_1 + n_2} \quad \text{or} \quad \frac{n_1 p_1 + n_2 p_2}{n_1 + n_2} = \frac{259 + 206}{954 + 770} = 0.2697.$$

Variance of the difference between p_1 and p_2: This is analogous to formula (23.4).

$$(23.8) \qquad s^2_{p_1 - p_2} = \frac{\bar{p}\bar{q}}{n_1} + \frac{\bar{p}\bar{q}}{n_2} \quad \text{or} \quad \bar{p}\bar{q}\left(\frac{1}{n_1} + \frac{1}{n_2}\right),$$

where $\bar{q} = 1 - \bar{p}$. For our problem $\bar{p}\bar{q} = (0.2697)(0.7303) = 0.19696$,

$$s^2_{p_1 - p_2} = \frac{0.19696}{954} + \frac{0.19696}{770} = 0.0004622, \quad \text{and}$$

$$s_{p_1 - p_2} = 0.02150.$$

Criterion of significance: Since the adverse consequences of rejecting H_0, if H_0 is not true, are not great, let us use $\alpha = .10$.

Rejection region: Since we are dealing with large samples,[4] we may consider that z, the ratio of the difference to its estimated standard error, is to be normally distributed. Therefore, since this is a two-sided test, the critical value of z is $z_{\alpha/2} = z_{.05} = 1.645$. If the sample value of z is greater numerically than 1.645, it falls in the rejection region.

Significance ratio:

$$(23.9) \qquad |z| = \frac{p_1 - p_2}{s_{p_1 - p_2}}$$

$$= \frac{0.2715 - 0.2675}{0.0215} = \frac{0.0040}{0.0215} = 0.19.$$

Conclusion: Since the sample value of z is smaller than $z_{\alpha/2}$ (i.e., $0.19 < 1.645$), we accept H_0 and conclude that the difference between p_1 and p_2 is not significant. If we wish also to evaluate the sample value of z, we

---

[4] For small samples a different treatment is advisable. See the section of Chapter 39 dealing with 2 × 2 contingency tables.

find that the probability of obtaining a value of $|z|$ as large as 0.19 is 0.85. Since $0.85 > 0.10$, we accept H_0.

Hypothesis that Two Populations have the Same Standard Deviation

The variance ratio. The variance ratio is the ratio between two independent estimates of the population variance.[5]

$$(23.10) \qquad F = \frac{s_1^2}{s_2^2}.$$

Since s^2 is always greater than zero, F cannot be negative, but can be indefinitely large. Values of F at various probability levels are given in Appendix 21. The probabilities given are the probabilities that F will equal or exceed the value recorded in the table. In Appendix 21, the values of F are always greater than 1. Thus only the upper probability points are given. These are the probability points that are most often useful.[6] In order to use Appendix Table 21 it is necessary to know the degrees of freedom ν_1 and ν_2 for s_1^2 and s_2^2, respectively. Although the number of degrees of freedom depend on the type of problem, it is always $n - 1$ for the problems of this chapter.

Test of hypothesis. Flex life of Supertwist cord and Regular cord were previously noted on page 354 to have $\Sigma x_1^2 = 11,668$ and $\Sigma x_2^2 = 9,967$, respectively. For each sample, $n = 50$. From this information we compute

$$s_1^2 = \frac{11,668}{49} = 238.12, \quad \text{and} \quad s_2^2 = \frac{9,967}{49} = 203.41.$$

Our hypothesis is that $\sigma_1^2 = \sigma_2^2$, the alternative hypothesis being that $\sigma_1^2 > \sigma_2^2$. For the criterion of significance we shall take $\alpha = 0.05$.

Next, we obtain

$$F = \frac{s_1^2}{s_2^2} = \frac{238.12}{203.41} = 1.171.$$

---

[5] A more complete definition is

$$F = \frac{\chi_1^2/\nu_1}{\chi_2^2/\nu_2},$$

where
$$\chi^2 = \sum_1^\nu \left(\frac{X - \mu}{\sigma}\right), \quad \text{with } \nu \text{ degrees of freedom,}$$

or
$$\chi^2 = \sum_1^n \left(\frac{X - \bar{X}}{\sigma}\right)^2, \quad \text{with } \nu = n - 1.$$

[6] The lower probability point is the reciprocal of F with ν_1 and ν_2 interchanged. Thus, if $\nu_1 = 5$ and $\nu_2 = 8$, the .05 *upper* probability point is 3.69. If $\nu_1 = 8$ and $\nu_2 = 5$, the *upper* probability point is 4.82, and the *lower* probability point is $1/3.69 = 0.271$.

The appropriate degrees of freedom are $v_1 = 50 - 1 = 49$ and $v_2 = 50 - 1 = 49$. Referring to Appendix 21 we find entries for $v_1 = 30$ and 60 and for $v_2 = 24$ and ∞. It is not necessary to interpolate, since $F = 1.171$ is less than the value of F shown in the table for any of the four combinations $v_1 = 30$, $v_2 = 24$; $v_1 = 30$, $v_2 = \infty$; $v_1 = 60$, $v_2 = 24$; and $v_1 = 60$, $v_2 = \infty$. Thus the probability of obtaining a value of s_1^2/s_2^2 as large as, or larger than, that observed is more than 0.05. We therefore accept the null hypothesis, and conclude that s_1^2 is not significantly larger than s_2^2.

The probability of obtaining a value of s_1^2/s_2^2 as large as, or larger than, the observed value is considerably more than 0.05. When $v_1 = v_2$, and the probability is 0.05 for a given value of s_1^2/s_2^2, then the probability is 0.10 of obtaining a value of s_1^2/s_2^2 as large as or larger than that obtained or a value of s_1^2/s_2^2 as small as or smaller than the reciprocal of that obtained, i.e., as large as 1.171 or as small as 0.854.

Data are shown in Tables 17.4 and 17.5 which enable us to compute the following estimates of the population variation in the strength of screw-drivers of valve caps:

National Equipment Company	Competitor
$n_2 = 34$	$n_1 = 36$
$\Sigma x_2^2 = 4{,}739.39$	$\Sigma x_1^2 = 35{,}115.97$
$s_2^2 = \dfrac{4{,}739.39}{33} = 143.62$	$s_1^2 = \dfrac{35{,}115.97}{35} = 1{,}003.31$

To determine if s_1^2 is significantly larger than s_2^2 we compute

$$F - \frac{s_1^2}{s_2^2} = \frac{1{,}003.31}{143.62} = 6.99.$$

$v_1 = 36 - 1 = 35$ and $v_2 = 34 - 1 = 33$. Referring to Appendix 21, we find that this value of F is beyond the 0.001 point, and we conclude that s_1^2 exceeds s_2^2 significantly. The National Equipment Company is almost certainly making a more uniform product than is its competitor.

Chapter 24

FITTING A STRAIGHT LINE

It is frequently very useful to be able to explain variations in one series by comparing them with variations in another related series. For instance, a concern buys large quantities of materials that must be of a certain tensile strength; these materials must be tested, but the only way of measuring tensile strength involves stretching a unit until it breaks, thereby destroying its usefulness. However, it appears that materials that possess great tensile strength are also likely to be hard, and those that are unusually weak in this respect tend also to be extremely soft. If the association between hardness and tensile strength is sufficiently close, it is possible to estimate with considerable accuracy the tensile strength of any piece on the basis of the relationship between hardness and tensile strength shown by a sample. This is an economical method of testing, since the test for hardness is not destructive.

The Scatter Diagram

In the second and third columns of Table 24.1 are shown the hardness X and tensile strength Y of a random sample of 27 pieces of wrought aluminum alloy, arranged according to hardness as shown by the tests. This, of course, is not the order in which the pieces were tested; it is used to enable one to see that, as hardness increases, there is a tendency for tensile strength to increase. Although this table enables one to observe each item separately, one cannot gain a clear impression of the nature of the relationship between the two variables; if hardness increases a given number of points, we do not know how much tensile strength increases. For the purpose of finding out, an extremely useful chart, known as the "scatter diagram" (Chart 24.1) is constructed by placing dots on coordinate paper, one dot for each pair of observations. For example, the fourth specimen listed in Table 24.1 shows a hardness of 27 and a tensile strength of 13. Therefore, the dot representing this item is located directly above the 27 value on the X axis, which represents hardness, and to the right of the 13 value on the Y axis, which represents tensile strength. Chart 24.1 shows each of the 27 items located in a similar fashion.

The straight line running through the diagram is the best fitting straight line that can be drawn, according to *one* criterion of goodness of fit. The equation type is

(24.1) $$Y_X = a + bX.$$

Table 24.1—Computation of Values Used in Determining Measures of Relationship Between Hardness and Tensile Strength of 27 Pieces of Wrought Aluminum Alloy
(Hardness is measured in units of Brinnell hardness; tensile strength represents thousands of pounds per square inch.)

Rank in hardness (lowest to highest)	Hardness X	Tensile strength Y	X^2	XY	Y^2
1	16	8	256	128	64
2	24	14	576	336	196
3	26	15	676	390	225
4	27	13	729	351	169
5	28	16	784	448	256
6	29	16	841	464	256
7	30	16	900	480	256
8	35	19	1,225	665	361
9	41	23	1,681	943	529
10	42	26	1,764	1,092	676
11	44	25	1,936	1,100	625
12	45	26	2,025	1,170	676
13	49	30	2,401	1,470	900
14	52	30	2,704	1,560	900
15	52	30	2,704	1,560	900
16	59	37	3,481	2,183	1,369
17	64	33	4,096	2,112	1,089
18	70	38	4,900	2,660	1,444
19	80	39	6,400	3,120	1,521
20	87	52	7,569	4,524	2,704
21	95	48	9,025	4,560	2,304
22	99	60	9,801	5,940	3,600
23	99	61	9,801	6,039	3,721
24	101	59	10,201	5,959	3,481
25	116	68	13,456	7,888	4,624
26	119	71	14,161	8,449	5,041
27	120	67	14,400	8,040	4,489
Total:	1,649	940	128,493	73,631	42,376
Mean	61.07407	34.81481	....	....	....
Correction term	....	....	*100,711.1	*57,409.6	*32,725.9
Variation or covariation			27,781.9	16,221.4	9,650.1

Source: Aluminum Research Laboratories, Aluminum Company of America.

$\overline{X}$ and $\overline{Y}$ are carried to 7 digits to permit formal internal checks. Actually only 3 or 4 digits are significant.

* These correction terms, which are subtracted from the sums of squares and products in order to obtain measures of variation and covariation, are:

$$\frac{(\Sigma X)^2}{n} = \overline{X}\Sigma X ; \quad \frac{(\Sigma X)(\Sigma Y)}{n} = \overline{X}\Sigma Y = \overline{Y}\Sigma X ; \quad \frac{(\Sigma Y)^2}{n} = \overline{Y}\Sigma Y.$$

Chart 24.1—Hardness and Tensile Strength of 27 Pieces of Wrought Aluminum Alloy

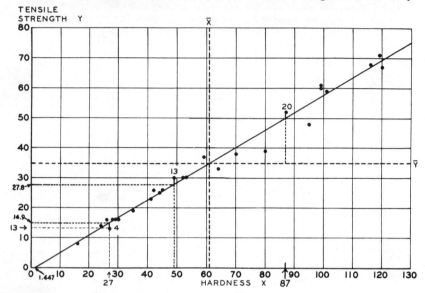

Source of data: Table 24.1.

The symbol Y_X, pronounced "Y sub X," or "Y of X," or "Y on X," means "Y as a function of X," or "estimate of Y when X has a specified value."[1] The statistical problem is to find numerical values for a and b such that the equation gives the best fitting straight line that can be obtained. As we shall see, this line has the equation

$$Y_X = -0.8451 + 0.58388X.$$

The straight line resulting from this equation is plotted on Chart 24.1, and is known as an *estimating line*, while the equation is known as an *estimating equation*. The reason for this terminology is that the purpose of the equation is to permit us to make estimates of Y for specified values of X. Consider two examples, using the specified value of X as a subscript to Y, and also substituting that value for X in the estimating equation.

Observation 4: $X = 27$, $Y_{27} = -0.8451 + (0.58388)(27) = 14.9197$;

Observation 13: $X = 49$, $Y_{49} = -0.8451 + (0.58388)(49) = 27.7650$.

The location of these values is shown by dotted lines on Chart 24.1.

The estimated values Y_X do not necessarily coincide with the actual values Y. Consider again observations 4 and 13.

Observation 4: $X = 27$, $Y = 13$, $Y_{27} = 14.92$, $Y - Y_{27} = -4.92$.

Observation 13: $X = 49$, $Y = 30$, $Y_{49} = 27.77$, $Y - Y_{49} = 2.23$.

---

[1] Sometimes $Y(X)$ is used instead of Y_X.

The Least Squares Criterion

Values of $Y - Y_X$ are called errors of estimate, since they are the amounts by which the estimates are in error. It would seem natural to want the sum of these errors (taken without regard to sign) to be as small as possible. But statisticians usually fit the line in such a way that the sum of the squares of these errors is as small as possible. From a graphic point of view, the

Chart 24.2—Effect on Sum of Squares of Deviations from Estimating Line Resulting From Wrong Values of *a* and *b* in Estimating Equation

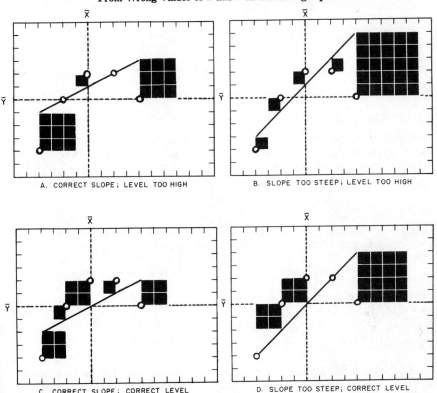

A. CORRECT SLOPE; LEVEL TOO HIGH

B. SLOPE TOO STEEP; LEVEL TOO HIGH

C. CORRECT SLOPE; CORRECT LEVEL

D. SLOPE TOO STEEP; CORRECT LEVEL

estimating line is drawn in such a way that the sum of the squares of the vertical deviations from it is as small as, or smaller than the sum, from any other straight line. Thus, in Chart 24.2, diagram A, which shows a line with the correct slope ($b = 0.5$) and the correct level (passing through the point $\overline{X}, \overline{Y}$), has the smallest shaded area. From a mathematical viewpoint we determine the values of a and b by the *method of least squares*, minimizing $\Sigma (Y - Y_X)^2$. But since $Y_X = a + bX$, we may say that we minimize $\Sigma (Y - a - bX)^2$.

It should be remembered that the equation

$$Y_X = a + bX$$

refers to a sample. It is an estimate of a similar equation for the entire population, which may be written

$$Y_X = A + BX.$$

Thus a in an estimate of A and b is an estimate of B. The chief reason for fitting an equation by the method of least squares is that when this is done, a and b are not only unbiased estimates of A and B, but have the smallest variance of all estimates that are unbiased.[2]

The Normal Equations

Minimizing $\Sigma(Y - a - bX)^2$ results in two equations:[3]

(24.2) $$na + b\Sigma X = \Sigma Y, \text{ normal equation I;}$$

(24.3) $$a\Sigma X + b\Sigma X^2 = \Sigma XY, \text{ normal equation II.}$$

We have now two simultaneous equations and two unknowns. The numerical values for ΣX, ΣY, ΣX^2, and ΣXY, which are needed for these equations, are computed in Table 24.1 and shown in the total row of that table. We may therefore substitute these values in the normal equations and solve for a and b.[4] It is easier, however, to use two single equations than

---

[2] This is true provided the values of $Y - Y_X$ for the entire population do not vary with the values of X, and have the same variance for all values of X. In order to apply the usual tests of significance it must also be assumed that the errors of estimate are normally distributed.

[3] Normal equations for any equation that is in linear form can be obtained as follows:
1. Multiply each of the n observation equations by the coefficient of the first unknown, and sum the resulting equations. In the present case, the first unknown is a, and its coefficient is 1. Thus we have

$$\sum_1^n [1(Y = a + bX)] \quad \text{or} \quad \sum_1^n (Y = a + bX) \quad \text{or} \quad \Sigma Y = Na + b\Sigma X.$$

2. Multiply each of the n observation equations by the coefficient of the second unknown, and sum the resulting equations. In the present case, the second unknown is b, and its coefficient is X. Thus we have

$$\sum_1^n X(Y = a + bX) \quad \text{or} \quad \sum_1^n (XY = aX + bX^2) \quad \text{or} \quad \Sigma XY = a\Sigma X + b\Sigma X^2.$$

3. If there are more than two unknowns, the procedure is continued in an analogous manner.

[4] The solution below is simple, though perhaps somewhat laborious. Substitute in the normal equations the numerical values given in Table 24.1:

I. $$27a + 1{,}649b = 940;$$

II. $$1{,}649a + 128{,}493b = 73{,}631.$$

a pair of simultaneous equations. From the normal equations it is easy to derive the following:[5]

(24.4) $b = \dfrac{\Sigma xY}{\Sigma x^2}$,   where $x = X - \bar{X}$.

(24.5) $b = \dfrac{\Sigma xy}{\Sigma x^2}$,   where $y = Y - \bar{Y}$.

(24.6) $a = \bar{Y} - b\bar{X}$.

The reader is already familiar with the fact that Σx^2, referred to as variation, is easily computed as follows:

$$\Sigma x^2 = \Sigma X^2 - \frac{(\Sigma X)^2}{n}.$$

Similarly, $\Sigma y^2 = \Sigma Y^2 - \dfrac{(\Sigma Y)^2}{n}.$

Multiply both sides of equation I by $\bar{X} = 1,649/27 = 61.07407$, subtract from equation II, and obtain b.

II. $1,649.0a - 128,493.0b = 73,631.0$

I. $1,649.0a - 100,711.1b = 57,409.6$

Difference: $27,781.9b = 16,221.4$

$b = 0.58388.$

Substitute 0.58388 for b in equation I.

I. $27a + (1,649)(0.58388) = 940;$

$27a = -22.818;$

$a = -0.8451.$

Check by substituting the values of a and b in equation II.

II. $(1,649)(-0.8451) - (128,493)(.58388) = 73,631.$

[5] The slope of a line is not changed by subtracting a constant from each value of X; the line is merely moved sideways. If therefore we subtract $\bar{X}$ from each value of X, normal equation II, which is

$$\Sigma XY = a\Sigma X + b\Sigma X^2$$

becomes

$$\Sigma (X - \bar{X})Y = a\Sigma (X - \bar{X}) - b\Sigma (X - \bar{X})^2, \quad \text{or}$$

$$\Sigma xY = a\Sigma x + b\Sigma x^2, \quad \text{since } x = X - \bar{X}, \quad \text{or}$$

$$\Sigma xY = b\Sigma x^2, \quad \text{since } \Sigma x = 0.$$

Likewise, the slope of a line is not changed by subtracting a constant from each value of Y; the line is merely moved up or down. If we subtract $\bar{Y}$ from each value of Y

$$\Sigma xY = b\Sigma x^2$$

becomes

$$\Sigma x(Y - \bar{Y}) = b\Sigma x^2, \quad \text{or}$$

$$\Sigma xy = b\Sigma x^2.$$

Equation (24.6) is obtained by dividing both sides of normal equation I by n.

Finally, $\Sigma\, xy$, referred to as covariation, and defined as $\Sigma\,(X - \bar{X})(Y - \bar{Y})$, is computed as follows:[6]

$$(24.7) \qquad\qquad \Sigma\, xy = \Sigma\, XY - \frac{(\Sigma\, X)(\Sigma\, Y)}{n}.$$

Covariation obviously is a measure of the extent to which x and y vary together. It is positive if the concomitant deviations are in the same direction, and negative if in opposite directions.

Computations

The values of $\Sigma\, X^2$, $\Sigma\, XY$, and $\Sigma\, Y^2$, as well as the correction terms and the measures of variation and covariation, $\Sigma\, x^2$, $\Sigma\, xy$, $\Sigma\, y^2$, are computed in Table 24.1. They are also repeated on page 369, together with their symbols.[7] Each measure of variation and covariation is obtained by subtracting a correction term from sum of squares or sum of products immediately above it.

It is worthwhile to compare Table 24.1 with Table 24.2. In the latter table the measures of variation and covariation are computed explicitly (and laboriously) by the definitional formulas:

$$\Sigma\, x^2 = \frac{\Sigma\,(X - \bar{X})^2}{n}\; ; \;\; \Sigma\, xy = \frac{\Sigma\,(X - \bar{X})(Y - \bar{Y})}{n}\; ; \;\; \Sigma\, y^2 = \frac{\Sigma\,(Y - \bar{Y})^2}{n}.$$

---

[6] The correction terms $(\Sigma\, X)^2/n$, $(\Sigma\, Y)^2/n$, and $(\Sigma\, X)(\Sigma\, Y)/n$ may also be written $\bar{X}\,\Sigma\, X$, $\bar{Y}\,\Sigma\, Y$, and $\bar{X}\,\Sigma\, Y$ or $\bar{Y}\,\Sigma\, X$, or they may be written $n\bar{X}^2$, $n\bar{Y}^2$, and $n\bar{X}\bar{Y}$. Since $\bar{X}$ and $\bar{Y}$ are needed for other purposes, there are advantages in the second method of computation (involving sums and means), provided the means are computed to a sufficient number of digits. It is recommended that they be carried to *at least* as many digits as the sum of squares or sum of products with the most digits. It is recommended also that $\bar{X}\,\Sigma\, Y$ and $\bar{Y}\,\Sigma\, X$ both be computed as a check.

The proof that $\Sigma\, xy = \Sigma\, XY - (\Sigma\, X)(\Sigma\, Y)/n$ is as follows:

$$\Sigma\, xy = \Sigma\,(X - \bar{X})(Y - \bar{Y})$$
$$= \Sigma\,(XY - \bar{X}Y - \bar{Y}X + \bar{X}\bar{Y})$$
$$= \Sigma\, XY - \bar{X}\,\Sigma\, Y - \bar{Y}\,\Sigma\, X + n\bar{X}\bar{Y}$$
$$= \Sigma\, XY - \frac{(\Sigma\, X)(\Sigma\, Y)}{n} - \frac{(\Sigma\, X)(\Sigma\, Y)}{n} + \frac{(\Sigma\, X)(\Sigma\, Y)}{n}$$
$$= \Sigma\, XY - (\Sigma\, X)(\Sigma\, Y)/n.$$

[7] It is not necessary to record the individual values of X^2, XY, and Y^2, for modern calculating machines will cumulate sums of products. Values of $\Sigma\, X^2$, $2\,\Sigma\, XY$, and $\Sigma\, Y^2$ can be obtained simultaneously. Note that $\bar{X}$ and $\bar{Y}$ are carried to 7 digits, since $\Sigma\, X^2$ contains 6 digits. This many is necessary in order that $\bar{X}\,\Sigma\, X = (\Sigma\, X)^2/n$. It is also necessary for other internal checks. It should be noted that a separate row is not needed for $(\Sigma\, X)^2$, $(\Sigma\, X)(\Sigma\, Y)$, and $(\Sigma\, Y)^2$. Not only can the correction terms be obtained by multiplying a sum by a product, $(\bar{X}\,\Sigma\, X$, $\bar{X}\,\Sigma\, Y$ or $\bar{Y}\,\Sigma\, X$, $\bar{Y}\,\Sigma\, Y)$ but all makes of modern calculating machines permit taking the product of two numbers and dividing the product by a third number without clearing the product from the machine.

Sum Mean	$\Sigma X = 1,649$ $\bar{X} = 61.07407$	....	$\Sigma Y = 940$ $\bar{Y} = 34.81481$
Sum of squares or products Correction term	$\Sigma X^2 = 128,493$ $\dfrac{(\Sigma X)^2}{n} = 100,711.1$	$\Sigma XY = 73,631$ $\dfrac{(\Sigma X)(\Sigma Y)}{n} = 57,409.6$	$\Sigma Y^2 = 42,376$ $\dfrac{(\Sigma Y)^2}{n} = 32,725.9$
Variation or covariation	$\Sigma x^2 = 27,781.9$	$\Sigma xy = 16,221.4$	$\Sigma y^2 = 9,650.1$

Table 24.2—Computation of Measures of Variation and Covariation

Item number	x $(X - \bar{X})$	y $(Y - \bar{Y})$	x^2	xy	y^2
1	−45.07407	−26.8148	2,031.67	1,208.65	719.03
2	−37.07407	−20.8148	1,374.49	771.69	433.26
3	−35.07407	−19.8148	1,230.19	694.99	392.63
4	−34.07407	−21.8148	1,161.04	743.32	475.89
5	−33.07407	−18.8148	1,093.89	622.28	354.00
6	−32.07407	−18.8148	1,028.75	603.47	354.00
7	−31.07407	−18.8148	965.60	584.65	354.00
8	−26.07407	−15.8148	679.86	412.36	250.11
9	−20.07407	−11.8148	403.97	237.17	139.59
10	−19.07407	−8.8148	363.82	168.13	77.70
11	−17.07407	−9.8148	291.52	167.58	96.33
12	−16.07407	−8.8148	258.38	141.69	77.70
13	−12.07407	−4.8148	145.78	58.13	23.18
14	−9.07407	−4.8148	82.34	43.69	23.18
15	−9.07407	−4.8148	82.34	43.69	23.18
16	−2.07407	2.1852	4.30	−4.53	4.78
17	2.92593	−1.8148	8.56	−5.31	3.29
18	8.92593	3.1852	79.67	28.43	10.15
19	18.92593	4.1852	358.19	79.21	17.52
20	25.92593	17.1852	672.15	445.54	295.33
21	33.92593	13.1852	1,150.97	447.32	173.85
22	37.92593	25.1852	1,438.38	955.17	634.29
23	37.92593	26.1852	1,438.38	993.10	685.66
24	39.92593	24.1852	1,594.08	965.62	584.92
25	54.92593	33.1852	3,016.86	1,822.73	1,101.26
26	57.92593	36.1852	3,355.41	2,096.06	1,309.37
27	58.92593	32.1852	3,472.27	1,896.54	1,035.89
Total	0.000	0.000	27,781.9	16,221.4	9,650.1

Source: Table 24.1. Values of x and y are carried to the minimum number of decimal places necessary to obtain the number of decimal places recorded in the total row.

The results are the same as for Table 24.1, but the amount of labor required is prohibitive except in the rare cases where $\bar{X}$ and $\bar{Y}$ are integers. It does however point up one fact: For all except two cases the x and y deviations are in the same direction.

From the values of Table 24.1 we now compute a and b.

$$b = \frac{\Sigma\, xy}{\Sigma\, x^2} = \frac{16{,}221.4}{27{,}781.9} = 0.58388.$$

$$a = \bar{Y} - b\bar{X} = 34.81481 - (0.58388)(61.07407) = -0.8451.$$

The estimating equation is therefore

$$Y_X = -0.8451 + 0.58388X.$$

This is the sloping line plotted on Chart 24.1. The value of Y_X for each of the 27 values of X is recorded in Table 24.3. Note[8] that $\Sigma\, Y = \Sigma\, Y_X$, and therefore the mean value of Y equals the mean value of Y_X.

Alternative Methods of Stating the Equation

Since the estimating equation is

$$Y_X = a + bX, \quad \text{equation (24.1),}$$

and

$$\bar{Y} = a + b\bar{X}, \quad \text{from equation (24.6),}$$

it is obvious that the value of Y_X is $\bar{Y}$ when $X = \bar{X}$; in other words, the estimating line goes through the point $\bar{X}, \bar{Y}$. Arithmetically this is demonstrated by substituting 61.07407 (the value of $\bar{X}$) for X in the estimating equation.

$$Y_{61.07407} = -0.8451 + (0.58388)(61.07407) = 34.8148,$$

which is the value of $\bar{Y}$. See also Chart 24.1. Since the estimating equation goes through the point $\bar{X}, \bar{Y}$, we may write the estimating equation in any of three ways:

$$Y_X = a + bX;$$

(24.8) $$Y_x = \bar{Y} + bx;$$

(24.9) $$y_x = bx, \quad \text{where } y_x = Y_X - \bar{Y}.$$

Suitability of the Equation

Another fact that is perhaps obvious is that a, the Y intercept of the

---

[8] This is easily proved.

$$Y_x = a + bX.$$
$$\Sigma\, Y_x = \Sigma\, (a + bX) = Na + b\,\Sigma\, X.$$

But $$\Sigma\, Y = Na + b\,\Sigma\, X, \quad \text{normal equation I.}$$

Therefore $$\Sigma\, Y = \Sigma\, Y_x.$$

**Table 24.3—Actual and Estimated Values, Using
Least Squares Estimating Equation**
$(Y_x = -0.8451 + 0.58388X)$

Item number	X	Y	Y_x
1	16	8	8.4970
2	24	14	13.1680
3	26	15	14.3358
4	27	13	14.9197
5	28	16	15.5035
6	29	16	16.0874
7	30	16	16.6713
8	35	19	19.5907
9	41	23	23.0940
10	42	26	23.6779
11	44	25	24.8456
12	45	26	25.4295
13	49	30	27.7650
14	52	30	29.5167
15	52	30	29.5167
16	59	37	33.6038
17	64	33	36.5232
18	70	38	40.0265
19	80	39	45.8653
20	87	52	49.9525
21	95	48	54.6235
22	99	60	56.9590
23	99	61	56.9590
24	101	59	58.1268
25	116	68	66.8850
26	119	71	68.6366
27	120	67	69.2205
Total	1,649	940	940.0005

Source: Table 24.1.

estimating equation, is the value of Y_X when $X = 0$; i.e., it is Y_0. Thus $Y_0 = -0.8451 + (0.58388)(0) = -0.8445$, which is the value of a.

It is somewhat perplexing that according to our estimating equation, a specimen with hardness of 1.447 would tend to be entirely lacking in tensile strength (see Chart 24.1 also), and a specimen of no hardness ($X = 0$) would tend to have negative tensile strength[9] ($Y_X = -0.8445$). Three comments are pertinent. (1) There is the possibility that the relationship between the variables is not exactly linear, though this does not seem plausible after examining Chart 24.1. If this is the case a different type of equation should

[9] If we insist that a be zero, so that the equation is $Y_X = cX$, the method of least squares gives $c = \Sigma XY / \Sigma X^2$.

be fitted. (Other types of equations are explained in Chapters 27 and 36.) (2) The equation was fitted to a sample of 27 items. The sample equation $Y_X = \overline{Y} + bx$ is an estimate of the population equation[10] $E(Y|X) = E(Y) + Bx$. Thus both $\overline{Y}$ and b are subject to sampling error. (3) It is hazardous to make estimates beyond the range of the data. This is because the sampling error of $Y_x = \overline{Y} + bx$ depends on the sampling errors of $\overline{Y}$ and bx, and therefore gets larger as x gets larger.

*Estimating Y from X and X from Y

Hitherto we have considered estimating Y for specified values of X, but have not considered the possibility that estimating X for specified values of Y might also be of interest. For example, knowing hardness we want to estimate tensile strength, but it is possible that we might know the tensile strength and want to estimate the hardness. The method of making estimates depends on three things:

1. Whether relationship is functional or regressional
2. Whether the data are obtained from an existent population, or result from a controlled experiment.
3. Whether X or Y or both are subject to errors of measurement.

If there is a functional relationship there is a "true" value of Y for each permissible value of X, and vice versa. Functional relationships are common in the physical sciences. An example is the relationship between the distance a body falls in a vacuum and the time it takes to fall that distance.

If the relationship is regressional there is no "true" value of Y for each value of X, and there is no "true" value of X for each value of Y. For each value of X there may be many values of Y, since Y is not completely determined by X or by causes affecting X. Similarly, X is not completely determined by Y or by causes affecting Y. But there is an *expected* value of Y for each value of X, and an *expected* value of X for each value of Y. Regressional relationships are common in the social sciences. An example is the relationship between ages of husbands and ages of wives. Propinquity, wealth, and social position affect one's choice of mate. But two people whose residences are in the same neighborhood, and who are in the same financial and social set, are not necessarily of the same age.

In a controlled experiment one of the variables is manipulated by the experimenter. Many, though not all, functional relationships are measured by means of a controlled experiment. For example, the distance that a body is allowed to fall may be regulated, and the time noted that it takes in falling. On the other hand, ages of husbands and their wives may be taken at random from the Census volumes, which are records of an existent population.

---

[10] The symbol $Y|X$ means value of Y for a specified value of X. The symbol $E(Y|X)$ therefore means expected value of Y for all observations having a specified value of X; i.e., mean of the conditional probability distribution of Y for a specified value of X. The symbol $E(Y)$ denotes mean value of the probability distribution of Y.

Regressional relationship, sampling from an existent population, neither variable subject to error. There are two regression equations.

$$(24.10) \qquad\qquad Y_X = a_{YX} + b_{YX}X;$$

$$(24.11) \qquad\qquad X_Y = a_{XY} + b_{XY}Y.$$

In deviation form the equations are

$$(24.12) \qquad\qquad Y_x = a_{Yx} + b_{Yx}x;$$

$$(24.13) \qquad\qquad X_y = a_{Xy} + b_{Xy}y.$$

In fitting equations (24.10) and (24.12) we minimize the sum of the squares of the vertical deviations; i.e., we minimize $\Sigma\,(Y - Y_X)^2$.

$$(24.14) \quad b_{YX} = b_{Yx} = \frac{\Sigma\,xy}{\Sigma\,x^2}, \quad a_{Yx} = \bar{Y}, \quad \text{and} \quad a_{YX} = a_{Yx} - b_{YX}\bar{X}.$$

In fitting (24.11) and (24.13) we minimize $\Sigma\,(X - X_Y)^2$.

$$(24.15) \quad b_{XY} = b_{Xy} = \frac{\Sigma\,xy}{\Sigma\,y^2}, \quad a_{Xy} = \bar{X}, \quad \text{and} \quad a_{XY} = a_{Xy} - b_{XY}\bar{Y}.$$

Unless every observation point falls on the regression line, the slope b_{XY} is steeper than the slope b_{YX}. See Chart 26.1.

Summary

A relationship between two variables can be shown graphically by means of a scatter diagram and estimating line, or mathematically by means of an estimating equation.

The purpose of an estimating equation is to permit one to make estimates of one variable from specified values of another. The dependent variable is the one to be estimated. The independent variable is the estimator.

An estimating equation is usually fitted by the method of least squares, because we want to make unbiased estimates of the true estimating equation, with minimum variance.

There are two types of relationship: functional and regressional. There are also two ways of obtaining data: from a controlled experiment, and by sampling from an existent population. Referring to the parameter B estimated by the statistic b, if the relationship is functional $B_{YX}B_{XY} = 1$; if it is regressional there are two regression equations, and $B_{YX}B_{XY} \leqslant 1$. In business administration and economics most relationships are regressional, and the data are obtained by sampling from an existent population.

If the independent variable is subject to errors of measurement, the slope b will be too small. The best way to compute b, in such a case, depends on the type of relationship and how the data were obtained.

Since many formulas have been used in this chapter, a recapitulation of some of the more important ones may be worthwhile.

Forms of Estimating Equation

(24.1) $$Y_x = a + bX.$$

(24.8) $$Y_x = \overline{Y} + bx.$$

(24.9) $$y_x = bx.$$

Normal Equations

(24.2) $$na + b \,\Sigma\, X = \Sigma\, Y, \text{ normal equation I;}$$

(24.3) $$a \,\Sigma\, X + b \,\Sigma\, X^2 = \Sigma\, XY, \text{ normal equation II.}$$

Computational Formulas

(24.5) $$b = \frac{\Sigma\, xy}{\Sigma\, x^2}.$$

(24.6) $$a = \overline{Y} - b\overline{X}.$$

(24.7) $$\Sigma xy = \Sigma\, XY - \frac{(\Sigma\, X)(\Sigma\, Y)}{n}.$$

Chapter 25

RELIABILITY OF REGRESSION ESTIMATES

Whether an estimate is useful depends on how reliable it is. In order to make an estimate of reliability we must first measure the amount of variation in the errors of estimate for the observed sample. From this measure of variation we can estimate the standard deviation of all the values of Y in the population around the true estimating line. This makes it possible to estimate the standard errors of a and b, and therefore of the estimated values.

Total Variation and its Additive Components

Definition of terms. The variability exhibited by a scatter diagram is composed of three types of deviations.

1. *Total deviations*: $y = Y - \bar{Y}$. We may, if we wish, refer to the deviation of each Y-value from the mean of the Y-values as a total deviation. Each total deviation is shown graphically by Chart 25.1.

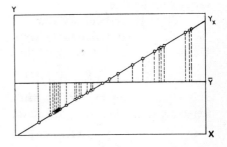

Chart 25.1—Deviations from Mean Tensile Strength of 27 Pieces of Wrought Aluminum Alloy
Total Deviations y

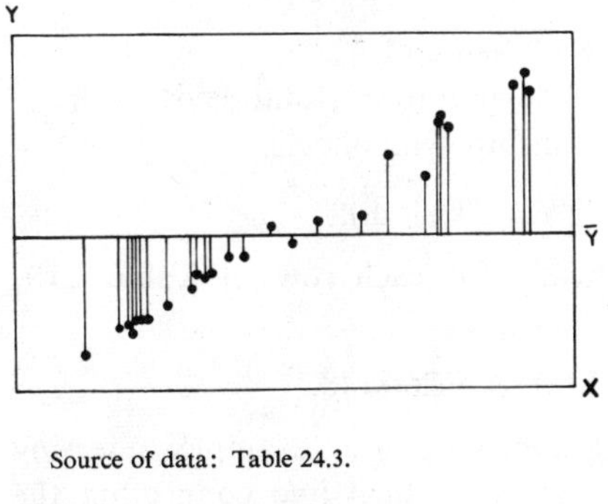

Chart 25.2—Deviations from Mean Tensile Strength of Regression Estimates of 27 Pieces of Wrought Aluminum Alloy
Explained deviations y_x

Source of data: Table 24.3.

Source of data: Table 24.3.

2. *Explained deviations*: $y_x = Y_x - \bar{Y}$. We may refer to the deviation of each estimated value of Y from the mean of the Y-values or Y_x values as an explained deviation. It is the part of the total deviation that is explained by the relationship between X and Y. It may help to recall that equation (24.9) is $y_x = bx$. Each explained deviation is shown by Chart 25.2. The individual Y-values are not plotted on this chart, since they are not needed, but there is a vertical broken line for each value of X. If the Y-values were plotted

as solid dots sometimes the broken line would pass through the solid dot, and sometimes the broken line would not reach the solid dot.

It should be understood that by "explained" we do not mean "caused," but merely "accounted for" by the estimating equation.

Chart 25.3—Deviations from Regression Line of 27 Pieces of Wrought Aluminum Alloy

Unexplained Deviations $y \cdot x$

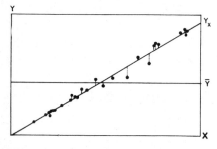

Source of data: Table 24.3.

3. *Unexplained deviations*: $y \cdot x = Y - Y_x$. Previously we have referred to the deviation of each Y-value from the corresponding estimated value as an error of estimate. Each such deviation may also be referred to as an unexplained deviation, since it is the part of the total deviation that is not explained by the relationship between X and Y. Each unexplained deviation is shown by Chart 25.3.

Comparison of Charts 25.1 and 25.3 reveals instantly that in nearly every instance the unexplained deviation is smaller than the corresponding total deviation. But there are a few exceptions. Table 25.1 shows three instances where $y \cdot x$ is larger numerically than y. These are observations 16, 17, and 19. Nevertheless, the marked tendency for $y \cdot x$ to be smaller than y indicates that one can estimate tensile strength much more accurately if he knows, not only the average tensile strength, but also the hardness of each specimen and how tensile strength varies with hardness.

Additive property of deviations. For each value of X,

(Unexplained deviation) + (explained deviation) = (total deviation).

This is apparent when we write the relationship symbolically.

$$(Y - Y_x) + (Y_x - \bar{Y}) = (Y - \bar{Y}).$$

This equality can be verified arithmetically for each row of Table 25.1. Referring to the first row, for example,

$$(-0.4970) + (-26.3178) = -26.8148.$$

The relationship can also be verified graphically. For example, referring to item number 20 on Chart 24.1, we see a vertical line connecting the observation point with the diagonal line. This line represents $(Y - Y_x)$, the unexplained deviation. A dotted vertical line connects the diagonal line with horizontal line. This line represents $(Y_x - \bar{Y})$, the explained deviation. The vertical line which is part solid and part dotted represents $(Y - \bar{Y})$, the total deviation.

For the sake of concise notation we may write

(25.1) $y \cdot x + y_x = y.$

Table 25.1—Computations Illustrating Concepts of the Three Types of Deviations
and Three Types of Variation: Unexplained; Explained; Total
(Unexplained, explained, and total deviations are computed from Table 24.3.)

Item number	$y \cdot x$ $Y - Y_x$	y_x $Y_x - \bar{Y}$	y $Y - \bar{Y}$	$(y \cdot x)^2$	y_x^2	y^2
1	−0.4970	−26.3178	−26.8148	0.25	692.63	719.03
2	0.8320	−21.6468	−20.8148	0.69	468.58	433.26
3	0.6642	−20.4790	−19.8148	0.44	419.39	392.63
4	−1.9197	−19.8951	−21.8148	3.69	395.82	475.89
5	0.4965	−19.3113	−18.8148	0.25	372.93	354.00
6	−0.0874	−18.7274	−18.8148	0.01	350.72	354.00
7	−0.6713	−18.1435	−18.8148	0.45	329.19	354.00
8	−0.5907	−15.2241	−15.8148	0.35	231.77	250.11
9	−0.0940	−11.7208	−11.8148	0.01	137.38	139.59
10	2.3221	−11.1369	−8.8148	5.39	124.03	77.70
11	0.1544	−9.9692	−9.8148	0.02	99.38	96.33
12	0.5705	−9.3853	−8.8148	0.33	88.08	77.70
13	2.2350	−7.0498	−4.8148	5.00	49.70	23.18
14	0.4833	−5.2981	−4.8148	0.23	28.07	23.18
15	0.4833	−5.2981	−4.8148	0.23	28.07	23.18
16	3.3962	−1.2110	2.1852	11.53	1.47	4.78
17	−3.5232	1.7084	−1.8148	12.41	2.92	3.29
18	−2.0265	5.2117	3.1852	4.11	27.16	10.15
19	−6.8653	11.0505	4.1852	47.13	122.11	17.52
20	2.0475	15.1377	17.1852	4.19	229.15	295.33
21	−6.6235	19.8087	13.1852	43.87	392.38	173.85
22	3.0410	22.1442	25.1852	9.25	490.37	634.29
23	4.0410	22.1442	26.1852	16.33	490.37	685.66
24	0.8732	23.3120	24.1852	0.76	543.45	584.92
25	1.1150	32.0702	33.1852	1.24	1,028.50	1,101.26
26	2.3634	33.8218	36.1852	5.59	1,143.91	1,309.37
27	−2.2205	34.4057	32.1852	4.93	1,183.75	1,035.89
Total	−0.0005	0.0009	0.0004	178.7	9,471.3	9,650.1*

* Because of rounding error, there is a discrepancy of one unit in the last digit between total and the sum of unexplained and explained variation.

Referring to Table 25.1, it is worth noting that in approximately half the cases y_x and $y \cdot x$ are of the same sign. In these cases we have explained too little. In the rest of the cases, where y_x and $y \cdot x$ have different signs, the estimating equation has explained too much. In two cases, observation 16 and 17, the signs of y and y_x are opposite, indicating that the explanation was in the wrong direction.

Additive property of variation. Although it is not obvious, it follows from the method of least squares, by which the estimating equation was obtained, that the sum of squares of the three types of deviations is also additive.

(Unexplained variation) + (explained variation) = (total variation).
Symbolically,[1]

(25.2) $\Sigma (y \cdot x)^2 + \Sigma y_x^2 = \Sigma y^2.$

This can be verified by examining the last row of Table 25.1.

$$178.7 + 9{,}471.4 = 9{,}650.1.$$

Additive property of variance. If we divide both sides of (25.2) by n we obtain[2]

(25.3) $\sigma_{y \cdot x}^2 + \sigma_{y(x)}^2 = \sigma_y^2.$

Arithmetically,

$$6.620 + 350.79 = 357.41.$$

The standard deviations, however, are not additive.

$$\sigma_{y \cdot x} + \sigma_{y(x)} > \sigma_y.$$

Thus

$$2.573 + 18.729 > 18.905.$$

Computational Procedures

The procedures used in Table 25.1 for computing measures of variation were intended solely as an explanation of concepts, rather than as practical methods of computation. The following procedures are more expeditious:

$$\Sigma y^2 = \Sigma Y^2 - \frac{(\Sigma Y)^2}{n} \, ;$$

(25.4) $\Sigma y_x^2 = b \, \Sigma xy$

$$\Sigma (y \cdot x)^2 = \Sigma y^2 - \Sigma y_x^2, \quad \text{from (25.2).}$$

For our data:

$$\Sigma y^2 = 42{,}376 - \frac{(940)^2}{27} = 9{,}650.1;$$

$$\Sigma y_x^2 = (0.58388)(16{,}221.4) = 9{,}471.4.$$

$$\Sigma (y \cdot x)^2 = 9{,}650.1 - 9{,}471.4 = 178.7.$$

Standard Error of Estimate of Sample

Testing tensile strength indirectly by testing a related characteristic, hardness, rather than testing directly and thereby destroying the specimen being tested, is a great money-saver, provided it works. We have not

---

[1] The algebraic proof of equation (25.2) is easy. Substituting symbolic definitions for the two terms on the left side of the equation, we obtain

$$\Sigma (y - y_x)^2 + \Sigma (bx)^2.$$

Expanding, this expression becomes Σy^2. Intermediate steps in this proof are left to the student.

[2] The subscript $y(x)$ rather than y_x is used for explained variation in order to avoid using a subscript with a subscript.

Chart 25.4—Estimating Line and Zones of Scatter for Tensile Strength of 27 Pieces of Wrought Aluminum Alloy

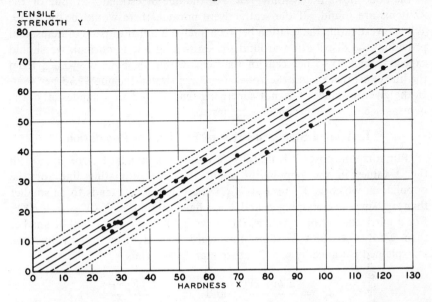

explained all the variability in tensile strength by using the apparent relationship between hardness and average tensile strength, for the dots on the scatter diagram do not all lie on the fitted curve. Some idea of the reliability of estimates can be obtained by computing the standard deviation of our errors of estimate. This measure, called the standard error of estimate of the sample, is

$$(25.5) \qquad \Delta_{y \cdot x} = \sqrt{\frac{\Sigma(y \cdot x)^2}{n}}.$$

This measure has already been computed. Let us recapitulate.

Unexplained variation: $\Sigma(y \cdot x)^2 = 178.7$.

Unexplained variance: $\qquad \Delta_{y \cdot x}^2 = \dfrac{\Sigma(y \cdot x)^2}{n} = \dfrac{178.7}{27} = 6.62.$

Standard error of estimate: $\quad \Delta_{y \cdot x} = \sqrt{6.62} = 2.57$ thousands of pounds per square inch.

The standard error of estimate is a measure of goodness of fit, since it is an average of the vertical distances between the points and the line. It may be interpreted in a manner strictly analogous to that of the standard deviation of a frequency distribution. It is the range above and below the line of estimation which encloses about 68.27 per cent of the items in the sample if the scatter is approximately normal. In practice we frequently think of this measure as the range within which about $\frac{2}{3}$ of the values are found. For the case in hand ($\Delta_{y \cdot x} = 2.57$), we should expect $\frac{2}{3}$ of the items of Chart 25.4

within the narrow band of $Y_x \pm s_{y \cdot x}$ shown on the diagram. A count of the dots shows that within $\pm s_{y \cdot x}$ of the line of estimate, 21 out of the 27 items are found. If the scatter were normal, there would be 18 or 19. When investigating the relation between a large number of pairs of items, and providing the distribution around the estimating line is normal, we should expect to find 95.45 per cent of the items within the zone of $\pm 2 s_{y \cdot x}$ from the line of estimate; and the zone of $\pm 3 s_{y \cdot x}$ should include 99.73 per cent. In the given instance it is not surprising that $Y_x \pm 3 s_{y \cdot x}$ includes all of the items, since only 27 specimens were tested.

Estimated Standard Error of Estimate of Population

For some purposes it is useful to estimate the standard error $\sigma_{y \cdot x}$ of all the Y-values in the population about the true estimating line for the population, which is $Y_X = A + BX$. The value of $s_{y \cdot x}$ tends to be smaller than $\sigma_{y \cdot x}$ since in obtaining a and b we have minimized $\Sigma (Y - a - bX)^2$. For a particular set of Y-values, therefore, $\Sigma (Y - a - bX)^2$ will be smaller than $\Sigma (Y - A - BX)^2$. This downward bias is offset by dividing the unexplained variance by $n - 2$ rather than by n. Thus

$$s_{y \cdot x}^2 = \frac{\Sigma (y \cdot x)^2}{n}, \quad \text{and} \quad s_{y \cdot x}^2 = \frac{\Sigma (y \cdot x)^2}{n - 2}.$$

The expected value[3] of $s_{y \cdot x}^2$ is $\sigma_{y \cdot x}^2$.

The quantity $n - 2$ is the number of degrees of freedom for the $y \cdot x$-values. There are $n - 2$ degrees of freedom since two points, or a point and a slope, determine a straight line. Or we may say that one degree of freedom is lost because of a and another because of b. For a particular set of X-values, all but two of the Y-values can be selected arbitrarily without affecting the values of a and b. But the other two Y-values determine a and b.

The formula for the estimated standard error is

(25.6) $$s_{y \cdot x} = \sqrt{\frac{\Sigma (y \cdot x)^2}{n - 2}}.$$

For our data

$$s_{y \cdot x} = \sqrt{\frac{178.7}{25}} = \sqrt{7.148} = 2.674.$$

*Other Estimated Standard Errors Used in Regression Analysis

It should be recalled that $s_{y \cdot x}^2 = \dfrac{\Sigma (y \cdot x)^2}{n - 2}$ is an estimate of the variance of the population values about the population estimating line.

---

[3] If $B_{YX} = 0$, the expected value of $s_{y \cdot x}^2 = \sigma_y^2$.

Values of Y_x, estimated from the equation $Y_x = a_{Yx} + b_{Yx}$, of course differ from the population regression values, because a and b in the above equation are subject to error.

Now, a is an average, and

(25.7)
$$s_a^2 = \frac{s_{y \cdot x}^2}{n}.$$

Also

(25.8)
$$s_b^2 = \frac{s_{y \cdot x}^2}{\Sigma x^2}.$$

Note that the variance of b becomes smaller as the sample size increases and as the values of x become more widely dispersed. Finally, $s^2{}_{Y_x} = s_a^2 + s_{bx}^2$. Therefore, since $s_{bx}^2 = x^2 s_b^2$,

(25.9)
$$s_{Y_x} = s_{y \cdot x} \sqrt{\frac{1}{n} + \frac{x^2}{\Sigma x^2}}.$$

Note that the estimates tend to differ farther from the true regression values as X departs farther from $\bar{X}$.

The actual values of Y, including those not represented in the sample, differ from the Y_x values obtained from the sample, and the value of these differences have a variance. The estimate of this variance is

$$s_{\text{prediction}}^2 = s_{y \cdot x}^2 + s^2{}_{Y_x},$$

and

(25.10)
$$s_{\text{prediction}} = s_{y \cdot x} \sqrt{1 + \frac{1}{n} + \frac{x^2}{\Sigma x^2}}.$$

Equations (26.9) and (26.10) can be used to obtain confidence limits for the estimating line and for predicted values. The limits for predictions will be wider than those for regression values, since the latter are really average values. The confidence limits become wider as x increases in size.

Summary

The standard error of estimate $s_{y \cdot x}$ for the sample is the standard deviation of the sample points about the sample estimating line. The quantity $s_{y \cdot x}$ is an estimate of $\sigma_{y \cdot x}$, which is the standard deviation of the population points about the population estimating line. The value of $s_{y \cdot x}^2$ is always larger than $s_{y \cdot x}^2$ because the unexplained variation is divided by degrees of freedom, rather than number of observations. $s_{y \cdot x}^2$ is an unbiased estimate of $\sigma_{y \cdot x}^2$.

The reliability of b depends on:

1. How close the points are to the line;
2. The number of observations;
3. How widely the X-values are dispersed.

The reliability of individual estimates and predictions depends also on the value of x. The larger the value of $|x|$ the less reliable is the estimate. One should therefore be wary of making estimates beyond the range of the data.

The most important formulas in this chapter are:

(25.2)
$$\Sigma \, (y \cdot x)^2 + \Sigma \, y_x^2 = \Sigma \, y^2;$$

(25.4)
$$\Sigma \, y_x^2 = b \, \Sigma \, xy;$$

(25.6)
$$s_{y \cdot x} = \sqrt{\frac{\Sigma \, (y \cdot x)^2}{n - 2}} \; ;$$

(25.8)
$$s_b^2 = \frac{s_{y \cdot x}^2}{\Sigma \, x^2} \; ;$$

(25.9)
$$s_{Yx} = s_{y \cdot x} \sqrt{\frac{1}{n} + \frac{x^2}{\Sigma \, x^2}} \; .$$

Chapter 26

THE CORRELATION COEFFICIENT

In Chapter 24 we learned how to fit a straight line by the method of least squares. Chapter 25 was concerned with reliability of estimates. Among other things we were concerned with the standard error of estimate $\mathcal{A}_{y \cdot x}$, which is a measure of closeness of fit. The smaller the value of $\mathcal{A}_{y \cdot x}$, the closer the fit. The standard error of estimate measures closeness of fit in an absolute sense, since it is stated in the units of measurement of the dependent variable. Its interpretation is therefore dependent on the data and problem under consideration.

The correlation coefficient r is also a measure of closeness of fit, but in a relative sense. It is a number that takes any value from $+1$ through 0 to -1. The sign of the coefficient is the same as b in the estimating equation, and indicates whether the correlation is positive or negative, whereas the arithmetic magnitude of the coefficient indicates the degree of association. Negative correlation indicates as close a degree of association as does positive. When there is no relationship between the variables, r is 0; when the relationship is perfect, it is $+1$ or -1.

Chart 26.1 contains scatter diagrams exhibiting various degrees of correlation. Examination of this chart should aid the student in obtaining an intuitive notion of the distinction between strong and weak correlation. Note especially two things that happen as the numerical value of the correlation coefficient gets larger.

(1) The points get closer to the regression lines.
(2) The two regression lines Y_x and X_y get closer to each other; the angle formed by their intersection gets smaller.

An idea of the meaning of negative correlation can be obtained by inspection of the time series plotted as Chart 26.2. Note that when free reserves are above average, borrowings are below average, and vice versa. If plotted as a scatter diagram these data would resemble rather closely the upper right section of Chart 26.1.

In this chapter, we shall indicate various concepts of r and various methods of computation. We shall also learn how to test the significance of r.

383

Chart 26.1—Scatter Diagrams Showing Varying Degrees of Correlation

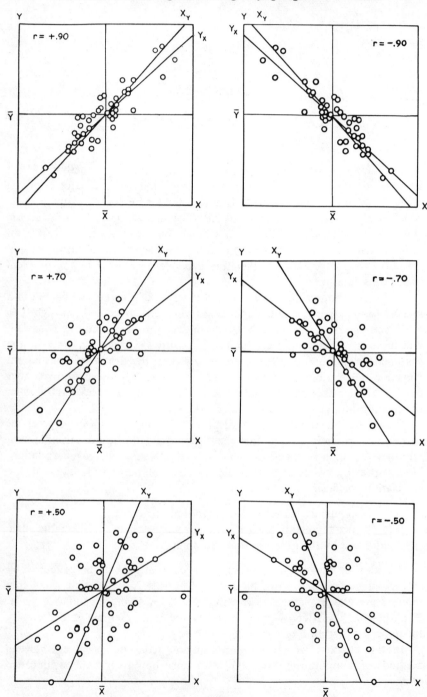

Source of data: E. C. Fieller, T. Lewis, and E. S. Pearson, *Correlated Random Normal Deviates*, Tracts for Computers No. XXVI, Cambridge University Press, Cambridge, 1955.

Chart 26.1—(cont.) Scatter Diagrams Showing Varying Degrees of Correlation

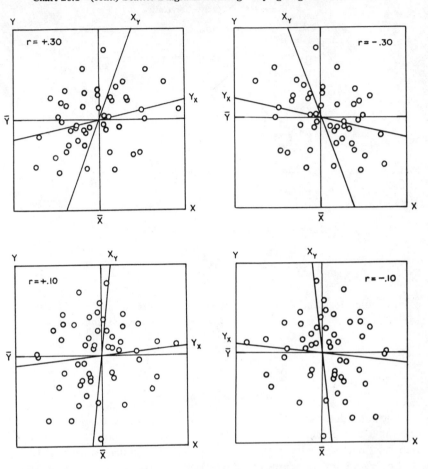

A Simple Method of Computation

If the estimating equation is not needed, but only the correlation coefficient, the easiest method of computation is

(26.1)
$$r = \frac{\Sigma\, xy}{\sqrt{(\Sigma\, x^2)(\Sigma\, y^2)}}.$$

This method of computation gives the sign of r automatically.

In (26.1) and all other formulas for r, the symbols x and y can be interchanged without affecting the value of the coefficient. To indicate that x is the independent variable, one writes r_{yx}; to indicate that y is the independent variable, one writes r_{xy}. Obviously $r_{xy} = r_{yx}$. In this chapter we shall omit the subscripts. Except for formula (26.1), the appropriate subscript, if used would be yx.

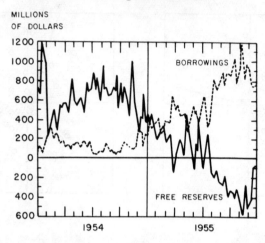

Chart 26.2—Member Bank Borrowings and Free Reserves: Negative Correlation

Source: Federal Reserve Bank of New York, *Annual Report*, 1955, p. 22.

In Tables 24.1 and 24.2 all of the values that are needed for substitution in formula (26.1) are given for the hardness and tensile strength data.

$$r = \frac{16,221}{\sqrt{(27,782)(9,650.1)}} = +0.9907.$$

Alternative Concepts

Formula (26.1) should not be thought of as a correlation concept, but only as a convenient method of computation. There are various ways of thinking about *r*, however, that contribute to one's understanding of it.

Covariance of standardized observations. It is apparent that formula (26.1) can also be written

$$r = \sum \left(\frac{x}{\sqrt{\sum x^2}} \frac{y}{\sqrt{\sum y^2}} \right),$$

and therefore

$$r = \frac{1}{n} \sum \left(\frac{x}{\sigma_x} \frac{y}{\sigma_y} \right),$$

or

(26.2)
$$r = \frac{\sum z_x z_y}{n},$$

where
$$z_x = \frac{X - \bar{X}}{\sigma_x} \quad \text{and} \quad z_y = \frac{Y - \bar{Y}}{\sigma_y}.$$

Thus we see that r measures the extent to which two variables vary together, when each has a mean of zero and a standard deviation of one. Formula (26.2) is sometimes called the product-moment formula.

Slope of standardized observations. If each variable has the same standard deviation, r varies directly with b; more explicitly,

$$(26.3) \qquad\qquad r = b_{z_y z_x}.$$

If the reader will glance at Chart 26.1 which shows several scatter diagrams, for each of which $\Delta_x \doteq \Delta_y \doteq 1$, he will notice that the steeper the slope of the y_x regression line, i.e., the larger the value[1] of b_{yx}, the larger the value of r.

It would be unduly laborious to use equation (26.3) explicitly. This would necessitate computing n values of z_x and n values of z_y. However, we can compute b and then adjust for differences in variability. Thus[2]

$$(26.4) \qquad\qquad r = b_{yx} \frac{\Delta_x}{\Delta_y}.$$

For our data:

$$b_{yx} = +0.58288;$$

$$\Delta_x = \sqrt{\frac{27{,}782}{27}} = 32.078;$$

$$\Delta_y = \sqrt{\frac{9{,}650.1}{27}} = 18.905.$$

Therefore

$$r = +0.58388 \, \frac{32.078}{18.905} = +0.9907.$$

It is also apparent from (26.4) that having computed r by formula (26.1) we may then compute b. Thus

$$(26.5) \qquad\qquad b_{yx} = r\frac{\Delta_y}{\Delta_x}, \quad \text{and} \quad b_{xy} = r\frac{\Delta_x}{\Delta_y}.$$

Geometric mean of the two slopes. If the reader will again look at Chart 26.1 he will see that there are two lines on each diagram, y_x with slope b_{yx} and x_y with slope b_{xy}. When these slopes are widely divergent the correlation is small, and as they get closer together the correlation gets larger. Symbolically,

$$(26.6) \qquad\qquad r = \sqrt{b_{yx} b_{xy}}.$$

---

[1] There are two estimating lines on each diagram. The one with the least slope is y_x with slope $b_{xy} = \Sigma\, xy/\Sigma\, x^2$. The one with the steepest slope is x_y with slope $b_{xy} = \Sigma\, xy/\Sigma\, x^2$. The slope is steeper because $1/bxy > byx$.

[2] It is also true that $r = b_{yx} \dfrac{\Delta_{x\cdot y}}{\Delta_{y\cdot x}}$, for $\Delta_x \Delta_{y\cdot x} = \Delta_y \Delta_{x\cdot y}$.

For our data:

$$b_{yx} = \frac{\Sigma\, xy}{\Sigma\, x^2} = \frac{16{,}221.4}{27{,}781.9} = 0.58388;$$

$$b_{xy} = \frac{\Sigma\, xy}{\Sigma\, y^2} = \frac{16{,}221.4}{9{,}650.1} = 1.68096$$

and $\qquad r = \sqrt{(0.58388)(1.68096)} = \sqrt{0.98148} = +0.9907.$

This formula does not give the sign automatically; but r takes the sign of b_{yx} and b_{xy}.

This formula is of some interest because it is convenient in connection with partial correlation, which will be considered in Chapter 35. Also it has a logical basis that may be appealing to some. We may think of b_{yx} as the ratio between the causes that are common to X and Y and all the causes that affect X; and we may think of b_{xy} as the ratio between the causes that are common to X and Y and all the causes that affect Y. Thus the correlation coefficient may be thought of as the geometric mean of these ratios.[3] This explanation is not completely realistic because it assumes all causes to be of

---

[3] Take 5 disks marked on one side as follows (the other side being blank):

$$\textcircled{X} \quad \textcircled{X} \quad \textcircled{\genfrac{}{}{0pt}{}{X}{Y}} \quad \textcircled{\genfrac{}{}{0pt}{}{X}{Y}} \quad \textcircled{Y}$$

If we should throw all 5 disks into the air, when they fall any number of disks from 0 to 4 with an X exposed might appear; also any number of disks from 0 to 3 with a Y exposed might appear. We may say that there are 4 causes (disks) operating to produce an X and 3 causes (disks) operating to produce a Y. Also there are 2 common causes (disks) that operate to produce both an X and a Y. Whenever an X appears the probability is $\frac{3}{4}$ that a Y will appear on the same disk; whenever a Y appears the probability is $\frac{2}{3}$ that an X will appear on the same disk. The expected distribution of the frequencies of occurrence of X and Y from 32 throws are as follows:

Y \\ X	0	1	2	3	4	Total
3	.	.	1	2	1	4
2	.	2	5	4	1	12
1	1	4	5	2	.	12
0	1	2	1	.	.	4
Total	2	8	12	8	2	32

Perhaps the student would enjoy verifying that there are 4 ways (sets of disks) that give 3 X's and 2 Y's. A little computation will show the following:

$$b_{YX} = \tfrac{3}{4}; \quad b_{XY} = \tfrac{2}{3}; \quad r = \sqrt{\tfrac{3}{4} \times \tfrac{2}{3}} = \sqrt{\tfrac{1}{2}} = +0.58.$$

equal magnitude. Nevertheless it serves to connect correlation with causes that are common to the two variables.

Ratio of standard deviation of explained deviations to standard deviation of total deviations. In symbolic form[4]

$$(26.7) \qquad r = \frac{\Delta_{y(x)}}{\Delta_y}.$$

This formula does not give the sign of the correlation coefficient. For our hardness and tensile strength data, these standard deviations were computed in Chapter 25. Substituting them in (26.7),

$$r = \frac{18.729}{18.905} = +0.9907.$$

Square root of the proportion of total variation that has been explained. This is the concept and method of computation that is looked upon with greatest favor in this book. It is instructive to write the formula for r^2 as well as r.

$$(26.8) \qquad r^2 = \frac{\Sigma \, y_x^2}{\Sigma \, y^2};$$

$$(26.9) \qquad r = \sqrt{\frac{\Sigma \, y_x^2}{\Sigma \, y^2}}.$$

The symbol r^2 refers to the coefficient of determination. It is the ratio of the explained variation to the total variation, and therefore the proportion of the total variation that has been explained.[5] This formula has two advantages over formula (26.7). One is purely computational. We avoid dividing the numerator and denominator[6] of (26.8) by n in order to obtain $\Delta_{y(x)}^2$ and Δ_y^2, and then taking the square roots of each of these quantities. The other

----

[4] Notation in which the parentheses and decimal point have the conventional meaning of "explained by" and "unexplained by," respectively, are also used in Chapter 35 dealing with multiple and partial correlation.

[5] It may be of interest to understand why formulas (26.1) and (26.9) are equivalent.

$$r = \sqrt{\frac{\Sigma \, y_x^2}{\Sigma \, y^2}} = \sqrt{\frac{b \, \Sigma \, xy}{\Sigma \, y^2}} = \sqrt{\frac{\frac{\Sigma \, xy}{\Sigma \, x^2} \Sigma \, xy}{(\Sigma \, y^2)}} = \sqrt{\frac{(\Sigma \, xy)^2}{(\Sigma \, x^2)(\Sigma \, y^2)}} = \frac{\Sigma \, xy}{\sqrt{(\Sigma \, x^2)\,(\Sigma \, y^2)}}.$$

Some students may enjoy proving that the other formulas for r are mathematically equivalent.

[6] It is easy to see that the coefficient of determination may also be thought of the proportion of the total variance that has been explained, i.e.,

$$r^2 = \frac{\Delta_{y(x)}^2}{\Delta_y^2}.$$

This formula is derived by squaring both sides of (26.7), or by dividing numerator and denominator of (26.8) by n.

advantage is that it is correct to speak of r^2 as being the proportion of variation that has been explained. This is because

$$\Sigma\, y_x^2 + \Sigma\, (y \cdot x)^2 = \Sigma\, y^2, \text{ and therefore}$$

(26.10) $$\frac{\Sigma\, y_x^2}{\Sigma\, y^2} + \frac{\Sigma\, (y \cdot x)^2}{\Sigma\, y^2} = 1.$$

But it is not correct to speak of r as being the proportion of the standard deviation that has been explained. This is because

$$\Delta_{y(x)} + \Delta_{y \cdot x} > \Delta_y, \text{ and therefore}$$

$$\frac{\Delta_{y(x)}}{\Delta_y} + \frac{\Delta_{y \cdot x}}{\Delta_y} > 1.$$

From (26.8) it is obvious that we can write the expression for the coefficient of determination in other ways that are instructive.

(26.11) $$r^2 = 1 - \frac{\Sigma\, (y \cdot x)^2}{\Sigma\, y^2}, \quad \text{or}$$

(26.12) $$r^2 = 1 - \frac{\Delta_{y \cdot x}^2}{\Delta_y^2}.$$

This concept is preferred by many for it states that the coefficient of determination is the relative reduction in variance when measured about the estimating equation rather than about the mean of the dependent variable. If we knew nothing about the relationship between X and Y, the best guess we could make concerning an item taken at random from some sample is that it is of average magnitude (i.e., $\bar{Y}$). Estimates so made would, of course, tend to be considerably in error. But if we also knew the value of x and the estimating equation $Y_x = \bar{Y} + bx$, we could utilize this additional information to make a better estimate (i.e., Y_x). Estimates so made would be subject to less error. The coefficient of determination tells us how much less, relatively.

If the reader will again refer to Chart 26.1 he will see that as the scatter around the estimating line becomes smaller, the correlation coefficient becomes larger. If the variance of the y-values remains constant, r^2 varies inversely with $\Delta_{y \cdot x}^2$.

Let us now return to our main approach. Substituting the values for variation already computed in Chapter 25 in formulas (26.8) and (26.9), we obtain

$$r^2 = \frac{9{,}471.4}{9{,}650.1} = 0.9815\,;$$

$$r = +0.9907.$$

What is a close degree of association? It is better not to answer that question categorically. The scatter diagrams of Chart 26.1 were partly for the purpose of letting the student answer that question for himself. It is a matter of opinion when the points are to be considered close to the line, just as it is a matter of opinion whether a given annual income is to be considered large. But possibly we could say that the dividing line is when half of the variation has been explained. If that is the case, the dividing line between strong and weak correlation is $r = \pm0.71$, for in that case $r^2 = 0.50$.

Interpretation of the Correlation Coefficient

The correlation coefficient cannot always be taken at its face value. It is necessary that one know something about the data, and plotting them as a scatter diagram will help greatly in interpreting the measure. Here are a few things to take into consideration.

1. *Are the data homogeneous?* In observational data heterogeneity can often be spotted by bimodality in either the X_1 distribution or the X_2 distribution, or the presence of a few items which are too far out of line with the other items to be considered a matter of chance. On the scatter diagram such heterogeneity may show up as a tendency for the dots to cluster into two or more groups, or for one or more dots to be far removed from the others on the chart. Where heterogeneity is observed it is better to classify the data on some rational basis and correlate each group separately. Individual items clearly governed by a different set of causes should be eliminated before correlating. If these common-sense steps are not taken, one may obtain a misleading impression, not only as to the degree of correlation, but sometimes even as to its sign.

2. *Are the data subject to large errors of measurement?* Since errors in the measurement of the two variables are ordinarily not correlated, such errors reduce the size of r below its true value. Such *attenuation* can be corrected if the magnitude of the errors is known.[7]

3. *Are the data individual measurements, or are they averages?* If the data to be correlated are first grouped into k size groups according to the independent variable, if $\bar{X}$ and $\bar{Y}$ are computed for each group, and if these means are correlated, the correlation among the means will be higher than among the individual items taken as a whole (unless $r = 1$ for the ungrouped data). This is because dispersion of the individual values around the k column means has been eliminated. Likewise, if the grouping and averaging is according to the r rows of the dependent variable, the correlation will be increased. Finally, if the data are grouped according to both variables so that there are rk cells, and if $\bar{X}$ and $\bar{Y}$ are computed for each cell and these paired cell means correlated, the correlation will be increased. The increase will be unimportant provided there is a large number of cells.

Often, the correlation of state averages will be higher than that of county values. This will be the case if differences among counties in the same state

---

[7] See J. P. Guilford, *Fundamental Statistics in Psychology and Education*, McGraw-Hill Book Co., Inc., New York, 1942, pp. 287–288.

are small compared with differences among states. If such is the case, grouping the counties according to states is much the same as grouping them according to size groups.

4. *Is the type of estimating equation appropriate?* If inspection of the scatter diagram reveals that a curved line could more appropriately be fitted to the data than a straight line, r is a misleading measure of closeness of

Chart 26.3—Effect of Correlation Coefficient of Using Straight Line Estimating Line when Relationship is Nonlinear
Equation Type $Y_x = a + bX$, $r_{YX} = +.11$

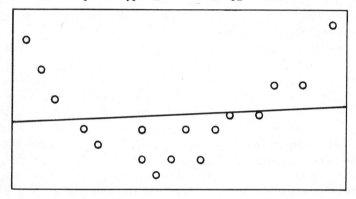

Equation Type $Y_{x,x^2} = a + bX + cX^2$, $r_{Y(x,x^2)} = .94$

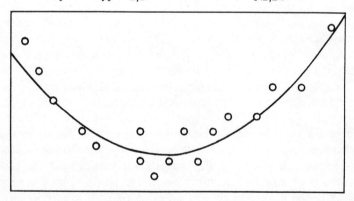

relationship. A curved line should be fitted, and a coefficient of nonlinear correlation should be computed, following the procedures explained in Chapter 27 or Chapter 36. So doing will yield a higher coefficient and one which reflects more accurately the closeness of the relationship. For the data of Chart 26.3, $r = +0.11$, but by using nonlinear correlation, the correlation is increased to 0.94. Sometimes it may be better to transform one or both of the variables into logarithms, reciprocals, or some other function before correlating.

5. *Have some of the data been eliminated?* For instance, if retail sales and payrolls are correlated for cities ranging from 100,000 to 500,000 population, the correlation will usually not be so high as if cities from 10,000 to 5,000,000 are included. This is because retail sales and payrolls are both positively correlated with population, and when the range of values along both axes is extended, $\Delta_{y(x)}$ is increased without a corresponding increase in $\Delta_{y\cdot x}$.

Chart 26.4—Effect on Correlation Coefficient of Censoring Data
Uncensored data: $r = +.92$

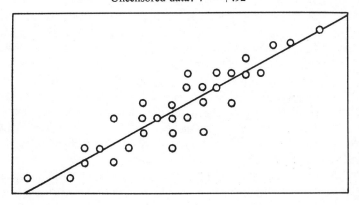

Central half of X values: $r = +.63$

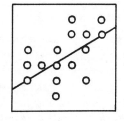

Consider Chart 26.4. In the scatter diagram at the top all the data are included. The one at the bottom is the same except that large and small values of X have been eliminated. The correlation coefficient has been reduced from $+0.92$ to $+0.63$.

6. *Have important variables been neglected?* The simple correlation of earnings of employees with placement scores will usually not be as great as the multiple correlation of earnings with placement scores and experience. Multiple correlation is considered in Chapter 35.

Causation and the Correlation Coefficient

The coefficient of correlation must be thought of, not as something that indicates a particular cause and effect relationship, but only as something that measures degree of association. Any one of the following situations may, in fact, occur.

1. *Either of the variables may be the cause of the other.* The variable that is supposed to be the cause of the variations in the other is usually taken as the independent variable and plotted along the horizontal axis. The statistician's belief that either of the two variables is the cause of the other, and his belief as to which is cause and which is effect are determined by considerations other than the magnitude of *r*.

2. *Co-variation of the two variables may be due to a common cause or causes affecting each of them in the same way, or in opposite ways.* If it should be found that there is correlation between the number of automobiles registered and the number of telephone subscribers in the various states, it should not be hastily concluded that having an automobile necessitates one's subscribing for telephone service, nor is it easy to see how using a telephone necessitates purchase of an automobile. It is apparent, however, that many persons feel that their incomes are high enough for both luxuries.

3. *The correlation may be due to chance.* Even though there may be no relationship whatever between the variables in the universe from which the sample is drawn, it may be that enough of the paired variables that are selected may vary together, just by accident, to give a fair degree of correlation. Thus if for a small group of typists we should find positive correlation between foot length and output, we might be inclined to attribute the result to chance. Because we usually deal with samples, and therefore with chance, it is advisable always to test the significance of the correlation coefficient.

Tests of Significance

One of the ideas that has been emphasized in this book is that any statistical measure is to be considered significant if the variability that is accounted for is large in comparison with that which is attributable to chance. It is therefore not surprising that analysis of variance is the most widely applicable method of testing the significance of correlation coefficients. Estimates of the variance of the dependent variable in a normal population in which there is no correlation between the paired observations is obtained by dividing variation by degrees of freedom. Thus:

$$s_y^2 = \frac{\Sigma y^2}{n-1};$$

(26.13)
$$s_{y(x)}^2 = \frac{\Sigma y_x^2}{m-1} = \Sigma y_x^2,$$

where *m* is the number of constants in the estimating equation;

$$s_{y \cdot x}^2 = \frac{\Sigma (y \cdot x)^2}{n-m} = \frac{\Sigma (y \cdot x)^2}{n-2}.$$

Of these three measures, $s_{y(x)}^2$ and $s_{y\cdot x}^2$ are independent, whereas s_y^2 depends on both $s_{y(x)}^2$ and $s_{y\cdot x}^2$. Since F may be regarded as the ratio between two independent estimates of the population variance,

$$(26.14) \qquad\qquad F = \frac{s_{y(x)}^2}{s_{y\cdot x}^2}.$$

Using the data of page 378, we obtain the results shown in the table below.

Source of variation	Amount of variation	Degrees of freedom	Estimate of variance
Total	$\Sigma y^2 = 9{,}650$	$n - 1 = 26$	$s_y^2 = 371$
Explained	$\Sigma y_x^2 = 9{,}471$	$m - 1 = 1$	$s_{y(x)}^2 = 9{,}471$
Unexplained . . .	$\Sigma (y\cdot x)^2 = 178.7$	$n - m = 25$	$s_{y\cdot x}^2 = 7.15$

Note that variation and degrees of freedom are additive, but estimated variance is not. If there were no correlation between the paired variables in the population from which the sample was drawn, estimates of the population variances based upon explained, and unexplained variations, obtained from individual samples, would tend to be approximately the same. In this case the explained variance is 1,325 times as large as the unexplained; that is,

$$F = \frac{s_{y(x)}^2}{s_{y\cdot x}^2} = \frac{\Sigma y_x^2 \div 1}{\Sigma (y\cdot x)^2 \div (n-2)} = \frac{9{,}471}{7.15} = 1{,}325.$$

From Appendix 21 we find that when the degrees of freedom in the numerator (ν_1 in the F table) and denominator (ν_2 in the F table) are 1 and 25, respectively, the ratio of the explained variance to the unexplained variance, if there is no correlation in the population, will be as large as 13.88 only one time in one thousand. As large a ratio as 1,325 will occur by chance much less frequently. We conclude, then, that since the probability is less than 0.001 the correlation coefficient r is highly significant. This also tells us that b is highly significant.

Since $t = \sqrt{F}$ when there is one degree of freedom in the numerator, we may also compute $t = \sqrt{1{,}325} = 36.4$. For $n = 25$ the required value of t at the 0.001 level is 3.725, and our conclusion is the same as before. In some cases there is an advantage in computing t, since our t table (Appendix 16) provides values of t at levels other than those shown in our F table of Appendix 21.

F and t may also be computed from the proportions of variation that have been explained (r^2) and unexplained[8] ($1 - r_{12}^2$), rather than from the amounts of variation Σy_x^2 and $\Sigma (y\cdot x)^2$. Thus,

$$(26.15) \qquad\qquad t = r\sqrt{\frac{n-2}{1-r^2}}.$$

---

[8] The quantity $r_{y\cdot x}^2 = 1 - r_{yx}^2$ is sometimes called the coefficient of nondetermination.

For a one-sided test t takes the sign of r. For a one-sided test when r is positive we would ordinarily have H_0: $\rho = 0$ and H_a: $\rho > 0$. Formula (26.15) would ordinarily be used when r is computed by use of formula (26.1).

F and t test the hypothesis that there is no correlation in the population. The distribution of sample correlation coefficients is symmetrical only around a population value of zero, in which case it approaches the normal form as n approaches ∞. If one wishes to obtain confidence limits for ρ, one may use David's tables.[9] For excellent approximations one may transform r into z_r, which is approximately normal in its distribution, except when n is very small.[10] Procedures for use of z_r are similar to those using z for testing hypotheses concerning μ and P, with which the student is familiar. A chart for reading values of z_r given r, and values of r given z_r is given in Appendix 6.

---

[9] F. N. David, *Tables of the Correlation Coefficient*, Biometrika Office, University College, London, 1938.

[10] z_r is used to distinguish it from

$$z_X = \frac{X - \mu}{\sigma} \; ; \quad z_{\bar{X}} = \frac{\bar{X} - \mu}{\sigma_{\bar{X}}} \; ; \quad z_p = \frac{p - P}{\sigma_p} \, .$$

The appropriate formulas are

$$z_r = \log_e \sqrt{\frac{1 + r}{1 - r}} = 1.15129 \log_{10} \left(\frac{1 + r}{1 - r} \right);$$

$$\sigma_{z_r} \doteq \frac{1}{\sqrt{n - m - \dfrac{2}{3}}} = \frac{1}{\sqrt{n - \dfrac{8}{3}}} = \sqrt{\frac{3}{3n - 8}}, \quad \text{for simple } r;$$

$$\sigma_{z_{r1} - z_{r2}} = \sqrt{\sigma_{z_{r1}}^2 + \sigma_{z_{r2}}^2}.$$

The z transformation is due to R. A. Fisher. The formula given above for σ_{z_r} is from Harold Hotelling, "New Light on the Correlation Coefficient and its Transforms," *Journal of the Royal Statistical Society*, Series B (Methodological), Vol. XV, No. 2, 1953. It is worth noting that z_r is the hyperbolic arctangent of r; i.e., $z_r = \tanh^{-1} r$. Tables of hyperbolic arctangents are found in various publications; for example, *Mathematical Tables from Handbook of Chemistry and Physics*, 8th ed., Chemical Publishing Co., Cleveland, 1946.

*Chapter 27

TYPES OF TWO-VARIABLE CORRELATION

Chapters 24 through 26 developed methods for correlating two variables when the magnitude of each observation is known, and when the dependent variable increases a constant amount for each unit increase of the independent variable. In this chapter the following special cases will be considered:

1. Correlation of grouped data.
2. Correlation of data classified into two classes for each variable.
3. Correlation of ranked data.
4. Curvilinear relationships that can be transformed into a linear equation.

Correlation for 2×2 tables and correlation of ranked data are said to be nonparametric methods when a specified form of population is not assumed. The procedures that will be illustrated involve little that is new in principle.

Correlation of Grouped Data

The analysis of the relationship between hardness and tensile strength, which was the subject matter of Chapters 24–26, involved only 27 items. When a large number of items are correlated, the computations may be shortened materially by first grouping the data into a two-way frequency distribution. To illustrate the procedure, circulation of *Holiday* magazine per 1,000 families in March 1955, Y, is correlated with retail sales per family, X, for a sample of 155 counties. A correlation such as this may serve various practical purposes. It may indicate sections of the country where *Holiday* does not conform to the general pattern, and thus point out weak spots to the publisher. It may also indicate to potential advisers whether the magazine is read by the type of reader to whom they wish to appeal. Thus if the correlation is extremely high, it would appear that *Holiday* is a good medium for advertising commodities which appeal primarily to people with large spending power, but not so good a medium for advertising goods intended primarily for persons with small spending power.

Correlation table. Table 27.1 is a tally sheet of these data.[1] Such a table is similar to a scatter diagram with one difference: whereas in a scatter

---

[1] Note, however, that the tally sheet is not strictly necessary; if the values of the different variables are entered on cards, the cards can be sorted and the entries made directly in the correlation table. Such a procedure has two advantages: it facilitates selecting the class interval and class limits; it avoids the rather large risk of making errors in tallying.

Table 27.1—Tally Sheet Showing Retail Sales Per Family in Dollars X, and *Holiday* Circulation per 1,000 Families in March 1955, for 155 Counties

Y \ X	1,000–1,399	1,400–1,799	1,800–2,199	2,200–2,599	2,600–2,999	3,000–3,399	3,400–3,799	3,800–4,199	4,200–4,599	4,600–4,999	5,000–5,399	5,400–5,799
30.0–32.4												
27.5–29.9						/		/	/			
25.0–27.4									/			
22.5–24.9		/										
20.0–22.4							//	//				
17.5–19.9						//	/	///	//			
15.0–17.4						///	///	///	卌 /		/	
12.5–14.9					/	////	卌	////	卌 /			/
10.0–12.4				/	//	卌 卌	卌 / 卌 /	///				/
7.5–9.9		/	//	卌	卌	////	卌	////				
5.0–7.4		////	///	卌	卌 /	////	//		/			
2.5–4.9	/	///	///	//	卌	/	/					
0.0–2.4	//	/	///									

Sources of data: Curtis Publishing Co., *Holiday Circulation*, March 1955 issue; *Sales Management Survey of Buying Power*, May 10, 1956, pp. 259–831.

diagram each dot is placed in its exact location, in a correlation table each tally mark is placed merely in its appropriate cell. In the calculations that follow, each item in a cell is treated as if it had the same value as the mid-point of that cell. Thus it is assumed that each of the six counties represented in the cell that is the intersection of the fifth column from the left and the third row from the bottom has a per capita sales of $2,800 and a *Holiday* circulation of 6.2 copies per 1,000 families. Although the mid-point assumption is not absolutely correct, if the items are numerous and there is a reasonably large number of cells, preferably not fewer than twelve classes in each distribution, the error from grouping is usually not large.

Table 27.2, which is a correlation table, is based upon the tally sheet Table 27.1. In the center of each cell is recorded the frequency tallied in Table 27.1. When these numbers are added vertically, the results are as indicated in the row labeled f_X. This row is the frequency distribution of variable X, retail sales per family. Horizontal addition of the cell frequencies shown in the column labeled f_Y gives the frequency distribution of variable Y, *Holiday* circulation per 1,000 families. The total of the frequencies, or counties, n, is 155 for each distribution. The last two columns of the table are largely self-explanatory; they are the columns necessary for computation of the mean and variation of variable Y. The two rows of $f_X d'_X$ and $f_X (d'_X)^2$ are those needed to compute the mean and variation of variable X. The algebraic totals of the different columns and rows are indicated in the lower right section of the table.

The number in the upper left corner of each cell printed in italics is the product of d'_X and d'_Y. The values in the first and third quadrants of the table are positive, while those in the second and fourth are, of course, negative. The lower right number in each cell, shown in boldface, is the result of the multiplication of the $d'_X d'_Y$ value for that cell by the corresponding f_{XY}. Algebraically adding these boldface numbers, $\Sigma f_{XY} d'_X d'_Y$ is found to be +568.

Computation of measures of relationship. In order to compute all of the final measures of relationship, certain intermediate measures must first be obtained:

$\overline{X}$ and $\overline{Y}$, the mean of each series (needed only for the estimating equation);
Σx^2 and Σy^2, the variation of each series;
Σxy, the co-variation.
The computation of these measures follows familiar patterns:

$$\overline{X} = X_0 + c_X \left(\frac{\Sigma f_X d'_X}{n}\right) = 3,199.50 + 400\left(\frac{6}{155}\right) = \$3,214.98.$$

$$\overline{Y} = Y_0 + c_Y \left(\frac{\Sigma f_Y d'_Y}{n}\right) = 11.20 + 2.5\left(\frac{-7}{155}\right) = 11.09 \text{ copies}.$$

Table 27.2—Correlation Table for Retail Sales Per Family in Dollars (X), and *Holiday* Circulation per 1,000 Families in March 1955, for 155 Counties

Cell notation: *(d'ₓd'ᵧ)* f **f·d'ₓd'ᵧ** — i.e. italic = $d'_X d'_Y$, centre = frequency f, bold = $f\,d'_X d'_Y$.

Y \ X	1,000–1,399	1,400–1,799	1,800–2,199	2,200–2,599	2,600–2,999	3,000–3,399	3,400–3,799	3,800–4,199	4,200–4,599	4,600–4,999	5,000–5,399	5,400–5,799	f_Y	d'_Y	$f_Y d'_Y$	$f_Y(d'_Y)^2$
30.0–32.4							*8* 1 **8**	*16* 1 **16**					2	8	16	128
27.5–29.9						*0* 1 **0**		*14* 1 **14**	*21* 1 **21**	*28* 1 **28**			4	7	28	196
25.0–27.4										*24* 1 **24**			1	6	6	36
22.5–24.9		*−20* 1 **−20**						*10* 1 **10**		*20* 1 **20**			3	5	15	75
20.0–22.4						*0* 2 **0**		*8* 2 **16**					4	4	16	64
17.5–19.9							*3* 2 **6**	*6* 1 **6**	*9* 2 **18**				5	3	15	45
15.0–17.4							*2* 3 **6**	*4* 3 **12**	*6* 6 **36**		*10* 1 **10**		13	2	26	52
12.5–14.9				*−2* 1 **−2**	*−1* 1 **−1**	*0* 4 **0**	*1* 5 **5**	*2* 4 **8**	*3* 6 **18**	*4* 2 **8**		*6* 1 **6**	24	1	24	24
10.0–12.4			*0* 2 **0**		*0* 2 **0**	*0* 11 **0**	*0* 6 **0**	*0* 3 **0**	*0* 3 **0**			*0* 1 **0**	28	0	0	0
7.5–9.9		*4* 1 **4**	*3* 2 **6**	*2* 5 **10**	*1* 5 **5**	*0* 2 **0**	*−1* 4 **−4**	*−2* 1 **−2**					20	−1	−20	20
5.0–7.4	*10* 2 **20**	*8* 4 **32**	*6* 3 **18**	*4* 5 **20**	*2* 6 **12**	*0* 4 **0**	*−2* 2 **−4**		*−6* 1 **−6**				27	−2	−54	108
2.5–4.9	*15* 1 **15**	*12* 3 **36**	*9* 3 **27**	*6* 2 **12**	*3* 5 **15**	*0* 1 **0**	*−3* 1 **−3**	*−6* 1 **−6**					17	−3	−51	153
0.0–2.4	*20* 2 **40**	*16* 1 **16**	*12* 3 **36**				*−4* 1 **−4**						7	−4	−28	112
f_X	5	10	13	13	19	25	25	18	19	5	1	2	155	…	−7	1,013
d'_X	−5	−4	−3	−2	−1	0	1	2	3	4	5	6	…	n	$\Sigma f_Y d'_Y$	$\Sigma f_Y(d'_Y)^2$
$f_X d'_X$	−25	−40	−39	−26	−19	0	25	36	57	20	5	12	$\Sigma f_X d'_X$			$\Sigma f_X d'_X d'_Y$
$f_X(d'_X)^2$	125	160	117	52	19	0	25	72	171	80	25	72	918	$\Sigma f_X(d'_X)^2$		$= +568$

Source of data: Table 27.1.

(27.1) $\quad \Sigma x^2 = c_X^2 \Sigma (x')^2 = c_X^2 \left[\Sigma f_X (d_X')^2 - \dfrac{(\Sigma f_X d_X')^2}{n} \right]$

$\qquad\qquad = (160{,}000)\left(918 - \dfrac{36}{155}\right) = (160{,}000)(917.768) = 146{,}843{,}000.$

(27.2) $\quad \Sigma y^2 = c_Y^2 \Sigma (y')^2 = c_Y^2 \left[\Sigma f_Y (d_Y')^2 - \dfrac{(\Sigma f_Y d_Y')^2}{n} \right]$

$\qquad\qquad = (6.25)\left(1{,}013 - \dfrac{49}{155}\right) = (6.25)(1{,}012.68) = 6{,}329.25.$

(27.3) $\quad \Sigma xy = c_X c_Y \Sigma x'y' = c_X c_Y \left[\Sigma f_{XY} d_X' d_Y' - \dfrac{(\Sigma f_X d_X')(\Sigma f_Y d_Y')}{n} \right]$

$\qquad\qquad = (400)(2.5)\left[568 - \dfrac{(6)(-7)}{155} \right] = (1{,}000)(568.271) = 568{,}271.$

If the estimating equation is needed, the various measures are computed in exactly the same manner as for ungrouped data.

$$b = \frac{\Sigma xy}{\Sigma x^2} = \frac{568{,}271}{146{,}843{,}000} = 0.0038699.$$

$$a = \bar{Y} - b\bar{X} = 11.09 - (0.0038699)(3{,}214.98)$$

$$= 11.09 - 12.44 = -1.35.$$

$$Y_X = -1.35 + 0.0038699\,X.$$

$$\Sigma y_x^2 = b\,\Sigma xy = (0.0038699)(568{,}271) = 2{,}199.15.$$

$$\Sigma (y \cdot x)^2 = \Sigma y^2 - \Sigma y_x^2 = 6{,}329.27 - 2{,}199.15 = 4{,}130.1.$$

$$s_{y \cdot x}^2 = \frac{\Sigma (y \cdot x)^2}{n - 2} = \frac{4{,}130.1}{153} = 26.99.$$

$$s_{y \cdot x} = 5.20.$$

$$r^2 = \frac{\Sigma y_x^2}{\Sigma y^2} = \frac{2{,}199.2}{6{,}329.3} = 0.3475.$$

$$r = +0.589.$$

If the estimating equation is not needed, but only r is to be found, it is easier to compute it directly from formula (26.1).

$$r = \frac{\Sigma xy}{\sqrt{(\Sigma x^2)(\Sigma y^2)}} = \frac{568{,}271}{\sqrt{(146{,}843{,}000)(6{,}329.25)}} = +0.589.$$

If the computations are carried through in class interval units, there is a further saving of labor.[2]

$$(27.4) \qquad r = \frac{\Sigma\, x'y'}{\sqrt{[\Sigma\, (x')^2][\Sigma\, (y')^2]}}$$

$$= \frac{568.27}{\sqrt{(917.768)(1{,}012.68)}} = +0.589.$$

Bias resulting from grouping. On page 399 it was pointed out that in calculating the measures of relationship from grouped data, each item is treated as if it had the same value as the mid-point of the cell in which it is located. Although this assumption is not correct, it results in no bias so far as $\Sigma\, xy$ is concerned. Values of $\Sigma\, x^2$ and $\Sigma\, y^2$, however, will tend to be somewhat too large when computed from grouped data. Consequently r computed from grouped data tends to be somewhat smaller than r computed from ungrouped data, unless a correction is made for the error of grouping.

The correction for grouping error is made by subtracting $n/12$ from $\Sigma\, (x')^2$ and from $\Sigma\, (y')^2$ of formula (27.4). For our illustration, $n = 155$, and $155 \div 12 = 12.917$. So we have

$$r = \frac{568.27}{\sqrt{(904.851)(999.76)}} = +0.597.$$

2 × 2 Tables

Correlation coefficient. If the data of Table 27.2 are reduced to a 2 × 2 table, as in 27.3, we have the ultimate in simplicity of presentation. In

Table 27.3—2 × 2 Correlation Table of Retail Sales per Family and *Holiday* Circulation per 1,000 Families in March 1955, for 155 Counties

Circulation	Retail sales		Total
	$1,000–$3,399	$3,400–$5,799	
10.0–32.4	25	59	84
0.00–9.9	60	11	71
Total	85	70	155

Source of data: Table 27.2.

---

[2] Formula (27.4) may also be stated in detail:

$$r = \frac{\Sigma f_{xy} d'_x d'_y - (\Sigma f_x d'_x)(\Sigma f_y d'_y)/n}{\sqrt{[\Sigma f_x (d'_x)^2 - (\Sigma f_x d'_x)^2/n][\Sigma f_y (d'_y)^2 - (\Sigma f_y d'_y)^2/n]}}$$

or

$$r = \frac{n \Sigma f_{xy} d'_x d'_y - (\Sigma f_x d'_x)(\Sigma f_y d'_y)}{\sqrt{[n \Sigma f_x (d'_x)^2 - (\Sigma f_x d'_x)^2][n \Sigma f_y (d'_y)^2 - (\Sigma f_y d'_y)^2]}}.$$

constructing this table $3,400 is considered the dividing line between small and large retail sales per family, and 10 copies per 1,000 families is considered the dividing line between small and large circulation of *Holiday*. The dividing line should be approximately the median of each series.

Let us use the following symbols to indicate the frequencies in a contingency table.

Category	1	2	Total
2	f_{21}	f_{22}	$n_2.$
1	f_{11}	f_{12}	$n_1.$
Total	$n_{.1}$	$n_{.2}$	N

There are many ways of measuring degree of association for a 2×2 table, and there is no agreement among authorities as to which is best. It is difficult, however, to conceive of a simpler one than the following, which might be referred to as the "net per cent" method:

$$(27.5) \qquad r_{NP} = \frac{(f_{11} + f_{22}) - (f_{21} + f_{12})}{N}.$$

Note that this coefficient can be computed on a desk calculator without recording intermediate steps.

For our data

$$r_{NP} = \frac{(60 + 59) - (25 + 11)}{155} = \frac{199 - 36}{155} = \frac{83}{155} = +0.535.$$

Thus the net per cent of entries that are in agreement (low, low, or high, high) is 53.5. For a 2×2 table there could be complete agreement ($r_{NP} = +1$) or complete disagreement ($r_{NP} = -1$), or any value between these two extremes.

Test of significance. Chi-square is used for testing significance. The method, except for determining the expected frequencies, is similar to that used in Chapter 19 to test goodness of fit.

If there were no connection between retail sales and size of circulation, we should expect $\frac{84}{155}$ of the 85 counties with small sales to have large circulation. An analogous statement can be made for the expected frequencies for each cell. Symbolically:

$$(27.6) \qquad \begin{cases} \hat{f}_{21} = \dfrac{n_2. n_{.1}}{N}; & \hat{f}_{22} = \dfrac{n_2. n_{.2}}{N}; \\[2ex] \hat{f}_{11} = \dfrac{n_1. n_{.1}}{N}; & \hat{f}_{12} = \dfrac{n_1. n_{.2}}{N}. \end{cases}$$

Numerically:

$$\hat{f}_{21} = \frac{(84)(85)}{155} = 46.06; \qquad \hat{f}_{22} = \frac{(84)(70)}{155} = 37.94;$$

$$\hat{f}_{11} = \frac{(71)(85)}{155} = 38.94; \qquad \hat{f}_{12} = \frac{(71)(70)}{155} = 32.06.$$

These results are tabulated in Table 27.4. Note that the marginal totals are the same as for Table 27.3.

Table 27.4—Expected Frequencies for Data of Table 37.3 Under the Hypothesis of No Correlation

Circulation	Retail sales		Total
	$1,000– $3,399	$3,400– $5,799	
10.0–32.4	46.08	37.94	84
0.0–9.9	38.94	32.06	71
Total	85	70	155

To compute χ^2 we use formula (19.11), which for a 2×2 table may be written

$$\chi^2 = \sum \frac{(f-\hat{f})^2}{\hat{f}} = \frac{(f_{21} - \hat{f}_{21})^2}{\hat{f}_{21}} + \frac{(f_{22} - \hat{f}_{22})^2}{\hat{f}_{22}} + \frac{(f_{11} - \hat{f}_{11})^2}{\hat{f}_{11}} + \frac{(f_{12} - \hat{f}_{12})^2}{\hat{f}_{12}},$$

or, since $|f - \hat{f}|$ is the same for each of the four cells,

$$(27.7) \qquad \chi^2 = (f-\hat{f})^2 \sum \left(\frac{1}{\hat{f}}\right) = (f-\hat{f})^2 \left(\frac{1}{\hat{f}_{21}} + \frac{1}{\hat{f}_{22}} + \frac{1}{\hat{f}_{11}} + \frac{1}{\hat{f}_{12}}\right).$$

For our data

$$\chi^2 = (21.06)^2 \left(\frac{1}{46.06} + \frac{1}{37.94} + \frac{1}{38.94} + \frac{1}{32.06}\right)$$

$$= 443.5(.02171 + .02636 + .02568 + .03119)$$

$$= (443.5)(.1049) = 48.5.$$

There is but one degree of freedom, since the marginal totals for the f and $\hat{f}$ distributions must be the same. This is equivalent to specifying:

$$\Sigma f = \Sigma \hat{f} = N;$$

$$f_{21} + f_{22} = \hat{f}_{21} + \hat{f}_{22} = n_{2.};$$

$$f_{21} + f_{11} = \hat{f}_{21} + \hat{f}_{11} = n_{.1}.$$

These constraints completely determine the frequencies in all but one cell. One cell, and one cell only, can be filled in arbitrarily. Consequently we enter the χ^2 table (Appendix 22) at $\nu = 1$. When $P = .001$, we find that χ^2 is only 10.827. There is thus virtually no doubt that *Holiday* circulation varies with retail sales.

One objection to the use of χ^2 to test the significance of r_P for a 2×2 table is that r_{NP} is not a simple function of χ^2.

**Table 27.5—Flexibility and Selling Ability of
20 Salesmen**

Selling ability	Flexibility		Total
	Poor	Good	
Good	3	7	10
Poor	8	2	10
Total	11	9	20

Source of data: Kornagy and Graham, *The Selection and Training of Salesmen*, McGraw Hill Book Co., Inc., New York, 1925, p. 294.

Qualitatively classified data. Occasionally one encounters data that not only are not designated by numerical values, but are classified according to characteristics that may or may not be fundamentally quantitative. For instance, a salesman may be considered good or poor, but it is not stated how good or poor he is. Likewise, a salesman's reactions to a psychological test may be either favorable or unfavorable. Now, suppose it is desired to discover from such data the extent to which it is true that selling ability is associated with the Downey Will-Temperament Test for flexibility, or the capacity to modify one's routine activities. The salesmen may be grouped as in Table 27.5, often referred to as a contingency table.

It is apparent at a glance that the better salesmen are superior in flexibility and that the poorer salesmen are inferior in flexibility. Only 5 out of 20 salesmen are exceptions to this general tendency. Observe that the traits shown in the table progress from left to right and from bottom to top as in the usual scatter diagram or correlation table.

If we apply formula (27.5), we obtain $r_{NP} = +0.500$.

It should be noted that the categories into which our data are classified are fundamentally quantitative. The procedures would be the same if they were fundamentally qualitative. For example, we could classify employees as white or negro, and agricultural or industrial. In such a case there would be no basis for affixing a sign to the correlation coefficient.

Correction for *continuity.* We again use χ^2 to test significance. However, when the sample size is small, it is desirable to make a correction for continuity, usually referred to as Yates' correction for continuity.[3] The correction consists merely of reducing the value of each of the $|f - \hat{f}|$ values by 0.5.

$$(27.8) \qquad \chi^2 = (|f - \hat{f}| - 0.5)^2 \sum \left(\frac{1}{\hat{f}}\right).$$

The expected frequencies for our data are given in Table 27.6.

Table 27.6—Expected Frequencies for Data of
Table 27.5 Under the Hypothesis of
No Correlation

Selling ability	Flexibility		Total
	Poor	Good	
Poor	5.5	4.5	10.0
Good	5.5	4.5	10.0
Total	11.0	9.0	20.0

$$\chi^2 = (2.5 - 0.5)^2 \left(\frac{1}{5.5} + \frac{1}{4.5} + \frac{1}{5.5} + \frac{1}{4.5}\right)$$

$$= 2^2(0.1818 + 0.2222 + 0.1818 + 0.2222)$$

$$= 4(0.8080) = 3.232.$$

With $\nu = 1$, Appendix 22 indicates that when $\chi^2 = 3.232$, $P \doteq .07$. Our sample therefore fails to show a significant relationship between flexibility and selling ability.

Correlation of Ranked Data

Sometimes statistical series are composed of items the exact magnitude of which cannot be ascertained, but which are ranked according to size. Thus the figures in column (2) of Table 27.7 show the ranks of twenty salesmen as determined by the sales manager, based upon their value to the concern. In column (3) their ranks are stated according to the results of two psychological tests. By comparing the rankings of the salesmen according to the subjective criterion and according to the average score on the two tests, it may be seen that the characteristics tested have something to do with selling ability. For instance, Mr. Millard was first and Mr. Holman was last

---

[3] Neither $\Sigma (f - \hat{f})^2/\hat{f}$ nor $\Sigma (|f - \hat{f}| - 0.5)^2/\hat{f}$ have the χ^2 distribution, but they approach that form of distribution as n approaches infinity. An exact test of significance for 2×2 contingency tables is given in Chapter 39.

by either method of judging. Sometimes two or more items may be tied in rank; in which case each is given the average of the two ranks. Thus if Borden and McNulty were tied for third and fourth, each would be given a rank of 3.5; if Borden, McNulty, and Mattern were tied for third, fourth, and fifth, each would be given a rank of 3.

Table 27.7—Rank of 20 Employees with Respect to Selling Ability and Results of Psychological Tests, and Computation of k for Obtaining Rank Correlation Coefficient τ

Salesmen	Rank by sales manager	Rank by two tests	Number of employees in rows below with larger test rank
(1)	(2)	(3)	(4)
Millard	1	1	19
Prentice	2	6	14
Borden	3	7	13
McNulty	4	9	11
Mattern	5	2	15
Peterson	6	10	10
Rosoff	7	3	13
Haddad	8	5	11
Weingard	9	15	5
Bochman	10	8	9
Gellers	11	4	9
Kelly	12	14	5
Lyon	13	17	3
Petty	14	18	2
Kennedy	15	16	2
Preston	16	12	3
Minnett	17	13	2
Tolan	18	11	2
Sullivan	19	19	1
Holman	20	20	0
Total	...	...	$k = 149$

A rank correlation coefficient for which there is an exact test significance is Kendall's τ. The procedure for computing is most easily explained by reference to a table such as Table 27.7. The first entry in column (4) is 19. This number is recorded because the rank in column (3) is 1, and there are 19 entries below it in column (3) that are larger than 1. The second entry in column (4) is 14. This number is recorded because there are 14 numbers below it in column (3) that are larger than 6. The other entries in column (4) are obtained in similar manner.[4] The total for column (4) is $k = 149$. We next compute

(27.9) $$S = 2k - \binom{n}{2}$$

$$= 2(149) - \binom{20}{2} = 298 - 190 = 108,$$

and

(27.10) $$\tau = \frac{S}{\binom{n}{2}}$$

$$= \frac{108}{190} = +0.568.$$

This is a nonparametric measure; it makes no assumptions concerning the nature of the distributions underlying the ranks.[5]

Test of significance. Appendix 26 provides an exact test of significance of S for sample sizes through $n = 10$. For larger samples it is satisfactory to assume that S is distributed normally with

(27.11) $$\sigma_S = \sqrt{\frac{n(n-1)(2n+5)}{18}},$$

and

(27.12) $$z_S = \frac{S-1}{\sigma_S}.$$

For our data

$$\sigma_S = \sqrt{\frac{(20)(19)(35)}{18}} = 27.18,$$

and $$z_S = \frac{108}{27.18} = 3.97.$$

---

[4] It is not necessary to convert either variable into ranks, since we need only to count the number of occurrences larger than a given value. But if the data in column (2) have not been arranged in rank order, it is necessary to draw a line through each row, as it is used, in order to keep the count straight.

[5] Another widely used rank correlation coefficient is Spearman's rank correlation coefficient.

$$r_{\text{rank}} = 1 - \frac{6 \Sigma D^2}{n(n^2 - 1)},$$

where D is the difference between a pair of ranks. For the above data

$$r_{\text{rank}} = 1 - \frac{6(314)}{(20)(400 - 1)} = +0.764.$$

See D. J. Cowden and F. E. Croxton, *Practical Business Statistics*, 2d ed., Prentice-Hall, Inc., New York, 1948, pp. 422–424. Use of r_{rank} obtains the same result that would be obtained by applying the ordinary product-moment formula to the ranks. The sampling distribution of r_{rank} has not been determined for all sample sizes.

Since the probability of obtaining a value of S as large as $+108$ or larger is smaller than 0.001, we consider S, and τ, to be significant.

Correlation of Transformed Data

Frequently the dots on a scatter diagram will cluster much more closely around a curved line than around a straight line. If such is the case, and the improvement in the fit is greater than could be accounted for by the accident of sampling, it may be better to base estimates on a curved rather than a straight line. One method is to transform one or both of the variables into some other form, such as logarithms; another is to use an equation with more than two constants. We shall here discuss the use of logarithms. The use of an equation with more than two constants will be considered in Chapter 36 as a special case of multiple correlation.

Choice of function. It is often difficult to decide what type of transformation to use, but one should consider for the various equation types:

1. What type is most logical;
2. What type results in a distribution of errors that is most nearly normal around the estimating line;
3. What type results in a distribution of errors that is most nearly uniform in variability around the estimating line;
4. What type results in the smallest errors within the range of data in which one is interested;
5. What type results in the closest correlation;
6. What type results in the simplest curve.

Use of logarithms. It is well known that as output on a new job progresses, the cost per unit decreases because workers learn to do the work more rapidly. If hours per unit of output can be expressed as a function of the total output, cost of production can be figured in such a way that gross profit per unit of time is more stable. In the aircraft frame industry it was found that each time the quantity of production was doubled, the cumulative labor hours was 80 per cent of the preceding.[6]

Consider the data of Table 27.8 where average hours per unit are a function of the cumulative production. Chart 27.1 shows that the relationship is obviously nonlinear, but when they are plotted on paper with logarithmic scales for each axis, as on Chart 27.2, or when the logarithms of the two series are plotted on arithmetic paper, as on Chart 27.3, the dots fluctuate around a straight line.

---

[6] See Rolfe Wyer, "Learning Curve Helps Figure Profits, Control Costs," *N.A.C.A. Bulletin*, Vol. XXXV, December, 1953, pp. 490–502. In this paper Wyer explains how to figure labor costs and gross profits. The coded data of Table 27.7 are read from a chart (Exhibit 2), p. 492, of that paper.

**Table 27.8—Cumulative Quantity Produced,
and Cumulative Hours per Unit, in
an Aircraft Frame Factory**
(Coded data)

Cumulative quantity X	Cumulative hours per unit Y
20	150
35	125
60	105
100	100
150	92
300	77
500	62
800	58
1,500	47

Source: See footnote 6.

**Chart 27.1—Scatter Diagram on Arithmetic Paper
Cumulative Quantity Produced and Cumulative
Hours per Unit in an Aircraft Frame Factory**

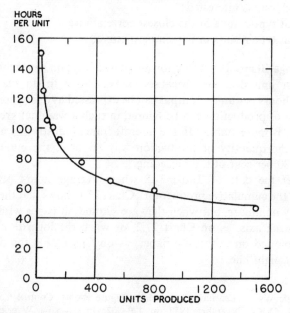

Source of data: Table 27.7 and 27.9.

**Chart 27.2—Scatter Diagram on Logarithmic Paper: Cumulative Quantity
Produced and Cumulative Hours per Unit in an Aircraft Factory**

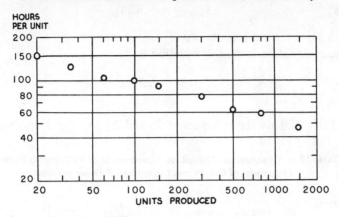

Source of data: Tables 27.8 and 27.10.

**Chart 27.3—Scatter Diagram on Arithmetic Paper: Logarithm
of Quantity Produced and Logarithm of Cumulative Hours
per Unit in an Aircraft Frame Factory**

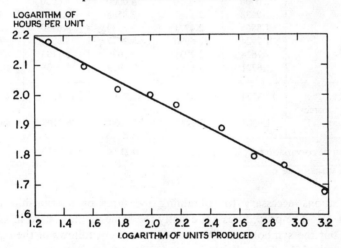

Source of data: Tables 27.9 and 27.10.

The equation describing the straight line on Chart 27.2 is of the type

(27.13) $$Y_X = AX^b.$$

This is a parabolic equation, or when b is negative, a hyperbolic equation.
If we take the logarithm of each side of the equation, we have

(27.14) $$\text{Log } Y_X = a + b \log X,$$

where $a = \log A$.

To make the notation a little simpler we may write

(27.15) $$X_{1(2)} = a + b_{12}X_2,$$

where $X_{1(2)} = \log Y_X$ and $X_2 = X$.
Finally, in deviation form, this equation is

(27.16) $$x_{1(2)} = b_{12}x_2,$$

where $x_2 = X_2 - \bar{X}_2$.

In Table 27.9 are shown values of X_1 and X_2 (i.e., $\log Y$ and $\log X$) and

Table 27.9—Computations Needed for Measurement of Relationship Between Logarithms of Output and Logarithms of Hours per Unit

Statistic:	X_1 (log Y)	X_2 (log X)	X_1^2	X_1X_2	X_2^2
	2.1761	1.3010	4.7354	2.8311	1.6926
	2.0969	1.5441	4.3970	3.2378	2.3842
	2.0212	1.7782	4.0852	3.5941	3.1620
	2.0000	2.0000	4.0000	4.0000	4.0000
	1.9638	2.1761	3.8565	4.2734	4.7354
	1.8865	2.4771	3.5589	4.6730	6.1360
	1.7924	2.6990	3.2127	4.8377	7.2846
	1.7634	2.9031	3.1096	5.1193	8.4280
	1.6721	3.1761	2.7959	5.3108	10.0876
Total	17.3724	20.0547	33.7512	37.8772	47.9104
Mean or correction term ...	1.9303	2.2283	33.5334	38.7109	44.6879
Variation or co-variation			0.2178	−0.8337	3.225

Source of data: Table 27.8.

computations necessary for obtaining measures of relationship between X_1 and X_2. The procedures are exactly the same as those used in Chapters 24–26, but the symbols are different. A statement follows of the equations that are needed. They should be studied carefully, since they will also be extended (in Chapters 35 and 36) for use in multiple and partial correlation.

Constants for estimating equation:

(27.17) $$b_{12} = \frac{\Sigma x_1x_2}{\Sigma x_2^2},$$

where $$\Sigma x_1x_2 = \Sigma X_1X_2 - (\Sigma X_1)(\Sigma X_2)/n.$$

(27.18) $$a = \bar{X}_1 - b_{12}\bar{X}_2.$$

Explained variation:

(27.19) $$\Sigma\, x_{1(2)}^2 = b_{12}\, \Sigma\, x_1 x_2.$$

Unexplained variation:

(27.20) $$\Sigma\, x_{1.2}^2 = \Sigma\, x_1^2 - \Sigma\, x_{1(2)}^2.$$

Standard error of estimate:

(27.21) $$s_{1.2} = \sqrt{\frac{\Sigma\, x_{1.2}^2}{n-2}}.$$

Coefficient of correlation:

(27.22) $$r_{12} = \sqrt{\frac{\Sigma\, x_{12}^2}{\Sigma\, x_1^2}},$$

or

(27.23) $$r_{12} = \frac{\Sigma\, x_1 x_2.}{\sqrt{(\Sigma\, x_1^2)(\Sigma\, x_x^2)}}.$$

Substituting the values from Table 27.8 in these formulas, we obtain

$$b_{12} = -\frac{0.8337}{3.2225} = -0.2587.$$

$$x_{1(2)} = -0.2587 x_2.$$

$$a = 1.9303 - (0.2587)(2.2283) = 2.5068.$$

$$X_{12} = 2.5068 - 0.2587 X_2.$$

$$\Sigma\, x_{1(2)}^2 = (-0.2587)(-0.8337) = 0.2157.$$

$$\Sigma\, x_{1(2)}^2 = 0.2178 - 0.2157 = 0.0021.$$

$$s_{1.2}^2 = \frac{0.0021}{7} = 0.0003; \quad s_{1.2} = 0.017.$$

$$r_{12}^2 = \frac{0.2157}{0.2178} = 0.9904; \quad r_{12} = -0.995.$$

$$r_{12} = \frac{-0.8337}{\sqrt{(0.2178)(3.2225)}} = -0.995.$$

Interpretation of estimating equation. The estimating equation is

$$X_{12} = 2.5068 - 0.2587 X_2.$$

Using logarithmic notation

$$\text{Log } Y_X = 2.5068 - 0.2587 \log X.$$

Using these equations, the Y_X values are computed in Table 27.9. The antilog of 2.5068 is 321.22, and the equation can be written in hyperbolic form,

$$Y_X = 321.22 X^{-0.2587}.$$

Table 27.9—Cumulative Hours per Unit, Estimated from Cumulative Output
(Log $Y_X = 2.5068 - 0.2587 \log X$)

Cumulative output X	Cumulative hours per unit Y	X_2 log X	X_1 log Y	$b_{12}X_2$	$X_{1(2)}$ log Y_X	Y_X antilog $X_{1(2)}$
20	150	1.3010	2.1761	−0.3366	2.1702	148.0
35	125	1.5441	2.0969	−.3995	2.1073	128.0
60	105	1.7782	2.0212	−.4600	2.0468	111.4
100	100	2.0000	2.0000	−.5174	1.9894	97.6
150	92	2.1761	1.9638	−.5630	1.9438	87.9
300	77	2.4771	1.8865	−.6408	1.8660	73.4
500	62	2.6990	1.7924	−.6982	1.8086	64.4
800	58	2.9031	1.7634	−.7510	1.7558	57.0
1500	47	3.1761	1.6721	−.8217	1.6851	48.4
Total	...	...	17.372	...	17.373	...

To put the meaning of this equation in words:[7] The percentage change in hours per unit relative to the percentage change in total output, at any point on the curve, is −0.2587. If we wish to know what happens as output doubles, we compute

$$\text{Log } \lambda = b \log 2$$
$$= (-0.2587)(0.30103) = -0.0779 = \bar{1}.9221.$$
$$\lambda = 0.836 = 83.6 \text{ per cent.}$$

Thus, if $X = 50$, $Y_X = 116.8$;

if $X = 100$, $Y_X = 97.6$;

if $X = 200$, $Y_X = 81.6$.

Now $$\frac{97.6}{116.8} = \frac{81.6}{97.6} = 0.836 = 83.6 \text{ per cent.}$$

The equation may therefore be said to describe an 83.6 per cent learning curve.

Interpretation of standard error of estimate. The standard error of estimate,

$$s_{1.2} = 0.017,$$

is the standard deviation of the unexplained deviations of the logarithms around the logarithmic estimating line. The symbol $s_{\log Y.\log X}$ may also be

[7] In the language of the economist, b may be referred to as the elasticity of hours per unit with respect to output.

used, since it is the standard error of estimate of the logarithms. Below are values of $X_{1(2)} \pm s_{1.2}$ for three values of X.

X	X_2 (log X)	$X_{1(2)}$	$X_{1(2)} \pm s_{1.2}$
50	1.6990	2.067	2.050 and 2.084
100	2.0000	1.989	1.972 and 2.006
200	2.3010	1.912	1.895 and 1.929

The antilog of $s_{1.2}$, for which the symbol s_{Y/Y_x} is appropriate, is 1.04. If we divide and multiply the values of Y_X by 1.04, we obtain:

X	Y_x (antilog $X_{1(2)}$)	$Y_x/1.04$	$1.04 Y_x$
50	116.8	112	121
100	97.6	94	101
200	81.6	78	85

These are the same values that are obtained when we take the antilogs of the values of $X_{1(2)} \pm s_{1.2}$. Thus $s_{Y/Y_x} =$ antilog $s_{1.2}$ may be thought of as the *relative* standard error of estimate.

A note on demand curves. One of the major problems of business management consists in determining the most profitable price at which to offer commodities for sale. Profit-making possibilities depend on the cost of producing (and selling) various quantities, and the prices at which various quantities can be sold. The control of costs has long engaged the attention of businessmen and is one of the objects of cost accounting; the determination of price has been for some time one of the central problems of economic theorists, but has been in the main considered only subjectively by business executives.

A table showing the relationship between the different amounts of a product offered for sale and the various prices at which they can be sold, or between various prices and the amounts that can be sold at these prices, is known as a *demand schedule*, and when plotted is known as a *demand curve*. It is often a very difficult problem to derive a demand curve statistically, although it is necessary for a businessman to know the demand curve for his product in order to adjust price and production if his aim is to obtain the maximum profit. A difficulty arises out of the fact that the true demand curve may be changing shape and shifting to the right or left with the passage of time. It is easiest to derive for relatively perishable commodities, the production of which is subject to considerable uncontrollable fluctuation but which are relatively stable in demand, so that the demand curve remains much the same in successive periods of time. One method of attempting to remove the influence of a gradual change in demand is to fit trends to a price and a production series and use deviations from trend or percentages of trend as the data to be correlated. (See Chapter 37, pp. 557–560.) This method is satisfactory if demand is gradually and continuously changing. Alternatively, time may be considered as a separate variable. This approach requires the technique of partial regression explained in Chapter 35. (See also Chapter 36, pp. 553–554.) Another method is to take into consideration the variable or variables that are responsible for the change in demand. For example, in measuring the relationship between production X and price Y of potatoes, the demand is affected by the price of the foods. The effect of food prices can be allowed for (1) by deflation, dividing the price of potatoes by a food price index or (2) by regression, using the price of potatoes as another independent variable.

It is usually appropriate, when deriving a demand curve statistically, to use the logarithms of the production series and the logarithms of the price series. If a constant elasticity of demand is assumed, a straight line is fitted to the logarithms, and the flexibility of price (reciprocal of elasticity of demand) is the slope of the line.

Flexibility of methods using transformed variables. We have considered only an equation of the type

$$\log Y_X = a + b \log X.$$

A large number of functions are available for which a logical basis could be found for some kinds of data. To state but a few:

$$\log Y_X = a + bX;$$
$$Y_X = a + b \log X;$$
$$\frac{1}{Y_X} = a + bX;$$
$$Y_X = a + b\frac{1}{X};$$
$$\frac{1}{Y_X} = a + b \log X.$$

All these, and many others, can be handled simply, by transforming them[8] into an equation of the type $X_{1(2)} = a + b_{12}X_2$.

---

[8] It is quite possible that the relationship between *Holiday* circulation and per family income could be improved by use of an equation with log Y as the dependent variable. Referring to the criteria on page 409:

1. It seems logical to suppose that expenditures for luxuries increase more rapidly than incomes.

2. Table 27.1 indicates positive skewness, not only for the Y distribution as a whole, but for most of the individual arrays of Y values for the different X classes. Use of log Y values tends to correct that difficulty.

3. The variances of the individual arrays seem to get larger as we progress from left to right in Table 27.1.

4. The correlation between X and Y is $+.59$; the correlation between X and log Y is $+.65$.

5. From the evidence it is not clear what type of equation should be used, but the preponderance of evidence suggests log $Y_x = a + bX$ is preferable to $Y_x = a + bX$, but that still better is log $Y_x = a + bX + cX^2$. For correlation methods using this type of relationship, see Chapter 36.

Chapter 28

ELEMENTS OF LINEAR TREND FITTING

A time series consists of data arranged chronologically. Typically an economic or business time series has these characteristic components: secular trend T; cycles C; seasonal movements S; irregular fluctuations I. Ordinarily we think of the original data Y as being the product of these components. Symbolically,

$$(28.1) \qquad\qquad Y = T \times C \times S \times I.$$

In this chapter we shall consider only secular trend, the gradual increase or decrease over a period of time that is long relative to the other components.

There are two reasons for trend measurement. One reason is that it aids directly in business planning. If analysis of the physical volume of sales over a period of many years indicates that they have tended to grow in a particular way, it is fair to assume that they will continue to grow in that manner until there is a fundamental change in the system of causes in operation. The growth may be by a constant amount each year, or by a constant percentage, or in some other manner describable by a mathematical formula. Once the trend formula has been discovered, it is a simple matter to extend the trend any desired distance into the future. Having done so, a basis is provided for planning the financing and construction of plant and equipment for future needs. It must be emphasized, however, (1) that projection of a trend is valid only so long as the underlying system of causes governing the growth remains the same, and (2) that the trend equation is subject to error, and amount of error in the trend values becomes larger, sometimes very rapidly, the farther the trend is extended beyond the data.

The other reason for being interested in the trend is to help one in studying the other movements, especially the cycles, which fluctuate around the trend. In order to isolate the cycles, the trend values must be computed and then statistically eliminated from the data. This is accomplished by dividing the original data by the trend values. If monthly data are used, they must also be adjusted for seasonal variation. When data have been adjusted for trend (or for seasonal and trend, if monthly data are used), they may be studied in order to make economic generalizations concerning cycles in the business or industry in question, and they may be compared with other similarly adjusted data to aid one in making forecasts.

In this chapter we shall consider the fitting of a straight line only. Annual data will be used, and the method of least squares will be employed.

Some Examples

Chart 28.1 shows the physical volume of production in the United States (1880–1943) expressed as a percentage of the average 1923–28 production, and also the same data on a per capita basis. The dotted lines are trend lines, and since the chart is a ratio chart, the straight lines indicate a *constant percentage rate* of growth.[1] The average rate of growth of the total productuation series is 3.4 per cent per annum, while for the per capita production

Chart 28.1—Indexes of Total Production and Production per Capita, 1880–1943, with Exponential Trends

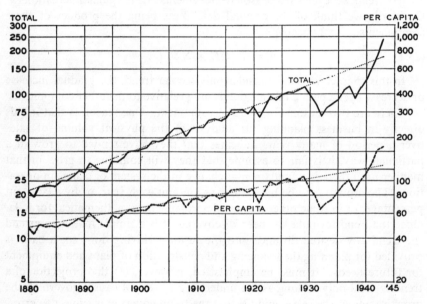

Source of data: Clark Warburton, "National Product, Income and Employment, 1945 to 1956," *The Southern Economic Journal*, Vol. XI, January 1945, pp. 222–223.

series it is 1.6 per cent per annum. Until about 1930 the trend for each series fits remarkably well; but after that both indexes depart rather widely from their trend lines, suggesting that the underlying forces at work in the more recent years are sufficiently different to justify the use of a different trend line. The fluctuations around the trend line are mainly of a cyclical, rather than a random, character; points above the line tend to come in groups, as do points below the line.

Although production as a whole seems to be growing at almost a constant percentage rate, this is not usually true for individual industries or individual

---

[1] The equation for such a trend is known as an exponential equation (see Chapter 14). Fitting an exponential is considered in Chapter 38.

**Chart 28.2—U. S. Consumption of Rayon and Acetate,
and Trend, 1911–1955**
A. Arithmetic Scale

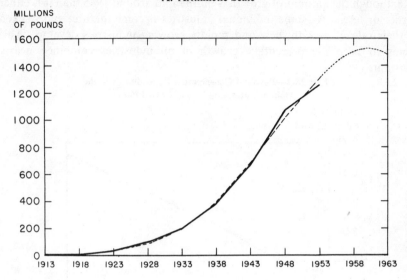

B. Ratio Scale

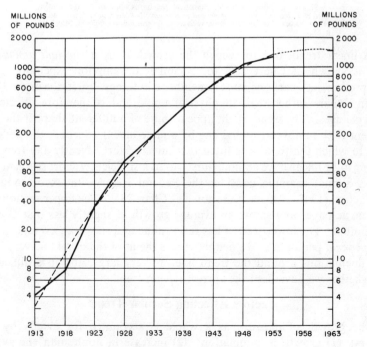

Source of data: See Table 38.2.

companies. For example, Chart 28.2 indicates clearly that United States consumption of rayon and acetate is growing at a decreasing percentage rate, though the amount of growth is more rapid around 1945 than it is either earlier or later. As some individual industries become mature, and slacken in their rate of growth, new and rapidly growing industries develop. This seems to keep the percentage growth of all industries combined nearly constant.

Chart 28.3—Personal Consumption Expenditures in the United States, and Trend, 1947–1956

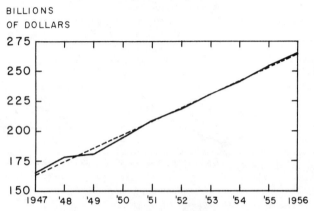

Source of data: Office of Statistical Standards, Bureau of the Budget, *Historical and Descriptive Supplement to Economic Indicator*, p. 11, and Board of of Governors of the Federal Reserve System, *Federal Reserve Bulletin*, May 1957, p. 581.

A linear trend, one for which the growth is by a *constant amount* per year is shown in Chart 28.3 for personal consumption expenditures. In interpreting this chart one must remember two things. First, the expenditures are in dollars rather than in physical units, and is therefore affected by price changes. The trend might appear to be of a different shape if the price element were removed (by dividing by a price index). Second, the period of time to which the trend was fitted is relatively short. Nearly any trend will appear to be linear if we confine ourselves to a sufficiently short segment of it.

As a final example consider the Federal Reserve Index of Industrial Production (1947–1949 = 100) shown as Chart 28.4. The upper section is on arithmetic paper and shows an average growth of slightly less than 3 *points* per annum. The lower section has ratio ruling and shows an average growth of 4 *per cent* per annum. In neither case is the fit of the trend line very good. The fluctuations around the trend line are very large, and it is difficult to tell whether we have used the correct *type* of trend.

Factors Affecting Secular Trend

The growth of industry as a whole is accounted for chiefly by four factors: (1) growth in population; (2) increase in nonhuman energy; (3)

**Chart 28.4—Federal Reserve Index of Industrial Production
and Estimates of Trend**

A. Straight line trend: arithmetic scale

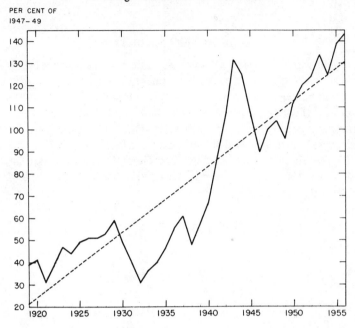

B. Exponential trend: ratio scale

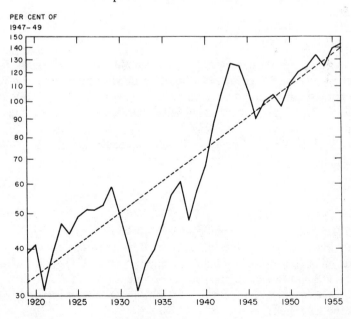

Source of data: Board of Governors of the Federal Reserve System, *Federal Reserve
Bulletin,* various issues.

capital accumulation; (4) improvement in technical methods. When referring to an individual industry or individual company, a fifth factor must be mentioned: the demand for the specific commodity relative to other commodities.

Test for Significance of Trend

It is foolish to fit a trend to a time series unless the time series is correlated with time. Because of the cyclical component of most time series, it is not valid to compute r and test its significance. Instead, Kendall's S is more appropriate. This is a nonparametric test, and makes no assumption concerning the nature of the trend (other than that of gradual growth or decline) or the form of the distribution of the residuals around the trend.

Let us see whether Sears, Roebuck and Company average monthly sales, 1946–1956, have a significant trend. Using the methods of Chapter 27, we find, from Table 28.1 that $k = 53$.

$$\binom{n}{2} = \binom{11}{2} = \frac{11 \cdot 10}{2 \cdot 1} = 55.$$

$$S = 2k - \binom{n}{2} = 2(53) - 55 = 51.$$

$$\sigma_S = \sqrt{\frac{n(n-1)(2n+5)}{18}} = \sqrt{\frac{(11)(10)(27)}{18}} = 12.845.$$

$$z = \frac{S-1}{\sigma_S} = \frac{50}{12,845} = 3.85.$$

Using the table of normal curve areas we find that the probability $P(z)$ of obtaining a value of S equal to or larger than 51 is approximately .00005. The hypothesis of no trend must therefore be rejected; the trend is highly significant. This is not surprising. The existence of a trend is obvious from a casual inspection of Chart 28.5.

If we wish also a correlation coefficient we use Kendall's τ.

$$\tau = \frac{S}{\binom{n}{2}} = \frac{51}{55} = +.927.$$

The fact that there is a significant trend does not tell us what kind of a trend to use. Before making this important decision one should first plot the data, on arithmetic and on semi-logarithmic paper. If the points fluctuate around a straight line on arithmetic paper, one should fit a straight line, if they fluctuate around a straight line on semi-logarithmic paper, one should fit an exponential curve. See Chapter 38.

Criteria for Fitting a Trend

Various methods are available for fitting trends, each of which uses a different criterion.

Least squares. The best trend equation is that which minimizes $\Sigma (Y - Y_x)^2$. A subsidiary property is that $\Sigma (Y - Y_x) = 0$. Although the theoretical superiority of this method is not obvious, since the fluctuations around the trend lines are usually cyclical, rather than random, and not usually distributed normally, it is a convenient method, and is the one used in this chapter.

**Table 28.1—Sears, Roebuck and Company Sales, 1946–1956, and
Computation of *k* for Testing Trend**
(Sales are in millions of dollars.)

Year	Total sales per year	Average monthly sales*	Number of years subsequent to current year with sales larger than those of current year
1946	1,666.5	138.875	10
1947	2,089.8	174.150	9
1948	2,417.8	201.483	7
1949	2,274.3	189.525	7
1950	2,623.6	218.633	6
1951	2,800.4	233.367	5
1952	3,048.4	254.033	4
1953	3,146.7	262.225	2
1954	3,066.4	255.533	2
1955	3,436.1	286.342	1
1956	3,687.0	307.250	0
Total	30,257.0	2,521.416	$k = 53$

* Average monthly sales are one-twelfth of total sales per year.
Source of data: Bureau of Foreign and Domestic Commerce, U.S. Department of Commerce, *Survey of Current Business*, various issues and supplements.

Maximum likelihood. The best estimate of the population trend, according to this criterion, is the one that makes the observed sample the most likely. For a straight line, with normally distributed deviations, the estimate is the same as the least squares estimate.

Method of moments. The trend is fitted in such a way that $\Sigma Y_x = \Sigma Y$ and $\Sigma x Y_x = \Sigma x Y$. For a straight line the method of moments also gives the same result as the method of least squares.

Selected points. A free-hand trend is fitted, and as many equidistant points are selected on this curve as there are constants in the trend equation. The trend is then fitted in such a way that it goes through these points. The method is very simple and easy, and we shall employ it in Chapter 35 to fit types of curves for which the method of least squares is too difficult.

Partial averages. The data are divided into as many equal parts as there are constants in the trend equation. The trend values are then made to agree with the observed values for each section of the data. This also is a satisfactory simple method, often used for complicated equations.

Least absolute deviations. The trend equation is that which minimizes $\Sigma |Y - Y_x|$. This is a cumbersome method, and is rarely used.

Fitting a Straight-line Trend by the Method of Least Squares

The description and fitting of a straight line was given in Chapter 24. The equation, it should be recalled, was

$$Y_X = a + bX,$$

where X refers to values of the independent variable, time. For a trend equation when n, the number of years, is odd, X takes the values[3] 0, 1, 2, ..., $n - 1$; when n is even, X takes the values 0, 2, 4, ..., $2(n - 1)$. If the values of the independent variable are deviations x from the mean value $\bar{X}$, the equation becomes

$$Y_x = \bar{Y} + bX.$$

The mean value of X is also the middle value of X, since X-values are spaced at equal intervals.

The formulas of Chapter 24 are applicable, without change, to the fitting of trends. Thus, for the equation $Y_X = a + bX$ we can use the normal equations:

$$na + b \Sigma X = \Sigma Y;$$

$$a \Sigma X + b \Sigma X^2 = \Sigma XY.$$

This is unnecessarily laborious, however, and we can compute:

$$b = \frac{\Sigma xY}{\Sigma x^2};$$

$$a - \bar{Y} = b\bar{X}.$$

These formulas are applicable for the computation of ΣxY and Σx^2:

$$\Sigma x^2 = \Sigma X^2 - \frac{(\Sigma X)^2}{n};$$

$$\Sigma xY = \Sigma xy = \Sigma XY - \frac{\Sigma X \Sigma Y}{n}.$$

However, since the X-values are usually spaced at equal intervals, $\bar{X}$ is the middle value of X, and the x-values are easily obtained by computing $x = X - \bar{X}$.

---

[3] Technically the X-values can be any series of numbers spaced at uniform intervals.

Several situations typically encountered in fitting a straight line by the method of least squares will now be considered.

Odd number of years, averages per month. Computation of values for fitting a trend to Sears, Roebuck and Company average monthly sales, 1946–1956 is in Table 28.2. This is a period of 11 years. A value of 0 is assigned to X for the first year for which we want a trend value, usually the first year of the data, and the X-values increase by 1 for each year. Thus the

Table 28.2—Sears, Roebuck and Company Average Monthly Sales, Odd Number of Years, 1946–1956, and Straight-Line Trend Fitted by the Method of Least Squares, Using x-values
(Sales are in millions of dollars.)

Year	X	x $X - \bar{X}$	Sales Y	x^2	xY	Trend value*
1946	0	−5	138.875	25	−694.375	154.97
1947	1	−4	174.150	16	−696.600	169.82
1948	2	−3	201.483	9	−604.449	184.67
1949	3	−2	189.525	4	−379.050	199.52
1950	4	−1	218.633	1	−218.633	214.37
1951	5	0	233.367	0	0.000	229.22
1952	6	1	254.033	1	254.033	244.07
1953	7	2	262.225	4	524.450	258.92
1954	8	3	255.533	9	766.599	273.77
1955	9	4	286.342	16	1,145.368	288.62
1956	10	5	307.250	25	1,536.250	303.47
Sum	55	0	2,521.416	110	1,633.593	2,521.42
Mean	5	0	299.220	...	...	229.22

* The same trend values are obtained by using either of these equations:
$$Y_x = 229.220 + 14.8508x; \quad Y_X = 154.966 + 14.8508X.$$
Source of data: Table 28.1.

X-values go from 0 through 10. The X column is not really necessary, but is included to show that the x-values are obtained by subtracting 5, the value of $\bar{X}$, from each X-value. (If the X-values had run from 1 for 1946 through 11 for 1956, ΣX would have been 66, and $\bar{X}$ would have been 6; but the x-values would have been unaffected.) The x^2 column is included only for expository purposes, since Appendix 4 shows that the sum of the squares of the first 5 natural numbers is 55. If a modern calculating machine is used the ΣxY values can be recorded without recording any of the individual products. Note that half of the xY values are negative and the other half positive, and that in obtaining ΣxY we must subtract the former from the latter. Thus $4,226.700 - 2,593.107 = 1,633.593$.

From equation (24.4) we compute

$$b = \frac{1,633.593}{110} = 14.8508,$$

and since $\overline{Y} = \dfrac{2,521.416}{11} = 229.220$, the trend equation, with origin at 1951, may be written

$$Y_x = 229.220 + 14.8508x.$$

Chart 28.5—Sears, Roebuck and Company Total Annual Sales and Average Monthly Sales, and Trend Lines, 1946–1956

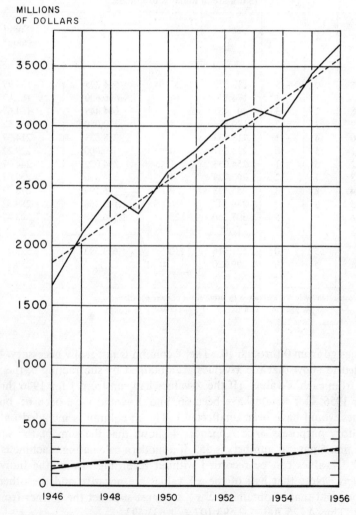

MILLIONS
OF DOLLARS

Source of data: Tables 28.4, 28.5, 28.7, and 28.8.

From equation (24.6) we compute

$$a = 229.220 - (14.8508)5 = 154.966,$$

and the trend equation, with origin at 1946, is

$$Y_X = 154.966 + 14.8508X.$$

Use of either the Y_X or the Y_x equation yields the results shown in the last column. It should be noted that the total of the Y-values is the same as the total of the trend values of Table 28.2. This is necessary, but does not assure us that b was computed correctly. Another useful check is to plot the trend and see if it looks reasonable. This has been done on Chart 28.5 (broken line, lower part), and it appears that the fit is good.

Odd number of years, annual totals. Computation of values for fitting a trend to Sears, Roebuck and Company total annual sales is in Table 28.3.

Table 28.3—Sears, Roebuck and Company Total Annual Sales, Odd Number
of Years, 1946–1956, and Straight Line-Trend Fitted by the
Method of Least Squares, Using x-values
(Sales are in millions of dollars.)

Year	X	x	Sales Y	xY	Trend values* Y_x
1946	0	−5	1,666.5	−8,332.5	1,859.59
1947	1	−4	2,089.8	−8,359.2	2,037.80
1948	2	−3	2,417.8	−7,253.4	2,216.01
1949	3	−2	2,274.3	−4,548.6	2,394.22
1950	4	−1	2,623.6	−2,623.6	2,572.43
1951	5	0	2,800.4	0.0	2,750.64
1952	6	1	3,048.4	3,048.4	2,928.85
1953	7	2	3,146.7	6,293.4	3,107.06
1954	8	3	3,066.4	9,199.2	3,285.27
1955	9	4	3,436.1	13,744.4	3,463.48
1956	10	5	3,687.0	18.435.0	3,641.69
Sum	55	0	30,257.0	19,603.1	30,257.04
Mean	5	0	2,750.636	. . .	2,750.64

* The same trend values are obtained by use of either of these equations:
$$Y_x = 2,750.636 + 178.2100x; \qquad Y_X = 1,859.586 + 178.2100X.$$
Source of data: Table 28.1.

Proceeding as before we obtain:

$$b = \frac{19,603.1}{110} = 178.2100;$$

$$\bar{Y} = 2,750.636;$$

$$Y_x = 2,750.636 + 178.2100x;$$

$$a = 2,750.636 - (178.2100)5 = 1,859.586;$$

$$Y_X = 1,859.586 + 178.2100X.$$

Since average monthly sales are one-twelfth as large as total annual sales, the a, b, and trend values are one-twelfth as large for the former as for the latter. This is shown graphically by Chart 28.5. We can therefore fit a trend to annual totals, if that is the form in which the data are available, and convert it to a trend for monthly average data very easily. Thus, for our data

$$Y_X = \frac{1{,}859.586}{12} + \frac{178.2100}{12} X$$

is the same as

$$Y_X = 154.966 + 14.8508X,$$

which was the trend equation for the preceding section.[4]

Even number of years, averages per month. Computation of values for fitting a trend to Sears, Roebuck and Company average monthly sales, 1947–1956, a period of 10 years, is shown in Table 28.4. The procedure is

Table 28.4—Sears, Roebuck and Company Average Monthly Sales, Even Number of Years, 1947–1956, and Straight-Line Trend Fitted by the Method of Least Squares, Using x-values
(Sales are in millions of dollars.)

Year	X	x	Sales Y	x^2	xY	Trend values* Y_x
1947	0	−9	174.150	81	−1,567.350	176.25
1948	2	−7	201.483	49	−1,410.381	190.03
1949	4	−5	189.525	25	−947.625	203.81
1950	6	−3	218.633	9	−655.899	217.59
1951	8	−1	233.367	1	−233.367	231.36
1952	10	1	254.033	1	254.033	245.14
1953	12	3	262.225	9	786.675	258.92
1954	14	5	255.533	25	1,277.665	262.70
1955	16	7	286.342	49	2,044.394	286.48
1956	18	9	307.250	81	2,765.250	300.26
Sum	90	0	2,382.541	330	2,273.395	2,382.54
Mean	9	0	238.254	...	...	238.25

* The same trend values are obtained by use of any of these equations:
$Y_x = 238.254 + 6.8891x$;
$Y_X = 176.252 + 6.8891X$ (X-units, one-half year);
$Y_X = 176.252 + 13.7782X$ (X-units, one year).
Source of data: Table 28.1.

[4] Since $x = X - 5$, we can obtain the equation $Y_X = 154.966 + 14.8508X$, which is the equation for averages per month, with origin at 1946, from the equation $Y_x = 2{,}750.636 + 178.2100x$, which is the equation for total annual sales, with origin at 1951, as follows:

$$Y_x = \frac{2{,}750.636}{12} + \frac{178.210}{12}(X - 5)$$

$$= 229.2197 + 14.8508X - (14.8508)(5)$$

$$= 154.966 + 14.8508X.$$

the same as for Table 28.3 except for the numerical values for X and x.

$$b = \frac{2,273.395}{330} = 6.8891.$$

$$\overline{Y} = \frac{2,382.541}{10} = 238.254.$$

$$Y_x = 238.254 + 6.8891x.$$

$$a = 238.254 - (6.8891)(9) = 176.252.$$

$$Y_X = 176.252 + 6.8891X.$$

If we wish to renumber our X-values, 0, 1, 2, ..., 9, (so that X-units will be one year instead of one-half year) we substitute $2X$ for X in the above equation

$$Y_X = 176.252 + (6.8891)(2X);$$

$$Y_X = 176.252 + 13.7782X.$$

Even number of years, annual totals. Table 28.5 is like Table 28.4 except that the Y-values are 12 times as large. The computations follow.

$$b = \frac{27,280.7}{330} = 82.6688.$$

$$\overline{Y} = \frac{28,590.5}{10} = 2,859.05.$$

$$Y_x = 2,859.05 + 82.6688x.$$

$$a = 2,859.05 - (82.6688)(9) = 2,115.031.$$

$$Y_X = 2,115.031 + 82.6688X.$$

With X-units of one year:

$$Y_X = 2,115.031 + (82.6688)(2X);$$

$$Y_X = 2,115.031 + 165.3376X.$$

The a and b values in the preceding section are, of course, one-twelfth those given above. This is true also of the trend values.[5]

---

[5] Since $x = 2(X - 9)$, we can also obtain an equation for average sales per month, X-units of one year, with origin at 1947, $Y_X = 176.25 + 13.778X$, directly from $Y_x = 2,859.050 + 82.6688x$ which is the equation for total annual sales, x-units of one-half year, with origin at 1951–1952, as follows:

$$Y_X = \frac{2,859.050}{12} + \frac{82.6688}{12}(2X - 9)$$

$$= 238.2542 + 13.778X - 62.0014;$$

$$Y_X = 176.25 + 13.778X.$$

A verbal statement which may help to clarify the mathematical operation is:
The average growth per annum in total annual sales is 165.3376;
The average rate of growth per 6 months in total annual sales is 82.6688;
The average growth per annum in average monthly sales is

$$\frac{165.3376}{12} = \frac{88.6688}{6} = 13.788$$

**Table 28.5—Sears, Roebuck and Company Total Annual Sales, Even
Number of Years, 1947–1956, and Straight-Line Trend Fitted by
Method of Least Squares, Using x-values**
(Sales are in millions of dollars.)

Year	X	x	Sales Y	x^2	$x^2 Y$	Trend values* Y_x
1947	0	−9	2,089.8	81	−18,808.2	2,115.03
1948	2	−7	2,417.8	49	−16,924.6	2,280.37
1949	4	−5	2,274.3	25	−11,371.5	2,445.71
1950	6	−3	2,623.6	9	−7,870.8	2,611.04
1951	8	−1	2,800.4	1	−2,800.4	2,776.38
1952	10	1	3,048.4	1	3,048.4	2,941.72
1953	12	3	3,146.7	9	9,440.1	3,107.06
1954	14	5	3,066.4	25	15,332.0	3,272.39
1955	16	7	3,436.1	49	24,052.7	3,437.73
1956	18	9	3,687.0	81	33,183.0	3,603.07
Sum	90	0	28,590.5	330	27,280.7	28,590.50
Mean	9	0	2,859.05	...	...	2,859.05

$Y_x = 2{,}859.050 + 82.6688x;$
$Y_X = 2{,}115.031 + 82.6688X$ (X-units, one-half year);
$Y_X = 2{,}115.03 + 165.3376X$ (X-units, one year).

Note that the constants of these trend equations, and the trend values, are 12 times as large as those of Table 28.4.
Source of data: Table 28.1.

Uses of Trend Equations

There are three principal uses of trend equations that will be commented on briefly.

Forecasting by extrapolation. By extrapolation is meant extending the trend in order to obtain an estimate or forecast for years beyond the data used in fitting the trend. Thus, if we wish to forecast Sears, Roebuck and Company sales for the year 1959, using the trend $Y_X = 1{,}859.586 + 178.2100X$ shown below Table 28.3, we substitute 13 for X in the equation, and obtain

$$Y_X = 1{,}859.586 + (178.2100)(13) = 4{,}176.32.$$

The forecast is thus $4,176,320,000.

Extreme caution is advisable in interpreting this forecast.

(1) It is not really a forecast of the actual sales, but only of the trend value for sales. A modification should be made for the effect of the cyclical component. This is not easy.

(2) The constants a and b in the trend equation are only estimates of A and B, the true constants. They are subject to error and the error in the forecast increases with the passage of time; i.e., the error in b is multiplied by x. Since only 11 years were used in fitting the trend, the error in b may be quite large; and since the extension of the trend beyond the data is relatively far (13 years beyond the center of the data, and 3 years beyond the 11 years covered), the forecast may be considerably in error.

(3) The same causal factors underlying the data for the period 1946–1956 may not persist in the future. This is perhaps the greatest obstacle to all forms of mechanical forecasting.

Measurement of cycles. Sometimes it is desired to observe how a business is progressing after taking into consideration the normal year-to-year growth. Trend may be eliminated either by subtracting the trend values from the original data obtaining cyclical residuals, or by dividing the original data by the trend values obtaining cyclical relatives. When the latter procedure is followed it is sometimes referred to as deflation. Symbolically,[6]

$$(28.2) \qquad \frac{Y}{Y_X} = \frac{TC}{T} = C.$$

Both cyclical residuals and cyclical relatives are computed in Table 28.6, and shown graphically in Chart 28.6. Percentage deviations from trend are also shown.

Table 28.6—Adjustment of Sears, Roebuck and Company Sales for Trend, 1946–1956

Year	Sales Y	Trend Y_x	Cyclical residuals $Y - Y_x$ (millions of dollars)	Cyclical relatives Y/Y_X (per cent)	Percentage deviations*
1946	1,666.5	1,859.6	−193.1	89.6	−10.4
1947	2,089.8	2,037.8	52.0	102.6	2.6
1948	2,417.8	2,216.0	201.8	109.1	9.1
1949	2,274.3	2,394.2	−119.9	95.0	−5.0
1950	2,623.6	2,572.4	51.2	102.0	2.0
1951	2,800.4	2,750.6	49.8	101.8	1.8
1952	3,048.4	2,928.8	119.6	104.1	4.1
1953	3,146.7	3,107.1	39.6	101.3	1.3
1954	3,066.4	3,285.3	−218.9	93.3	−6.7
1955	3,436.1	3,463.5	−27.4	99.2	−0.8
1956	3,687.0	3,641.7	45.3	101.2	1.2
Total	30,257.0	20,257.0	0.0	1,099.2	−0.8

*Percentage deviations may be computed as

$$100\,\frac{Y - Y_x}{Y_x}, \quad \text{or} \quad 100\left(\frac{Y}{Y_x} - 1\right)$$

Source of data: Table 28.3.

---

[6] Actually there may be a small amount of irregular movements; in which case it is better to write

$$\frac{Y}{Y_X} = \frac{TCI}{T} = CI.$$

The CI values are called cyclical-irregular movements. For monthly data the irregular component is likely to be fairly large.

Usually adjustment for trend is made by *dividing* the original data for trend because of these reasons.

1. Usually the cyclical residuals tend to become larger numerically as the trend values become larger, but the cyclical relatives remain more or less

Chart 28.6—Sears, Roebuck and Company Sales, with Trend, Cyclical Residuals, and Cyclical Relatives, 1946–1956

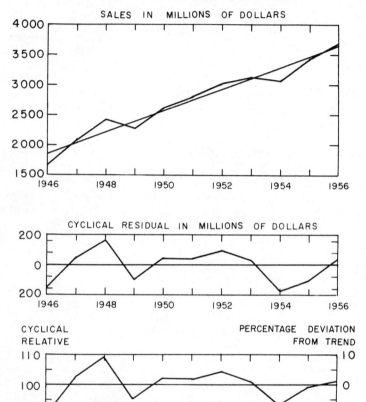

Source of data: Table 28.6.

constant, as in Chart 28.1. This is not the case, however, for our Sears, Roebuck and Company data. In fact, the cyclical relatives seem to be getting smaller.

2. For purposes of comparing the cycles of one series with those of another, percentages are more satisfactory. In Table 28.6, total annual sales were used. But if average monthly sales are used, the cyclical relatives and percentages deviating from trend are exactly the same. More important is

the case where the units of measurement are different in kind. One can not, for example, compare the amplitude of fluctuation of two series, one of which is measured in tons, and the other in kilowatt-hours.

Table 28.6 and Chart 28.6 shows that cycles in Sears, Roebuck and Company sales do not have very great amplitude, seldom departing from trend by more than 10 per cent from the trend line. This is characteristic of retail sales, especially of nondurable goods. Production series, especially durable goods, fluctuate a great deal more violently. See Charts 28.8 and 28.9.

Comparison of growth of different series. The coefficient b tells us the amount of growth per unit of time. Ordinarily, it is of little interest to compare amounts of growth. The average rates of growth is shown by the constant B in the exponential equation $Y_X = AB^X$. This type of equation is considered in Chapter 38.

Selection of Period to Which to Fit Trend

The period of time to which the trend is fitted often makes considerable difference. For example, the trend fitted to the Federal Reserve Index of Industrial Production for 1919 through 1956 (Chart 28.8) is considerably different from that fitted to the data from 1919 through 1930 or from 1931 through 1956.

Table 28.7—Artificial Data, Trend, and Cyclical Residuals
$$Y_x = 8.5 + 1x$$

Year X	$X - \bar{X}$ x	Data Y	Trend Y_X	Cyclical residuals $Y - Y_x$
0	−4.5	2	4	−2
1	−3.5	3	5	−2
2	2.5	8	6	2
3	−1.5	9	7	2
4	−0.5	6	8	−2
5	0.5	7	9	−2
6	1.5	12	10	2
7	2.5	13	11	2
8	3.5	10	12	−2
9	4.5	11	13	−2

If the data cover only 10 or 15 years it may be important to consider the stage of the cycle at the initial and terminal years; for longer periods this is less important. Consider the data of Table 28.7. The true trend equation is

$$Y_x = 8.5 + 1x,$$

with origin between year 4 and year 5. This equation can be obtained by fitting a trend to the data of years 1–8, or 3–6. The cyclical residuals are of a periodic nature, the length of each cycle being 4 years. The data and 3 trend lines are plotted on Chart 28.7. The solid line is the true trend.

Using these data as an example we can make certain generalizations.

1. The first year should not be one of depression and the last year one of prosperity, for that will make *b* too large. Thus, fitting to years 0–7,

Chart 28.7—Artificial Data and Three Trends

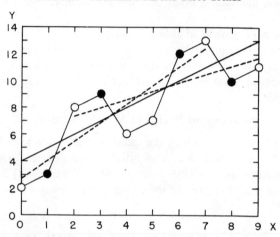

we obtain $b = 1.38$. This trend, plotted on Chart 28.7, is too steep.[7] Conversely the first year should not be one of prosperity and the last year one of depression, for that will make *b* too small. Thus, fitting to years 2–9, we obtain $b = 0.62$. This trend is also plotted on Chart 28.7 and is not steep enough. (Note that the average value of the two *b*-values is 1, which is the correct *b*-value).

2. The beginning and ending years should not be at the same point in their respective cycles   Thus if we fit the trend to years 0–8, which are first years of depressions, $b = 1.13$. If we fit to years 1–9, which are second years of depression, $b = 0.87$. These discrepancies are not so spectacular as those of the preceding paragraph, but they are substantial.

3. If the number of depression years exceed the number of prosperity years, the level of the trend will tend to be too small even though the slope may be correct. Thus, if we fit to years 0–9, the trend equation is

$$Y_x = 8.1 + 1x.$$

Thus $a = 8.1$ instead of 8.5. If the number of prosperity years exceeds the number of depression years, the level of the trend will be too large, even

---

[7] Note that for our Sears, Roebuck and Company data the slope is somewhat steeper for the 1946–1956 trend than for the 1947–1956 trend. This is because 1946 was a mild depression year. See Chart 28.6.

though the slope may be correct. Thus, if we fit to years 2–7, the trend equation is

$$Y_x = 9.2 + 1x.$$

Thus a is 9.2 instead of 8.5.

4. If the number of prosperity years is the same as the number of depression years, and also the first and last years are on opposite sides of the cycle (not opposite sides of the trend), both the level a and the slope b will tend to be correct. As stated earlier, if the trend is fitted to years 1–8 or 3–6, the correct trend will be obtained.

In general, bias in the slope is more to be feared than bias in the level, for a trend becomes cumulatively worse as x increases if b is wrong. None of the trends we have mentioned have a value of 8.5 when $X = 4.5$ (and $x = 0$) except those fitted to years 1–8 or 3–6. However it is only for trends fitted to years 0–9 or 2–6 that the discrepancy is noteworthy.

Effect of Choice of Trend on Estimates of Cycles

There are three subjective elements in trend fitting.

1. Choice of period of time to which trend is fitted.
2. Choice of type of trend.
3. Choice of method of fitting.

Of these, the first two often make a great deal of difference. Usually it makes little difference for a given type of trend whether the method of least squares or some other reasonable method is used.

Chart 28.8 shows three trends fitted to the Federal Reserve Index of Industrial Production.

1. Straight line fitted to 1919–1946 data (constant amount of growth).
2. Exponential curve fitted to 1919–1946 data (constant percentage growth).
3. Straight lines fitted to different segments of data.

Chart 28.9 shows the estimates of cycles resulting from adjusting the data for these three trends. Obviously the appearance of the "cycles" depends greatly on the nature of the trend that is selected. In general the trends become more flexible as we progress from the top toward the bottom of the page, and consequently the cycles become more numerous but of smaller amplitude. (If deseasonalized monthly data were used, the amplitude would be greater and wavelike movements would appear which are now concealed.) It is not easy to decide which of the trends brings out the cycles most accurately. If we knew what the cycles were supposed to look like, it would be much easier to select a good trend. On the other hand, if we knew the correct trend, the cycles could easily be obtained. One wonders whether to consider cycles to be what are left after adjusting for trend, or to consider trend to be a line that one draws through the cycles.

Chart 28.8—Federal Reserve Index of Industrial Production and Three Types of Trend, 1919–1956

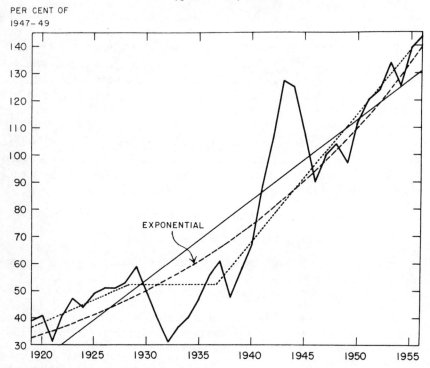

Source of data: *Federal Reserve Bulletin*, various issues.

Chart 28.9—Estimates of Cyclical Relatives in Industrial Production Resulting from Three Types of Trend

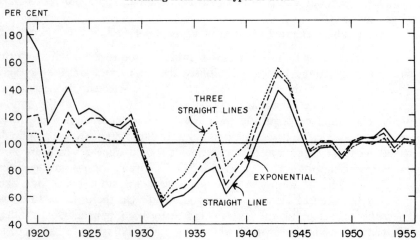

Source of data: See Chart 28.12.

Summary

Before a trend can be fitted intelligently it is necessary to define what is meant by trend. Three possible definitions may be mentioned.

1. Trend is the tendency of a series to change gradually in value over a long period of time. More specifically, it is the series of explained values of the Y variable when the independent variable is time, denoted by X (or the independent variables may be not only X, but also X^2, and even X^3). This definition leaves the word *long* undefined, and also does not directly relate the trend to any causal factors.

2. Trend is the amount of production that could be achieved at any time if the physical equipment were utilized at economic capacity. For this definition economic capacity is difficult both to define and to measure.

3. Trend is the line around which the cycles fluctuate. This definition can be applied only subjectively, for it is necessary first to identify the different *cycles* and their turning points. Different trained economists would often come to different conclusions on this subject.

Partly because of the difficulty of knowing exactly what one is trying to measure, different estimates of trend are obtained by different persons. The differences are mainly the result of:

1. Type of trend selected;
2. Period of time to which the trend is fitted.

The method of least squares is generally used for fitting a straight trend and many other trends, not because of its theoretical justification, but because of its convenience.

Chapter 29

MOVING AVERAGE OR RELATED SERIES
AS TREND

The two topics considered in this chapter are not related except that they both have to do with trends not employing an equation with time the independent variable.

Moving Averages

A centered moving average is a series of averages of r consecutive values, each average being placed at the chronological center of these consecutive values. Thus, for a 3-year moving average of the data of Table 29.1, we compute:

$$1920: \quad \frac{39 + 41 + 31}{3} = 37;$$

$$1921: \quad \frac{41 + 31 + 39}{3} = 37;$$

$$1922: \quad \frac{31 + 39 + 47}{3} = 39;$$

and so on.

When each average covers an even number of years the procedure is slightly more laborious, since centering requires another step: taking a 2-year moving average of the r-year moving average. Suppose we wish to take a 4-year moving average. We proceed as follows:

$$1920\text{--}21: \quad \frac{39 + 41 + 31 + 39}{4} = \frac{150}{4} = 37.50;$$

$$1921\text{--}22: \quad \frac{41 + 31 + 39 + 47}{4} = \frac{158}{4} = 39.50;$$

$$1922\text{--}23: \quad \frac{31 + 39 + 47 + 44}{4} = \frac{161}{4} = 40.25;$$

and so on.

Each of the above averages is centered, not at any year, but *between* two years. To center each average *at* a year we take a 2-year moving average of the 4-year moving average:

$$1921: \quad \frac{37.50 + 39.50}{2} = \frac{77.00}{2} = 38.500;$$

$$1922: \quad \frac{39.50 + 40.25}{2} = \frac{79.75}{2} = 39.875.$$

Obviously we could accomplish the same result, somewhat more easily as follows:

$$1921: \quad \frac{150 + 158}{8} = \frac{308}{8} = 38.500;$$

$$1921: \quad \frac{158 + 161}{8} = \frac{319}{8} = 39.875.$$

Finally, and perhaps most easily of all, we can compute each average all in one step:

$$1921: \quad \frac{39 + 2(41) + 2(31) + 2(39) + 47}{8} = \frac{308}{8} = 38.500;$$

$$1922: \quad \frac{41 + 2(31) + 2(39) + 2(47) + 44}{8} = \frac{319}{8} = 39.875.$$

Thus, a centered r-year moving average may also be regarded as an $(r + 1)$-year weighted moving average, the $(r - 1)$ central values being given double weight.

The purpose of a moving average is to smooth out fluctuations. If the fluctuations are random, the larger the value of r the smoother will be the results.

Moving averages of uniform length. Occasionally a time series will have a trend that cannot be fitted adequately by a simple mathematical curve. In such a case a moving average may be used.

Although a moving average becomes smoother as r is increased when the fluctuations are random, this statement must be modified if the fluctuations are periodic. In this case r should coincide with the length of the periodic movements. Consider the following hypothetical data, which include those of Table 28.7. The symbol $\bar{Y}_4$ is used to mean centered 4-year moving average.

Y	$\bar{Y}_4$	$Y - \bar{Y}_4$
2	..	..
3	..	..
8	6	2
9	7	2
6	8	−2
7	9	−2
12	10	2
13	11	2
10	12	−2
11	13	−2
16	..	..
17	..	..

The residual fluctuations apparently have a period of 4 years around a linear trend.

Thus we see that if the cycles are uniformly of length r, an r-year moving average will completely smooth out the cycles, leaving only the trend (assuming the trend to be linear). But since cycles in economic time series are not usually of uniform length, the number of observations should approximate the average length of one cycle, or perhaps of 2 consecutive cycles. Actually this advice is hard to follow because the cycles vary greatly in duration, and also the mean length, the median length, and the typical length may not agree very well. About the best that can be done is to proceed by trial and error until a trend is obtained that visually seems reasonably satisfactory.

Table 29.1 shows the computation of a 7-year moving average of the Federal Reserve Index of Industrial Production, 1919–1956. In this table the computations consist of two steps: (1) computation of a 7-year moving total; (2) division of the moving totals by 7 in order to obtain moving averages. For the first 3 moving totals we have:

$$39 + 41 + 31 + 39 + 47 + 44 + 49 \qquad = 290;$$
$$41 + 31 + 39 + 47 + 44 + 49 + 51 \qquad = 302;$$
$$31 + 39 + 47 + 44 + 49 + 51 + 51 = 312.$$

It is apparent from the above arrangement that the various moving totals, other than the first total, can be computed in a different manner:

$$290 - 39 + 51 = 302.$$
$$302 - 41 + 51 = 312.$$

In order to facilitate computations, a blank card of length sufficient to cover exactly 6 entries may be used. Table 29.1 shows the outline of this card, covering values 41 through 49, but exposing values 39 and 51, the numbers that were subtracted from and added to 290 in order to obtain 302. After obtaining each total the card is moved down one space. The calculating machine is, of course, not cleared after obtaining the successive totals. The last total in Table 29.1, which is 897, was obtained both by the subtraction and addition process we have described, and also by direct addition of the last 7 values. This provides an important check on our computations.

Chart 29.1 shows the moving average as a dotted line. It is perhaps too sensitive to the data to agree with many people's concept of a secular trend. Moving averages of 9, 11, or 13 years would of course progressively straighten out the trend.

Moving averages of variable length. One solution to the problem created by the fact that cycles are of variable length is to let r vary from year to year. The computational procedure is as follows:

(1) Ascertain the length of each cycle, measured from cyclical high to cyclical high. The length of each cycle is the value of r for the center of that cycle.

**Table 29.1—Federal Reserve Index of Industrial
Production, 1919–1956, and Seven-year
Moving Average
(1947–1949 = 100)**

Year	Index number	7-year moving total	7-year moving average
1919	39	...	...
1920	41	...	...
1921	31	...	...
1922	39	290 ✓	41.4
1923	47	302	43.1
1924	44	312	44.6
1925	49	334	47.7
1926	51	354	50.6
1927	51	356	50.9
1928	53	352	50.3
1929	59	334	47.7
1930	49	320	45.7
1931	40	309	44.1
1932	31	303	43.3
1933	37	300	42.9
1934	40	312	44.6
1935	47	320	45.7
1936	56	347	49.6
1937	61	377	53.9
1938	48	424	60.6
1939	58	483	69.0
1940	67	554	79.1
1941	87	618	88.3
1942	106	677	96.7
1943	127	709	101.3
1944	125	742	106.0
1945	107	759	108.4
1946	90	750	107.1
1947	100	735	105.0
1948	104	730	104.3
1949	97	747	106.7
1950	112	791	113.0
1951	120	816	116.6
1952	124	851	121.6
1953	134	897 ✓	128.1
1954	125	...	...
1955	139	...	...
1956	143	...	...

Source of data: Board of Governors of the Federal Reserve System,
Federal Reserve Bulletin, May, 1957, p.566.

(2) Ascertain the length of each cycle, measured from cyclical low to cyclical low. The length of each cycle is the value of r for the center of that cycle.

(3) Obtain values of r for other years by interpolation.

(4) Compute a centered average for each year using the appropriate value of r.

Chart 29.1—Federal Reserve Index of Industrial Production, 1919–1956, and Seven-year Moving Average, and Moving Average of Variable Length

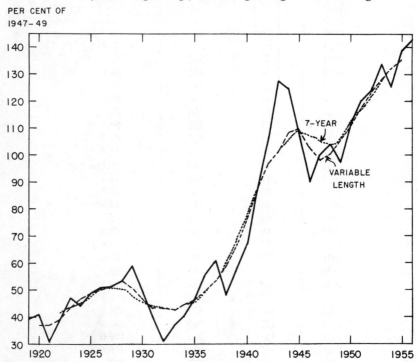

PER CENT OF
1947–49

Source of data: Table 29.1.

This has been done for the data of Table 29.1. The results, plotted in Chart 29.1, resemble rather closely those of the 7-year moving average. The most notable difference is that the moving average of variable length shows 1947 and 1948 to be years of prosperity, while the 7-year moving average shows them to be years of depression. The purpose of this method of computing a trend is to make it go through the center of each cycle. If one considers a secular trend to be the line around which the cycles fluctuate, a moving average of variable length, by definition, comes pretty close to being the true trend.

The chief objection to a moving average of variable length is its extremely subjective nature. In particular, people often disagree as to what movements should be considered as cycles. A movement that some would consider a cycle others consider a minor wave within a cycle.

In order to compare the results obtained with one of the trends of Chapter 28 we show on Chart 29.2: (1) straight lines fitted to different segments of

Chart 29.2—Federal Reserve Index of Industrial Production, 1919–1956,
Straight-Line Trend Fitted to Different Segments, and
Moving Average of Variable Length

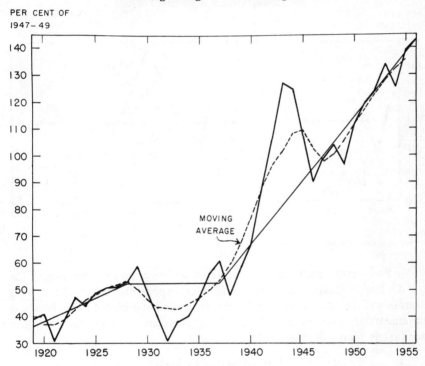

Source of data: Table 29.1.

data; (2) moving average of variable length. Chart 29.3 shows the estimates of cycles resulting from adjusting the data for these two trends. The chief differences in the results are that the percentages of the straight line trends show a deeper 1932 depression and much higher wartime peak in 1943.

Disadvantages of moving average trends. Moving averages have certain inherent defects that militate against their common use:

1. They never cover the complete period. In the case of a three-year moving average, the first and last years are eliminated in the process of averaging; a four-year moving average eliminates the first two and last two items. More specifically, if r is odd $(r-1)/2$ averages are sacrificed at each end; if r is even $r/2$ averages are sacrificed at each end.

2. Moving averages cannot easily be described by mathematical equations. Hence they cannot be thought of as describing "laws" of growth.

3. Simple moving averages tend to follow the curve into those peaks and troughs that are of greatest amplitude or duration.

Chart 29.3—Cycles in Federal Reserve Index of Industrial Production, 1919–1956, as Indicated by Straight Line Fitted to Different Segments, and Moving Average of Variable Length

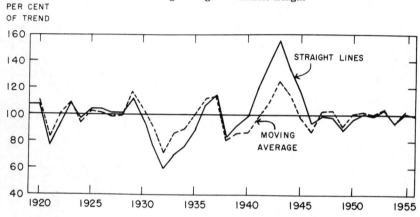

Source of data: See Table 29.1.

4. Frequently, simple moving averages will misrepresent the level of the trend. For instance, if the true trend is an exponential curve, the moving average will smooth out part of the curvature, and at each point will be above the true trend; in other cases the moving average may lie below the line which adequately represents the trend.

Related Series as Trend

Sometimes it is instructive to think of some related series as constituting the trend. This is particularly true of production series when it is possible to determine the theoretical or economic capacity of the equipment available for production. Thus Chart 29.4 shows total production of ingots and castings by the United States Steel Corporation, and the theoretical capacity for such production, while Chart 29.5 shows the per cent of capacity operated. It is apparent that the equipment is seldom fully utilized, and so the cyclical relatives are usually smaller than 100. Occasionally, however, equipment is utilized beyond economic capacity. This is possible because economic capacity allows time out for maintenance and repairs. Maintenance can be postponed for short periods of time.

Another case where a related series is used in trend analysis is where a broad production or income series is divided by population figures, thus

Chart 29.4—Production of Steel Ingots and Castings by U.S.
Steel Corporation, and Productive Capacity, 1910–1956

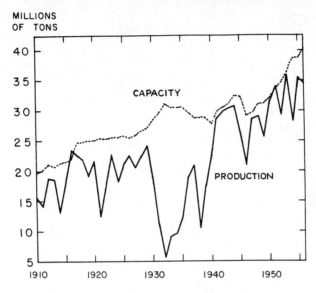

Source of data: U.S. Steel Corporation, *Annual Report*, 1956.

Chart 29.5—Production of Steel Ingots and Castings by U.S. Steel
Corporation as Per Cent of Capacity, 1910–1956

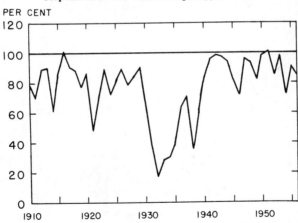

Source of data: U.S. Steel Corporation, *Annual Report*, 1956

being expressed as production or income per capita (see Chart 28.1). This
does not usually eliminate the trend, though it sometimes permits a simpler
type of trend to be used for the per capita data.

If it were able to account satisfactorily for the behavior of a time series,
we could substitute regression analysis for trend analysis for most purposes.

This would be desirable, since we would be substituting causal variables for the unknown causes that vary systematically with time.

Summary

A moving average does not provide constants for summarizing a trend, for making generalizations, or for comparing different time series. On the other hand, a moving average is flexible, and can be made to go through the centers of the different cycles, if they can be identified. A series adjusted for a well-selected moving average trend will therefore show the cycles as envisioned by the statistician. A related series, though not customarily used, has a logical basis lacking in other trends we have thus far considered.

Chapter 30

SEASONAL MOVEMENTS

Seasonal variation is a type of periodic fluctuation which has a duration of one year. Changes in the weather—amount of daylight, temperature, humidity, rainfall, wind velocity—affect consuming habits and producing ability. Certain holidays, notably Christmas and Easter, likewise are important factors in business fluctuations occurring within a year.

There are various reasons for measuring seasonal movements. If it is known that prices of some commodity typically fluctuate in a particular fashion, it may be profitable to buy while the price is low, holding the commodity for subsequent use or sale. Before deciding on such a course one must know the cost of storage and other costs involved. Similarly, if it is desirable to have stable production within a year even though sales show seasonal fluctuation, one can plan his fluctuating inventory so as to have at all times a large enough stock on hand to take care of expected sales, and yet keep his inventory close to the minimum. If, on the other hand, it seems better to keep small inventories, allowing production of a particular commodity to fluctuate, it may still be possible to maintain a constant labor force by manufacturing commodities the sales of which are complementary in their seasonal movements. Finally, it may be possible to reduce the seasonal fluctuations in sales by a proper advertising or price policy, or in production by artificial control of temperature, humidity, and so on, in the plant.

A less obvious reason for measuring seasonal movements is to adjust the data statistically for such movements, thus leaving the series composed only of trend, cyclical movements, and irregular fluctuations. Data in this form are easier to interpret for many purposes, since one is less likely to confuse the reason for any observed movement. For instance, if the data have not been adjusted, one may mistake a seasonal upswing for an improvement in business conditions; or he may become pessimistic when the reason for a decline is merely the usual seasonal slump. When data have been properly adjusted for seasonal movements there is no tendency for any one month of a year to be higher or lower than the average of the two adjacent months, or for any pattern to repeat itself in successive years. The method of making this adjustment is to divide the original data by the seasonal index. The data are then said to be deseasonalized. Thus:

$$(30.1) \qquad \text{Deseasonalized data:} \quad \frac{Y}{S} = \frac{TCSI}{S} = TCI.$$

447

In the present chapter we shall describe the computation of a seasonal index and its use in adjustment of data for seasonal variation.

Two types of seasonal movement are: (1) the stable seasonal, the pattern of which is constant for a period of years; and (2) the changing seasonal, the pattern of which is gradually changing during a period of time. Sometimes a stable pattern is maintained for a number of years, after which the pattern suddenly changes. In that case two stable seasonal indexes must be computed.

Another type of fluctuation that is considered in the chapter is that which is due to calendar variation. This might be considered a quasi-seasonal type of variability.

**Chart 30.1—Fire Losses in the United States, by Months,
1953–1955, and Average Values**

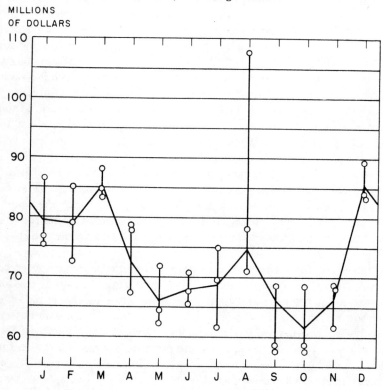

Source of data: Table 30.1.

A Crude Method of Estimating Seasonal

The simplest possible method of computing a seasonal index S is to compute the average value for January, for February, etc., and then express these averages as percentages, so that the 12 percentages will average 100. The reason we want the seasonal index to average 100 per cent is that we may wish to deseasonalize the original data (by dividing by the seasonal index). If the seasonal index averages 100 per cent, the deseasonalized data will have approximately the same average value as the original data.[1]

Table 30.1 and Chart 30.1 show fire losses in the United States for 1953–1955. The mean for August is not the mean of the three observations, but of 1954 and 1955 only. The value for 1953 was discarded because an assignable cause for its extremely high value was found. The fire losses for August 1953 were the highest on record, reflecting the loss from General Motor's Livonia, Michigan plant destruction.

The seasonal index S was obtained by multiplying each of the 12 means by the correction factor

$$c = \frac{100.00}{72,959} = 0.0013706.$$

Chart 30.2—Seasonal Index of Monthly Fire Losses, and of Average Losses per Day, 1953–1955

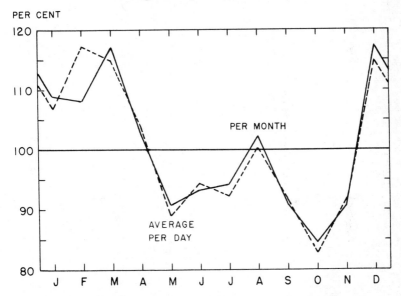

Source of data: Tables 30.1, 30.2, and 30.3.

This results in seasonal index numbers that average 100 per cent. The seasonal index is shown graphically by the solid line of Chart 30.2.

---

[1] A different kind of seasonal index can be obtained which is in units of measurement of the original data, and which totals zero. The data are then deseasonalized by subtracting these deviations from the original data. If this is done, the average value of the deseasonalized data is *exactly* the same as the average value of the original data. However, since the amplitude of seasonal fluctuations typically gets larger in an absolute sense as the trend values get larger, (see for example Chart 30.3) it is necessary to have a separate seasonal estimate for each year.

Table 30.1—Fire Losses in the United States and Computation of a Crude Seasonal Index, 1953–1955
(Losses are in thousands of dollars.)

Year	Jan.	Feb.	Mar.	Apr.	May	June	July	Aug.	Sept.	Oct.	Nov.	Dec.	Average
1953	76,659	72,706	83,471	67,362	64,239	67,644	74,938	107,713	68,613	68,551	68,064	83,440	
1954	86,493	78,928	84,821	77,933	62,282	65,533	69,532	78,163	64,087	57,668	61,663	83,881	72,959
1955	75,265	85,046	88,197	78,632	71,789	70,828	61,614	71,103	65,970	58,778	68,784	89,212	
Mean	79,472	78,893	85,496	74,642	66,103	68,002	68,695	74,633*	66,223	61,666	66,170	85,511	72,959
S	108.9	108.1	117.2	102.3	90.6	93.2	94.2	102.3	90.8	84.5	90.7	117.2	100.0

* This is a modified mean, after rejecting 107,713 because of its unrepresentative character.   74,663 = (78,163 + 71,103) ÷ 2.
S = monthly means multiplied by correction factor c, where c = 100.0 ÷ 72,959 = 0.0013706.
Source of data: National Board of Fire Underwriters, Fire Insurance Facts and Trends, Vol. XII, February, 1956, p. 1.

The method used in Table 30.1 is seldom useful. It assumes that the data do not have a trend component; the economic model is $Y = CSI$. Most economic time series have a trend component, however, and if the above method is used the result will not be an index of seasonal movements S, but an index of combined trend and seasonal TS. Actually, fire losses have an upward trend; but the trend is small compared with the seasonal movements, and for the three years under consideration the trend was not apparent. Perhaps this was because the trend and cycle offset each other.

The seasonal index of Table 30.1 is not very reliable, since it is based on data for only 3 years. Ordinarily a large number of years would be used.

Calendar Variation

Values per calendar day. It is rather obvious that the amount of fire loss must bear some relationship to the amount of time exposed to risk. Thus we find that the seasonal index for February, which usually has 28 days, is

Table 30.2—Fire Losses per Month, per Calendar Day, and Adjusted for
Variability in Calendar Days, 1955
(Thousands of dollars)

Month	Losses per month Y	Number of days D	Losses per day Y/D	Adjustment factor d	Losses adjusted for calendar-day variability Y/d
January ...	75,265	31	2,428	0.981183	73,849
February ..	85,046	28	3,037	1.086310	92,386
March	88,197	31	2,846	0.981183	86,537
April	78,632	30	2,621	1.013889	79,724
May	71,789	31	2,316	0.981183	70,438
June	70,828	30	2,361	1.013889	71,812
July	61,614	31	1,988	0.981183	60,455
August	71,103	31	2,294	0.981183	69,765
September .	65,970	30	2,199	1.013889	66,886
October ...	58,778	31	1,896	0.981183	57,672
November .	68,784	30	2,293	1.013889	69,739
December .	89,212	31	2,878	0.981183	87,533

Source of data: Table 30.1. Adjustment factors are from Table 30.3.

smaller than that for March, which has 31 days. Table 30.2 shows the reduction of fire losses in 1955 to a per calendar-day basis.

The broken line of Chart 30.2 shows a seasonal index computed from fire losses per calendar day. February, April, June, September, and November have been raised; the other seven months have been lowered. There is now a peak at February, instead of March. It appears that fire losses are related rather closely to temperature, except for December, where the Christmas season increases the risk.

Values adjusted for variability in calendar days. Fire losses per calendar day are approximately one-thirtieth as large as fire losses per month. If we wish to adjust for calendar day variability, without disturbing the *level* of the

Table 30.3—Adjustment Factors for Adjusting Monthly Values for
Variation in Number of Calendar Days

Month	Ordinary year		Leap year	
	Days	Adjustment factor	Days	Adjustment factor
January	31	0.981183	31	0.983871
February	28	1.086310	29	1.051724
March	31	0.981183	31	0.983871
April	30	1.013889	30	1.016667
May	31	0.981183	31	0.983871
June	30	1.013889	30	1.016667
July	31	0.981183	31	0.983871
August	31	0.981183	31	0.983871
September	30	1.013889	30	1.016667
October	31	0.981183	31	0.983871
November	30	1.013889	30	1.016667
December	31	0.981183	31	0.983871
Total	365	...	366	...
Average	30.41667	...	30.5	...

data, we must divide the original data by an index of calendar day variability, which is

$$\frac{\text{actual number of days in the month}}{\text{average number of days per month}}.$$

More convenient is to multiply the original data by a calendar day adjustment factor, which is

$$\frac{\text{average number of days per month}}{\text{actual number of days in the month}}.$$

The adjustment factors are shown is Table 30.3. They are also applied to the original data in Table 30.2. The fire losses adjusted for variability in calendar days are of course 30.41667 times as large as the fire losses per calendar day. A seasonal index computed from values adjusted for variability in calendar days is the same, however, as one computed from values per calendar day.

Values per working day. There is even greater variation in the number of working days than there is in calendar days. There may be either four or five Sundays, and four or five Saturdays, in a month. Some months have many holidays and others none. Holidays may fall on Sunday, Saturday, or a weekday. Easter and Good Friday slip from March to April and back again in a manner quite unintelligible to the layman.

Needless to say, a variation in production brought about by an increase in working days is of limited significance. If the data are to be put on a working day basis, one must first obtain the number of working days for each month of each year. This is done by subtracting the number of holidays from the number of calendar days in each month. The schedule of holidays varies from industry to industry and from region to region. It must be ascertained also whether Sunday is to be considered a holiday, and whether Saturday is a working day, a full holiday, or a half-holiday. Furthermore, it may or may not be the custom to grant as a holiday all of part of the Monday following a holiday that falls on a Sunday or Saturday. Finally, some holidays may be observed by only a part of the firms in an industry or only a part of the employees of a firm. In such cases the day may be considered a fractional working day. In Appendix 27 will be found a flexible arrangement that permits one quickly to ascertain the number of calendar or working days in any month from 1898 to 1976.

Having obtained the number of working days for each month of each year, production per working day is obtained by dividing the production figures by the number of working days.

Values adjusted for variability in working days per month. Once the number of working days in each month of each year has been computed, one multiplies the original data for each month by the working day adjustment factor,

$$\frac{\text{average number of working days per month}}{\text{actual number of working days in the month}}.$$

A final word of caution is necessary regarding adjustments for calendar variation. As indicated above, while a working-day basis is likely to be appropriate for production series, this need not be true for sales figures. Neither can the statistician blindly adopt any set of holidays to be used in adjusting time series to a working-day basis. He must discover what holidays are pertinent to *that particular series*. Some holidays, in fact, tend to cause sales to increase. Retail sales of many kinds show a marked pick-up at Easter. It may be that some adjustment more complex than either calendar-day or working-day adjustment may, in some cases, produce best results.

In general, adjustment either for calendar days or working days should smooth out the data somewhat. If this is not accomplished, the usefulness of the adjustment is open to suspicion.

In the remainder of this chapter we shall be dealing with Sears, Roebuck and Company monthly sales. The original data are in Tables 30.4 and

30.6. There is much to be said in favor of making a calendar-day adjustment for these data, since we should expect more sales in long months than in short ones. However, except for February, Table 30.8 does not provide convincing evidence that sales do fluctuate in this manner. We have therefore adopted the simpler procedure of computing the seasonal index from the unadjusted data. Since the number of calendar days is constant from year to year (excluding leap years), the seasonal index will incorporate in it any calendar-day variation that may exist.

Conventional Method of Estimating Seasonal

The method of estimating seasonal that was given in Table 30.1 is satisfactory only if the data have no trend and the cyclical component is unimpor-

Chart 30.3—Sears, Roebuck and Company Sales, and Centered 12-Month Moving Average, 1946–1956

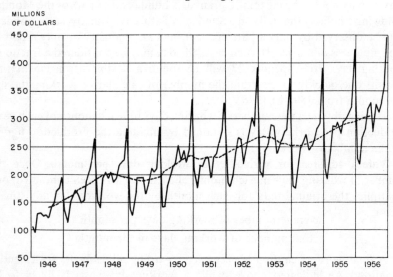

Source of data: Table 30.4.

tant. In the method that follows, we shall undertake to eliminate the trend and the cyclical components before averaging the different months. Briefly, we shall use the following procedure:

1. Estimate *TC*, using a 12-month moving average.
2. Eliminate *TC*, obtaining estimates of *SI*:

$$SI = \frac{TCSI}{TC}.$$

3. Average the *SI* estimates by months, obtaining an estimate of *S*.

Estimate of TC. Table 30.4 and Chart 30.3 show Sears, Roebuck and Company sales, by months, from 1946 through 1956. The years 1949 through

1953 are omitted for purposes of condensation. The broken line running through the chart is a 12-month moving average. It is a preliminary estimate

Table 30.4—Sears, Roebuck and Company Sales, 1946–1956, and Computation of Percentages of Centered 12-Month Moving Average
(Sales are in millions of dollars.)

Year and month	Sales	13-month weighted sum	12-month centered mov. av.	Per cent of moving average	Year and month	Sales	13-month weighted sum	12-month centered mov. av.	Per cent of moving average
(1)	(2)	(3)	(4)	(5)	(1)	(2)	(3)	(4)	(5)
1946: Jan.	105.8	...	...	...	1954: Jan.	179.1	6041.3	251.72	71.2
Feb.	95.1	...	...	...	Feb.	175.6	6047.5	251.98	69.7
Mar.	128.6	...	...	...	Mar.	210.6	6051.0	252.12	83.5
Apr.	129.8	...	...	...	Apr.	249.6	6059.9	252.50	98.9
May	126.4	...	...	...	May	257.6	6080.4	253.35	101.7
June	126.5	...	...	...	June	271.3	6114.3	254.76	106.5
July	121.8	3361.2	140.05	87.0	July	243.8	6166.6	256.94	94.9
Aug.	140.9	3408.9	142.04	99.2	Aug.	250.2	6215.4	258.98	96.6
Sep.	148.5	3451.5	143.81	103.3	Sep.	264.3	6262.6	260.94	101.3
Oct.	171.6	3505.5	146.06	117.5	Oct.	282.2	6332.6	263.86	107.0
Nov.	175.1	3581.6	149.23	117.3	Nov.	290.9	6398.5	266.60	109.1
Dec.	196.4	3663.8	152.66	128.7	Dec.	391.2	6448.4	268.68	145.6
1947: Jan.	134.0	3726.6	155.28	86.3	1955: Jan.	212.9	6499.6	270.82	78.6
Feb.	114.6	3768.9	157.04	73.0	Feb.	190.6	6572.6	273.86	69.6
Mar.	151.7	3826.0	159.42	95.2	Mar.	242.8	6651.1	277.13	87.6
Apr.	160.7	3901.0	162.54	98.9	Apr.	287.4	6715.5	279.81	102.7
May	171.6	3986.3	166.10	103.3	May	285.7	6775.6	282.32	101.2
June	163.5	4108.4	171.18	95.5	June	293.1	6839.2	284.97	102.9
July	147.6	4202.3	175.10	84.3	July	273.2	6887.4	286.98	95.2
Aug.	157.4	4250.3	177.10	88.9	Aug.	293.8	6929.6	288.73	101.8
Sep.	189.1	4318.4	179.93	105.1	Sep.	299.2	6979.4	290.81	102.9
Oct.	206.0	4404.5	183.52	112.2	Oct.	311.7	6995.2	291.47	106.9
Nov.	226.0	4469.5	186.23	121.4	Nov.	321.5	7020.1	292.50	109.9
Dec.	267.6	4531.2	188.80	141.7	Dec.	424.2	7087.9	295.33	143.6
1948: Jan.	156.7	4610.4	192.10	81.6	1956: Jan.	228.1	7126.6	296.94	76.8
Feb.	139.9	4686.0	195.25	71.7	Feb.	217.6	7162.5	298.44	72.9
Mar.	194.5	4750.1	197.92	98.3	Mar.	265.6	7207.2	300.30	88.4
Apr.	204.0	4793.8	199.74	102.1	Apr.	280.4	7234.7	301.45	93.0
May	193.3	4809.7	200.40	96.5	May	317.6	7291.5	303.81	104.5
June	203.5	4822.6	200.94	101.3	June	329.0	7353.2	306.38	107.4
July	186.8	4818.1	200.75	93.1	July	276.0	...	...	...
Aug.	193.8	4789.0	199.54	97.1	Aug.	326.9	...	...	...
Sep.	216.8	4752.4	198.02	109.5	Sep.	310.8	...	...	...
Oct.	222.0	4718.0	196.58	112.9	Oct.	327.6	...	...	...
Nov.	225.9	4707.9	196.16	115.2	Nov.	362.4	...	...	...
Dec.	280.6	4697.3	195.72	143.4	Dec.	445.0	...	...	...

Col. (2): Source of data is Office of Business Economics, U.S. Department of Commerce, *Survey of Current Business*, various issues.
Col. (3): Sum of each consecutive 13 values with the 11 central values counted twice.
Col. (4): Column (3) values divided by 24.
Col. (5): 100 [Col. (2) ÷ Col. (4)].

of the TC movements. It was shown in Chapter 29 that if the number of observations in each average of a moving average is the same as the length of the periodic movements we wish to smooth out, the desired result will be obtained. Therefore, since seasonal swings are periodic and last 12 months, a 12-month moving average will entirely eliminate these seasonal swings.

At the same time it will largely smooth out irregular movements. Unfortunately, it will also smooth out a small amount of the cyclical movements. It is mainly for that reason that we speak of a 12-month moving average as being only an *estimate* of the *TC* movements. The following is a compact method of obtaining a 12-month moving average. Computations are in Table 30.4.

1. At intervals of approximately 12 months, compute the sum of the values for 13 consecutive months, counting the 11 central months twice. Place this weighted sum in column (3) opposite the seventh month. Thus, for July 1946 we have recorded 3,361.2, which is equal to

$$105.8 + 2(95.1) + 2(128.6) + 2(129.8) + 2(126.4) + 2(126.5) + 2(121.8)$$
$$+ 2(140.9) + 2(148.5) + 2(171.6) + 2(175.1) + 2(196.4) + 134.0.$$

Thus the weighted sum for July 1946 involves values for January 1946 through January 1947; i.e., from 6 months earlier through 6 months later. Similar weighted sums are placed after July of each year, except 1956, where the weighted sum is placed after June (the values running from December 1955 through December 1956).

2. Cut out a card of size sufficient to cover exactly 10 months. Place it over column (2), exposing January and February 1946. The outline of the card is shown in Table 30.6. Now put 3,361.2 is the calculating machine, subtract the values for January and February 1946, add the values for January and February 1947, and record the resulting sum in the row for August. Thus,

$$3,408.9 = 3,361.2 - 105.8 - 95.1 + 134.0 + 114.6.$$

Now, slide down the card one space, and *without clearing the machine*, subtract the values for February and March 1946, add the values for February and March 1947, and record the resulting sum in the row for September. Thus

$$3,451.5 = 3,408.9 - 95.1 - 128.6 + 114.6 + 151.7.$$

Continue this procedure until a weighted sum is obtained for each month of each year.[2]

---

[2] This is a more compact, though perhaps more confusing, method than one suggested in Chapter 29. The method of Chapter 29, for the first two months is as follows:

$$\Sigma_1 = J_1 + F_1 + M_1 + A_1 + M_1 + J_1 + J_1 + A_1 + S_1 + O_1 + N_1 + D_1$$
$$\Sigma_2 = \quad\quad F_1 + M_1 + A_1 + M_1 + J_1 + J_1 + A_1 + S_1 + O_1 + N_1 + D_1 + J_2$$
$$\Sigma_3 = \quad\quad\quad\quad M_1 + A_1 + M_1 + J_1 + J_1 + A_1 + S_1 + O_1 + N_1 + D_1 + J_2 + F_2$$

Now the first 13-month weighted sum is $\Sigma_1 + \Sigma_2$:

(1) $J_1 + 2F_1 + 2M_1 + 2A_1 + 2M_1 + 2J_1 + 2A_1 + 2S_1 + 2O_1 + 2N_1 + 2D_1 + J_2.$

The second 13-month weighted sum is $\Sigma_2 + \Sigma_3$:

(2) $F_1 + 2M_1 + 2A_1 + 2M_1 + 2J_1 + 2A_1 + 2S_1 + 2O_1 + 2N_1 + 2D_1 + 2J_2 + F_2.$

Subtracting equation (1) from equation (2) we obtain

$$J_2 + F_2 - J_1 - F_1.$$

Therefore,

$$\Sigma_2 + \Sigma_3 = (\Sigma_1 + \Sigma_2) - J_1 - F_1 + J_2 + F_2.$$

The results obtained by this procedure will agree with those obtained by step 1 for July of each year, except 1956, where it will agree with June. The check mark after these values indicates that an agreement has been obtained.

3. Divide the values in column (3) by 24 (or multiply them by $1/24 = 0.041666667$), and record the results in column (5). The reason the divisor is 24, rather than 12, is that 24 observations enter into each weighted sum. Column (4) could just as well be labeled "weighted 13-month moving average" as "centered 12-month moving average," for it is an average of 13 months, the 11 central months being given double weight.

Chart 30.4—Percentages of Centered 12-Month Moving Average of Sears, Roebuck and Company Sales, 1946–1956

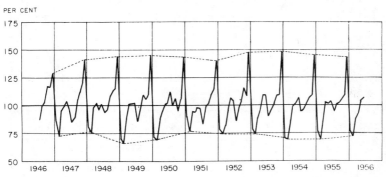

Source of data: Table 30.4.

Estimate of *SI*. In column (5) of Table 30.4 are shown the percentages of centered 12-month moving average, obtained by dividing the original data of column (2) by the moving average values[3] of column (4). They are plotted on Chart 30.4. These are the estimates of *SI*. Actually they are slightly biased estimates, having a slight positive correlation with the cyclical movements. This is because the 12-month moving average smooths out a little of the cycle at the peaks and troughs. Note the close resemblance between the fluctuations around the 100 per cent line of Chart 30.4 and those of the moving average of Chart 30.3. In one respect, however, they differ. The seasonal movements seem from Chart 30.3 to be getting larger in an absolute sense, but the seasonal percentages of Chart 30.4 show approximately constant amplitude.

Before deciding whether to compute a single seasonal index, two or more seasonal indexes for different periods of time, or a moving seasonal (one that gradually changes its pattern), it is well to study Chart 30.4. A casual

---

[3] Exactly the same seasonal index would result if we used percentages of the 13-month weighted sum. Although the saving of labor is considerable, such a procedure is more difficult to understand.

inspection of this chart does not indicate a change in the seasonal pattern. The two dotted lines connect the successive Decembers and the successive Februarys. There is no obvious trend in these values, though the value for December 1946 is unusually small. We shall, therefore, compute a single seasonal index from these data.

Chart 30.5—Seasonal-Irregular Movements and Stable Seasonal Index, Sears, Roebuck and Company Sales, 1946–1956

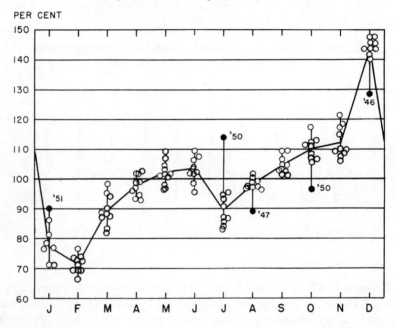

Source of data: Table 30.5.

Averaging out irregular movements. The estimates of *SI* of Table 30.5 are taken directly from column (5) of Table 30.4. They are also plotted on Chart 30.5. If the irregular component of the *SI* values is a random variable, normally distributed, with mean of zero, then monthly means of the *SI* values will average out the irregular movements, leaving only *S*, the seasonal component.

An examination of Chart 30.5 reveals that several extreme values deviate considerably from the bulk of the values of the different arrays. They are indicated on the chart by numerals stating the years in which they occur. July 1950 and January 1951 represent consumer panic buying as a result of the outbreak of the Korean war and the entrance of Communist China into the war. The sharp drop in October 1950 apparently resulted from belief that the war would be short following spectacular United Nation victories. It

Table 30.5—Sears, Roebuck and Company Estimate of Seasonal Irregular Movements, and Computation of Stable Seasonal Index by Conventional Method, 1946–1956

(Per cent of centered 12-month moving average)

Year	Jan.	Feb.	Mar.	Apr.	May	June	July	Aug.	Sep.	Oct.	Nov.	Dec.	Total
1946	...	...	...	...	...	...	87.0	99.2	103.3	117.5 H	117.3	128.7 L	...
1947	86.3	73.0	95.2	98.9	103.3	95.5 L	84.3 L	88.9 L	105.1	112.2	121.4 H	141.7	...
1948	81.6	71.7	98.3 H	102.1	96.5 L	101.3	93.1	97.1	109.5 H	112.9	115.2	143.4	...
1949	71.6	66.5 L	88.2	101.8	101.5	102.2	86.0	97.1	109.5	105.6	109.9	145.7	...
1950	70.6 L	69.3	87.7	93.4	100.4	101.9	113.7 H	100.6	106.8	96.4 L	106.1 L	143.8	...
1951	90.1 H	77.0 H	94.2	94.3	98.1	98.4	83.2 L	99.4	102.8	111.1	118.6	140.1	...
1952	77.3	73.9	82.0 L	96.9	107.2	104.1	86.8	97.6	104.8	115.1	107.7	147.6	...
1953	77.1	73.5	90.0	96.0	109.4 H	109.4 H	90.9	96.7	101.3	108.4	108.4	147.8 H	...
1954	71.2	69.7	83.5	98.9	101.7	106.5	94.9	96.6	101.3 L	107.0	109.1	145.6	...
1955	78.6	69.6	87.6	102.7 H	101.2	102.9	95.2	101.8 H	102.9	106.9	109.9	143.6	...
1956	76.8	72.9	88.4	93.0 L	104.5	107.4	...	...	...	...	...	...	...
Selected sum	620.5	573.6	714.8	782.3	817.9	824.7	718.2	784.3	836.5	879.2	896.1	1,151.5	9,599.6
Modified mean	77.56	71.70	89.35	97.79	102.24	103.09	89.78	98.04	104.56	109.90	112.01	143.94	1,199.96
Seasonal index S	77.6	71.7	89.4	97.8	102.2	103.1	89.8	98.0	104.6	109.9	112.0	143.9	1,200

Source of data: Table 30.4, column (5), percentages of centered 12-month moving average.
Selected sum: Values labeled H and L have been discarded.
Modified means: Selected sums divided by 8.
Seasonal index: Modified means multiplied by correction factor 1.00003 = 1,200.00 ÷ 1,199.96.

would be logical to discard the observations for these months, but in order to avoid bias, it seems better to follow conventional practice and treat each monthly array alike, and discard the same number of extremes from each array, depending on the appearance of the chart. Therefore we discard the *largest* and *smallest* percentage of each array, and compute modified means from the 8 central values for each month. This would have been done even if assignable causes had not been found. The sum of the 12 modified means is 1,199.96. This is very close to the desired total of 1,200.00 (or average of 100.0). When we multiply each modified mean by the correction factor 1.00003, we obtain seasonal index numbers[4] that total 1200.0 and average 100.0.

Adjustment for Seasonal Movements

Table 30.6 shows the original data, with a separate column for each month. At the bottom of the table is the seasonal index S, and also $100/S$, the seasonal adjustment factor. The seasonal adjustment can be computed by dividing by the seasonal index:

$$TCI = \frac{Y}{S} = \frac{TCSI}{S}.$$

Somewhat easier to multiply each month by its seasonal adjustment factor. The deseasonalized data are shown in Table 30.7.

A check is provided on the computations by multiplying the total row of Table 30.6 by the seasonal adjustment factors. This should result in the same numbers that are recorded in the total row of Table 30.7. The total *columns* of the two tables are not supposed to check exactly, but the discrepancy is not great.

An Iterative Procedure

Because a 12-month moving average tends to smooth out part of the cyclical movements is is sometimes considered worthwhile to make a revised estimate of TC. This may be done by computing a 5-month moving average[5] of the deseasonalized data. After this is done the original data are divided by the 5-month moving average. These percentages of 5-month moving average are considered the revised SI revised, and a seasonal index is computed from the revised estimates, using the method of Table 30.5.

---

[4] Actually we get the same results by rounding off the modified means. The application of the correction factor is included as part of the procedure solely because it is usually a desirable final step in the computations.

[5] Alternatively, the deseasonalized data may be plotted, smoothed free-hand, and the TC estimates read from the smooth curve. This is the method used by the Federal Reserve System. A 5-month moving average can of course be used as an aid to drawing the free-hand curve.

Table 30.6—Sears, Roebuck and Company Sales, and Stable Seasonal Index, 1946–1956

Year	Jan.	Feb.	Mar.	Apr.	May	June	July	Aug.	Sep.	Oct.	Nov.	Dec.	Total
1946	105.8	95.1	128.6	129.8	126.4	126.5	121.8	140.9	148.5	171.6	175.1	196.4	1,666.5
1947	134.0	114.6	151.7	160.7	171.6	163.5	147.6	157.4	189.1	206.0	226.0	267.6	2,089.8
1948	156.7	139.9	194.5	204.0	193.3	203.5	186.8	193.8	216.8	222.0	225.9	280.6	2,417.8
1949	139.2	128.3	169.5	194.6	192.6	193.6	163.1	184.7	209.6	202.9	212.1	284.1	2,274.3
1950	141.2	142.3	182.8	196.8	213.8	220.7	251.8	226.9	244.0	222.3	246.1	334.9	2,623.6
1951	208.1	176.0	215.1	216.6	228.0	229.7	193.4	230.1	237.4	256.9	277.4	331.7	2,800.4
1952	185.0	178.3	199.8	239.1	266.7	262.0	221.3	250.4	271.3	300.6	283.0	390.9	3,048.4
1953	205.5	196.3	240.0	254.7	289.0	287.6	237.3	250.5	260.5	277.1	275.5	372.7	3,146.7
1954	179.1	175.6	210.6	249.6	257.6	271.3	243.8	250.2	264.3	282.2	290.9	391.2	3,066.4
1955	212.9	190.6	242.8	287.4	285.7	293.1	273.2	293.8	299.2	311.7	321.5	424.2	3,436.1
1956	228.1	217.6	265.6	280.4	317.6	329.0	276.0	326.9	310.8	327.6	362.4	445.0	3,687.0
Total	1,895.6	1,754.6	2,201.0	2,413.7	2,542.3	2,580.5	2,316.1	2,505.6	2,651.5	2,780.9	2,895.9	3,719.3	30,257.0
Seasonal index S	77.6	71.7	89.4	97.8	102.2	103.1	89.8	98.0	104.6	109.9	112.0	143.9	1,200.0
Seasonal adjust-ment factor	1.28866	1.39470	1.11857	1.02249	0.97847	0.96993	1.11359	1.02041	0.95602	0.90992	0.89286	0.69493	...

Source of data: Original data are from Table 30.4; seasonal index numbers are from Table 30.5.

Table 30.7—Sears, Roebuck and Company Sales Adjusted by Stable Seasonal, 1946–1956

Year	Jan.	Feb.	Mar.	Apr.	May	June	July	Aug.	Sep.	Oct.	Nov.	Dec.	Total
1946	136.3	132.6	143.8	132.7	123.7	122.7	135.6	143.8	142.0	156.1	156.3	136.5	1,662.1
1947	172.7	159.8	169.7	164.3	167.9	158.6	164.4	160.6	180.8	187.4	201.8	186.0	2,074.0
1948	201.9	195.1	217.6	208.6	189.1	197.4	208.0	197.8	207.3	202.0	201.7	195.0	2,421.5
1949	179.4	178.9	189.6	199.0	188.5	187.8	181.6	188.5	200.4	184.6	189.4	197.4	2,265.1
1950	182.0	198.5	204.5	201.2	209.2	214.1	280.4	231.5	233.3	202.3	219.7	232.7	2,609.4
1951	268.2	245.5	240.6	221.5	223.1	222.8	215.4	234.8	227.0	233.8	247.7	230.5	2,810.9
1952	238.4	248.7	223.5	244.5	261.0	254.1	246.4	255.5	259.4	273.5	252.7	271.6	3,029.3
1953	264.8	273.8	268.5	260.4	282.8	279.0	264.3	255.6	249.0	252.1	246.0	259.0	3,155.3
1954	230.8	244.9	235.6	255.2	252.1	263.1	271.5	255.3	252.7	256.8	259.7	271.9	3,049.6
1955	274.4	265.8	271.6	293.9	279.5	284.3	304.2	299.8	286.0	283.6	287.1	294.8	3,425.0
1956	293.9	303.5	297.1	286.7	310.8	319.1	307.4	333.6	297.1	298.1	323.6	309.2	3,680.1
Total	2,442.8	2,447.1	2,462.1	2,468.0	2,487.7	2,503.0	2,579.2	2,556.8	2,535.0	2,530.3	2,585.7	2,584.6	30,182.3

Source of data: Table 30.6. Deseasonalized data are obtained by multiplication of original data by seasonal adjustment factors.

Test of Seasonal Index

There can be no reasonable doubt concerning the existence of seasonal fluctuations in Sears, Roebuck and Company sales. Chart 30.5 shows so much variability among the monthly means, and so little variability within the monthly arrays, that the possibility of apparent seasonality occurring by chance is precluded. Whether the seasonal index is adequate is another matter.

Table 30.8—Sears, Roebuck and Company Sales, Deseasonalized by a Stable
Seasonal Index, Expressed as Percentages of Preceding and
Following Months, 1946–1956

Year	Jan.	Feb.	Mar.	Apr.	May	June	July	Aug.	Sep.	Oct.	Nov.	Dec.
1946	...	95	108	99	97	95	102	104	95	105	107	83
1947	117	93	105	97	105	95	103	93	104	98	108	92
1948	106	93	108	103	93	99	105	95	104	99	102	102
1949	96	97	100+	105	98	101	97	99	107	95	99	106
1950	92	103	102	97	101	87	126	90	108	89	101	95
1951	112	97	103	96	100+	102	94	106	97	99	108	95
1952	99	108	91	101	105	100+	97	101	98	107	93	105
1953	97	103	100+	94	105	102	99	100-	101	102	96	109
1954	92	105	94	105	97	100+	105	97	99	100+	98	102
1955	102	97	97	107	97	97	104	102	97	99	99	101
1956	98	103	101	94	103	103	94	110	94	96	107	...

Source of data: Table 30.7.

Whether a seasonal index is adequate depends ultimately on how well it eliminates seasonal. If the seasonal adjustment is satisfactory there will be no tendency for the deseasonalized values of any month to be either larger than or smaller than the average of the adjacent months. Nor will there be such a tendency for several years in succession. The computational steps are as follows.

1. For each month obtain the average of the preceding and following months. Thus, using the data of Table 30.7 for February 1946, we obtain $0.5(136.3 + 143.8) = 140.05$.

2. Divide the deseasonalized value for each month by the average of the preceding and following months. Thus, Table 30.8 shows that for February 1946, $132.6 \div 140.05 = 0.95 = 95$ per cent.

There does not seem to be any tendency for any month to be larger than, or smaller than, the average of the adjacent months. But there are many runs of 3 or more that are either greater than 100 or smaller than 100, and seven months have runs of 3 or more above 100 followed by runs of 3 or more below 100, or vice versa, again suggesting that the seasonal pattern is a progressively changing one. Our original judgment, based on casual observation, thus appears to be in error.

*Moving Seasonal

Since our test of the preceding section indicates that the seasonal pattern of Sears, Roebuck and Company sales is gradually[6] changing, we shall compute a moving seasonal index.[7]

Table 30.9—Preliminary Estimate of Moving Seasonal for Sears, Roebuck and Company Sales, 1946–1956

Year	Jan.	Feb.	Mar.	Apr.	May	June	July	Aug.	Sep.	Oct.	Nov.	Dec.
1946	79.8	71.3	92.5	98.3	100.0	100.5	88.7	97.8	107.1	110.2	114.1	143.0
1947	79.8	71.3	92.5	98.3	100.0	100.5	88.7	97.8	107.1	110.2	114.1	143.0
1948	79.8	71.3	92.5	98.3	100.0	100.5	88.7	97.8	107.1	110.2	114.1	143.0
1949	79.8	71.3	92.5	98.3	100.0	100.5	87.8	97.9	107.1	109.6	114.6	143.0
1950	76.8	71.6	90.0	97.7	100.0	101.8	88.6	98.0	107.0	109.9	110.9	144.3
1951	75.3	72.2	88.6	95.7	103.0	102.7	87.9	97.9	104.8	108.4	108.7	145.7
1952	75.2	72.4	87.1	95.7	103.1	104.2	90.9	97.9	103.0	108.8	108.4	145.7
1953	77.7	72.4	87.0	97.3	103.4	104.5	90.9	97.9	102.3	108.8	109.1	145.6
1954	77.1	72.0	86.5	97.3	104.5	106.0	90.9	97.9	102.3	108.8	109.1	145.6
1955	77.1	72.0	86.5	97.3	104.5	106.0	90.9	97.9	102.3	108.8	109.1	145.6
1956	77.1	72.0	86.5	97.3	104.5	106.0	90.9	97.9	102.3	108.8	109.1	145.6

Source of data: Table 30.5.

Preliminary estimate. Using the *SI* estimates of Table 30.5, we compute in Table 30.9 a 5-year moving modified mean for each month. The modified mean used in the central three items in an array of five items. Thus, for January 1949, the 5 values are 86.3, 81.6, 71.6, 70.6, 90.1. In order of magnitude they are 70.6, 71.6, 81.6, 86.3, 90.1. The modified mean is $(71.6 + 81.6 + 86.3) \div 3 = 79.8$. For January 1950 the value is $(81.6 + 71.6 + 77.3) \div 3 = 76.8$. The modified mean, rather than the mean of all 5 items, is used in order to reduce the influence of possibly unrepresentative items and also of any cyclical component resulting from our method of estimating *SI*. The result of this procedure is that the seasonal index numbers for a specified month change rather gradually. Although a 5-year moving average does not provide us with values for the first two years and the last two years, the first two years are arbitrarily given the values of the third year,

---

[6] We sometimes find that the seasonal pattern suddenly changes. In such a case it is logical to use two stable seasonal indexes instead of a moving seasonal.

[7] The method described in this section is similar to that described by Julius Shiskin in "Seasonal Computations on Univac," *The American Statistician*, Vol. 9, February, 1955, pp. 19–23. According to Shiskin, the computations for a 10-year series (including several steps not shown in this section) takes about one minute on the Univac. The Univac method is a mechanical approximation to the method currently used by the Federal Reserve System. See footnote 9. The second approximation by the Shiskin method is an iteration of the first approximation, while we introduce slight modifications that call for exercise of judgment. The inability to exercise judgment is considered by some to be a weakness of all pure mechanical methods.

Table 30.10—Sears, Roebuck and Company Sales Adjustment for Preliminary Moving Seasonal, Revised Estimates of TC, SI, and Revised Moving Seasonal, 1946–1956
(Sales are in millions of dollars; 1949—1953 not shown.)

Year and month	Sales	Preliminary seasonal index	Deseasonalized data	5-month moving average	Per cent of moving average	Revised moving seasonal index	Year and month	Sales	Preliminary seasonal index	Deseasonalized data	5-month moving average	Per cent of moving average	Revised moving seasonal index
(1)	(2)	(3)	(4)	(5)	(6)	(7)	(1)	(2)	(3)	(4)	(5)	(6)	(7)
1946:							**1954:**						
Jan.	105.8	79.8	132.6	...	...	85.0	Jan.	179.1	77.1	232.3	245.6	72.9	76.0
Feb.	95.1	71.3	133.4	...	...	72.0	Feb.	175.6	72.0	243.9	246.4	71.3	72.0
Mar.	128.6	92.5	139.0	132.7	96.9	93.0	Mar.	210.6	86.5	243.5	244.5	86.1	87.0
Apr.	129.8	98.3	132.0	131.3	98.9	101.0	Apr.	249.6	97.3	256.5	249.3	100.1	96.0
May	126.4	100.0	126.4	132.1	95.7	99.0	May	257.6	104.5	246.5	254.1	101.4	103.0
June	126.5	100.5	125.9	133.1	95.0	97.0	June	271.3	106.0	255.9	256.5	105.8	105.0
July	121.8	88.7	137.3	134.5	90.6	91.0	July	243.8	90.9	268.2	256.9	94.9	90.0
Aug.	140.9	97.8	144.1	140.3	100.4	96.0	Aug.	250.2	97.9	255.6	259.5	96.4	100.0
Sept.	148.5	107.1	138.7	145.9	101.8	106.0	Sep.	264.3	102.3	258.4	261.6	101.0	102.5
Oct.	171.6	110.2	155.7	145.9	117.6	115.0	Oct.	282.2	108.8	259.4	261.7	107.8	108.0
Nov.	175.1	114.1	153.5	150.6	116.3	117.0	Nov.	290.9	109.1	266.6	265.8	109.4	110.0
Dec.	196.4	143.0	137.3	155.0	126.7	138.0	Dec.	391.2	145.6	268.7	267.1	146.5	147.0
1947:							**1955:**						
Jan.	134.0	79.8	167.9	156.7	85.5	33.0	Jan.	212.9	77.1	276.1	271.4	78.4	76.0
Feb.	114.6	71.3	160.7	158.7	72.2	72.0	Feb.	190.6	72.0	264.7	277.1	68.8	72.0
Mar.	151.7	92.5	164.0	165.5	91.7	92.0	Mar.	242.8	86.5	280.7	278.1	87.3	87.0
Apr.	160.7	98.3	163.5	164.5	97.7	100.0	Apr.	287.4	97.3	295.4	278.1	103.3	97.0
May	171.6	100.0	171.6	165.6	103.6	99.5	May	285.7	104.5	273.4	285.3	100.1	103.5
June	163.5	100.5	162.7	165.0	99.1	98.0	June	293.1	106.0	276.5	289.2	101.3	106.0
July	147.6	88.7	166.4	167.6	88.1	90.0	July	273.2	90.9	300.6	288.6	94.7	90.5
Aug.	157.4	97.8	160.9	170.7	92.2	96.5	Aug.	293.8	97.9	300.1	291.2	100.9	100.5
Sep.	189.1	107.1	176.6	177.8	106.4	106.0	Sep.	299.2	102.3	292.5	294.9	101.5	102.0
Oct.	206.0	110.2	186.9	181.9	113.2	113.0	Oct.	311.7	108.8	286.5	293.0	106.4	107.0
Nov.	226.0	114.1	198.1	189.0	119.6	116.5	Nov.	321.5	109.1	294.7	291.7	110.2	110.0
Dec.	267.6	143.0	187.1	192.9	138.7	141.0	Dec.	424.2	145.6	291.3	293.7	144.4	147.0
1948:							**1956:**						
Jan.	156.7	79.8	196.4	197.6	79.3	81.0	Jan.	228.1	77.7	293.6	297.8	76.6	76.0
Feb.	139.9	71.3	196.2	199.5	70.1	72.0	Feb.	217.6	72.0	302.2	296.5	73.4	72.0
Mar.	194.5	92.5	210.3	200.7	96.9	91.0	Mar.	265.6	86.5	307.1	299.0	88.8	88.0
Apr.	204.0	98.3	207.5	202.0	101.0	99.0	Apr.	280.4	97.3	288.2	302.4	92.7	97.5
May	193.3	100.0	193.3	204.8	94.4	100.0	May	317.6	104.5	303.9	302.6	105.0	104.0
June	203.5	100.5	202.5	202.4	100.5	99.0	June	329.0	106.0	310.4	308.0	106.8	107.0
July	186.8	88.7	210.6	201.4	92.8	89.0	July	276.0	90.9	303.6	311.1	88.7	91.0
Aug.	193.8	97.8	198.2	203.0	95.5	97.0	Aug.	326.9	97.9	333.9	310.6	105.2	101.0
Sept.	216.8	107.1	202.4	202.1	107.3	106.0	Sep.	310.8	102.3	303.8	314.9	98.7	101.5
Oct.	222.0	110.2	201.5	199.3	111.4	111.0	Oct.	327.6	108.8	301.1	315.3	103.9	105.5
Nov.	225.9	114.1	198.0	194.5	116.1	115.0	Nov.	362.4	109.1	332.2	...	...	110.0
Dec.	280.6	143.0	196.2	190.0	147.7	144.0	Dec.	445.0	145.6	305.6	...	...	147.0

Col. (2): Source of data is Tables 30.6 and 30.9.
Col. (3): Table 30.10.
Col. (4): Col. (2) ÷ Col. (3).
Col. (5): 5-month moving average of column (4).
Col. (6): Col. (2) ÷ Col. (5).
Col. (7): Read from chart 26.8.

and the last two years are given the values of the year preceding. This procedure errs on the conservative side, since it does not assume a continuation of the trends indicated by the moving averages.

Table 30.10 shows the adjustment of the data for the preliminary estimate of moving seasonal. There is not a separate column for each month, as in Tables 30.6 and 30.7, because there is a separate seasonal index number each

Chart 30.6—Sears, Roebuck and Company Sales, Deseasonalized by
Moving Seasonal Index, 1946–1956

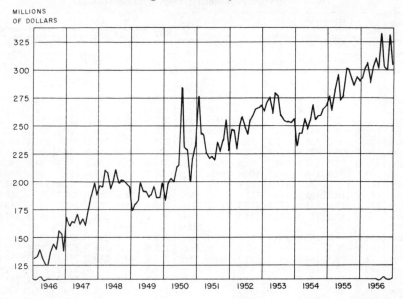

Source of data: Table 30.10.

year for each month. The deseasonalized data are plotted on Chart 30.6.

Test of preliminary estimate. The numbers in Table 30.11 were obtained
from column (4) of Table 30.10 in the same way that those of Table 30.8 were
obtained from Table 30.7. The results show that the moving seasonal index
is more satisfactory than the stable seasonal index in these respects. (1) The
runs of 3 or more on one side of 100 are not so frequent or so long. (2) The

Table 30.11—Sears, Roebuck and Company Sales, Deseasonalized by a Preliminary
Moving Seasonal Estimate, as Percentages of Preceding and Following
Months, 1946–1956

Year	Jan.	Feb.	Mar.	Apr.	May	June	July	Aug.	Sep.	Oct.	Nov.	Dec.
1946	...	98	105	99	98	95	102	104	93	107	105	85
1947	113	97	101	97	105	96	103	94	102	100_	106	95
1948	102	96	104	103	94	100+	105	96	101	101	100_	105
1949	93	101	97	105	99	102	97	99	105	97	96	108
1950	93	103	102	97	102	87	127	90	105	90	102	93
1951	116	94	103	98	98	101	96	105	96	98	110	91
1952	104	104	92	102	103	100+	96	101	99	105	96	102
1953	98	100+	104	94	104	102	98	99	100_	100+	99	106
1954	93	103	97	105	96	99	105	97	100+	99	101	99
1955	104	95	100+	107	96	96	104	101	100_	98	102	99
1956	99	101	104	94	102	102	94	110	96	95	110	...

Source of data: Table 30.10.

percentages are slightly closer to 100. However, there still seem to be too many runs, especially (as we should expect) those involving the first 3 years and the last 3 years. We shall therefore proceed to a second approximation.

Second approximation. In Table 30.10 we first adjust our original data by use of the preliminary moving seasonal. The results are shown in column

Chart 30.7—Sears, Roebuck and Company Sales, Deseasonalized by Moving Seasonal Index, 5-Month Moving Average of Deseasonalized Data, and 12-Month Moving Average of Original Data, 1946–1956

Source of data: Tables 30.4 and 30.10.

(4). Next we take a 5-month moving average of the column (4) figures, obtaining revised *TC* estimates.[8] The 5-month moving average of the deseasonalized data, and the 12-month moving average of the original data are plotted on Chart 30.7. The deseasonalized data are plotted as unconnected dots. Because of the smaller number of months included in each average, the 5-month moving average smooths out only a negligible amount of the

---

[8] Before computing this moving average, however, we made three substitutions in column (4).

  July, 1950: 224.2, the average of June and August, for 284.2, the true value.
  October, 1950: 225.0, the average of September and November, for 202.3, the true value.
  January, 1951: 238.0, the average of December, 1950, and February, 1951, for 276.4, the true value.

These substitutions are made because use of the data for these unrepresentative months would distort the moving average, and make it a poor estimate of the *TC* movements.

Chart 30.8—Revised Estimates of Sears, Roebuck and Company
Moving Seasonal Index, 1946–1957

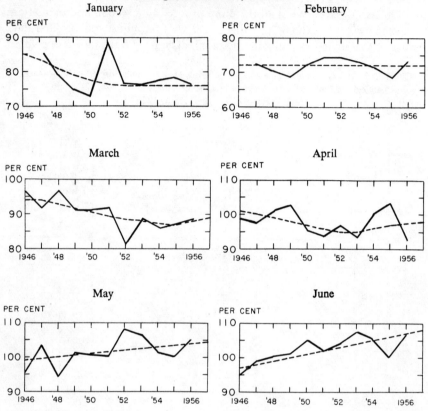

Source of data: Table 30.10.

cyclical movements. Notice that in Chart 30.7 the 5-month moving average reaches further into the cyclical peaks and troughs than does the 12-month moving average. Also the cyclical turning points of the 5-month moving average are more accurate; notice in particular 1949, 1951, and 1954. Another advantage of the 5-month moving average is that we have 8 more TC values than before, because a 5-month moving average sacrifices only 2 values at each end, compared with 6 for a 12-month moving average.

Next we divide the original data by the 5-month moving average, obtaining a revised estimate of the SI movements.

We now compute the second approximation moving seasonal in the same manner as before, with these exceptions.[9]

1. The data and the modified means have been plotted on Chart 30.8.
2. The modified means have been smoothed somewhat by inspection trends.

_____

[9] The Federal Reserve method differs from the one illustrated chiefly in these respects:
1. The preliminary estimate of CI is obtained by making a free-hand adjustment to

Chart 30.8 (cont).

July

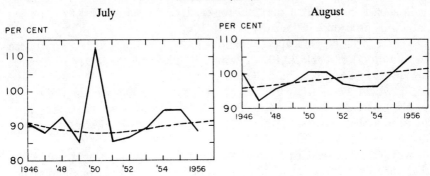

August

September

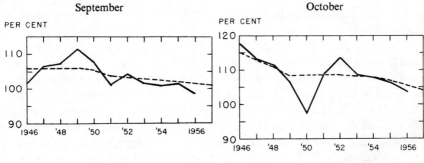

October

November

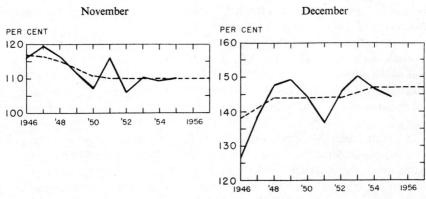

December

3. The trends have been extended to the edges of the chart.
4. The seasonal index numbers have been read from the trend lines on the chart.

---

a 12-month moving average. (The 12-month moving is not centered.)

2. The final estimate of *CI* is obtained by making a free-hand smoothing of the data which have been deseasonalized by the preliminary seasonal index.

3. The trends for the different months are made free-hand, both for the preliminary moving seasonal and the final moving seasonal.

4. In making the free-hand trends, the trend values are ordinarily made to total 1,200 for each year.

In smoothing and extending the trends it would be desirable also to do it in such a manner that the total for each year would be 1,200. This is a laborious procedure if done carefully.

The revised (second approximation) moving seasonal index is recorded in column (7) of Table 30.10. As would be expected, the largest differences are in the first two years and the last two years.

It would be possible to make a third approximation, adjusting the original data by the second approximation moving seasonal index. It is to be doubted, however, whether the improvement in the results would justify the additional labor.

Use of polynomial equations. The following method is more objective than the methods previously considered, and results in a seasonal index that averages 100 per cent each year.[10]

1. Compute percentages of a centered 12-month moving average in the usual manner.

2. Adjust these percentages, by multiplying by a constant (a different constant each year) so that they will total 1,200 each year. This step accomplishes two objects. (1) The bias due to inflexibility of the 12-month moving average will be partly overcome. More specifically, the percentages will be lowered somewhat for depression years (where the 12-month moving average fails to reach far enough into the troughs); and the percentages will be raised somewhat in prosperity years (where the 12-month moving average fails to reach far enough into the peaks). (2) If polynomial trends are fitted by the method of least squares each month, the trend values (moving seasonal index numbers) will total 1,200 for each year.

3. Fit a separate trend of the type $Y_x = a + bx$ to the adjusted percentages for each *month* separately, so that there will be 12 trend equations. The total of the a values will be 1,200.0, while the total of the total of the b values will be zero. These totals check the accuracy of the computations, and insure that the sum of the trend values (seasonal index numbers) for the 12 months of any one *year* will be 1,200.0.

If it seems desirable, a polynomial trend of higher degree $Y_x = a + bx + cx^2 + \ldots$ can be fitted (see Chapter 34). If this is done, the total of the c, and higher, order constants will also be zero. In practice, it is desirable to compute and plot the first-degree trends before proceeding to compute second-degree trends, for a first-degree trend may be adequate to represent the moving seasonal. Similarly, one should compute and plot second-degree trends before proceeding with third-degree trends. It is almost imperative that orthogonal

---

[10] The method of obtaining a moving seasonal which is illustrated in this section was suggested and more fully explained by the writer in 1942. See Dudley J. Cowden, "Moving Seasonal Indexes," *Journal of the American Statistical Association*, Vol. 37, December, 1942, pp. 523–524. In this article some advantages of computing a seasonal index using logarithms of the original data are also explained.

polynomials be used; otherwise, the labor of solving simultaneous equations, recomputing trend constants, and computing trend values will be prohibitive.

4. If it seems worthwhile, the original data can now be deseasonalized, and smoothed by a 5-month moving average (or in some other way). Then the original data can be expressed as percentages of the smoothed deseasonalized data, and steps 2 and 3 repeated.

Chapter 31

CYCLES AND IRREGULAR MOVEMENTS

Business cycles are undulatory movements representing alternating rises and declines in economic activity. For instance, depression troughs in American business activity may be observed in Chart 31.1 in 1919, 1921, 1924, 1927, 1932, 1938, 1946, 1949, 1952, 1954, and 1956, while prosperity

Chart 31.1—American Business Activity, 1918–1958

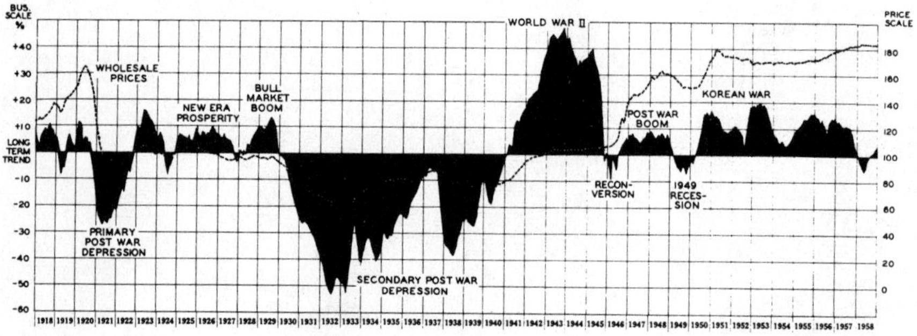

Source of data: Cleveland Trust Co.

peaks occurred in intermediate years. Although these cyclical movements vary greatly from one another with respect to amplitude and duration, they average a little less than 4 years in length. Statistically, therefore, cycles differ from seasonal movements in that cycles are not periodic in character.

The causes of cyclical movements are not so obvious as the causes of secular trend and seasonal fluctuations. Theories of business cycles are many, and some are difficult to understand; but some factors that affect cyclical movements should be mentioned.

1. Expansion or contraction of money (especially bank deposits) permits, and may cause, expansion or contraction of business activity.

2. Although there is a fairly constant demand for services and nondurable consumers' goods, purchases of durable goods, whether producers' or consumers', can be postponed. This permits periods of alternating activity and inactivity in these industries.

3. Increases in sales necessitate increased inventories, and therefore increases in production are more than proportionate to sales. Decreases in sales have the opposite effect.

472

4. Increases in production beyond a certain point necessitate further production of new capital goods, in addition to the normal replacement of worn out capital goods.

5. An increase in expenditures in any sector of the economy may gradually spread into other sectors of the economy, so that the original increase may have a multiplicative effect.

6. When business increases beyond a certain point, costs tend to rise faster than income, and when it falls below a certain point, costs may decline faster than income.

7. Human nature is such that we expect a continuation of prosperity when times are good, and a continuation of depression when times are bad. Since business activity depends on the carrying out of the plans of individuals, this psychological factor tends to perpetuate and accentuate any cyclical upswing or downswing.

8. Important specific events, not necessarily related closely to business conditions, or a combination of fortuitous events, may bring about (or prevent) a turning point in the business cycle.

Some people think that a period of prosperity develops within itself a poison which tends to cause a degeneration into a business recession. For example, when business is far above normal, money becomes tight, interest rates rise, and costs get out of line. The converse of this theory is not so widely held.

Irregular movements I are of two types.

1. Random R
2. Specific Q

Random irregular movements are the result of a large number of small independent causes. Individual random deviations are not predictable, but considered as a whole they may reasonably be expected to have an approximately normal distribution with mean of zero. Their occurrence over time also should be random; the sign of any deviation should not have any bearing on the sign of the next deviation. In statistical jargon, we say there should not be any significant autocorrelation.

Cyclical movements differ from random fluctuations in that cyclical observations for successive months are interdependent. Runs above the trend line, runs below the trend line, runs up, and runs down are longer than can be accounted for by chance. In statistical jargon we say that most economic time series, even after adjustment for trend and seasonal, have significant autocorrelation.

Specific irregular movements are movements for which we can assign a specific cause. For example, Chart 31.2 has four sharp troughs which are the direct effect of strikes in the steel industry. One stock market analyst lists a number of events which caused serious though temporary declines in the prices of corporation stocks.

Chart 31.2—Production of Steel Ingots and Castings, by Months, 1945–1956

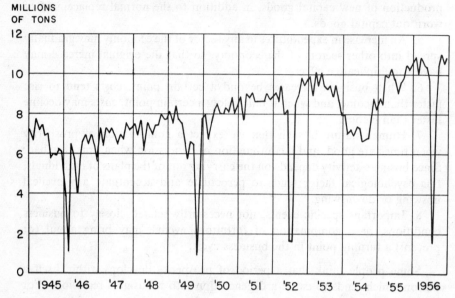

Source of data: Office of Business Statistics, United States Department of Commerce, *Survey of Current Business*, various issues and supplements. Data were compiled by the American Iron and Steel Institute.

Year	Event	Days of decline	Per cent loss
1898	Battleship Maine sunk	32	16
1906	San Francisco earthquake	14	11
1915	Lusitania sunk	32	11
1918	End World War I	49	10
1938	Austrian crisis	31	27.5
1938	Munich crisis	53	14
1939	Czechoslovakian crisis	24	22
1939	Poland invaded	17	7
1940	Fall of France	26	25
1941	Pearl Harbor	17	9
1945	End World War II	2	1
1948	Berlin crisis	72	9
1950	Korean crisis	13	12.5
1951	Korean truce proposed	9	4.5
1955	President Eisenhower's illness	1	6.5

It is not always easy to distinguish between a specific irregular movement and a cycle, for the former may generate the latter and merge into it.

From what has been said, it may be appropriate to reformulate our economic model in some cases. Instead of

$$Y = TCSI,$$

we may well write

(31.1) $$Y = TCSQR.$$

Estimate of Cyclical-irregular Movements

In order to estimate CI from the original data, $Y = TCSI$, we may follow any of these procedures.

First alternative:

1. Eliminate trend by dividing the original data by trend values: $CSI = TCSI \div T$.

2. Eliminate seasonal by dividing the results by S: $CI = CSI \div S$.

Second alternative:

1. Eliminate seasonal by dividing the original data by seasonal index: $TCI = TCSI \div S$.

2. Eliminate trend by dividing the results by T: $CI = TCI \div T$.

Third alternative:

1. Estimate TS by multiplying trend values by seasonal index numbers.

2. Eliminate TS by dividing original data by TS: $CI = TCSI \div TS$.

Table 31.1—Sears, Roebuck and Company Sales, and Computation of Cyclical-irregular Movements, 1946
(Sales are in millions of dollars.)

Month	Sales Y $TCSI$	Seasonal index S (per cent)	Deseasonalized data TCI $(TCSI - S)$	Trend Y_x T	Cyclical-irregular movements CI $(TCI \div T)$
January ...	105.8	85.0	124.5	156.16	79.7
February ...	95.1	72.0	132.1	157.31	84.0
March	128.6	94.0	136.8	158.46	86.3
April ...	129.8	101.0	128.5	159.60	80.5
May	126.4	99.0	127.7	160.75	79.4
June	126.5	97.0	130.4	161.90	80.5
July	121.8	91.0	133.8	163.05	82.1
August	140.9	96.0	146.8	164.20	89.4
September ..	148.5	106.0	140.1	165.34	84.7
October ...	171.6	115.0	149.2	166.49	89.6
November ..	175.1	117.0	149.7	167.64	89.3
December ..	196.4	138.0	142.3	168.79	84.3

Source: Tables 30.10 and 28.4.

These three procedures are mathematically equivalent, and yield identical results.[1] The first alternative is not often followed because there is usually no use for the CSI values. The second alternative is convenient when the data have already been deseasonalized. Table 31.1 shows this procedure for 1946, using the Sears, Roebuck and Company data. (The method of obtaining

---

[1] The method of adjustment by dividing by an adjustor is sometimes referred to as *deflation*. Thus, we deflate for trend by dividing by T, we deflate for seasonal by dividing by S, and we deflate for combined trend and seasonal by dividing by TS.

Table 31.2—Sears, Roebuck and Company Sales, and Computation of *CI* Movements
Using *TS* Estimates, 1946–1956
(Sales are in millions of dollars; 1949–1953 not shown.)

Year and month TCSI	Sales TCSI	Trend T	Seasonal S	TS	CI TCSI/TS	Year and month TCSI	Sales TCSI	Trend T	Seasonal S	TS	CI TCSI/TS
(1)	(2)	(3)	(4)	(5)	(6)	(1)	(2)	(3)	(4)	(5)	(6)
1946:						**1954:**					
Jan.	105.8	156.16	85.0	132.7	79.7	Jan.	179.1	266.38	76.0	202.4	88.5
Feb.	95.1	157.31	72.0	113.3	83.9	Feb.	175.6	267.53	72.0	192.6	91.2
Mar.	128.6	158.46	94.0	149.0	86.3	Mar.	210.6	268.68	87.5	235.1	89.6
Apr.	129.8	159.60	101.0	161.2	80.5	Apr.	249.6	269.83	96.0	259.0	96.4
May	126.4	160.75	99.0	159.1	79.4	May	257.6	270.98	103.0	279.1	92.3
June	126.5	161.90	97.0	157.0	80.6	June	271.3	272.13	105.0	285.7	95.0
July	121.8	163.05	91.0	148.4	82.1	July	243.8	273.27	90.0	245.9	99.1
Aug.	140.9	164.20	96.0	157.6	89.4	Aug.	250.2	274.42	100.0	274.4	91.2
Sep.	148.5	165.34	106.0	175.3	84.7	Sep.	264.3	275.57	102.5	282.5	94.6
Oct.	171.6	166.49	115.0	191.5	89.6	Oct.	282.2	276.72	108.0	298.9	94.4
Nov.	175.1	167.64	117.0	196.1	89.3	Nov.	290.9	277.87	110.0	305.7	95.2
Dec.	196.4	168.79	138.0	232.9	84.3	Dec.	391.2	279.01	147.0	410.1	95.4
1947:						**1955:**					
Jan.	134.0	169.94	83.0	141.1	95.0	Jan.	212.9	280.16	76.0	212.9	100.0
Feb.	114.6	171.09	72.0	123.2	93.0	Feb.	190.6	281.13	72.0	202.4	94.2
Mar.	151.7	172.23	94.0	161.9	93.7	Mar.	242.8	282.46	87.0	245.7	98.8
Apr.	160.7	173.38	100.0	173.4	92.7	Apr.	287.4	283.61	97.0	275.1	104.5
May	171.6	174.53	99.5	173.7	98.8	May	285.7	284.76	103.5	294.7	96.9
June	163.5	175.68	98.0	172.2	94.9	June	293.1	285.90	106.0	303.1	96.7
July	147.6	176.83	90.0	159.1	92.8	July	273.2	287.05	90.5	259.8	105.2
Aug.	157.4	177.97	96.5	171.7	91.7	Aug.	293.8	288.20	100.5	289.6	101.5
Sep.	189.1	179.12	106.0	189.9	99.6	Sep.	299.2	289.35	102.0	295.1	101.4
Oct.	206.0	180.27	113.0	203.7	101.1	Oct.	311.7	290.50	107.0	310.8	100.3
Nov.	226.0	181.42	116.5	211.4	106.9	Nov.	321.5	291.64	110.0	320.8	100.2
Dec.	267.6	182.57	141.0	257.4	104.0	Dec.	424.2	292.79	147.0	430.4	98.6
1948:						**1956:**					
Jan.	156.7	183.72	81.0	148.8	105.3	Jan.	228.1	293.94	76.0	223.4	102.1
Feb.	139.9	184.86	72.0	133.1	105.1	Feb.	217.6	295.09	72.0	212.5	102.4
Mar.	194.5	186.01	93.0	173.0	112.4	Mar.	265.6	296.24	88.0	260.7	101.9
Apr.	204.0	187.16	99.0	185.3	110.1	Apr.	280.4	297.39	97.5	290.0	96.7
May	193.3	188.31	100.0	188.3	102.7	May	317.6	298.53	104.0	310.5	102.3
June	203.5	189.46	99.0	187.6	108.5	June	329.0	299.68	107.0	320.7	102.6
July	186.8	190.60	89.0	169.6	110.1	July	276.0	300.83	91.0	273.8	100.8
Aug.	193.8	191.75	97.0	186.0	104.2	Aug.	326.9	301.98	101.0	305.0	107.2
Sep.	216.8	192.90	106.0	204.5	106.0	Sep.	310.8	303.13	101.5	307.7	101.0
Oct.	222.0	194.05	111.0	215.4	103.1	Oct.	327.6	304.27	105.5	321.0	102.1
Nov.	225.9	195.20	115.0	224.5	100.6	Nov.	362.4	305.42	110.0	336.0	107.8
Dec.	280.6	196.35	144.0	282.7	99.3	Dec.	445.0	306.57	147.0	450.7	98.7

Source of data: Tables 30.10 and 28.4.

the trend values is explained on page 477.) The third alternative is illustrated in Table 31.2 for the Sears, Roebuck and Company data, 1946–1956.

Obtaining trend values by months. In Chapter 28 we fitted a trend equation to annual data representing average monthly sales for two periods of time:

1946–1956, $Y_X = 154.996 + 14.8508X$ (Table 28.2);

1947–1956, $Y_X = 176.252 + 13.7782$ (Table 28.4).

In the first equation, $X = 0$ for 1946; in the second equation, $X = 0$ for 1947. There is some question as to which equation gives the better representation of trend. We have selected the 1947–1956 equation, even though the period of time to which the trend was fitted is one year shorter, and therefore the trend will be extrapolated to obtain the 12 trend values for 1946. The reason for the choice is that 1946 was a cyclical trough, and 1956 was perhaps a cyclical peak, and therefore the b-value for the 1946–1956 trend may have an upward bias; the slope of the trend may be too steep.

Since the average increase per month is one-twelfth the average increase per year, and since the middle of January, 1946, is 17.5 months earlier than the middle of the year 1947, we convert the equation for use with monthly data by the following simple procedure.[2]

$$Y_X = 176.252 + \left(\frac{13.7782}{12}\right)(X - 17.5)$$

$$= 176.252 + 1.14818X - (1.14818)(17.5), \text{ and}$$

$$Y_X = 156.159 + 1.14818X.$$

For this equation the X-values change by 1 each month (X-units are one month), and $X = 0$ for January, 1946 (X-origin is January, 1946). The trend values, using this equation, are shown in Tables 31.1 and 31.2. When using a calculating machine the trend values are easily obtained by putting 156.159 in the machine, 1.14818 on the keyboard (aligning the decimal points properly), and adding 1.14818 repeatedly without clearing the dials or keyboard. A check on the last entry is obtained by noting that $156.159 + (1.14818)(131) = 306.571$. (There are 131 months between January 1946 and December 1957.)

Obtaining *CI* values. Table 31.2 shows the *TS* values, obtained by multiplying *T* by *S*. These values are shown by the heavy broken line of Chart 31.3. The line may be thought of as representing the systematic part of the fluctuations in our data. The *CI* values of Tables 31.1 and 31.2, and Chart 31.4 are what is left over after adjusting for the systematic *TS* movements.

Estimates of Cycles

In order to make an estimate of the cyclical movements we must remove the irregular movements from our *CI* movements. We cannot do this by dividing the *CI* values by *I*, because the irregular movements are what remain after adjusting our original data for *T*, *C*, and *S*.

---

[2] Sometimes monthly data are given at annual rates, which are 12 times as large as the actual monthly sales of production. In that case the equation that is converted (in precisely the same manner) is $Y_x = 2,115.031 + 165.3376X$. See Table 28.5.

Chart 31.3—Sears, Roebuck and Company Sales, and Estimates of TS, 1946–1956

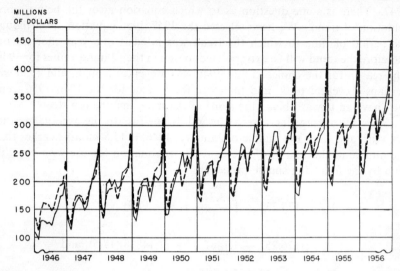

Source of data: Table 31.2.

Smoothing out irregularities by a moving average. To estimate C, the usual procedure is to take a moving average of CI, in the hope that this will smooth out the irregular movements. The method is not very satisfactory, but is perhaps the best we can do.

In the choice of a moving average two not completely independent choices must be made.

THE LENGTH OF THE MOVING AVERAGE. Often a 3-month or 5-month moving average is used. These have the advantage of ease of computation. Also, they smooth out only a negligible part of the cycle. On the other hand, they are not very smooth. If a longer (simple) moving average is used the cyclical estimates will be smoother, but the tendency to smooth out part of the cycles will be considerable.

SYSTEM OF WEIGHTING. Three systems of weighting are worth mentioning.

Simple. Simple moving averages assign the same weight to each observation. In Chapter 30, a 5-month moving average was used to smooth deseasonalized data. The results are plotted in Chart 30.7, together with a 12-month moving average of the original data. Both 3-month and 5-month moving averages are widely used for smoothing purposes. Even a 5-month moving average, however, is not very smooth; some of the irregularities still remain.

Binomial. For a 3-month moving average, the central value is given double weight. The weights are 1, 2, 1, and the sum of the weights is 4; or decimal weights 0.25, 0.50, 0.25 may be used, the sum of the weights being 1. Using decimal weights eliminates the need of dividing by 4. Smoother results will be obtained if a 5-month binomially weighted moving average is used. The weights[3] are 1, 4, 6, 4, 1, and the sum of the weights is 16. Binomially weighted moving averages may be computed by successive smoothings. For example, a binomial 5 is also a binomial 3 of a binomial 3, a binomial 7 is a binomial 3 of a binomial 5, and so on. This permits successive smoothings until the desired degree of smoothness is attained.

In general, a binomially weighted moving average produces a smoother curve than does a simple moving average of the same length. Also it is more sensitive in that it preserves more of the amplitude of the cycles.

Polynomial. In an endeavor to preserve the amplitude of the cycles, and at the same time get smooth results, weights are sometimes used that are equivalent of fitting a polynomial trend of second or higher degree to each successive *r* item, and using the trend value at the central point in time as the cyclical estimate.[4] Such cyclical estimates are usually referred to as moving arcs. Below are weights for 5- and 7-month moving arcs.[5]

5-month second degree	7-month second degree	7-month fourth degree
..	−2	5
−3	3	−30
12	6	75
17	7	131
12	6	75
−3	3	−30
..	−2	5
—	—	—
35	21	231

[3] Decimal weights that total 1 are 0.0625, 0.2500, 0.3750, 0.2500, 0.0625. A slightly simpler set of weights, that is not quite binomial, is 0.1, 0.2, 0.4, 0.2, 0.1. It is not apparent that the simpler set of weights is less satisfactory.

[4] A second-degree equation is $Y_x = a + bx + cx^2$; a fourth-degree equation is $Y_x = a + bx + cx^2 + dx^3 + ex^4$. The cyclical estimates are the values of a for the equations fitted to r successive months; or each estimate may be thought of the value of Y_0, the value of Y_x when $x = 0$. Equations of second and third degree have the same value of a as do those of fourth and fifth degree, and so on. Second-degree equations are described in Chapter 14. The fitting of polynomial equations is considered in Chapter 34.

[5] Weights for other moving arcs are given in Gerhard Tintner, *The Variate Difference Method*, Principia Press, Inc., Bloomington, Indiana, 1940, pp. 101–105. The weight patterns are referred to by Tintner as Sheppard's smoothing formulas. The weight patterns given by Tintner are in decimal form, so that the weights total 1.

Note that the weight pattern of a second-degree moving arc is also a second-degree curve, and the weight pattern of a fourth-degree moving arc is also a fourth-degree curve; the second differences of any second-degree moving arc weight pattern are constant, and the fourth differences of any fourth-degree moving arc weight pattern are constant.

An easier 5-month moving average that is not the *a*-value of successive second-degree curves fitted to the data, but which has the possibly desirable property of not smoothing out a second-degree curve to which it is applied, is −1, 4, 8, 4, −1. The sum of the weights is 14.

The reason moving arcs (and also binomially weighted moving averages) are relatively smooth is because their weight patterns are smooth. The central value receives the greatest weight, and the weights assigned to other values get gradually smaller as their position departs farther and farther from the central position. The result is that any unusually large (or small) value has a small influence when it is first included in the moving average, gradually increases in influence, and then gradually fades away. The function of the negative weights at or near the end of the weight pattern of a moving

Table 31.3—Sears, Roebuck and Company Cyclical-Irregular Movements, Cyclical Estimates, and Irregular Movements, 1946–1956

Year and month	CI	7-month 2nd degree moving arc		I $(CI \div C)$ per cent	Percentage deviations $(I - 100)$	Year and month	CI	7-month 2nd degree moving arc		I $(CI \div C)$ per cent	Percentage deviations $(I - 100)$
		C_1	C_2					C_1	C_2		
1946:						**1954:**					
Jan.	79.7	...	...	...	...	Jan.	88.5	91.1	91.8	96.4	−3.6
Feb.	83.9	...	...	...	...	Feb.	91.2	91.0	90.9	100.3	+3.0
Mar.	86.3	...	...	...	...	Mar.	89.6	91.0	91.4	98.0	−2.0
Apr.	80.5	82.3	...	...	...	Apr.	96.4	92.8	93.0	103.7	+3.7
May	79.4	80.0	...	...	...	May	92.3	95.0	94.3	97.9	−2.1
June	80.6	81.0	...	...	...	June	95.0	95.6	95.3	99.7	−0.3
July	82.1	83.2	83.2	98.7	−1.3	July	99.1	94.8	95.3	104.0	+4.0
Aug.	89.4	85.7	85.6	104.4	+4.4	Aug.	91.2	94.9	94.4	96.6	−3.4
Sep.	84.7	88.2	87.0	97.4	−2.6	Sep.	94.6	94.2	94.2	100.4	+0.4
Oct.	89.6	87.5	87.9	101.9	+1.9	Oct.	94.4	93.4	94.6	99.8	−0.2
Nov.	89.3	87.8	88.6	100.8	+0.8	Nov.	95.2	96.1	95.0	100.2	+0.2
Dec.	84.3	89.9	89.3	94.4	−5.6	Dec.	95.4	96.1	96.0	99.4	−0.6
1947:						**1955:**					
Jan.	95.0	91.1	91.2	104.2	+4.2	Jan.	100.0	96.3	97.4	102.7	+2.7
Feb.	93.0	92.3	92.8	100.2	+0.2	Feb.	94.2	98.5	97.9	96.2	−3.8
Mar.	93.7	94.9	94.2	99.5	−0.5	Mar.	98.8	99.5	98.8	100.0	0.0
Apr.	92.7	94.9	94.9	97.7	−2.3	Apr.	104.5	98.5	99.6	104.9	+4.9
May	98.8	95.6	95.2	103.8	+3.8	May	96.9	100.3	99.7	97.2	−2.8
June	94.9	94.3	94.2	100.7	+0.7	June	96.7	100.3	100.3	96.4	−3.6
July	92.8	94.1	94.0	98.7	−1.3	July	105.2	100.5	101.4	103.7	+3.7
Aug.	91.7	93.9	95.1	96.4	−3.6	Aug.	101.5	102.2	101.5	100.0	0.0
Sep.	99.6	97.9	98.0	101.6	+1.6	Sep.	101.4	102.2	101.3	100.1	+0.1
Oct.	101.1	101.8	101.1	100.0	0.0	Oct.	100.3	99.9	100.7	99.6	−0.4
Nov.	106.9	104.8	103.8	103.0	+3.0	Nov.	100.2	99.9	100.3	99.9	−0.1
Dec.	104.0	104.6	105.4	98.7	−1.3	Dec.	98.6	100.3	100.4	98.2	−1.8
1948:						**1956:**					
Jan.	105.3	106.1	106.5	98.9	−1.1	Jan.	102.1	101.6	101.0	101.1	+1.1
Feb.	105.1	107.9	107.3	97.9	−2.1	Feb.	102.4	101.0	101.2	101.2	+1.2
Mar.	112.4	108.4	108.4	103.7	+3.7	Mar.	101.9	100.9	100.7	101.2	+1.2
Apr.	110.1	108.2	108.4	101.6	+1.6	Apr.	96.7	100.5	100.3	96.4	−3.6
May	102.7	108.5	107.9	95.2	−4.8	May	102.3	99.9	101.0	101.3	+1.3
June	108.5	106.8	107.6	100.8	+0.8	June	102.6	102.0	101.7	100.9	+0.9
July	110.1	107.0	107.3	102.6	+2.6	July	100.8	103.7	...	...	...
Aug.	104.2	107.3	106.4	97.9	−2.1	Aug.	107.2	102.6	...	...	...
Sep.	106.0	104.9	105.6	100.4	+0.4	Sep.	101.0	104.1	...	...	...
Oct.	103.1	103.5	103.3	99.8	−0.2	Oct.	102.1	...	...	...	...
Nov.	100.6	100.8	99.8	100.8	+0.8	Nov.	107.9	...	...	...	...
Dec.	99.3	95.9	96.2	103.2	+3.2	Dec.	98.7	...	...	...	...

Source of data: *CI* values are from Table 31.2.

arc is to make the amplitude of the cyclical swings larger: to make them reach more faithfully into the cyclical peaks and troughs.

The proper choice of a moving average requires considerable judgement, since an inappropriate moving average may smooth out movements that one wishes to preserve, or it may create waves that have no economic basis. Also a moving average may change the timing of cyclical and other turning points.

Chart 31.4—Sears, Roebuck and Company Cyclical-Irregular Movements, and Cycles, 1946–1956

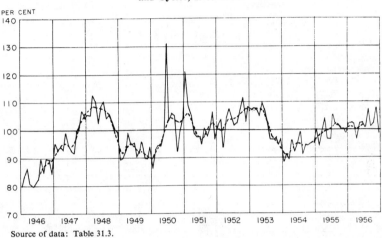

Source of data: Table 31.3.

The 5- and 7-year moving arcs are sufficiently sensitive, but on account of their short length, they are not sufficiently smooth. If, however, two successive smoothings by a 7-month second-degree moving arc are used (i.e., if we take a 7-month moving arc of the first 7-month moving arc) the results are both sufficiently sensitive and sufficiently smooth.[6] This can be seen from an inspection of Chart 31.4, where the data from the CI and C_2 columns of Table 31.3 are plotted.

In Table 31.3, the first value in the C_1 column is 82.3. It was obtained as follows:

$$\frac{-(2)(79.7) + 3(83.9) + 6(86.3) + 7(80.5) + 6(79.4) + 3(80.6) - 2(82.1)}{21}.$$

The other C_1-values were obtained similarly. The first value in the C_2 column is 83.2. It was obtained as follows:

$$\frac{-(2)(82.3) + 3(80.0) + 6(81.0) + 7(83.2) + 6(85.7) + 3(88.2) - 2(87.5)}{21}.$$

---

[6] The C_2-values can also be obtained by one smoothing of the CI estimates. The moving average weight pattern is

$$4, -12, -15, 8, 54, 108, 147, 108, 54, 8, -15, -12, 4.$$

The sum of the weights is 441, which is $(21)^2$.

The other C_2-values were obtained similarly. The C_2-values are the estimates of the cyclical movements.

Irregular Movements

An estimate of the irregular movements is obtained by dividing the cyclical irregular estimates by the cyclical estimates.

$$(31.2) \qquad\qquad I = \frac{CI}{C}.$$

Chart 31.5—Sears, Roebuck and Company Irregular Movements, by Months, 1946–1956

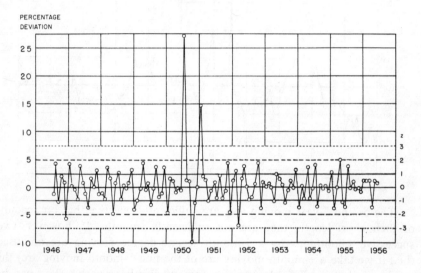

Source of data: Table 31.3.

This is done in Table 31.3, in the column labeled I. The last column shows the irregular movements as percentage deviations. These are plotted in Chart 31.5. It is apparent that the values for July 1950, October 1950, and January 1951 are far out of line. The standard deviation of the irregular movements, excluding these values, is 2.8, and expressed as standard measures these values and their probabilities under the hypothesis that the irregular movements are normally distributed with mean zero are:[7]

> July, 1950: $z = 9.71$; $P(z) \doteq 0.0$.
>
> October, 1950: $z = -3.50$; $Q(z) \doteq 0.0002$.
>
> January, 1951: $z = 5.25$; $P(z) \doteq 0.00000008$.

---

[7] In computing the cyclical estimates, arbitrary values for these three months were used because assignable causes were found for these three extreme deviations. See p. 458.

Because of their small probabilities, and because assignable causes were found (see p. 458), the irregular movements for these three months should be considered to be of a specific, rather than random, character.

*Test of normality. Chart 31.5 shows horizontal lines at distances of 1, 2, and 3 standard deviations from the central line. All three of the extreme values for which a cause could be assigned (see page 458) are beyond the 3-sigma limits. Thus the statistical evidence and the economic evidence reinforce each other.

Table 31.4—Irregular Percentage Deviations
Classified by Size, and Expected
Normal Frequencies
(Three values are not tabulated: −9.8; 14.7; 27.2)

Mid-value	f	$\hat{f}$
−6.5	1	0.88
−5.5	1	1.65
−4.5	4	3.62
−3.5	8	7.08
−2.5	14	11.21
−1.5	10	15.87
−0.5	19	18.18
0.5	21	18.18
1.5	16	15.87
2.5	5	11.21
3.5	11	7.08
4.5	7	3.62
5.5	0	1.65
6.5	0	0.88
Total	117	117.0

Source of data: Table 31.3.

Theoretically, 95.45 per cent of the points should be within the 2-sigma limits, and 99.73 should be within the 3-sigma limits. Therefore, of the 120 observations 5 or 6 should be beyond the 2-sigma limits ($0.0455 \times 120 = 5.5$), and not more than one beyond the 3-sigma limits ($0.0027 \times 120 = 0.3$). Inspection of Chart 31.5 reveals 6 observations beyond the broken line; and there are none beyond the dotted lines other than the three considered to be unrepresentative, though one other is rather close. These facts support the hypothesis that the irregular movements (excluding the 3 unrepresentative values) are normally distributed.

Table 31.4 shows the percentage deviations as a frequency distribution, while Chart 31.6 shows them as a histogram. The broken line of Chart 31.6 is a normal curve fitted to the data (excluding the 3 unrepresentative items). The goodness of fit has been tested by means of χ^2. The value of χ^2 (excluding

**Chart 31.6—Sears, Roebuck and Company Irregular Deviations,
Classified by Size, 1946–1956, and Normal Curve**

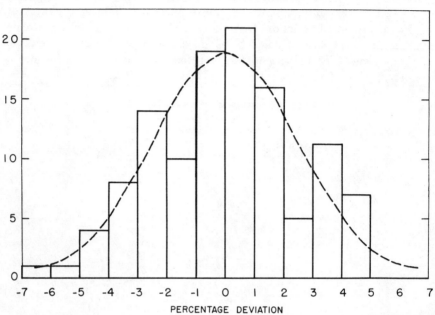

Source of data: Table 31.4.

the 3 unrepresentative items) is 14.923, and with 10 degrees of freedom $P(\chi^2) > 0.10$.   Therefore χ^2 is not significant at the 0.05 level, and the hypothesis that the presumably random irregular movements are normally distributed is accepted.[8]

*Test of independence. If the irregular movements are randomly distributed over time, the successive values will be independent; there will be no correlation between the values of the irregular movements and their values one month later.   It simplifies the problem considerably if we use the percentage deviations and consider not their exact values, but only whether they are positive or negative.[9]   If we look at first six values we find their signs to be

$$- + - + + -$$

---

[8] The chi-square test was considered in Chapter 19.   The reason for using 10 degrees of freedom is that there are 12 classes, after combining the end classes so that $\hat{f} \geq 1$ for each class, and there are 2 restrictions placed on the fitted curve: $\Sigma \hat{f} = \Sigma f$ and $\Sigma \hat{f} X^2 = \Sigma f X^2$.   By hypothesis, $\Sigma \hat{f} X = 0$.

[9] Of course we throw away some information by ignoring the exact values; but we gain in generality, for we are not tied to the assumption that the irregular movements are normally distributed.   We earlier concluded that there are three values that do not fit into the normal pattern.   Tests of significance that make no assumption concerning the form of the data are called nonparametric tests.

Now if we consider successive pairs we find

$$(- \ +) \ (+ \ -) \ (- \ +) \ (+ \ +) \ (+ \ -)$$

Obviously, if we consider all successive pairs we will find that sometimes the signs of the deviations do not change because they are both negative or both positive, and sometimes they change from negative to positive, or positive to negative. Thus the four possibilities are

$+ \ -$	$+ \ +$
$- \ -$	$- \ +$

If the percentage deviations are independent, we should expect the same number of observations in each cell.

Given month	Next month	
	$-$	$+$
$+$	29.75	29.75
$-$	29.75	29.75

Actual tabulation shows these results.[10]

Given month	Next month	
	$-$	$+$
$+$	35	28
$-$	20	36

There is thus some evidence that the irregular movements change direction too often. This could result from use of too sensitive a moving average for obtaining the cyclical estimates.

The computed value of χ^2 is 5.57. Using 3 degrees of freedom (since the only restriction placed on the $\hat{f}$-values is that $\Sigma \hat{f} = 119$), we find that the

---

[10] Where the value of $(I - 100)$ was 0.0, it was arbitrarily considered to have a positive sign.

probability of a value of χ^2 as large as that obtained or larger is greater than 0.10. The hypothesis of independence is therefore accepted.

If, in a similar manner, we should compare the sign of the current month with the sign of the month two months ahead, three months ahead, etc., our hypothesis of independence would not be rejected. Other tests of independence are possible, but not considered here. For example, we could examine the distribution of the length of runs of the same sign, or of first differences of the same sign.

Chapter 32

FUNDAMENTALS OF INDEX NUMBER
CONSTRUCTION

Index numbers are devices for comparing the magnitude of groups of related variables. They may compare (1) changes occurring over time, (2) differences between places, and (3) differences between like categories, such as persons, organizations, or objects. An index number is obtained by combining the variables by means of a total or average. Usually each index number in a series is expressed as a percentage of some convenient base. When a series of index numbers is obtained, it is customary to refer to it as an *index*.

The most common indexes measure variations over time. The total amount of money spent each year, relative to some base year, varies from year to year because of changes in the number of units of the different commodities bought, and because of changes in the unit prices of these commodities. Thus, we have three variables:

V, the value relative to some base year of the group of commodities, sometimes referred to as a value index number;

Q, the physical quantity of the commodities relative to some base year considered as a group, or the quantity index number;

P, the price relative to the base year of the commodities considered as a group, or the price index number.

The relationship between these three index numbers is, ideally,

$$V = PQ.$$

This seems reasonable when we consider that the amount of money spent for any commodity, say for cigarettes, is the price per package multiplied by the number of packages bought.

Uses of Index Numbers

1. Price movements are a guide to business policy. Rising prices call for one policy, while falling prices necessitate a different one. A stable or slowly rising price level is generally considered as a condition favorable to business stability. Stock market prices are considered especially significant, since changes in stock prices are sometimes forerunners of changes in other prices.

2. Indexes of industrial production are useful not only as indicators of business conditions, but also as a base with which to compare production in one's own business. For the latter purpose it is usual to compare production in the individual business with production in the industry.

3. Sometimes it is possible to combine series that are causally related to one's own business in such a way that changes in the index will forecast changes in one's own business.

Table 32.1—Deflation of Nominal Hourly Wage Rates in Manufacturing, 1950–1955

Year	Nominal wage rates (current dollars)	Consumer price index (per cent of 1950)	Wage rates in 1950 dollars	Nominal wage rates (per cent of 1950)	Real wage rates (per cent of 1950)
	W	P	$\dfrac{W}{P}$	V	$\dfrac{V}{P}$
1950	1.465	100.0	1.465	100.00	100.0
1951	1.59	108.0	1.472	108.53	100.5
1952	1.67	110.4	1.513	113.99	103.3
1953	1.77	111.3	1.590	120.82	108.6
1954	1.81	111.7	1.620	123 55	110.6
1955	1.88	111.4	1.688	128.33	115.2
1956	1.98	113.0	1.752	135.15	119.6

Source: U.S. Department of Labor, Bureau of Labor Statistics, *Monthly Labor Review*. The base of consumer price index has been shifted, by the writer, from 1947–49 to 1950. See Table 33.3.

4. It may be difficult to tell whether a company's sales are increasing in *physical volume*, as opposed to *dollar value*. The products sold may be numerous and diverse; some may be increasing while others are falling off in regard to the number of units sold. Likewise, the unit prices may be changing. An index of physical volume of company sales may therefore be constructed, or the dollar value of the sales "deflated" by dividing them by an index of company prices.

In Table 32.1, average hourly earnings of manufacturing wage earners are deflated by the consumer price index, obtaining wages in dollars of 1950 purchasing power. The deflated series W/P, which represents wages in dollars of constant value show a substantial rise in wages though not so spectacular as that of the W series, which represents wages in dollars of variable value. The series labeled V is obtained by dividing each W entry by the W entry for 1950. The column labeled real wages can be obtained either by dividing V by P, or by dividing each W/P entry by the W/P entry for 1950.

5. An index of company prices may also provide favorable publicity in case company prices have fallen in comparison with company wages rates or other price indexes.

6. Many wage contracts contain an escalator clause providing for adjustment of wages on the basis of changes in the consumer price index, CPI as it is usually called. Usually these contracts call for adjustments quarterly. For example, if the hourly wage rate has been $1.86 per hour and the CPI changes during the quarter from 120.2 to 120.8, the new wage rate will be increased from $1.86 to $120.8/120.2 \times 1.86 = 1.0050 \times 1.86 = \$1.87$ per hour, if the escalator clause calls for adjustment in wage rates proportionate to changes in CPI. Although a change in 1 cent per hour does not sound like much, the aggregate effect is considerable when it applies to millions of workers.

Sometimes other long term contracts call for payments to be adjusted on the basis of the CPI. An example is the payment for expensive products manufactured to special order and taking a long time to make.

Problems in Index Number Construction

In this section we will discuss, in order, the selection of a base, the type of formula to use, and the selection of suitable data.

Selection of base. Selection of a base with which to compare the various index numbers does not raise difficult theoretical questions. The choice depends on the purpose of the index. For a general purpose index number, a "normal" period should be chosen as base. Since comparisons among indexes are often made, one should also consider what base period has already been selected for related indexes. The United States Government has suggested that the three-year period 1947–49 is appropriate for many indexes; and there now seems to be a tendency to adopt this period as a base. Nevertheless, a number of different bases are in current use and it does not seem that a given set of years is necessarily "normal" for all series of data, or appropriate for all purposes.

Type of formula. Selection of a type of formula that is technically sound, and appropriate for the particular purpose in view, is a subject which has occupied the attention of statisticians for decades, and which has resulted in divergent solutions. The problem is perhaps of greater theoretical than practical importance.

Weighting system. Weighting the different series according to their importance is a troublesome problem, especially if their importance is changing. It will be shown, however, that only approximate accuracy in weights is required.

The data for index numbers. Too much emphasis cannot be put upon the practical problem of selecting the data that are the raw material of the index. Without doubt, the most important problem in index number construction is the selection of suitable data. The data must be accurate and comparable, and the sample adequate in size and as nearly representative as possible. The usefulness of an index is usually enhanced if it can be made available without delay. Hence, preference should be given to data taken from sources that report promptly. Needless to say, the data to be used depend on what one is trying to measure. A wholesale price index requires wholesale prices; a consumer price index necessitates data not only on retail prices of food, clothing, and house furnishings, but on rents, gas and electric rates, and so on, applying to the class of persons for whom the index is intended.

Accuracy. Although prices and quantities are likely to be accurate if gathered from the internal records of one's own company, one cannot always be sure of the accuracy of data reported by others. For example, the housewife may not keep accurate records of the quantities she purchases, and prices reported by shoppers at retail stores may be for commodities other than those specified for the price index.

Comparability. Standard grades of the same commodity are, of course, comparable between different dates. But is a 1930 automobile comparable with a 1957 one? Obviously one would rather have a 1957 car than a 1930 model of the same general type. Likewise, any physical volume index that treats an old carbon filament clear glass lamp as the equivalent of a modern nitrogen-filled inside-frosted bulb contains a serious mistake.

Representativeness. Since index numbers are usually obtained from samples, one must try to obtain a sample that behaves like the universe from which it is drawn. Probably the most satisfactory way to do this is to divide the original data into groups and subgroups, and try to obtain proportionate representation in each group. Thus, if the value of farm products marketed is three times as large as that of processed foods, the value of the former items in the sample should be three times that of the latter, for any index of prices or quantities. These large groups can each be split into smaller ones, such as fresh and dried fruits and vegetables, grains, etc., and the same procedure can be followed. In short, the problem is similar to that of stratified sampling. In practice the weight attached to the commodities in any group is adjusted so that the value of the sample will be correct for each group; i.e., each commodity is weighted, not according to its own importance, but according to the importance of the group of commodities that it represents. Commodities selected to represent a group of commodities in a price index should, of course, be those which, taken together, are typical of the price movements of all the commodities in the group.

Adequacy. It has been pointed out that the reliability of the mean of a random sample increases with the square root of the *number* of items included. Likewise the larger the *proportion* of items included, the more reliable is the mean. In index number construction this should be interpreted to mean proportion of total *value*. It would appear, then, that one should ordinarily select the most important items first, and as many other suitable items as it seems worthwhile to include. The absolute number of items to use or the proportion of total value to include are questions that cannot be answered in general terms. The problem is further complicated because of these factors:

1. The commodities are usually selected partly on the basis of judgment.
2. The sampling plan is stratified rather than simple.
3. Weights are values, rather than frequencies.
4. Weights are assigned to individual commodities or groups of commodities on a partly arbitrary basis.
5. The prices (and quantities) of the different commodities are interdependent.

Index Number Symbols

Index numbers are computed from prices and/or quantities of individual commodities. These are designated by lower case letters.

p is the price of an individual commodity;
q is the quantity of an individual commodity.

Usually a subscript is attached to p or q. The subscript 0 is generally (though not always) used to refer to the base year, while 1, 2, etc., refer to other years in chronological order.

p_0 is the price of a commodity in the base year;
p_1 is the price of a commodity in year 1;
p_2 is the price of a commodity in year 2;
and so on.

Analogous meanings are attached to the symbols q_0, q_1, q_2, etc.

Capital letters are used to refer to index numbers.
P means price index number;
Q means quantity index number.

Subscripts attached to P or Q refer to the years being compared.

P_{01} means price index for year 1 relative to year 0;
P_{02} means price index for year 2 relative to year 0;
P_{12} means price index for year 2 relative to year 1.

Analogous meanings are attached to the symbols Q_{01}, Q_{02}, Q_{12}, etc.

For the sake of simplicity we shall follow the practice of giving the formula for year 1 relative to year 0. Where different years are being compared, different subscripts are easily substituted.

Illustrative Data

In Tables 32.2 and 32.3 are listed data from which we shall construct various indexes of the price of textile fibers and of mill consumption of textiles.

Certain peculiarities of the data should be noted. The textile labeled *rayon* includes also acetate; nonorganic man-made fibers, such as orlon, dacron, and fiber glass, are excluded. The quantities refer to shipments to domestic mills of all grades of each textile, while the prices are those of only one specific grade of each textile. The use of separate prices and quantities of each grade shipped would make the illustration too cumbersome for purposes of exposition, and would result in little gain in accuracy. The price series for rayon and acetate is a weighted average of the prices of viscose staple and acetate staple, giving the former a weight of 0.8 and the latter a weight of 0.2. This is better than an average that weighs each according to its actual importance each year, for such an average changes each year, not only because the price of each series has changed, but also because of changes in the relative quantities consumed. If there are two commodities, one cheap and one expensive, and both go *up* in price, the average price might go *down* because of the shift in purchases from the expensive to the cheap commodity. An index number, under these circumstances, should show an *increase* in price.

Simple Index Numbers

Simple aggregative index numbers. The simplest method, but one of the least satisfactory methods, of index number construction is to ascertain the total cost in each year of buying one unit of each commodity and to express this total cost each year as a per cent of the base year cost. This is done in Table 32.2. The formula is

(32.1)
$$P_{01} = \frac{\Sigma p_1}{\Sigma p_0}.$$

The simple aggregative assigns equal importance to the absolute change of each commodity. The result is that a commodity with a high price per unit tends to exert more influence on the aggregative index number than does a commodity with a low price per unit. If cotton were quoted by the bale

Table 32.2—Textile Fiber Prices, 1953–1956, and Simple Aggregative
Price Index
(Prices are in dollars per pound.)

Textile	1953	1954	1955	1956
	p_0	p_1	p_2	p_3
Cotton	0.338	0.350	0.349	0.348
Wool	1.729	1.706	1.421	1.371
Rayon	0.351	0.340	0.341	0.320
Silk	5.295	4.920	4.594	4.486
Total	7.713	7.316	6.705	6.526
Index number*	100.0	94.9	86.9	84.6

* Formula (32.1).
Source: Textile Economic Bureau, Inc., *Textile Organon*, various issues.

Table 32.3—United States Mill Consumption of Textiles, 1953–1956,
and Simple Aggregative Quantity Index
(Quantities are in millions of pounds.)

Textile	1953	1954	1955	1956
	q_0	q_1	q_2	q_3
Cotton	4521.0	4125.2	4384.2	4339.1
Wool	503.8	389.9	428.2	454.9
Rayon	1223.0	1154.8	1419.2	1201.1
Silk	5.4	6.4	7.2	7.7
Total	6,253.2	5,676.3	6,238.8	6,002.8
Index number*	100.0	90.8	99.8	96.0

* Formula (32.2).
Source: Textile Economic Bureau, *Textile Organon*, Vol. XXVIII, March, 1957, p. 42.

instead of by the pound, its influence on the aggregative index number would be approximately 500 times as great. In our present illustration silk exerts 15 times as much influence in the simple aggregative index number as cotton, whereas the value of cotton fiber consumed by mills in 1953 was more than 50 times as great as that of silk. The weighting is, in fact, haphazard and illogical: the unit price quotation for different commodities may be such units as grain, pound, ton, gallon, barrel, inch, foot, yard, kilowatt-hour, and so on, and the fact that a particular unit happens to be the one quoted commercially may have nothing to do with its economic importance.

The analogous quantity index number formula is

$$(32.2) \qquad Q_{01} = \frac{\Sigma \, q_1}{\Sigma \, q_0}.$$

This formula compares the cost in the given year with the cost in the base year of buying the goods actually bought in each year if the price for each

Table 32.4—Textile Fiber Prices Relative to 1953, and Simple Arithmetic
Average of Relatives Index
(Per cent)

Textile	1953 $\dfrac{p_0}{p_0}$	1954 $\dfrac{p_1}{p_0}$	1955 $\dfrac{p_2}{p_0}$	1956 $\dfrac{p_3}{p_0}$
Cotton	100.00	103.55	103.26	102.96
Wool	100.00	98.67	82.19	79.29
Rayon	100.00	96.87	97.15	91.17
Silk	100.00	92.92	86.76	84.72
Total	400.00	392.01	369.36	358.14
Index number*	100.0	98.0	92.3	89.5

* Formula (32.3).
Source of data: Table 32.2.

commodity each year was $1.00 per unit. This is obviously an unrealistic assumption.

Simple average of relatives index numbers. Table 32.4 and Chart 32.1 show the prices of the different textiles relative to 1953, the year selected for base. These relative prices p_x/p_0 are usually referred to as price relatives. The price of each of the commodities is moving gradually downward except that of cotton, which shows only a slight upward movement. But since each price is affected by special factors as well as by factors common to textiles in general, they do not move in unison. The dispersion among the price relatives is obviously increasing with the passage of time. Little central tendency is observable, which is not surprising in view of the small number of commodities. Nevertheless, any index number of textile prices must lie somewhere between the highest price relative for any given year, and the lowest.

A crude price index can be obtained by simply averaging these price relatives for each year, as in Table 32.4. This type of index number is known

**Chart 32.1—Textile Fiber Price Relatives, and Simple Arithmetic
Average of Relatives Index, 1953–1956**

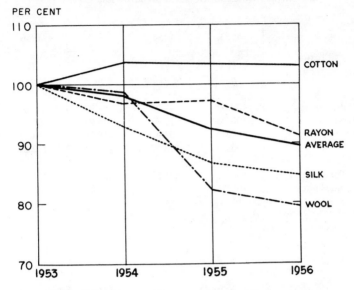

Source of data: Table 32.4.

as the *simple average of price relatives*, and is indicated by the formula

$$(32.3) \qquad P_{01} = \frac{1}{n} \sum \left(\frac{p_1}{p_0} \right).$$

The index is plotted as a heavy line on the chart.

The chief objection to this index number is that each price relative exercises an equal influence, whereas economically some are more important than others. Another objection that is sometimes raised is that the simple arithmetic mean is not an appropriate type of average to use with ratios since it results in too high a value and is therefore said to have an "upward bias." The geometric mean is considered by many to be better.[1]

Table 32.5 and Chart 32.2 show quantity relatives q_x/q_0. The tendency is slightly upward, except in the case of silk, which is steeply upward. A simple average-of-relatives index is computed in Table 32.5 and plotted on Chart 32.2. The formula is

$$(32.4) \qquad Q_{01} = \frac{1}{n} \sum \left(\frac{q_1}{q_0} \right).$$

It should be noted that silk has exerted an influence far out of line with its economic importance. (For these data also there is also a large rounding off error, since the silk quantities have only two significant digits.)

---

[1] For a discussion of this point see pages 234–235.

Table 32.5—United States Mill Consumption of Textiles Relative to 1953, and Simple Arithmetic Average of Relatives Index, 1953–1956

(Per cent)

Textile	1953 $\frac{q_0}{q_0}$	1954 $\frac{q_1}{q_0}$	1955 $\frac{q_2}{q_0}$	1956 $\frac{q_3}{q_0}$
Cotton	100.00	91.25	96.97	95.98
Wool	100.00	77.39	84.99	90.29
Rayon	100.00	94.42	116.04	98.21
Silk†	100.00	118.52	133.33	142.59
Total	400.00	381.58	431.33	427.07
Index number*	100.0	95.4	107.8	106.8

* Formula (32.4).
† There are only 2 significant digits for silk.
Source of data: Table 32.3.

Chart 32.2—United States Mill Consumption of Rayon Relatives, and Simple Arithmetic Average of Relatives Index, 1953–1956

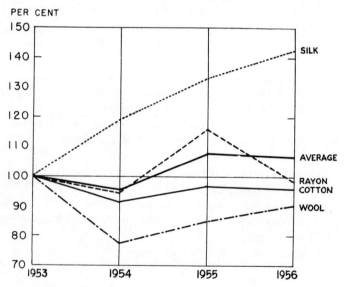

Source of data: Table 32.5.

Aggregative Price Index Numbers

It is often better to think of a price index number, not as an average of relatives, frequently of heterogeneous data, but as a measure of the relative value in two different years of a fixed aggregate of goods. This type of price index number answers the question: "If we buy the same assortment of goods in each of two years, but at different prices, how much will we spend in the given year relative to the base year?" This is a particularly useful concept for consumer price indexes, which indicate how much it would cost in a given year as compared with the base year to support a particular plane of living.

Weighted aggregative price index numbers. In order to allow each commodity to have an appropriate influence on the index, it is advisable to use a weighted rather than a simple[2] aggregate. To construct a weighted aggregative index number, a list of definite quantities of specified commodities is taken, and calculations are made to determine what this aggregate of goods is worth in each of the two or more years under comparison. The value in any given year relative to the value in the base year is an aggregative price index number. Aggregative index numbers show merely the changing value of a fixed aggregate of goods. Since the total value changes while the components of the aggregate do not, the changes must be due to price.

There are innumerable kinds of aggregative price index numbers, depending on the list of commodities, and the number of units of each being compared. A few systems of weighting are discussed below, and in some cases illustrated. In each of the illustrations, the quantity used is not that of the particular grade of textile included in the index, but of all grades of that kind of textile.

1. *Base period quantities.* The formula for this method, sometimes known as Lespeyre's index, is

$$(32.5) \qquad P_{01} = \frac{\Sigma p_1 q_0}{\Sigma p_0 q_0} .$$

It is the one illustrated in Table 32.6. When used for a consumer price index number, this formula compares the theoretical cost in the given year with the actual cost in the base year of maintaining the standard of living of the base year. It has been noted, however, that the base period quantities may not be typical of those consumed in later years.

2. *Given period quantities.* The formula for this method, sometimes known as Paasche's index, is

$$(32.6) \qquad P_{01} = \frac{\Sigma p_1 q_1}{\Sigma p_0 q_1} .$$

---

[2] A simple aggregative index number is not, strictly speaking, unweighted. The weight assigned to each price is one unit of the commodity concerned.

**Table 32.6—Construction of Aggregative Price Index of Textile Fibers,
Using Base Year Quantity Weights**

(Quantities are in millions of pounds; values are in millions of dollars.)

Textile	Quantity	Price per pound			
	1953	1953	1954	1955	1956
	q_0	p_0	p_1	p_2	p_3
Cotton	4,521.0	$0.338	$0.350	$0.349	$0.348
Wool	503.8	1.729	1.706	1.421	1.371
Rayon	1,223.0	0.351	0.340	0.341	0.320
Silk	5.4	5.295	4.920	4.594	4.486

Textile	Theoretical value of 1953 quantities at price of given year			
	1953†	1954	1955	1956
	$p_0 q_0$	$p_1 q_0$	$p_2 q_0$	$p_3 q_0$
Cotton	1,528.1	1,582.4	1,577.8	1,573.3
Wool	871.1	859.5	715.9	690.7
Rayon	429.3	415.8	417.0	391.4
Silk	28.6	26.6	24.8	24.2
Total	2,857.1	2,884.3	2,735.5	2,679.6
Index number*	100.0	101.0	95.7	93.8

* Formula (32.5).
† Actual value.
Source of data: Tables 32.2 and 32.3.

It is illustrated in Table 32.7. When used for a consumer price index, this formula compares the actual cost in the given year with the theoretical cost in the base year of maintaining the plane of living of the given year. This method involves the selection of a new set of weights each year, or even each month. Often it is impossible to obtain a revised set of weights that frequently. Even if this is possible, Table 32.7 clearly illustrates that the amount of computation required is nearly double that of the base year weighted method. A more serious objection is that given year weights may not be typical of earlier years.[3] Furthermore, although each period is thereby directly compared with the base year, the comparison among the different years is not entirely valid, for the reason that the quantities of the different goods changes each year.

---

[3] When the correlation of price and quantity relatives is positive, given year weights give a higher result for a price (or quantity) index than do base year weights. The opposite is true when the correlation is negative. It can be argued that whether given year weighting makes the index too high or too low depends to a considerable extent on whether the changes are due mainly to demand or mainly to supply. Since changes in demand and supply are ordinarily both at work, it often does not make much difference which system of weighting is employed.

**Table 32.7—Construction of Aggregative Price Index of Textile Fiber Prices,
Using Given Year Quantity Weights**
(Quantities are in millions of pounds; values are in millions of dollars.)

Textile	Price per pound				Actual value in given year			
	1953	1954	1955	1956	1953	1954	1955	1956
	p_0	p_1	p_2	p_3	p_0q_0	p_1q_1	p_2q_2	p_3q_3
Cotton ...	0.338	0.350	0.349	0.348	1,528.1	1,443.8	1,530.1	1,510.0
Wool	1.729	1.706	1.421	1.371	871.1	665.2	608.5	623.7
Rayon ...	0.351	0.340	0.341	0.320	429.3	392.6	483.9	384.4
Silk	5.295	4.920	4.594	4.486	28.6	31.5	33.1	34.5
Total ..	...	...	...	...	2,857.1	2,533.1	2,655.6	2,552.6

Textile	Quantity				Theoretical value of given year quantities at 1953 prices			
	1953	1954	1955	1956	1953†	1954	1955	1956
	q_0	q_1	q_2	q_3	p_0q_0	p_0q_1	p_0q_2	p_0q_3
Cotton ...	4,521.0	4,125.2	4,384.2	4,339.1	1,528.1	1,394.3	1,481.9	1,466.6
Wool	503.8	389.9	428.2	454.9	871.1	674.1	740.4	786.5
Rayon ...	1,223.0	1,154.8	1,419.2	1,201.1	429.3	405.3	498.1	421.6
Silk	5.4	6.4	7.2	7.7	28.6	33.9	38.1	40.8
Total ..	...	...	...	...	2,857.1	2,507.6	2,758.5	2,715.5
Index numbers	...	...	...	...	100.0	101.0	96.3	94.0

* Formula (32.6).
† Actual value.
Source of data: Tables 32.2 and 32.3.

3. *Average quantities of base and given years.*

$$(32.7) \qquad P_{01} = \frac{\Sigma p_1 \bar{q}_{0,1}}{\Sigma p_0 \bar{q}_{0,1}}.$$

This is a compromise solution. But again, as with given year quantity weights, we have shifting weights and a resultant lack of comparability among the different years.

4. *Average quantities in several years.* The years selected should be such that the average quantities are typical. This is a solution that has often been adopted. If it is decided to use as weights the average quantity for the three years 1947, 1948, and 1949, the formula is

$$(32.8) \qquad P_{01} = \frac{\Sigma p_1 \bar{q}_{47-49}}{\Sigma p_0 q_{47-49}}.$$

The weights used will, however, eventually become obsolete. When this is the case, a new index can be constructed and spliced to the old one, using the method shown on pages 506–507.

5. *Average of quantities for all the years included in the index.* Though perhaps an excellent solution for an historical study, this plan is impractical if the index is to be kept up to date, since it means current revision of weights and continuous revision of the complete set of index numbers.

6. *Hypothetical quantities.* For example, the quantities might refer to the quantities of different commodities necessary to support some desirable standard of living.

7. *Geometric average of a pair of index numbers with different systems of weighting.* When the two index numbers are, respectively, those with base and given year weights, the resulting average is frequently referred to as Fisher's index number or the "ideal" index number.

$$(32.9) \qquad P_{01} = \sqrt{\frac{\Sigma p_1 q_0}{\Sigma p_0 q_0} \times \frac{\Sigma p_1 q_1}{\Sigma p_0 q_1}} .$$

Although this method has certain technical advantages,[4] it is difficult to say precisely just what it does measure.

Combining the results of Tables 32.6 and 32.7 ideal index numbers are easily computed. (Note that in each year the arithmetic mean and the geometric mean give the same results to one decimal place.)

Index number	1953	1954	1955	1956
Base year weights .	100.0	101.0	95.7	93.8
Given year weights	100.0	101.0	96.3	94.2
Ideal	100.0	101.0	96.0	94.0

The alternatives mentioned may seem to be much ado about nothing. As a matter of fact, it often makes little difference which of the systems of weighting is used. A comparison of the various index numbers thus far computed shows that only the simple average of relatives and the simple aggregative give results that are far out of line. The illogical nature of their weights has already been explained.

Even if the quantity weights are only approximate, it makes little difference. Table 32.8 shows the results of using base year quantity weights which have been rounded to one digit. It is interesting to note that when the index numbers of Tables 32.6 and 32.8 are both rounded to the nearest per cent, the results are the same. (If the *prices* are rounded to one digit, however, the effect on the index numbers is considerable.)

But if it so happens that commodities that are changing *greatly* in relative importance during the period are also undergoing price changes materially different from the average, then the matter of weighting becomes important. Over a considerable period of time the changes in the prices and quantities

---

[4] See Chapter 33.

are likely to be so great that any fixed base index number will become inaccurate. In recent years there has been a tendency to employ a type of index in which "link-relative" index numbers are chained together to form a "chain" index. Each link relative is an index number with the preceding year as base, and with weights appropriate for the two years under comparison. Chain index numbers will be considered in Chapter 33.

Table 32.8—Construction of Aggregative Index of Textile Fiber Prices, Using Base Year Quantity Weights Rounded to One Significant Digit
(Quantities are in millions of pounds; values are in millions of dollars.)

Textile	q_0	p_0q_0	p_1q_0	p_2q_0	p_3q_0
Cotton	5,000	1,690	1,750	1,745	1,740
Wool	500	864	853	710	686
Rayon	1,000	351	340	341	320
Silk	5	26	25	23	22
Total	....	2,931	2,968	2,819	2,768
Index number .	....	100.0	101.3	96.2	94.4

Source of data: Tables 32.2 and 32.3.

Weighted aggregative quantity index numbers. An aggregative index number of physical volume is the counterpart of the analogous aggregative price index number. Just as the aggregative index number of price measures the changing value of an aggregate of goods when the quantities have been held constant, so the aggregative index number of physical volume measures the changing value of a varying aggregate of goods when the prices have been held constant. The price index number answers the question: "If we buy the same assortment of goods in each of two years, but at *different prices*, how much will we spend in the given year relative to the base year?" The quantity index number answers the question: "If we buy *varying quantities* of specified goods in each of two years, but at the same price, how much will we spend in the given year relative to the base year?" While in the former case the difference in the amount spent was due to price change, in the latter case the difference must, of course, be attributed to changes in quantities bought and sold, since prices were held constant. Three weighting systems are illustrated here:

1. *Base period prices.*

(32.10)
$$Q_{01} = \frac{\Sigma\, p_0 q_1}{\Sigma\, p_0 q_0}.$$

2. *Given period prices.*

(32.11)
$$Q_{01} = \frac{\Sigma\, p_1 q_1}{\Sigma\, p_1 q_0}.$$

Since the different sums of products for these two formulas were all computed for Tables 32.6 and 32.7, they are recombined in the tabular arrangement that follows. The results by the two methods turn out to be almost identical.

$$\Sigma p_1 q_1 = 1443.8 \quad \Sigma p_2 q_2 = 1530.1 \quad \Sigma p_3 q_3 = 1510.0$$
$$\Sigma p_1 q_0 = 1582.4 \quad \Sigma p_2 q_0 = 1577.8 \quad \Sigma p_3 q_0 = 1573.3$$
$$_1 Q_{01} = 91.241 \quad\quad _2 Q_{02} = 96.977 \quad\quad _3 Q_{03} = 95.977$$

$$\Sigma p_0 q_1 = 1394.3 \quad \Sigma p_0 q_2 = 1481.9 \quad \Sigma p_0 q_3 = 1466.6$$
$$\Sigma p_0 q_0 = 1528.1 \quad \Sigma p_0 q_0 = 1528.1 \quad \Sigma p_0 q_0 = 1528.1$$
$$_0 Q_{01} = 91.244 \quad\quad _0 Q_{02} = 96.977 \quad\quad _0 Q_{03} = 95.975$$

3. *"Ideal" index number.*

(32.12)
$$Q_{01} = \sqrt{\frac{\Sigma p_0 q_1}{\Sigma p_0 q_0} \times \frac{\Sigma p_1 q_1}{\Sigma p_1 q_0}}.$$

In general, the merits and defects of the different types of quantity index numbers are the same as for the corresponding type of price index number.

Chapter 33

SELECTED TOPICS IN INDEX NUMBER CONSTRUCTION

Weighted Average-of-Relatives Index Numbers

Construction of index numbers by simple[1] averages of price relatives and quantity relatives were mentioned briefly in Chapter 32, and found to be unsatisfactory because of inappropriate weighting.

Weighted averages of relatives are obtained by multiplying each relative by its weight, summing these products, and dividing by the sum of the weights. The formulas thus are

(33.1)
$$P = \frac{\sum \left[v \left(\frac{p_1}{p_0} \right) \right]}{\sum v} ;$$

(33.2)
$$Q = \frac{\sum \left[v \left(\frac{q_1}{q_0} \right) \right]}{\sum v} .$$

The weights are always values, the value weight for any commodity being the product of a price and a quantity ($v = pq$). For a price index number the value is the product of the base year price and whatever quantity has been decided upon. For the quantity index number the value weight is the product of the base year quantity and whatever price has been decided upon.

Exactly the same results can be obtained by the use of aggregate values as by averaging relatives. Two systems of weighting averages of price relatives, and two systems of weighting quantity relatives, together with their equivalent aggregative types, are as follows:

Index number	Average of relatives formula	Equivalent aggregative formula
PRICE:		
(33.3) Base year weights, $_0P_{01}$:	$\dfrac{\sum \left[p_0 q_0 \left(\frac{p_1}{p_0} \right) \right]}{\sum p_0 q_0}$	$\dfrac{\sum p_1 q_0}{\sum p_0 q_0}$
(33.4) Given year weights, $_1P_{01}$:	$\dfrac{\sum \left[p_0 q_1 \left(\frac{p_1}{p_0} \right) \right]}{\sum p_0 q_1}$	$\dfrac{\sum p_1 q_1}{\sum p_0 q_1}$

[1] A simple average-of-relatives index number is not, strictly speaking, unweighted. The value weight assigned to each relative is the same.

	Index number QUANTITY:	Average of relatives formula	Equivalent aggregative formula
(33.5)	Base year weights, $_0Q_{01}$:	$\dfrac{\Sigma\left[p_0q_0\left(\dfrac{q_1}{q_0}\right)\right]}{\Sigma\, p_0q_0}$	$\dfrac{\Sigma\, p_0q_1}{\Sigma\, p_0q_0}$
(33.6)	Given year weights, $_1Q_{01}$:	$\dfrac{\Sigma\left[p_1q_0\left(\dfrac{q_1}{q_0}\right)\right]}{\Sigma\, p_1q_0}$	$\dfrac{\Sigma\, p_1q_1}{\Sigma\, p_1q_0}$

Only one illustration of a price index constructed by using a weighted average of relatives will be provided here, an average of price relatives weighted with base year values. The construction of such an index is shown in Table 33.1. Notice that the last three columns of this table agree (within permissible limits of errors of rounding) with the last three columns of Table 32.6.

Table 33.1—Construction of Average-of-Relatives Price Index of Textile Fibers, Weighted with Base Year Values

(Value weights are in millions of dollars; price relatives are percentages of 1939.)

Textile	Value	Price relative			Weighted price relative		
	1953	1954	1955	1956	1954	1955	1956
	v_0 (p_0q_0)	$\dfrac{p_1}{p_0}$	$\dfrac{p_2}{p_0}$	$\dfrac{p_3}{p_0}$	$v_0\left(\dfrac{p_1}{p_0}\right)$	$v_0\left(\dfrac{p_2}{p_0}\right)$	$v_0\left(\dfrac{p_3}{p_0}\right)$
Cotton ...	1,528.1	103.55	103.26	102.96	1,582.3	1,577.9	1,573.3
Wool	871.1	98.67	82.19	79.29	859.5	716.0	690.7
Rayon ...	429.3	96.87	97.15	91.17	415.9	417.1	391.4
Silk	28.6	92.92	86.76	84.72	26.6	24.8	24.2
Total ...	2,857.1	...	...	...	2,884.3	2,735.8	2,679.6
Index number*	100.0	...	...	...	101.0	95.8	93.8

* Formula (33.3).
Source of data: Price relatives are from Table 32.4; value weights are from Table 32.6.

There is a saving of labor if the weights are made to total unity, as in Table 33.2.

$$(33.7) \qquad P_{01} = \Sigma\left[w_0\left(\frac{p_1}{p_0}\right)\right], \qquad \text{where } w_0 = \frac{p_0q_0}{\Sigma\, p_0q_0}.$$

The resulting figures are, of course, the same as in Table 33.1. This refinement also permits one to see how many points each commodity contributed to the index number each year. Thus we see that in 1956 cotton contributed 55 out of the 94 percentage points to the index number.

Various situations in which it is necessary or advantageous to use the average-of-relative method of index number construction should be mentioned.

1. When a commodity is used to represent a group of commodities, its price relative is weighted by the value of the group. The alternative is to use a fictitious quantity weight obtained by dividing the value of the group of commodities by the price of the group representative. This is at best a confusing procedure.

Table 33.2—Construction of Average-of-Relatives Price Index of Textile Fibers, with Weights Proportionate to Base Year Values Totaling Unity

(1953 = 100)

Textile	Proportionate value in base year w_0	Price relative			Weighted price relative		
		1954 $\dfrac{p_1}{p_0}$	1955 $\dfrac{p_2}{p_0}$	1956 $\dfrac{p_3}{p_0}$	1954 $w_0\left(\dfrac{p_1}{p_0}\right)$	1955 $w_0\left(\dfrac{p_2}{p_0}\right)$	1956 $w_0\left(\dfrac{p_3}{p_0}\right)$
Cotton........	0.53484	103.55	103.26	102.96	55.38	55.23	55.07
Wool	0.30489	98.67	82.19	79.29	30.08	25.06	24.17
Rayon	0.15026	96.87	97.15	91.17	14.56	14.60	13.70
Silk	0.01001	92.92	86.76	84.72	0.93	0.87	0.85
Total	1.00000	. . .	. . .	. . .	101.0	95.8	93.8
Index number*..	. . .	. . .	. . .	. . .	101.0	95.8	93.8

* Formula (33.7).
Source of data: Table 33.1.

2. When a commodity or series is to be substituted for one formerly used, the relative for the "new" commodity may be spliced to the relative for the "old" commodity, using the former value weights.

3. The individual price or quantity relatives may be worth studying. Having computed the individual relatives, it is very simple to utilize them in constructing the index.

4. An index may be constructed by combining several previously constructed indexes, all of which have the same base.

5. When an index of cyclical fluctuations is to be constructed it is necessary to adjust each original series for trend and seasonal variation. Usually the adjustment is made by dividing *TCSI* by *TS*, obtaining *CI*, or cyclical-irregular *relatives*. The different series are thus also put in comparable form.

6. Indexes of plant efficiency, level of living, and the like, may be based on raw data which are not analogous to prices or quantities. Such data may take various forms, such as ratio of defectives to output, cost of production,

median number of years of schooling, and so on. Such series can be made comparable by expressing them as ratios to (or percentages of) some base.

Changing the Base of an Index

It may be desirable to change the base of an existing index for various reasons, including: (1) to make the base more recent; (2) to permit easy comparison with some date of special interest (such as entry of the United States into World War II); (3) to provide a better comparison with some other index or series of relatives which has a different base; (4) to splice two overlapping indexes together; (5) to construct a chain index.

Table 33.3—Changing Base of Consumer Price Index from 1947–49 to 1950

Year	Index number	
	1947–49 = 100	1950 = 100 (col. 2 ÷ 1.028)
(1)	(2)	(3)
1947	95.5	92.9
1948	102.8	100.0
1949	101.8	99.0
1950	102.8	100.0
1951	111.0	108.0
1952	113.5	110.4
1953	114.4	111.3
1954	114.8	111.7
1955	114.5	111.4
1956	116.2	113.0

Source of data: See Table 32.1.

Shifting to a more recent base. As an illustration of procedure, let us shift the consumer price index shown in Table 33.3 from its 1947–49 base to a 1950 base. This is accomplished by the simple device of dividing each of the index numbers of the original index by the index number for the new base year. Thus, the index number for 1950 was 102.8. If we divide each of the index numbers by 1.028, or multiply them by 1/1.028 = 0.97276, we obtain the index numbers shown in the last column of Table 33.3.

Splicing two overlapping indexes. In Table 32.6 an aggregative price index number was constructed, using 1953 as a base, with 1953 quantity weights. Now let us assume that we consider the 1953 weights to be outmoded, and we wish to use 1955 weights. Table 33.4 illustrates computation of the 1956 and 1957 index numbers with 1955 base and 1955 weights.

Table 33.4—Construction of Aggregative Price Index of Textile Fibers, with 1955 Base and 1955 Quantity Weights

Textile	q_{55}	p_{55}	p_{56}	p_{57}	$p_{55}q_{55}$	$p_{55}q_{56}$	$p_{55}q_{57}$
Cotton ...	4,384.2	0.349	0.348	0.340	1,530.1	1,525.7	1,490.6
Wool	428.2	1.421	1.371	1.675	608.5	587.1	717.2
Rayon ...	1,419.2	0.341	0.320	.298	483.9	454.1	422.9
Silk	7.2	4.594	4.486	4.484	33.1	32.3	32.3
Total ...	...	...	...	...	2,655.6	2,599.2	2,663.0
Index number .	...	...	...	...	100.0	97.9	100.3

Source of data: See Tables 32.2 and 32.3. The price data for 1957 are those of July, 1957.

We now have two indexes: index A from 1953 through 1955 with 1953 base and weights, and index B beginning 1955 with 1955 base and weights. There is one overlapping year, which is 1955. We wish to splice these two indexes together to form a continuous series. In Table 33.5 the two indexes are reconstructed from the total values of Tables 32.6 and 33.4. In column (6)

Table 33.5—Construction of Two Overlapping Indexes of Textile Fibers, and Splicing them Together

Year X	$p_X q_{53}$	Index A	$p_X q_{55}$	Index B	Spliced index	
					1953 = 100 (col. 5 × 0.9574)	1955 = 100 (col. 3 ÷ 0.9574)
(1)	(2)	(3)	(4)	(5)	(6)	(7)
1953	2,857.1	100.00	...	...	100.0	104.4
1954	2,884.3	100.95	...	...	101.0	105.4
1955	2,735.5	95.74	2,655.6	100.00	95.7	100.0
1956	...	...	2,599.2	97.88	93.7	97.8
1957	...	...	2,663.0	100.28	96.0	100.3

Index A. $\Sigma p_X q_{53}/\Sigma p_{53}q_{53}$.
Index B: $\Sigma p_X q_{55}/\Sigma p_{55}q_{55}$.
Source of data: Tables 32.6 and 33.4.

both indexes are put on a 1953 basis, by multiplying index B by the 1955 value for index A. In column (7) both indexes are put on a 1955 basis by dividing index A by the 1955 value for index A.

A procedure equivalent to that of Table 33.5 is followed whenever an index is revised. Such a revision usually involves not only changing the weights, but changing the list of commodities also.[2]

---

[2] Changing the list of commodities is of course a special case of changing weights. When a commodity is dropped its weight is changed from a positive quantity to zero; when a commodity is added its weight is changed from zero to a positive quantity.

Table 33.6—Construction of Link-Relative Index Numbers of Textile Fiber Prices, Using Average Quantities as Weights

Textile	$\bar{q}_{53,54}$	p_{53}	p_{54}	$p_{53}\bar{q}_{53,54}$	$p_{54}\bar{q}_{53,54}$
Cotton	4,323.1	0.338	0.350	1,461.2	1,513.1
Wool	446.8	1.729	1.706	772.5	762.2
Rayon	1,188.9	0.351	.340	417.3	404.2
Silk	5.9	5.295	4.920	31.2	29.0
Total	...	...	...	2,682.2	2,708.5
$P_{53,54}$	...	...	...	...	100.98

Textile	$\bar{q}_{54,55}$	p_{54}	p_{55}	$p_{54}\bar{q}_{54,55}$	$p_{55}\bar{q}_{54,55}$
Cotton	4,254.7	0.350	0.349	1,489.1	1,484.9
Wool	409.0	1.706	1.421	697.8	581.2
Rayon	1,287.0	0.340	0.341	437.6	438.9
Silk	6.8	4.920	4.594	33.5	31.2
Total	...	...	...	2,658.0	2,536.2
$P_{54,55}$	...	...	...	...	95.42

Textile	$\bar{q}_{55,56}$	p_{55}	p_{56}	$p_{55}\bar{q}_{55,56}$	$p_{56}\bar{q}_{55,56}$
Cotton	4,361.6	0.349	0.348	1,522.2	1,517.8
Wool	441.6	1.421	1.371	627.5	605.4
Rayon	1,310.2	0.341	0.320	446.8	419.3
Silk	7.4	4.594	4 486	34.0	33.2
Total	...	...	...	2,630.5	2,575.7
$P_{55,56}$	...	...	...	...	97.92

Source of data: Average quantities are computed from Table 32.3. Prices are from Table 32.2.

Link-relative index numbers	Computations	Chain index numbers
$P_{53,54} = 100.98$	....	$P_{53,54} = 101.0$
$P_{54,55} = 95.42$	$P_{53,54} \times P_{54,55} = 100.98 \times 0.9542 = 96.36$	$P_{53,55} = 96.4$
$P_{55,56} = 97.92$	$P_{53,55} \times P_{55,56} = 96.36 \times 97.92 = 94.36$	$P_{53,56} = 94.4$

*Chain index. Sometimes the list of commodities and the system of weights are revised each year. The procedure is similar to that just explained. A series of link-relative index numbers is constructed in which each member is expressed as a percentage of the preceding year. This procedure yields a set of figures showing year-to-year comparisons, and it is in such terms that the businessman often thinks. These link relatives, if desired, may then be chained back to a fixed base by *successive* multiplication. Since the object of the chain index is to obtain maximum year-to-year comparability, the weighting system should be strictly up-to-date. Possibly the best solution is to use the ideal index number formula for each link relative.

$$P_{X-1,X} = \sqrt{\frac{\Sigma p_X q_{X-1}}{\Sigma p_{X-1} q_{X-1}} \times \frac{\Sigma p_X q_X}{\Sigma p_{X-1} q_X}} \; .$$

A solution that gets almost the same result is to use as quantity weights the average quantities of the current and preceding year.

$$P_{X-1,X} = \frac{\Sigma p_X \bar{q}_{X,X-1}}{\Sigma p_{X-1} \bar{q}_{X,X-1}} \; .$$

This is the solution used in Table 33.6, where link-relative index numbers are constructed. The chain index numbers are easily obtained from the link relatives.

Although maximum comparability between successive years is obtained by a chain index, only the year following the fixed base is strictly comparable with that base. With the passage of time, involving many link relatives, the meaning of the chain index becomes increasingly doubtful. Another objection to the chain index is that if some types of relationships exist, not only will the chain index diverge more and more from an index with fixed weights, but it will diverge in a predictable direction from the "true" index. In other words, it will be biased.

*Tests of Index Numbers

There are two sometimes conflicting purposes in constructing index numbers. One purpose is to find the answer to a specific question. For instance, one question might be: "What is the cost this year as compared with 1955 of supporting this year's scale of living?" Another question might be: "What is the cost this year as compared with 1955 of supporting the actual scale of living enjoyed each year, but at 1955 prices?" (It is suggested that the student write down the formula for the index numbers that will answer each of these questions.) The appropriate question to ask is a matter of economics or business administration, rather than of statistics.

But often an index is to be used by many persons for many purposes. Thus a general-purpose index number is wanted: one that will answer many questions approximately, but no question exactly.[3] The formula for such

---

[3] Some people would say that the following is a general question: "How much has the price level increased since 1955?" Others regard it as a specific question.

an index number is to be judged, in the opinion of some authorities, by whether it meets certain mathematical tests. The apparently reasonable assumption is made that since an index number is computed from a group of commodities, the index number should behave in the same manner as any individual commodity. For instance, for any individual commodity:

$$(1) \quad \frac{p_1}{p_0} \times \frac{p_0}{p_1} = 1;$$

$$(2) \quad \frac{p_1}{p_0} \times \frac{q_1}{q_0} = \frac{p_1 q_1}{p_0 q_0} = v, \text{ or value relative.}$$

Therefore two analogous tests, the time reversal test and the factor reversal test, have been laid down.

Time reversal test. This test holds that an index number should work backward as well as forward; an index number for position 0 relative to position 1 (the backward index number) should be the *reciprocal* of the index number for position 1 relative to position 0 (the forward index number). The backward index number formula is derived from the forward index number formula by reversing the time subscripts (0 and 1) of the forward index number formula. Thus, if $\frac{\Sigma p_1 q_0}{\Sigma p_0 q_0}$ is the forward index number, $\frac{\Sigma p_0 q_1}{\Sigma p_1 q_1}$ is the backward index number. Obviously

$$\frac{\Sigma p_1 q_0}{\Sigma p_0 q_0} \times \frac{\Sigma p_0 q_1}{\Sigma p_1 q_1} \neq 1,$$

and $\frac{p_1 q_0}{p_0 q_0}$ does not meet the time reversal test.[4]

Factor reversal test. This test holds that the product of a price index number and the corresponding quantity index number should accurately measure relative total value:

$$P \times Q = \frac{\Sigma p_1 q_1}{\Sigma p_0 q_0} = V.$$

Where a price index is likely to be used as a deflator, obtaining $Q = V \div P$, a plausible argument can be made for this test. A quantity index number formula corresponding to a price index number formula is derived from the latter by interchanging the factors (p and q). Thus if $\frac{\Sigma p_1 q_0}{\Sigma p_0 q_0}$ is the price

---

[4] The "circular" test is an extension of the time reversal test. It says that if $P_{01} \times P_{12} \times \dots \times P_{k-1,k} \times P_{k0} = 1$, using the same method of construction for each link relative, then the circular test is met. Most people who believe in the time reversal test do not, however, believe in the circular test.

index number, $\dfrac{\Sigma\, q_1 p_0}{\Sigma\, q_0 p_0} = \dfrac{\Sigma\, p_0 q_1}{\Sigma\, p_0 q_0}$ is the quantity index number. Obviously

$$\frac{\Sigma\, p_1 q_0}{\Sigma\, p_0 q_0} \times \frac{\Sigma\, p_0 q_1}{\Sigma\, p_0 q_0} \neq \frac{\Sigma\, p_1 q_1}{\Sigma\, p_0 q_0},$$

and $\dfrac{\Sigma\, p_1 q_0}{\Sigma\, p_0 q_0}$ does not meet the factor reversal test.

There are several index number formulas which meet both tests, but only one is simple enough to justify serious consideration. This is the "ideal" index number, of which Irving Fisher was the leading advocate. As already stated,

$$P_{01} = \sqrt{\frac{\Sigma\, p_1 q_0}{\Sigma\, p_0 q_0} \times \frac{\Sigma\, p_1 q_1}{\Sigma\, p_0 q_1}},$$

If the p and q factors are reversed we obtain the ideal quantity index number

$$Q_{01} = \sqrt{\frac{\Sigma\, p_0 q_1}{\Sigma\, p_0 q_0} \times \frac{\Sigma\, p_1 q_1}{\Sigma\, p_1 q_0}}.$$

It is apparent that the product of these two index numbers is $\dfrac{\Sigma\, p_1 q_1}{\Sigma\, p_0 q_0}$, and that the ideal index number therefore meets the factor reversal test. If the time subscripts for the price index are interchanged we obtain

$$P_{10} = \sqrt{\frac{\Sigma\, p_0 q_1}{\Sigma\, p_1 q_1} \times \frac{\Sigma\, p_0 q_0}{\Sigma\, p_1 q_0}}.$$

It is again apparent that $P_{01} \times P_{10} = 1$, and that the ideal price index number therefore meets the time reversal test. It can be shown similarly that the ideal quantity index meets the time reversal test.

The chief objections to ideal index are: (1) it is laborious to compute; (2) current quantity data are often difficult to obtain; (3) it seems impossible to say specifically what it measures.

*Chapter 34

POLYNOMIAL TRENDS

In Chapter 14 the mathematical characteristics of polynomial equations were stated. These are summarized below through fourth degree.

First degree (straight line): $Y = a + bX$
    Constant first difference b
Second degree (parabola): $Y = a + bX + cX^2$
    Two directions of slope
    Constant second difference $2c$
Third degree (cubic): $Y = a + bX + cX^2 + dX^3$
    Three directions of slope are possible
    One point of inflection
    Constant third difference $6d$
Fourth degree (quartic): $Y = a + bX + cX^2 + dX^3 + eX^4$
    Four directions of slope are possible
    Two points of inflection
    Constant fourth difference $24e$

As the degree of equation increases one degree, one new term is added to the equation, one new direction of slope is possible, and there is one more point of inflection. For trend fitting it is seldom desirable to use a polynomial of higher degree than third.

In this chapter we shall explain the fitting of second-degree simple polynomials, and illustrate the use of a simplifying and labor-saving device, orthogonal polynomials, for second-degree and third-degree equations.

Second-degree Trend

As stated in the introduction to this chapter, a second-degree polynomial equation has the form

$$Y_X = a + bX + cX^2.$$

If n is odd, X takes the values $0, 1, 2, \ldots, (n-1)$.
If n is even, X takes the values $0, 2, 4, \ldots, 2(n-1)$.

In order to fit a second-degree curve one must have three normal equations, since there are three constants. The procedure followed for a straight line is extended for a second-degree curve: each of the first two equations receives a new term, and the third is obtained by multiplying by the coefficient of the third unknown, and summing. Thus, for the equation $Y_X = a + bX + cX^2$, we perform these operations,

I. $\Sigma [Y = a + bX + cX^2]$

II. $\Sigma [X(Y = a + bX + cX^2)]$

III. $\Sigma [X^2(Y = a + bX + cX^2)]$

and obtain

(34.1)
$$\begin{cases} \text{I.} \quad na + b\,\Sigma\,X + c\,\Sigma\,X^2 = \Sigma\,Y; \\ \text{II.} \quad a\,\Sigma\,X + b\,\Sigma\,X^2 + c\,\Sigma\,X^3 = \Sigma\,XY; \\ \text{III.} \quad a\,\Sigma\,X^2 + b\,\Sigma\,X^3 + c\,\Sigma\,X^4 = \Sigma\,X^2Y. \end{cases}$$

If, as usual, time-variable is in deviation form, $x = X - \bar{X}$, and the equation

$$Y_x = a + bx + cx^2$$

has these normal equations (since $\Sigma\,x = \Sigma\,x^3 = 0$)

(34.2)
$$\begin{cases} \text{I.} \quad na + c\,\Sigma\,x^2 = \Sigma\,Y; \\ \text{II.} \quad b\,\Sigma\,x^2 = \Sigma\,xY; \\ \text{III.} \quad a\,\Sigma\,x^2 + c\,\Sigma\,x^4 = \Sigma\,x^2Y. \end{cases}$$

It is apparent from equation II that the value of b is the same as for a straight line, but that to obtain a and c, normal equations I and III must be solved.[1]

For illustrative purposes we shall fit a second-degree trend to annual sales of Pittsburgh Plate Glass Company, 1947–1956.

From Table 34.1 we obtain our values for obtaining the trend constants.

$$b = \frac{\Sigma\,xY}{\Sigma\,x^2} = \frac{6,279.6}{330} - 19.0291.$$

I. $10a + 330c = 4,073.8.$

II. $330a + 19,338c = 139,121.8.$

Multiplying equation I by 33, which is $330 \div 10$, and subtracting from equation III, we solve for c.

I.$'$ $330a + 10,890c = 134,435.4$

III. $330a + 19,338c = 139,121.8$

III − I.$'$ $8,448c = 4,686.4$

$c = 0.55473$

---

[1] The values of a and c are not the same for the two equations,

$$Y_X = a + bX + cX^2, \quad \text{and}$$
$$Y_X = a + bx + cx^2,$$

because the time origin of the former is arbitrary, but usually the first year to which the equation is fitted; while the latter is always at the mean value of X, or mid-point in time, when no observations are missing.

Table 34.1—Sales of Pittsburgh Plate Glass Company, Sums of Powers and Sums of Products for Computing Second-degree Trend, and Trend Values, 1947–1956

(Sales are in millions of dollars.)

Year	x	x^2	x^4	Y	xY	x^2Y	Straight line trend $Y+bx$ $Y_{z(1)}$	Second-degree trend $a+bx+cx^2$		
								$a+bx$	cx^2	$Y_{z(2)}$
1947	−9	81	6,561	265.1	−2,385.9	21,473.1	236.12	217.81	44.93	262.74
1948	−7	49	2,401	283.1	−1,981.7	13,871.9	274.18	255.87	27.18	283.05
1949	−5	25	625	286.8	−1,434.0	7,170.0	312.23	293.93	13.87	307.80
1950	−3	9	81	339.4	−1,018.2	3,054.6	350.29	331.99	4.99	336.98
1951	−1	1	1	407.6	−407.6	407.6	388.35	370.04	0.55	370.59
1952	1	1	1	407.5	407.5	407.5	426.41	408.10	0.55	408.65
1953	3	9	81	457.1	1,371.3	4,113.9	464.47	446.16	4.99	451.15
1954	5	25	625	435.7	2,178.5	10,892.5	502.53	484.22	13.87	498.09
1955	7	49	2,401	586.9	4,108.3	28,758.1	540.58	522.28	27.18	549.46
1956	9	81	6,561	604.6	5,441.4	48,972.6	578.64	560.34	44.93	605.27
Total	0	330	19,338	4,073.8	6,279.6	139,121.8	4,073.8	3,890.74	183.04	4,073.8

Source of data: *Seventy-third Annual Report,* 1956, Pittsburgh Plate Glass Co.

The trend equations are:

$Y_{z(1)} = 407.380 + 19.0291x$;

$Y_{z(2)} = 389.074 + 19.0291x + 0.55473x^2$

The value of a is obtained by substituting the value of c in equation I.

I. $10a + (330)(0.055473) = 4,073.8$
     $10a = 4,073.8 - 183.0609 = 3,890.7391$
     $a = 389.07391.$

To check the solution of these equations, the values of a and c are now substituted in equation III.

III. $(330)(389.07391) + (19,338)(0.055473) = 139,121.8.$

**Chart 34.1—Sales of Pittsburgh Plate Glass Company, Linear
Trend, and Second-degree Trend**

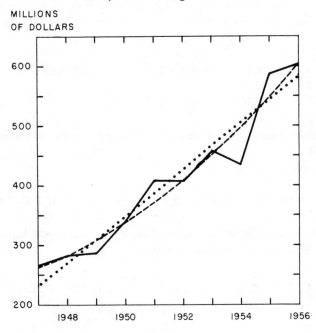

Source of data: Table 34.1.

The trend equation, therefore, is

$$Y_x = 389.074 + 19.0291x + 0.55473x^2.$$

This equation was used in obtaining the trend values of Table 34.1. Note that $\Sigma Y_x = \Sigma Y$ in this table, as was the case with a straight line.

Table 34.1 and Chart 34.1 show both the straight line trend and the second-degree trend. The equations are:[2]

Straight line: $Y_{x(1)} = 407.380 + 19.0291x.$

Second degree: $Y_{x(2)} = 389.074 + 19.0291x + 0.55473x^2.$

---

[2] The numeral in parentheses after subscript x in an equation indicates the degree of equation.

Notice that the values of a are not the same for the two equations. In the first equation, $a = \bar{Y}$, but in the second one it was necessary to solve simultaneous equations.

Changing units and shifting origin. If we wish to change the time units from $\frac{1}{2}$ year to 1 year, we substitute $2x$ for x on the right side of the equation.

$$Y_x = 389.074 + 19.0291(2x) + 0.55473(2x)^2;$$

$$Y_x = 389.074 + 38.0582x + 2.2189x^2.$$

Thus a is unchanged, b is multiplied by 2, and c is multiplied by 4.

If we wish to have the time origin at the first year of our data, we substitute $X - \bar{X} = X - 4.5$ for x in the last equation.

$$Y_X = 389.074 + 38.0582(X - 4.5) + (2.2189)(X - 4.5)^2;$$

$$Y_X = 262.745 + 18.088X + 2.2189X^2.$$

Note that the a-value for this equation is the same as the 1947 trend value of Table 31.1.

Both operations can be combined, if preferred.

$$Y_X = 389.074 + (19.0291)[2(X - 4.5)] + (0.55473)[2(X - 4.5)]^2.$$

Finally, if we wish to find the trend values for each month beginning with January 1947, another step is necessary.

$$Y_X = \frac{1}{12}\left[262.745 - (18.088)\frac{X - 5.5}{12} + (2.2189)\left(\frac{X - 5.5}{12}\right)^2\right],$$

which gives

$$Y_X = 21.243 + 0.11148X + 0.0012842X^2.$$

The reason for subtracting 5.5 is that the middle of January 1947 is 5.5 months earlier than the middle of the year 1947. The division by 12 within the brackets is because one month is one-twelfth of one year. The division by 12 outside the brackets is because monthly sales are one-twelfth of annual sales.

Orthogonal Polynomials

Use of simple polynomials is somewhat laborious for various reasons.

1. Each time the degree of the equation is increased, approximately half

of the trend constants must be recomputed. Thus, comparing[3]

$$Y_{x(1)} = a_1 + b_1 x \quad \text{with}$$
$$Y_{x(2)} = a_2 + b_2 x + c_2 x^2,$$

the values of b_1 and b_2 are the same, but the values of a_1 and a_2 are different. Now, comparing

$$Y_{x(2)} = a_2 + b_2 x + c_2 x^2 \quad \text{with}$$
$$Y_{x(3)} = a_3 + b_3 x + c_3 x^2 + d_3 x^3,$$

examination of the normal equations shows that $a_2 = a_3$ and $c_2 = c_3$, but $b_2 \neq b_3$.

2. Solving of simultaneous equations is required for all simple polynomial equations beyond a straight line.

3. The values of x^2, x^3, x^4, etc., become rather large when n is large, while the corresponding orthogonal polynomials t_1, t_2, t_3, etc., are typically rather small.

4. Testing the significance of simple polynomial trend constants is laborious. The greater simplicity and ease of testing orthogonal polynomial trend constants is considered by some to be their greatest advantage.

An orthogonal polynomial equation of degree s is of the type

$$Y_{t(s)} = \sum_{n=0}^{s} B_r t_r; \qquad \text{i.e.,}$$

(34.3) $$\qquad Y_{t(s)} = B_0 t_0 + B_1 t_1 + B_2 t_2 + \ldots + B_s t_s.$$

By definition, $t_0 = 1$ and $t_1 = x$. (The *numerical* values of x are 0, 1, 2, ..., if n is odd; and 1, 3, 5, ..., if n is even.) The t_r values are related to the x^r values in a manner explained in Appendix 7 of this book. The computation of the equation constants is extremely simple:

(34.4) $$\qquad B_r = \frac{\Sigma\, t_r Y}{\Sigma\, t_r^2}.$$

Thus,

$$B_0 = \frac{\Sigma\, t_0 Y}{\Sigma\, t_0^2} = \frac{\Sigma\, Y}{n} = \bar{Y};$$

$$B_1 = \frac{\Sigma\, t_1 Y}{\Sigma\, t_1^2}; \quad B_2 = \frac{\Sigma\, t_2 Y}{\Sigma\, t_2^2}; \quad B_3 = \frac{\Sigma\, t_3 Y}{\Sigma\, t_3^2}.$$

Another important advantage of orthogonal polynomials is their convenience in testing significance of the trend constants. The *net* amount of variation explained by any trend constant is

(34.5) $$\qquad \Sigma\, y_{t(r)}^2 = B_r \Sigma\, t_r Y.$$

---

[3] The numeral in parenthesis after subscript x in an equation indicates the degree of equation, as do the subscripts to a, b, and c.

Thus,[4]

$$\Sigma \, y_{t(1)}^2 = B_1 \, \Sigma \, t_1 \, Y;$$

$$\Sigma \, y_{t(2)}^2 = B_2 \, \Sigma \, t_2 \, Y;$$

$$\Sigma \, y_{t(3)}^2 = B_3 \, \Sigma \, t_3 \, Y.$$

Appendix 7 of this book gives values of t_r through $r = 3$, for values of n from 5 through 16. At the bottoms of the different columns are also shown values of $\Sigma \, t_r^2$, needed for computing values of B_r, and formulas for obtaining values of t_r from values of x^r. More extensive tables of orthogonal polynomials are readily available.[5]

Fitting a second-degree trend. As an illustration of polynomial trend fitting by use of orthogonal polynomial we shall again use the Pittsburgh Plate Glass Company data. Table 34.2 is self-contained, but we repeat the computation of the B_r below for the sake of clarity.

---

[4] The F test is used in testing significance, the *net* explained variance being divided by the residual variance. Using orthogonal polynomials:

$$F_1 = \frac{\Sigma \, y_{t(1)}^2}{[\Sigma \, y^2 - \Sigma \, y_{t(1)}^2] \div (n-2)} \, ;$$

$$F_2 = \frac{\Sigma \, y_{t(2)}^2}{[\Sigma \, y^2 - \Sigma \, y_{t(1)}^2 - \Sigma \, y_{t(2)}^2] \div (n-3)} \, ;$$

$$F_3 = \frac{\Sigma \, y_{t(3)}^2}{[\Sigma \, y^2 - \Sigma \, y_{t(1)}^2 - \Sigma \, y_{t(2)}^2 - \Sigma \, y_{t(3)}^2] \div (n-4)} \, .$$

In these equations, $\Sigma \, y^2 = \Sigma \, (Y - \bar{Y})^2 = \Sigma \, Y^2 - \bar{Y} \Sigma \, Y$. The number of degrees of freedom for each of the numerators is 1, so that net explained variance is the same as net explained variation. The number of degrees of freedom for each denominator is the quantity enclosed in the parentheses.

Using simple polynomial equations, in order to compute the net explained variation it is necessary to compute the *gross* explained variation for any degree of equation, and then subtract from that quantity the *gross* explained variation for the equation of one degree smaller. The gross explained variation is computed as follows:

First degree: $a_1 \, \Sigma Y + b_1 \, \Sigma \, xY - \bar{Y} \Sigma \, Y.$

Second degree: $a_2 \, \Sigma \, Y + b_2 \, \Sigma \, xY + c_2 \, \Sigma \, x^2 Y - \bar{Y} \Sigma \, Y.$

Third degree: $a_3 \, \Sigma \, Y + b_3 \, \Sigma \, xY + c_3 \, \Sigma \, x^2 Y + d_3 \, \Sigma \, x^3 Y - \bar{Y} \Sigma \, Y.$

[5] R. A. Fisher and F. Yates, *Statistical Tables for Biological, Agricultural and Medical Research*, Oliver and Boyd Ltd., Edinburgh, 1949, give values through $r = 5$ and $n = 52$. The symbol ξ' is used instead of t. E. S. Pearson and H. O. Hartley, *Biometrika Tables for Statisticians*, Vol. I, Cambridge University Press, 1954, give values through $r = 6$ and $n = 52$. The symbol ϕ is used instead of t.

$$B_0 = \frac{\Sigma\,Y}{n} = \frac{4,073.8}{10} = 407.38.$$

$$B_1 = \frac{\Sigma\,t_1 Y}{\Sigma\,t_1^2} = \frac{6,279.6}{330} = 19.029\,;$$

$$B_2 = \frac{\Sigma\,t_2 Y}{\Sigma\,t_2^2} = \frac{585.8}{132} = 4.438.$$

The trend equation is

$$Y_{t(2)} = 407.38 + 19.029t_1 + 4.438t_2.$$

Table 31.2 shows the trend values not only for this equation, but also for the straight line equation

$$Y_{t(1)} = 407.38 + 19.029t_1.$$

The trend values are the same as obtained by use of simple polynomials (compare with Table 34.1), but the computation is much easier. Note especially:

1. It was not necessary to recompute B_0 when the degree of equation was increased from straight line to second degree.

2. It was not necessary to solve simultaneous equations.

Table 34.2—Sales of Pittsburg Plate Glass Company, and Computation of
Trend Values by Use of Orthogonal Polynomials, 1947–1956
(Sales are in millions of dollars.)

Year	t_1	t_2	Sales Y	$t_1 Y$	$t_2 Y$	$Y_{t(1)}$ $B_0 + B_1 t_1$	$B_2 t_2$	$Y_{t(2)}$ $Y_{t(1)} + B_2 t_2$
1947	−9	6	265.1	−2,385.9	1,590.6	236.12	26.63	262.75
1948	−7	2	283.1	−1,981.7	566.2	274.18	8.88	283.06
1949	−5	−1	286.8	−1,434.0	−286.8	312.24	−4.44	307.80
1950	−3	−3	339.4	−1,018.2	−1,018.2	350.29	−13.31	336.98
1951	−1	−4	407.6	−407.6	−1,630.4	388.35	−17.75	370.60
1952	1	−4	407.5	407.5	−1,630.0	426.41	−17.75	408.66
1953	3	−3	457.1	1,371.3	−1,371.3	464.47	−13.31	451.16
1954	5	−1	435.7	2,178.5	−435.7	502.52	−4.44	498.08
1955	7	2	586.9	4,108.3	1,173.8	540.58	8.88	549.46
1956	9	6	604.6	5,441.1	3,627.6	578.64	26.63	605.27
Sum	0	0	4,073.8	6,279.6	585.8	4,073.8	0.0	4,073.8
$\Sigma\,t_r^2$	330	132	...	...	...	...	...	...
B_r	...	...	407.38	19.029	4.438	...	...	...

Source of data: Table 34.1. Orthogonal polynomials are from Appendix 7.
The trend equation is $Y_{t(2)} = 407.38 + 19.029t_1 + 4.438t_2.$

Fitting a third-degree trend. The fitting process is no more complicated than for a second-degree trend. For an illustration we use miles of railroad track operated in the United States, 1905–1955, at 5-year intervals. Computation of the constants for the trend equations is in Table 34.3. For the B_r values we have

$$B_0 = \frac{\Sigma \, Y}{n} = \frac{4,315}{11} = 392.272;$$

$$B_1 = \frac{\Sigma \, t_1 Y}{\Sigma \, t_1^2} = \frac{616}{110} = 5.600;$$

$$B_2 = \frac{\Sigma \, t_2 Y}{\Sigma \, t_2^2} = \frac{-2,542}{858} = -2.9627;$$

$$B_3 = \frac{\Sigma \, t_3 Y}{\Sigma \, t_3^2} = \frac{2,111}{4,290} = 0.4921.$$

Table 34.3—Miles of Railroad Track Operated, at 5-Year Intervals, 1905–1955, and Computation of Constants for Third-degree Trend Equation, Using Orthogonal Polynomials

(*Y*-values are in thousands of miles.)

Year	t_1	t_2	t_3	Y	$t_1 Y$	$t_2 Y$	$t_3 Y$
1905	−5	15	−30	307	−1,535	4,605	−9,210
1910	−4	6	6	352	−1,408	2,112	2,112
1915	−3	−1	22	391	−1,173	−391	8,602
1920	−2	−6	23	407	−814	−2,442	9,361
1925	−1	−9	14	418	−418	−3,762	5,852
1930	0	−10	0	430	0	−4,300	0
1935	1	−9	−14	419	419	−3,771	−5,866
1940	2	−6	−23	406	812	−2,436	−9,338
1945	3	−1	−22	398	1,194	−398	−8,756
1950	4	6	−6	396	1,584	2,376	−2,376
1955	5	15	30	391	1,955	5,865	11,730
Sum	0	0	0	4,315	616	−2,542	2,111
$\Sigma \, t_r^2$ or							
B_r	110	858	4,290	392.272	5.6000	−2.9627	0.4921

Source of data: Association of American Railroads, *A Chronology of American Railroads*, 1957, p. 8.
The trend equation is $Y_{t(3)} = 392.272 + 5.6000t_1 - 2.9627t_2 + 0.4921t_3$.

The trend equations are therefore as follows.

Straight line: $\quad Y_{t(1)} = 392.272 + 5.600t_1.$

Second degree: $\quad Y_{t(2)} = 392.272 + 5.600t_1 - 2.9627t_2.$

Third degree: $\quad Y_{t(3)} = 392.272 + 5.600t_1 - 2.9627t_2 + 0.4921t_3.$

Notice again that there are no simultaneous equations to be solved, and no trend constants to be recomputed as the degree of equation is increased. With simple polynomials there would be considerable computational labor.[6]

Computation of the trend values is shown in Table 34.4. Notice that the different terms in the equation (B_1t_1, B_2t_2, and B_3t_3) each total zero over

Table 34.4—Computation of Third-degree Polynomial Trend for Miles of All Track Operated, 1905–1955, Using Orthogonal Polynomials
(*Y*-values are in thousands of miles.)

Year	B_1t_1	$Y_{t(1)}$ $B_0 + B_1t_1$	B_2t_2	$Y_{t(2)}$ $Y_{t(1)} + B_2t_2$	B_3t_3	$Y_{t(3)}$ $Y_{t(2)} + B_3t_3$
1905	−28.000	364.27	−44.440	319.83	−14.763	305.07
1910	−22.400	369.87	−17.776	352.10	2.953	355.05
1915	−16.800	375.47	−2.963	378.44	10.826	389.26
1920	−11.200	381.07	−17.776	398.85	11.318	410.17
1925	−5.600	386.67	−26.664	413.34	6.889	420.23
1930	0.000	392.27	−29.627	421.90	0.00	421.90
1935	5.600	397.87	−26.664	424 54	−6.889	417.65
1940	11.200	403.47	−17.776	421.25	−11.318	409.93
1945	16.800	409.07	−2.963	412.04	−10.826	401.21
1950	22.400	414.67	−17.776	396.90	−2.953	393.94
1955	28.000	420.27	−44.440	375.83	14.763	390.60
Total	0.000	4,315.0	0.00	4,315.0	0.00	4,315.0

Source: B_r values are computed in Table 34.3.
The trend equation is $Y_t = 392.272 + 5.600t_1 - 2.9627t_2 + 0.4921t_3$. Values of t_r are given in Table 34.3.

the n observations. Also, in computing successively $Y_{t(1)}$, $Y_{t(2)}$, and $Y_{t(3)}$ there is no recomputing of trend values; the new term is just added on. Thus,

$$Y_{t(1)} = B_0 + B_1t_1;$$
$$Y_{t(2)} = Y_{t(1)} + B_2t_2;$$
$$Y_{t(3)} = Y_{t(2)} + B_3t_3.$$

---

[6] More specifically, the computations required are as follows.

Straight line: $a_1 = \dfrac{\Sigma Y}{n}$;

$$b_1 = \frac{\Sigma xY}{\Sigma x^2}$$

Second degree: $b_2 = b_1$;

$$\begin{cases} na_2 + c_2 \Sigma x^2 = \Sigma Y; \\ a_2 \Sigma x^2 + c_2 \Sigma x^4 = \Sigma x^2 Y \end{cases}$$

Third degree: $a_3 = a_2$;

$c_3 = c_2$;

$$\begin{cases} b_3 \Sigma x^2 + d_3 \Sigma x^4 = \Sigma x^3 Y; \\ b_3 \Sigma x^4 + d_3 \Sigma x^6 = \Sigma x^4 Y. \end{cases}$$

With simple polynomials there would be a considerable amount of recomputation to obtain all three trend equations. Of course it is not necessary to find the values of $Y_{t(1)}$ and $Y_{t(2)}$ in order to find the values of $Y_{t(3)}$, for $Y_{t(3)} = B_0 + B_1t_1 + B_2t_2 + B_3t_3$.

In Chart 34.2 the data, and trends of first, second, and third degree are shown. By looking at the chart we can get some idea of when our equation

Chart 34.2—Miles of Railroad Track Operated, and Polynomial
Trends, 1905–1955

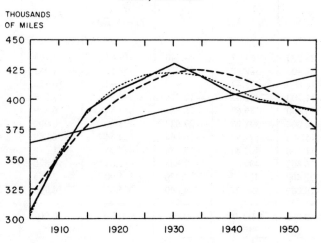

Source of data: Tables 34.3 and 34.4.

is of a high enough degree to be a satisfactory representation of the trend. We can also test the significance of B_1, B_2, and B_3, in that order.

The nature of orthogonal polynomials. Orthogonal polynomials are, as the name indicates, polynomials.[7] Consider the case where $n = 7$, Table 34.5.

Table 34.5—Orthogonal Polynomials
Through Third Degree for $n = 7$

t_0	t_1	t_2	t_3
1	−3	5	−1
1	−2	0	1
1	−1	−3	1
1	0	−4	0
1	1	−3	−1
1	2	0	−1
1	3	5	1

---

[7] A computational formula for computing values of t_r is given in Appendix 7. It is interesting to note that x^2 − mean value of $x^2 = t_2$ when n is odd, and is equal to $4t_2$ when n is even.

The values of t_0 are constant, the first differences of the t_1 values are constant, the second differences of the t_2 values are constant, and the third differences of the t_3 values are constant.

As can be seen $t_0 = 1$ and $t_1 = x$. That $\Sigma\, t_1 = \Sigma\, t_2 = \Sigma\, t_3 = 0$ can easily be verified. The polynomials are called orthogonal because they are uncorrelated; the sum of each of the cross-products is zero:

$$\Sigma\, t_0 t_1 = \Sigma\, t_0 t_2 = \Sigma\, t_0 t_3 = \Sigma\, t_1 t_2 = \Sigma\, t_1 t_3 = \Sigma\, t_2 t_3 = 0.$$

Conversion of orthogonal polynomial equations into simple polynomial equations. In Table 34.2 we obtained the orthogonal polynomial equation

$$Y_{t(2)} = 407.38 + 19.029 t_1 + 4.438 t_2.$$

When $n = 10$, we find from Appendix 7 that

$$t_2 = \frac{1}{8} x^2 - \frac{33}{8} = 0.125 x^2 - 4.125.$$

Substituting into the orthogonal polynomial equation:

$$Y_{x(2)} = 407.38 + 19.029 x + (4.438)(0.125 x^2 - 4.125);$$

$$Y_{x(2)} = 389.07 + 19.029 x + 0.55475 x^2.$$

As a check let us compute the 1956 trend value.

$$Y_{x(2)} = 389.07 + (19.029)(9) + (0.55475)(81) = 605.27.$$

This agrees with Tables 34.1 and 34.2.

In Table 34.3 we obtained the orthogonal polynomial equation

$$Y_{t(3)} = 392.272 + 5.6000 t_1 - 2.9627 t_2 + 0.4921 t_3.$$

When $n = 11$, we find from Appendix 7:

$$t_2 = x^2 - 10;$$

$$t_3 = \frac{5}{6} x^3 - \frac{89}{6} x = 0.8333 x^3 - 14.8333 x.$$

Substituting into the orthogonal polynomial equation:

$$Y_x = 392.272 + 5.6000 x - (2.9627)(x^2 - 10) \\ + (0.4921)(0.8333 x^3 - 14,8333 x);$$

$$Y_x = 421.899 - 1.699 x - 2.9627 x^2 + 0.4101 x^3.$$

As a check let us compute the 1955 trend value.

$$Y_x = 421.899 - (1.699)(5) - (2.9627)(25) + (0.4101)(125) = 390.60$$

This agrees with Table 34.4.

It will be recalled that the values of x are 5 years apart. If we wish trend values for each year, conversion of the equation is very simple. We merely substitute $x/5$ for x.

$$Y_x = 421.899 - 1.699\left(\frac{x}{5}\right) - 2.9627\left(\frac{x}{5}\right)^2 + 0.4101\left(\frac{x}{5}\right)^3;$$

$$Y_x = 421.899 - 0.3398x - 0.11851x^2 + 0.0032808x^3.$$

Using this equation, the 1955 trend value is

$$Y_x = 421.899 - (0.3398)(25) - (0.11851)(625)$$
$$+ (0.003281)(15,625) = 390.60.$$

This agrees with Table 34.4.

Extrapolation. In order to extrapolate, two alternative procedures are possible. We may first convert our orthogonal polynomial equation into a simple polynomial equation and extrapolate in the usual manner. The other procedure is to use the appropriate formulas at the bottoms of the columns of Appendix 7, and obtain the necessary polynomials.

An Appraisal of Polynomial Trends

Polynomial trends are simple to fit, and can be extended to any degree. As the degree of equation is larger the variation around the trend line gets smaller; i.e., the quantity $\Sigma (Y - Y_X)^2$ gets smaller. However, the number of degrees of freedom declines by one every time an additional term is added to the equation. If there are as many constants in the equation as there are observations, the trend will coincide with every point, but the trend equation will be meaningless.

Polynomial equations lend themselves to labor-saving devices such as orthogonal polynomials.

Polynomial equations often fit the data well within the range of the data. However, it is usually impossible to find any logical basis for a polynomial equation. This will perhaps seem obvious when we note that a straight line or a third-degree trend will, upon extension, become negative in one direction and increase without limit in the other direction. Second- and fourth-degree trends will increase or decrease without limit at both ends. On the other hand, most economic time series can not have negative values, and tend to reach an upper or lower limit in one or both directions.

*Chapter 35

MULTIPLE AND PARTIAL CORRELATION

One method of reducing the magnitude of the error of estimate and increasing the magnitude of the correlation coefficient is to use not one, but two or more, independent variables in the estimating equation. Thus, tensile strength could be estimated on the basis of hardness and specific gravity; *Holiday* circulation per 1,000 families by counties could be estimated from retail sales per family and per cent urban.

The methods used in this chapter are extensions of the methods used in simple correlation, and anyone who has mastered that subject should have little difficulty with multiple and partial correlation. The notation we shall use is that of Chapter 27, pages 412-413, since the X and Y notation is not sufficiently flexible for our purposes. A review of that section is recommended at this point. However, a brief summary is given below. Note that in each case the parentheses, when used, means "explained by" while the decimal point always means "unexplained by."

Estimating equation:

$$x_{1(2)} = b_{12}x_2, \quad \text{and}$$

$$X_{1(2)} = a_{12} + b_{12}X_2.$$

Computational formulas for estimating equation:

$$b_{12} = \frac{\Sigma\, x_1 x_2}{\Sigma\, x_2^2}\,;$$

$$a_{12} = \bar{X}_1 - b_{12}\bar{X}_2.$$

Measures of variation:

Total $\quad\quad \Sigma\, x_1^2 \ = \Sigma\, X_1^2 - (\Sigma\, \bar{X}_1)^2/n;$

Explained $\quad \Sigma\, x_{1(2)}^2 = b_{12}\, \Sigma\, x_1 x_2;$

Unexplained $\quad \Sigma\, x_{1.2}^2 = \Sigma\, x_1^2 - \Sigma\, x_{1(2)}^2.$

Estimated standard error of estimate:

$$s_{1.2} = \sqrt{\frac{\Sigma\, x_{1.2}^2}{n-2}}.$$

525

Coefficient of correlation:

$$r_{12} = \sqrt{\frac{\Sigma x_{1(2)}^2}{\Sigma x_1^2}} \, .$$

Variance ratio for test of significance:

$$F = \frac{\Sigma x_{1(2)}^2 \div (m-1)}{\Sigma x_{1.2}^2 \div (n-m)} \, ,$$

where m is the number of constants in the estimating equation.

A Three-variable Illustration

In this section we shall use an illustration from the field of personnel testing, the ultimate object of which is to enable management to discriminate among applicants for employment as to their degree of aptitude for specific jobs.[1]

A peg-board or manual dexterity test, and a copying or finger-dexterity test was administered to each of 51 aircraft riveter trainees at San Diego, California. The statistical problem is how to weight these separate tests and thus combine them into a battery of tests which is in closest agreement with a suitable criterion. In this case, the criterion is an objective test, the number of rivets set correctly per minute. Our variables, then, are:

Dependent variable:

1. Ability to set rivets;

Independent variables:

2. Manual dexterity score;
3. Finger-dexterity score.

The values of all three variables are recorded in Table 35.1, and indicate achievement per unit of time.

---

[1] Correlation analysis is used a great deal in developing tests of various kinds. A test should be reliable. Reliability results from the selection of items that measure the same thing, and by having a sufficiently large number of items in the test. For example, if there are a large number of questions, and the results from the odd-numbered questions and the even-numbered questions are highly correlated, the test will be reliable. A test should also be valid, measuring what it purports to measure. If the correlation with a suitable criterion is sufficiently high, the test is valid. Both reliability and validity of a test can be improved by item analysis. The use of correlation in test construction is more fully treated in F. E. Croxton and D. J. Cowden, *Practical Business Statistics*, 2d ed., Prentice-Hall, Inc., Englewood Cliffs, N. J. 1948, pp. 297–298. A more detailed exposition is given in J. P. Guilford, *Fundamental Statistics in Psychology and Education*, McGraw-Hill Book Co., Inc., New York, 1942, Chapter XIV.

Table 35.1—Data for Multiple Correlation of Manual-dexterity and Finger-dexterity Score with Criterion

independent variables

Trainee number	Criterion X_1 *(Dependent)*	Manual dexterity X_2	Finger dexterity X_3
1	230	135	107
2	81	93	67
3	100	108	81
4	212	138	93
5	216	123	81
6	156	116	86
7	201	119	86
8	194	112	96
9	164	128	80
10	166	116	86
11	146	125	78
12	196	114	89
13	202	128	84
14	203	129	80
15	201	125	99
16	195	120	86
17	180	126	92
18	174	136	95
19	120	104	82
20	198	116	76
21	189	112	80
22	184	109	85
23	174	113	75
24	168	113	87
25	143	104	69
26	131	103	65
27	130	125	84
Sum ...	4,654	3,190	2,269
Mean ...	170.370	118.148	84.037
Product of sums.	21,659,716 14,846,260 10,559,926	14,846,260 10,176,100 7,238,110	10,559,926 7,238,110 5,148,361
ΣX_j $\bar{X}_j$	ΣX_1 $\bar{X}_1$	ΣX_2 $\bar{X}_2$	ΣX_3 $\bar{X}_3$
$\Sigma X_1 \Sigma X_j$ $\Sigma X_2 \Sigma X_j$ $\Sigma X_3 \Sigma X_j$	$(\Sigma X_1)^2$ $\Sigma X_2 \Sigma X_1$ $\Sigma X_3 \Sigma X_1$	$\Sigma X_1 \Sigma X_2$ $(\Sigma X_2)^2$ $\Sigma X_3 \Sigma X_2$	$\Sigma X_1 \Sigma X_3$ $\Sigma X_2 \Sigma X_3$ $(\Sigma X_3)^2$

Source: War Manpower Commission, courtesy of C. L. Shartle, Chief, Division of Occupational Analysis and Manning Tables.

Table 35.2—Computation of Values for Multiple Correlation of Manual-dexterity and Finger-dexterity Scores with Criterion

Trainee	X_1^2	$X_1 X_2$	$X_1 X_3$	X_2^2	$X_2 X_3$	X_3^2
1	52,900	31,050	24,610	18,225	14,445	11,449
2	6,561	7,533	5,427	8,649	6,231	4,489
3	10,000	10,800	8,100	11,664	8,748	6,561
4	44,944	29,256	19,716	19,044	12,834	8,649
5	46,656	26,568	17,496	15,129	9,963	6,561
6	24,336	18,096	13,416	13,456	9,976	7,396
7	40,401	23,919	17,286	14,161	10,234	7,306
8	37,636	21,728	18,624	12,544	10,752	9,216
9	26,896	20,992	13,120	16,384	10,240	6,400
10	27,556	19,256	14,276	13,456	9,976	7,396
11	21,316	18,250	11,388	15,625	9,750	6,084
12	38,416	22,344	17,444	12,996	10,146	7,921
13	40,804	25,856	16,968	16,384	10,752	7,056
14	41,209	26,187	16,240	16,641	10,320	6,400
15	40,401	25,125	19,899	15,625	12,375	9,801
16	38,025	23,400	16,770	14,400	10,320	7,396
17	32,400	22,680	16,560	15,876	11,592	8,464
18	30,276	23,644	16,530	18,496	12,920	9,025
19	14,400	12,480	9,840	10,816	8,528	6,724
20	39,204	22,968	15,048	13,456	8,816	5,776
21	35,721	21,168	15,120	12,544	8,960	6,400
22	33,856	20,056	15,640	11,881	9,265	7,225
23	30,276	19,662	13,050	12,769	8,475	5,625
24	28,224	18,984	14,616	12,769	9,831	7,569
25	20,449	14,872	9,867	10,816	7,176	4,761
26	17,161	13,493	8,515	10,609	6,695	4,225
27	16,900	16,250	10,920	15,625	10,500	7,056
Sum of squares or products ..	836,924	556,637	396,486	380,040	269,820	193,021
Correction term	802,211.70	549,861.48	391,108.37	376,892.59	268,078.15	190,680.04
Variation or co-variation	34,712.30	6,775.52	5,377.63	3,147.41	1,741.85	2,340.96
$\Sigma X_i X_j$	ΣX_1^2	$\Sigma X_1 X_2$	$\Sigma X_1 X_3$	ΣX_2^2	$\Sigma X_2 X_3$	ΣX_3^2
$\dfrac{\Sigma X_i \, \Sigma X_j}{n}$	$\dfrac{(\Sigma X_1)^2}{n}$	$\dfrac{\Sigma X_1 \, \Sigma X_2}{n}$	$\dfrac{\Sigma X_1 \, \Sigma X_3}{n}$	$\dfrac{(\Sigma X_2)^2}{n}$	$\dfrac{\Sigma X_2 \, \Sigma X_3}{n}$	$\dfrac{(\Sigma X_3)^2}{n}$
$\Sigma x_i x_j$	Σx_1^2	$\Sigma x_1 x_2$	$\Sigma x_1 x_3$	Σx_2^2	$\Sigma x_2 x_3$	Σx_3^2

Source: Table 35.1.

Tables 35.1 and 35.2 show the computation of the measures of variation and co-variation required for our problem. A symbolic statement of the entries at the bottoms of these two tables is given also.[2]

---

[2] An internal check on the accuracy of computations is desirable. For each row of the check table on p. 530, $X_T = X_1 + X_2 + X_3$. Thus, for the first row $230 + 135 + 107 = 472$. The entries at the bottom of the X_T row are the sum, mean, and squared sum of the individual X_T values. A check is provided, also, for the sums, means, and squares and products of sums of Table 35.1, as well as for sums of squares and sums of products, correction terms, and measures of variation, and co-variation of Table 35.2.

Sums:

$$\Sigma X_1 + \Sigma X_2 + \Sigma X_3 = \Sigma X_T;$$

$$4{,}654 + 3{,}190 + 2{,}269 = 10{,}113.$$

Means:

$$\bar{X}_1 + \bar{X} + \bar{X}_3 = \bar{X}_T;$$

$$172.370 + 118.148 + 84.037 = 374.555.$$

The discrepancy in the last digit is due to rounding error.

Squares and products of sums:

This check is obtained by expanding $(\Sigma X_1 + \Sigma X_2 + \Sigma X_3)^2$, which results in

$$2(\Sigma X_1 \Sigma X_2 + \Sigma X_1 \Sigma X_3 + \Sigma X_2 \Sigma X_3) + (\Sigma X_1)^2 + (\Sigma X_2)^2 + (\Sigma X_3)^2 = (\Sigma X_T)^2;$$

$$2(14{,}846{,}260 + 10{,}599{,}926 + 7{,}238{,}110) + 21{,}659{,}716 + 10{,}176{,}100 + 5{,}148{,}261 =$$

$$102{,}272{,}769.$$

Sums of squares and sums of products:

This check is obtained by expanding $\Sigma (X_1 + X_2 + X_3)^2$. The expansion gives

$$2(\Sigma X_1 X_2 + \Sigma X_1 X_3 + \Sigma X_2 X_3) + \Sigma X_1^2 + \Sigma X_2^2 + \Sigma X_3^2 = \Sigma X_T^2;$$

$$2(556{,}637 + 396{,}486 + 269{,}820) + 836{,}924 + 380{,}040 + 193{,}021 = 3{,}855{,}871.$$

This check is also applicable for each row of Table 35.2. For any row, $2(X_1 X_2 + X_1 X_3 + X_2 X_3) + X_1^2 + X_2^2 + X_3^2 = X_T^2$. Thus for the first row, $2(31{,}050 + 24{,}610 + 14{,}445) + 52{,}900 + 18{,}225 + 11{,}449 = 222{,}784$. The applicability of the check, row by row permits one to locate any possible error without recomputing each square or product. If one wishes, he may make partial totals for groups of rows, and prove the different sections of the table separately.

Correction terms:

$$2\left(\frac{\Sigma X_1 \Sigma X_2}{n} + \frac{\Sigma X_1 \Sigma X_3}{n} + \frac{\Sigma X_2 \Sigma X_3}{n}\right) + \frac{(\Sigma X_1)^2}{n} + \frac{(\Sigma X_2)^2}{n} + \frac{(\Sigma X_3)^2}{n} = \frac{(\Sigma X_T)^2}{n};$$

$$2(549{,}861.48 + 391.108.37 + 268{,}078.51) + 802{,}211.70 + 376.892.59 + 190{,}680.04$$

$$= \frac{(10{,}113)^2}{27} = 3{,}787{,}880.33.$$

Variation and covariation:

$$2(\Sigma x_1 x_2 + \Sigma x_1 x_3 + \Sigma x_2 x_3) + \Sigma x_1^2 + \Sigma x_2^2 + \Sigma x_3^2 = \Sigma X_T^2 - \frac{(\Sigma X_T)^2}{n} = \Sigma x_T^2;$$

$$2(6{,}775.52 + 5{,}337.63 + 1{,}741.85) + 34{,}712.30 + 3{,}147.41 + 2{,}340.96$$

$$= 3{,}855{,}871 - 3{,}787{,}880.33 = 67{,}990.67$$

Check Table

X_T	X_T^2
472	222,784
241	58,081
289	83,521
443	196,249
420	176,400
358	128,164
406	164,836
402	161,604
372	138,384
368	135,424
349	121,801
399	159,201
414	171,396
412	169,744
425	180,625
401	160,801
398	158,404
405	164,025
306	93,636
390	152,100
381	145,161
378	142,884
362	131,044
368	135,424
316	99,856
299	89,401
339	114,921

$\Sigma X_T = 10{,}113$ $\Sigma X_T^2 = 3{,}855{,}871$

$\bar{X}_T = 374.556$ $\dfrac{(\Sigma X_T)^2}{n} = 3{,}787{,}890.33$

$(\Sigma X_T)^2 = 102{,}272.769$ $\Sigma x_T^2 = 67{,}990.67$

Multiple estimating equation. The estimating equation is

(35.1) $$X_{1(23)} = a_{1(23)} + b_{12.3}X_2 + b_{13.2}X_3.$$

In this equation $a_{1(23)}$ is the computed value $X_{1(23)}$ of variable 1 when X_2 and X_3 are each zero. Since $X_{1(23)} = \bar{X}_1$ when $X_2 = \bar{X}_2$ and $X_3 = \bar{X}_3$, the equation in deviation form is

(35.2) $$x_{1(23)} = b_{12.3}x_2 + b_{13.2}x_3.$$

The statistic $b_{12.3}$ refers to the amount of change in variable 1 which is associated with a unit change in variable 2 when variable 3 is held constant. It is an estimate of the parameter $B_{12.3}$, which is the value of B_{12} for all observations in the population having the same value for variable 3. Similarly,

$b_{13.2}$ refers to the amount of change in variable 1 which is associated with a unit change in variable 3, when variable 2 is held constant. The way in which we hold a variable constant is to adjust, by subtraction, for its affect. Just as

$$b_{12} = \frac{\Sigma\, x_1 x_2}{\Sigma\, x_2^2} \quad \text{and} \quad b_{13} = \frac{\Sigma\, x_1 x_3}{\Sigma\, x_3^2},$$

so[3]

$$b_{12.3} = \frac{\Sigma\, x_{1.3} x_{2.3}}{\Sigma\, x_{2.3}^2} \quad \text{and} \quad b_{13.2} = \frac{\Sigma\, x_{1.2} x_{3.2}}{\Sigma\, x_{3.2}^2},$$

where $x_{1.3}$, $x_{2.3}$, $x_{1.2}$, and $x_{3.2}$ are unexplained deviations. For example, $x_{1.3} = x_1 - x_{1(3)}$. However, we can avoid computing the n individual values of $x_{1.3}$, $x_{2.3}$, $x_{1.2}$, and $x_{3.2}$ by various devices that will be indicated.

Normal equations.[4] The normal equations for equation (35.1) are:

(35.3)
$$\begin{cases} (1)\ Na_{1(23)} + b_{12.3}\, \Sigma\, X_2 + b_{13.2}\, \Sigma\, X_3 = \Sigma\, X_1; \\ (2)\ a_{1(23)}\, \Sigma\, X_2 + b_{12.3}\, \Sigma\, X_2^2 + b_{13.2}\, \Sigma\, X_2 X_3 = \Sigma\, X_1 X_2; \\ (3)\ a_{1(23)}\, \Sigma\, X_3 + b_{12.3}\, \Sigma\, X_2 X_3 + b_{13.2}\, \Sigma\, X_3^2 = \Sigma\, X_1 X_3. \end{cases}$$

For equation (35.2) the normal equations are,

(35.4)
$$\begin{cases} (2)\ b_{12.3}\, \Sigma\, x_2^2 + b_{13.2}\, \Sigma\, x_2 x_3 = \Sigma\, x_1 x_2; \\ (3)\ b_{12.3}\, \Sigma\, x_2 x_3 + b_{13.2}\, \Sigma\, x_3^2 = \Sigma\, x_1 x_3. \end{cases}$$

The b coefficients have the same meaning and same numerical value whether the equation is in original form or in deviation form. Furthermore, if we divide both sides of normal equation (1) by n we obtain

(35.5)
$$a_{1(23)} = \bar{X}_1 - b_{12.3}\bar{X}_2 - b_{13.2}\bar{X}_3.$$

If we substitute in normal equations (35.4) the values for variation and co-variation shown at the bottom of Table 35.2 we obtain

(2) $3{,}147.41 b_{12.3} + 1{,}741.85 b_{13.2} = 6{,}775.52;$

(3) $1{,}741.85 b_{12.3} + 2{,}340.96 b_{13.2} = 5{,}377.62.$

If we divide equation (2) by 3,147.41 and then multiply it by 1,741.85, or else multiply it by $0.5534233 = 1{,}741.85/3{,}147.41$, we have

(2) $1{,}741.85 b_{12.3} + 963.98 b_{13.2} = 3{,}749.73.$

---

[3] This is the method of computation explicitly used in the abbreviated Doolittle method. See Dudley J. Cowden, "Correlation Concepts and the Doolittle Solution," *Journal of the American Statistical Association*, Vol. 38, September, 1943, p. 330.

[4] The procedural rules of footnote 3, Chapter 24, apply here.

This permits us to subtract normal equation (2) from normal equation (3), obtaining an equation with only one unknown. From this equation $b_{13.2}$ is readily computed.

(3) $1,741.85b_{12.3} + 2,340.96b_{13.2} = 5,377.62$

(2) $1,741.85b_{12.3} + 963.98b_{13.2} = 3,749.73$

$$1,376.98b_{13.2} = 1,627.89$$

$$b_{13.2} = 1.18222.$$

We obtain $b_{12.3}$ by substituting 1.18222 for $b_{13.2}$ in normal equation (2):

$$3,147.41b_{12.3} - (1,741.85)(1.18222) = 6,775.52;$$

$$b_{12.3} = 1.49846.$$

A check is obtained by substituting 1.18222 for $b_{13.2}$ and 1.49846 for $b_{12.3}$ in normal equation (3):

$$(1,741.85)(1.498.46) + (2,340.96)(1.18222) = 5,377.62.$$

Our estimating equation in deviation form is therefore

$$x_{1(23)} = 1.49846x_2 + 1.18222x_3.$$

To convert this equation into original form we must find $a_{1(23)}$, using equation (35.5).

$$a_{1(23)} = \overline{X}_1 - b_{12.3}\overline{X}_2 - b_{13.2}\overline{X}_3$$

$$= 172.370 - (1.49846)(118.148) - (1.18222)(84.037)$$

$$= -104.02.$$

The estimating equation in original form is, then,

$$X_{1(23)} = -104.02 + 1.49846X_2 + 1.18222X_3.$$

In combining the two tests into a battery of tests the manual-dexterity test and the finger-dexterity test are given weights of $b_{12.3} = 1.49846$ and $b_{13.2} = 1.18222$, respectively. The score values are multiplied by their weights and added to $a_{1(23)}$ (that is, 104.02 is subtracted). Thus, if we wish to estimate the aptitude of a person with test scores such as those of the first trainee listed in Table 35.1, we substitute in the equation the test scores there recorded. Thus,

$$X_{1(23)} = -104.02 + (1.49846)(135) + (1.18222)(107) = 225.$$

This is rather close to the criterion score. The person would be expected to set 225 rivets per minute, but he actually set 230.

The distinction between a simple and a multiple estimating equation may be clarified if one thinks of the simple equation as describing a line and the multiple equation as describing a plane. Chart 35.1 shows the plane described by the equation $X_{1(23)} = -104.02 + 1.49846X_2 + 1.18222X_3$. The diagonal line on the right face of the solid indicates the change in X_1 for each unit change in X_2, but a fixed value of X_3. Its slope is 1.49846. By inspection of the diagram it is apparent that the slope is the same for any value of X_3.

Chart 35.1—Plane Described by Multiple Regression Equation:
$$X_{1(23)} = -104.0 + 1.50X_2 + 1.18X_3$$

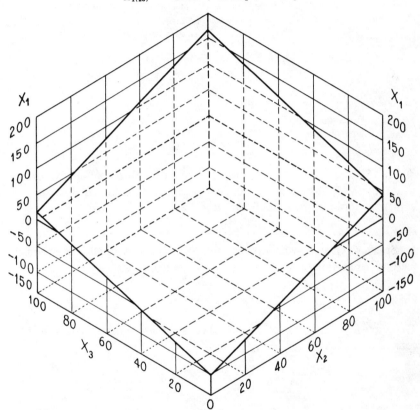

Source of data: Equation was fitted to data of Table 35.1.

The diagonal line on the left face of the solid indicates the change in X_1 for each unit change in X_3, but a fixed value of X_2. Its slope is 1.18222. By inspection of the diagram it is apparent that the slope is the same for any value of X_2. The chart also shows that when $X_2 = \bar{X}_2$ and $X_3 = \bar{X}_3$, $X_{1(23)} = \bar{X}_1$. One thing that the chart does not show is the cloud of 27 observation points above and below the plane. This is left to the reader's imagination. The plane depicted is the plane that best fits this cloud of observation points.

Sources of variation. The sum of the squares of the deviations of the computed values $\Sigma\, x^2_{1(23)} = \Sigma\, (X_{1(23)} - \bar{X}_1)^2$ is computed by methods similar to those with which the student is familiar. Explained variation is

(35.6) $$\Sigma\, x^2_{1(23)} = b_{12.3}\, \Sigma\, x_1 x_2 + b_{13.2}\, \Sigma\, x_1 x_3.$$

Substituting in this equation we obtain

$$\Sigma\, x^2_{1(23)} = (1.49846)(6,775.52) + (1.18222)(5,377.63) = 16,510.4.$$

Table 35.3—Total, Explained, and Unexplained Variation
for Multiple Correlation of Manual-dexterity and
Finger-dexterity Score with Criterion

Source of variation	Symbol	Amount of variation
Total	$\Sigma\, x_1^2$	34,712
Explained	$\Sigma\, x^2_{1(23)}$	16,510
Unexplained	$\Sigma\, x^2_{1.23}$	18,202

In Table 35.3 the different measures of variation are summarized in the usual manner. Note that unexplained variation is obtained by subtracting explained variation from total variation.

(35.7) $$\Sigma\, x^2_{1.23} = \Sigma\, x_1^2 - \Sigma\, x^2_{1(32)}$$

Standard error of estimate and multiple correlation coefficient. The usual methods are followed in computing these measures.

(35.8) $$s_{1.23} = \sqrt{\frac{\Sigma\, x^2_{1.23}}{n - 3}}.$$

There are $n - 3$ degrees of freedom because the estimating equation has 3 constants: $a_{1(23)}$, $b_{12.3}$, and $b_{13.2}$. Substituting,

$$s_{1.23} = \sqrt{\frac{18,202}{24}} = \sqrt{758.4} = 27.54.$$

(35.9) $$r_{1(23)} = \sqrt{\frac{\Sigma\, x^2_{1(23)}}{\Sigma\, x_1^2}}.$$

Substituting,

$$r_{1(23)} = \sqrt{\frac{16,510}{34,712}} = \sqrt{0.4756} = 0.690.$$

No sign is affixed to the coefficient of multiple correlation, since the different b coefficients do not necessarily have the same sign.

Partial correlation. Partial correlation coefficients show the *net* correlation between each independent variable and the dependent variable. In this sense they show the relative importance of each independent variable. It is enlightening to compare the concepts of partial correlation with those of simple and multiple correlation.

The simple correlation coefficient r_{12} is the square root of the proportion of total variation that has been explained by use of the equation $X_{1(2)} = a_{12} + b_{12}X_2$ or $x_{12} = b_{12}x_2$. Also, it may be regarded as the simple correlation between X_1 and $X_{1(2)}$ or between x_1 and $x_{1(2)}$.

The multiple correlation coefficient $r_{1(23)}$ is the square root of the proportion of total variation that has been explained by use of the equation $X_{1(23)} = a_{1(23)} + b_{12.3}X_2 + b_{13.2}X_3$ or $x_{1(23)} = b_{12.3}x_2 + b_{13.2}x_3$. Also, it may be regarded as the simple correlation between X_1 and $X_{1(23)}$ or between x_1 and $x_{1(23)}$.

The partial correlation coefficient $r_{12.3}$ may be regarded as the simple correlation between the variables 1 and 2 when variable 3 has been "held constant." More precisely, $r_{12.3}$ is the simple correlation between variables 1 and 2 when each of these has been adjusted for the effect of variable 3; that is, the simple correlation between $x_{1.3}$ and $x_{2.3}$. (Likewise, $r_{13.2}$ is the simple correlation between $x_{1.2}$ and $x_{3.2}$.) For computational purposes it is perhaps the simplest to regard $r_{12.3}^2$ as the *net* proportion of variation explained[5] by variable 2; that is, the proportion of variation unexplained after use of variable 3 which was explained by variable 2. Thus, $r_{12.3}^2$ is obtained by finding the *increase* in the explained variation brought about by use of the equation $x_{1(23)} = b_{12.3}x_2 + b_{13.2}x_3$ instead of the equation $x_{13} = b_{13}x_3$, dividing this quantity by the amount of variation still to be explained after using the latter equation alone, and extracting the square root. $r_{13.2}$ is obtained in an analogous manner. Thus:

(35.10)
$$\begin{cases} r_{12.3}^2 = \dfrac{\Sigma\, x_{12.3}^2}{\Sigma\, x_{1.3}^2} = \dfrac{\Sigma\, x_{1(23)}^2 - \Sigma\, x_{1(3)}^2}{\Sigma\, x_1^2 - \Sigma\, x_{1(3)}^2}; \\[2ex] r_{13.2}^2 = \dfrac{\Sigma\, x_{13.2}^2}{\Sigma\, x_{1.2}^2} = \dfrac{\Sigma\, x_{1(23)}^2 - \Sigma\, x_{1(2)}^2}{\Sigma\, x_1^2 - \Sigma\, x_{1(2)}^2}. \end{cases}$$

Note that for both the multiple coefficient and the partial coefficients the subscript to r is always the same as the subscript to $\Sigma\, x^2$ in the numerator. For partial coefficients, the variable that has been held constant follows the decimal point in the subscript to the coefficient, and also in the formula itself. Thus,

$$r_{12}^2 = \frac{\Sigma\, x_{1(2)}^2}{\Sigma\, x_1^2},$$

and we affix .3 everywhere to obtain

$$r_{12.3}^2 = \frac{\Sigma\, x_{12.3}^2}{\Sigma\, x_{1.3}^2}.$$

---

[5] Another way of looking at the net proportion of variation explained is enlightening. Just as $\Sigma\, x_{12}^2 = b_{12}\,\Sigma\, x_1 x_2$ and $\Sigma\, x_{13}^2 = b_{13}\,\Sigma\, x_1 x_3$, so $\Sigma\, x_{12.3}^2 = b_{12.3}\,\Sigma\, x_{1.3}x_{2.3}$ and $\Sigma\, x_{13.2}^2 = b_{13.2}\,\Sigma\, x_{1.2}x_{3.2}$. This is the main approach used in the Doolittle method.

Note also that the full formula is the same as the multiple correlation formula, except that both the numerator and the denominator are adjusted for variation explained by the variable held constant. Thus

$$r^2_{1(23)} = \frac{\Sigma\, x^2_{1(23)}}{\Sigma\, x^2_1},$$

but

$$r^2_{12.3} = \frac{\Sigma\, x^2_{1(23)} - \Sigma\, x^2_{1(3)}}{\Sigma\, x^2_1 - \Sigma\, x^2_{1(3)}}.$$

The signs of $r_{12.3}$ and $r_{13.2}$, respectively, are the same as those of $b_{12.3}$ and $b_{13.2}$

A summary of the formulas for simple, multiple, and partial correlation at this point may be useful.

Type of relationship	Coefficient of determination		Explained variation
	Symbol	Formula	
Simple	r^2_{12}	$\dfrac{\Sigma\, x^2_{1(2)}}{\Sigma\, x^2_1}$	$\Sigma\, x^2_{1(2)} = b_{12}\, \Sigma\, x_1 x_2$
Multiple	$r^2_{1(23)}$	$\dfrac{\Sigma\, x^2_{1(23)}}{\Sigma\, x^2_1}$	$\Sigma\, x^2_{1(23)} = b_{12.3}\, \Sigma\, x_1 x_2$ $+\, b_{13.2}\, \Sigma\, x_1 x_3$
Partial	$r^2_{12.3}$	$\dfrac{\Sigma\, x^2_{12.3}}{\Sigma\, x^2_{1.3}}$	$\Sigma\, x^2_{12.3} = \Sigma\, x^2_{1(23)} - \Sigma\, x^2_{1(3)}$
Partial	$r^2_{13.2}$	$\dfrac{\Sigma\, x^2_{13.2}}{\Sigma\, x^2_{1.2}}$	$\Sigma\, x^2_{13.2} = \Sigma\, x^2_{1(23)} - \Sigma\, x^2_{1(2)}$

To illustrate the method of computation, recall that for multiple correlation we had:

Normal equations:

$$\begin{cases} b_{12.3}\, \Sigma\, x^2_2 + b_{13.2}\, \Sigma\, x_2 x_3 = \Sigma\, x_1 x_2; \\ b_{12.3}\, \Sigma\, x_2 x_3 + b_{13.2}\, \Sigma\, x^2_3 = \Sigma\, x_1 x_3. \end{cases}$$

$$\begin{cases} 3{,}147.41 b_{12.3} + 1{,}741.85 b_{13.2} = 6{,}755.52; \\ 1{,}741.85 b_{12.3} + 2{,}340.96 b_{13.2} = 5{,}377.63. \end{cases}$$

Variation explained by variables 2 and 3 together:

$$\Sigma \, x_{1(23)}^2 = b_{12.3} \, \Sigma \, x_1 x_2 + b_{13.2} \, \Sigma \, x_1 x_3;$$
$$16,510 = (1.49846)(6,775.52) + (1.18222)(5,377.63).$$

b Coefficients:

$$b_{12} = \frac{\Sigma \, x_1 x_2}{\Sigma \, x_2^2}; \qquad\qquad b_{13} = \frac{\Sigma \, x_1 x_3}{\Sigma \, x_3^2}$$

$$2.15273 = \frac{6,775.52}{3,147.41}. \qquad 2.29719 = \frac{5,377.63}{2,340.96}.$$

Gross variation explained by each variable:

$$\Sigma \, x_{1(2)}^2 = b_{12} \, \Sigma \, x_1 x_2; \qquad\qquad \Sigma \, x_{1(3)}^2 = b_{13} \, \Sigma \, x_1 x_3;$$
$$14,585.87 = (2.15272)(6,775.52). \qquad 12,353.44 = (2.29719)(5,377.63).$$

Net explained variation;

$$\Sigma \, x_{13.2}^2 = \Sigma \, x_{1(23)}^2 - \Sigma \, x_{1(2)}^2; \qquad\qquad \Sigma \, x_{12.3}^2 = \Sigma \, x_{1(23)}^2 - \Sigma \, x_{1(3)}^2;$$
$$1,924.52 = 16,510.39 - 14,585.87. \qquad 4,156.95 = 16,510.39 - 12,353.44.$$

Variation remaining after use of one independent variable:

$$\Sigma \, x_{1.2}^2 = \Sigma \, x_1^2 - \Sigma \, x_{1(2)}^2; \qquad\qquad \Sigma \, x_{1.3}^2 = \Sigma \, x_1^2 - \Sigma \, x_{1(3)}^2;$$
$$20,126.43 = 34,712.30 - 14,585.87. \qquad 22,358.86 = 34,712.30 - 12,353.44.$$

The relationships among the coefficients of simple, multiple, and partial correlation will perhaps be still further clarified by reference to Chart 35.2, in which the total variation is broken down into the various types of explained and unexplained variation. The method of obtaining the various coefficients of determination (squares of coefficients of correlation) from the values shown on the charts is indicated below.

$$r_{12}^2 = \frac{\Sigma \, x_{1(2)}^2}{\Sigma \, x_1^2}; \qquad r_{1(23)}^2 = \frac{\Sigma \, x_{1(23)}^2}{\Sigma \, x_1^2}; \qquad r_{13}^2 = \frac{\Sigma \, x_{1(3)}^2}{\Sigma \, x_1^2};$$

$$0.4202 = \frac{14,586}{34,712}. \qquad 0.4756 = \frac{16,510}{34,712}. \qquad 0.3559 = \frac{12,353}{34,712}.$$

$$r_{13.2}^2 = \frac{\Sigma \, x_{13.2}^2}{\Sigma \, x_{1.2}^2}; \qquad\qquad\qquad r_{12.3}^2 = \frac{\Sigma \, x_{12.3}^2}{\Sigma \, x_{1.3}^2};$$

$$0.0956 = \frac{1,925}{20,126}. \qquad\qquad\qquad 0.1859 = \frac{4,157}{22,359}.$$

By extracting the square roots we obtain the coefficients of correlation.

$$r_{12} = +0.648; \quad r_{1(23)} = 0.690; \quad r_{13} = +0.597;$$
$$r_{13.2} = +0.309; \qquad\qquad\qquad r_{12.3} = +0.431.$$

One important principle is brought out by the chart. There is a great deal of overlapping between $\Sigma x_{1(2)}^2$ and $\Sigma x_{1(3)}^2$ (10,429 in this case). This is the amount of variation explained jointly by variables 2 and 3. As the chart indicates, $\Sigma x_{1(23)}^2 = \Sigma x_{12.3}^2 + \Sigma x_{13.2}^2 +$ joint explained variation. The total variation explained by variables 2 and 3 together is equal to the net amount explained by variable 2 plus the net amount explained by variable 3

Chart 35.2—Diagrammatic Representation of Sources of Variation in Dependent Variable with Two Independent Variables

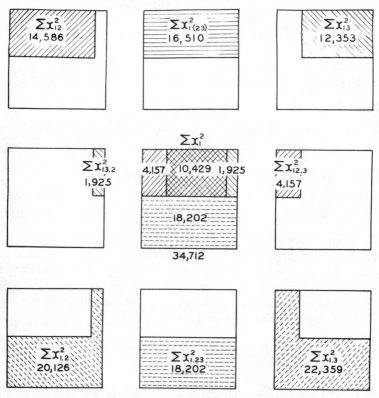

Source of data: Table 35.1.

plus the amount explained jointly by them. It is this duplication that prevents the coefficient of multiple determination from being the sum of the two coefficients of simple correlation. The chart also shows that $\Sigma x_{1(23)}^2 = \Sigma x_{1(2)}^2 + \Sigma x_{13.2}^2 = \Sigma x_{1(3)}^2 + \Sigma x_{12.3}^2$; i.e.,[6] the total variation explained by

[6] Accordingly,

$$\Sigma x_{1(23)}^2 = b_{12} \Sigma x_1 x_2 + b_{13.2} \Sigma x_{1.2} x_{3.2}, \quad \text{or}$$
$$\Sigma x_{1(23)}^2 = b_{13} \Sigma x_1 x_3 + b_{12.3} \Sigma x_{1.3} x_{2.3}.$$

This method of computation is the main approach used in the abbreviated Doolittle method.

variables 2 and 3 together is equal to the gross amount explained by variable 2 plus the net amount explained by variable 3, or the gross amount explained by variable 3 plus the net amount explained by variable 2.

Still another way of looking at Chart 35.2 is that $\Sigma\, x^2_{1(23)} = \Sigma\, x^2_{1(2)} + \Sigma\, x^2_{1(3)}$ — joint explained variation; i.e., the total variation explained by variable 2 and 3 together is equal to the gross amount explained by variable 2 plus the gross amount explained by variable 3 minus the amount explained jointly by them. For given values of r_{12} and r_{13} having the same sign, the duplication between $\Sigma\, x^2_{12}$ and Σx^2_{13} will be large if r_{23} is large and positive, and will become smaller as r_{23} gets closer to zero. It follows that for given values of r_{12} and r_{13} having the same sign,[7] the smaller, algebraically, the value of r_{23}, the larger will be the value[8] of $r_{1(23)}$. Consequently, if a number of independent variables are available for use in multiple correlation with the dependent variable, and if each of these is correlated positively with the dependent variable, one should select those variables that have large correlation with the dependent variable and small correlation (algebraically) with each other.[9]

Alternative Approaches to Regression and Correlation

Instead of solving simultaneous equations, one can first obtain b_{12}, b_{13}, b_{23}, and other *zero-order* regression coefficients. From these, $b_{13.2}$, $b_{12.3}$, and other *first-order* coefficients can quickly be obtained. The procedure can be extended indefinitely, to obtain coefficients of any order,[10] though it is not so fast as the abbreviated Doolittle method if there are more than 4 variables.

---

[7] $+0.2$ and -0.2 are both smaller *numerically* than is -0.3, but they are both larger *algebraically* than -0.3; $+0.4$ is larger than any of these numbers, both numerically and algebraically.

[8] This is apparent from a consideration of the relationship

$$r^2_{1(23)} = \frac{r^2_{12} + r^2_{13} - 2r_{12}r_{13}r_{23}}{1 - r^2_{23}}.$$

In applying this formula it must be remembered that for a given value of r_{12} and r_{13} only a certain range of values for r_{23} is possible when dealing with real numbers.

[9] If r_{12} and r_{13} are of opposite signs, $\Sigma\, x^2_{1(23)} > \Sigma\, x^2_{1(2)} + \Sigma\, x^2_{1(3)}$, and the larger, algebraically, the value of r_{23}, the larger will be the value of $r_{1(23)}$. If the sign of the correlation with the independent variable is negative for any of the variables, one should change (one at a time) the sign of the coefficient of correlation of each such variable with the dependent variable and each of the other independent variables. This process, called reflection, results in each independent variable showing a positive correlation with the dependent variable. After reflection, the relationships among the different measures of variation and the different correlation coefficients is as described in the text.

[10] This topic is fully explained and illustrated in Dudley J. Cowden, "A Procedure for Computing Regression Coefficients," *Journal of the American Statistical Association*, Vol. 53, March, 1958, pp. 144–150.

Let i denote the dependent variable; j denote the "active" independent variable; $t, u, v, \ldots$, denote the "passive" independent variables (those held constant). Then,

$$(35.11) \quad \begin{cases} b_{ij.t} = \dfrac{b_{ij} - b_{it}b_{tj}}{1 - b_{jt}b_{tj}}; \\[2ex] b_{ij.tu} = \dfrac{b_{ij.u} - b_{it.u}b_{tj.u}}{1 - b_{jt.u}b_{tj.u}}; \\[1ex] \text{and so on.} \end{cases}$$

Partial correlation coefficients can be obtained from the partial regression coefficients.

$$(35.12) \quad \begin{cases} r_{ij.t} = \sqrt{b_{ij.t}b_{ji.t}}; \\[1ex] r_{ij.tu} = \sqrt{b_{ij.tu}b_{ji.tu}}; \\[1ex] \text{and so on.} \end{cases}$$

Also, partial correlation coefficients can be obtained from correlation coefficients of lower order.[11] Thus:

$$(35.13) \quad \begin{cases} r_{ij.t} = \dfrac{r_{ij} - r_{it}r_{jt}}{\sqrt{1 - r_{it}^2}\ \sqrt{1 - r_{jt}^2}}; \\[3ex] r_{ij.tu} = \dfrac{r_{ij.t} - r_{it.u}r_{jt.u}}{\sqrt{1 - r_{it.u}^2}\ \sqrt{1 - r_{jt.u}^2}}; \\[1ex] \text{and so on.} \end{cases}$$

Testing Significance

Use of variance ratio F. Analysis of variance can be used for testing significance, not only of simple, but also multiple and partial correlation, as well as the constants in the estimating equation. Reference to Chart 35.2 will help one in understanding Table 35.4. Further explanation concerning degrees of freedom is helpful. There are $n = 27$ sets of observations and $m = 3$ constants; one degree of freedom is lost through use of the mean, so that total variation has $n - 1 = 26$ degrees of freedom. Two additional $(m - 1)$ degrees of freedom are lost through use of the constants $b_{12.3}$ and $b_{13.2}$. (It would be duplication to count both $\bar{X}_1$ and $a_{1(23)}$.) Note that degrees of freedom are additive in the same way as are the amounts of variation; thus for $\Sigma x_{1.23}^2$,

$$(n - 1) - (m - 1) = 26 - 2 = 24, \quad \text{or}$$
$$n - m = 27 - 3 = 24.$$

[11] See F. E. Croxton and D. J. Cowden, *Applied General Statistics*, 2d ed., Prentice-Hall, Inc., Englewood Cliffs, N.J., 1955, pp. 552–555.

The various tests of significance are as follows:

Multiple correlation:

$$H_0: \quad \rho_{1(23)} = 0; \qquad H_a: \quad \rho_{1(23)} \neq 0.$$
$$\alpha = .05; \qquad F_{.05;2,24} = 3.403.$$

Table 35.4—Analysis of Variance for Testing Significance of Relationship Between Manual-dexterity Score and Finger-dexterity Score, and Criterion

Source of variation	Symbol	Amount of variation	Degrees of freedom	Estimated variance*
Total	Σx_1^2	34,712	$n - 1 = 26$	...
Less:				
Explained by X_2 and X_3..	$\Sigma x_{1(23)}^2$	16,510	$m - 1 = 2$	$s_{1(23)}^2 = 8,255$
Unexplained	$\Sigma x_{1.23}^2$	18,202	$n - m = 24$	$s_{1.23}^2 = 758$
Explained by X_2 and X_3 ..	$\Sigma x_{1(23)}^2$	16,510	2	...
Less:				
Gross explained by X_3 ..	$\Sigma x_{1(3)}^2$	12,353	1	...
Net explained by X_2	$\Sigma x_{12.3}^2$	4,157	1	$s_{12.3}^2 = 4,157$
Explained by X_2 and X_3 ..	$\Sigma x_{1(23)}^2$	16,510	2	...
Less:				
Gross explained by X_2 ..	$\Sigma x_{1(2)}^2$	14,586	1	...
Net explained by X_3	$\Sigma x_{13.2}^2$	1,925	1	$s_{13.2}^2 = 1,925$

* Each of these is an unbiased estimate of the population variance if the population is uncorrelated.

The null hypothesis is to be rejected is the sample value of the variance ratio, $F_{1(23)}$, is equal to or greater than 3.403.

$$(35.14) \qquad F_{1(23)} = \frac{s_{1(23)}^2}{s_{1.23}^2} = \frac{\Sigma x_{1(23)}^2 \div (m - 1)}{\Sigma x_{1.23}^2 \div (n - m)}$$
$$= \frac{16,510 \div 2}{18,202 \div 24} = \frac{8,255}{758} = 10.89.$$

Actually, when $\nu_1 = 2$ and $\nu_2 = 24$, the probability of obtaining a value of F as large as 10.89 or larger is less than 0.001. Therefore we reject H_0, and conclude that $r_{1(23)}$ is highly significant.

Partial correlation:

$$H_0: \quad \rho_{12.3} = 0; \qquad H_a: \quad \rho_{12.3} \neq 0.$$
$$\alpha = .05; \qquad F_{.05;1,24} = 4.260.$$

$$(35.15) \qquad F_{12.3} = \frac{s_{12.3}^2}{s_{1.23}^2} = \frac{\Sigma x_{12.3}^2 \div (m - p - 1)}{\Sigma x_{1.23}^2 \div (n - m)},$$

where p is the number of "passive" variables; i.e., the number held constant.

$$F_{12.3} = \frac{4,157 \div 1}{18,202 \div 24} = \frac{4,157}{758} = 5.484.$$

When $\nu_1 = 1$ and $\nu_2 = 24$, the probability of obtaining a value of F as large or larger than 5.484 is between .05 and .01. Therefore $r_{12.3}$ and $b_{12.3}$ are significant.

$$H_0: \quad \rho_{13.2} = 0; \qquad H_a: \quad \rho_{13.2} \neq 0.$$

$$\alpha = .05; \qquad F_{.05;1,24} = 4.260.$$

(35.16)
$$F_{13.2} = \frac{s_{13.2}^2}{s_{1.23}^2} = \frac{\Sigma x_{13.2}^2 \div (m - p - 1)}{\Sigma x_{1.23}^2 \div (n - m)}$$

$$= \frac{1,925 \div 1}{18,202 \div 24} = \frac{1,925}{758} = 2.540.$$

When $\nu_1 = 1$ and $\nu_2 = 24$, the probability of obtaining a value of F as large as as or larger than 2.540 is between .20 and .10. Therefore we conclude that $r_{13.2}$ and $b_{13.2}$ are not significant.[12]

The reason $\Sigma x_{1.23}^2 = 18,202$ is used for the unexplained variation for both $F_{12.3}$ and $F_{13.2}$ may not be obvious. Table 35.4, in which the total variation is analyzed into various additive components, may make this clear. The following equalities are easily seen by inspection of Chart 35.1.

$$\Sigma x_1^2 = \Sigma x_{12}^2 + \Sigma x_{13.2}^2 + \Sigma x_{1.23}^2 = 14,586 + 1,925 + 18,202 = 34,712;$$

$$\Sigma x_1^2 = \Sigma x_{13}^2 + \Sigma x_{12.3}^2 + \Sigma x_{1.23}^2 = 12,353 + 4,157 + 18,202 = 34,712.$$

In nonmathematical language we may say that total variation is made up of the gross amount explained by one independent variable plus the net amount explained by the other independent variable plus the amount not explained by the two taken together. Notice also:

$$\Sigma x_{1.23}^2 = \Sigma x_1^2 - \Sigma x_{12}^2 - \Sigma x_{13.2}^2 = \Sigma x_{1.2}^2 - \Sigma x_{13.2}^2;$$

$$\Sigma x_{1.23}^2 = \Sigma x_1^2 - \Sigma x_{13}^2 - \Sigma x_{12.3}^2 = \Sigma x_{1.3}^2 - \Sigma x_{12.3}^2.$$

---

[12] If desired, F may be computed from the values of the coefficients of determination and nondetermination, instead of from the values of the explained and unexplained variation. Thus

$$F_{1(23)} = \frac{r_{1(32)}^2 \div (m - 1)}{[1 - r_{1(23)}^2] \div (n - m)} = \frac{0.4756 \div 2}{0.5244 \div 24} = \frac{0.2378}{0.02185} = 10.9;$$

$$F_{12.3} = \frac{r_{12.3}^2 \div 1}{(1 - r_{12.3}^2) \div (n - m)} = \frac{0.1859}{0.1841 \div 24} = \frac{0.1859}{0.03392} = 5.48;$$

$$F_{13.2} = \frac{r_{13.2}^2 \div 1}{(1 - r_{13.2}^2) \div (n - m)} = \frac{0.09562}{0.9044 \div 24} = \frac{0.09562}{0.03768} = 2.54.$$

This method is the mathematical equivalent of that used above, and the results are of course the same.

In other words, if we subtract the amount of variation we have explained from the amount we are trying to explain, we have the amount still unexplained $\Sigma\, x_{1.23}^2$.

Use of t. If we wish, we may now take the square roots of $F_{12.3}$ and $F_{13.2}$, obtaining $t_{12.3}$ and $t_{13.2}$. Thus

$$t_{12.3} = \sqrt{5.484} = 2.342; \quad \nu = 24; \quad .05 > P > .02.$$

$$t_{13.2} = \sqrt{2.540} = 1.594; \quad \nu = 24; \quad .2 > P > .1.$$

The advantage of computing t is that t tables ordinarily record values of t at a relatively large number of probability points. One cannot compute t to test the multiple correlation coefficient, because the explained variation has more than one degree of freedom.

Usually t is computed directly as follows:

$$(35.17) \quad \begin{cases} t_{12.3} = r_{12.3}\sqrt{\dfrac{n-3}{1 - r_{12.3}^2}}\,; \\[3mm] t_{13.2} = r_{13.2}\sqrt{\dfrac{n-3}{1 - r_{13.2}^2}}\,. \end{cases}$$

Thus

$$t_{12.3} = 0.4312\sqrt{\frac{24}{0.8141}} = 2.34;$$

$$t_{13.2} = 0.3092\sqrt{\frac{24}{0.9044}} = 1.59.$$

Use of formula (35.17) gives the sign of t automatically.

In the present case, $r_{13.2}$ and $b_{13.2}$ are not significant. The evidence that the finger-dexterity test has any value for estimating the criterion, in addition to that provided by the manual-dexterity test, is not convincing. Since $r_{13.2}$ and $b_{13.2}$ are not significant, we should test r_{12} and b_{12}.

$$F_{12} = \frac{\Sigma\, x_{12}^2 \div 1}{\Sigma\, x_{1.2}^2 \div 25} = \frac{14{,}586 \div 1}{20{,}126 \div 25} = \frac{14{,}586}{805} = 18.12.$$

$$t_{12} = \sqrt{18.12} = 4.26.$$

t_{12} can also be computed from formula (26.15):

$$t_{12} = r_{12}\sqrt{\frac{n-2}{1 - r_{12}^2}}\,.$$

When $\nu = 25$, the probability of obtaining a value of t as large as 4.26 or larger is less than 0.001. Therefore r_{12} and b_{12} are highly significant.

An alternative procedure is to test r_{12} and r_{13} for significance, and then if both are significant, proceed with the computation of $r_{12.3}$ and $r_{13.2}$. If both of these are significant, at some appropriate level, the multiple estimating equation is justified. In the present instance r_{13} is significant, almost at the 0.001 level. But as we have seen $r_{13.2}$ is not significant even at the 0.10 level. The reason for this is the great amount of duplication between X_2 and X_3. Chart 35.2 shows that the joint contribution of X_2 and X_3 to the explained variation is much larger than the net contribution of either of them, and almost as large as either of their gross contributions.

z Transformation. The z transformation can be used for a partial, but not a multiple, correlation coefficient. The formula for the transformation is the same as for simple r. However, the degrees of freedom for the standard error are different.

$$(35.18) \qquad \sigma_{z_{12.3}} \doteq \frac{1}{\sqrt{n - m - 2/3}} = \frac{1}{\sqrt{n - 11/3}} = \sqrt{\frac{3}{3n - 11}}.$$

It should be recalled that the z transformation is for use when testing the hypothesis that ρ is some value other than zero, or when testing the significance of the difference between two correlation coefficients.

*Chapter 36

SPECIAL TOPICS IN MULTIPLE CORRELATION

In Chapter 27 we saw that curvilinear relationships can sometimes be reduced to linear form by transforming one or both variables into logarithms or some other function. Another type of nonlinear relationship is described by a polynomial equation of the type $Y = a + bX + cX^2 + \dots$. In this chapter we shall see how the methods with which we are already familiar can be used for this type of relationship. No new symbols, formulas, or computational methods are required.

Another topic that will be considered briefly is multiple nonlinear correlation, where the relationship of the dependent variable with at least one of two or more independent variables is nonlinear.

Finally, joint correlation will be touched upon. This is the case where the slope of variable 1 on variable 2 depends partly on the value of variable 3, and the slope of variable 1 on variable 3 depends partly on the value of variable 2.

Use of Second-degree Equation

Business management is interested, not only in the most profitable adjustment of volume of production and selling price to each other, but also in the relationship between volume of production and cost of production. A thorough investigation of this relationship would include the way in which individual types of costs, such as direct labor, indirect labor, and overhead, vary with output for a given amount of plant and equipment; and also how these costs change as the amount of plant and equipment changes. Finally, some account should be taken of the tendency, if any, for efficiency to improve with the passage of time. Our present illustration is limited to the relationship between total output and total employment costs of the United States Steel Corporation. Total production is here defined as ingots and castings produced, plus steel products shipped. Employment costs are adjusted for changes in hourly earnings, relative to 1955.[1]

Computation of estimating equation. In Chart 36.1 the output and labor cost data are plotted as a scatter diagram. The relationship is clearly curvilinear. The estimating equation is of the type

$$Y_{X,X^2} = a + bX + cX^2.$$

---

[1] This adjustment is made by the process of deflation: employment costs are divided by the ratio of the hourly earnings in the given year to hourly earnings in 1955.

Chart 36.1—Output and Employment Costs of the United States Steel Corporation, 1931–1941 and 1946–1955

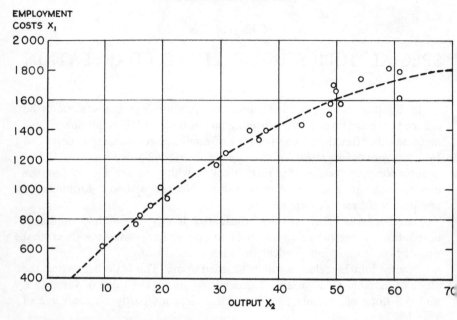

Source of data: Tables 36.1 and 36.2.

The student is already familiar with the use of this type of equation as a trend equation in Chapter 34 (pages 512–516). The methods of that chapter cannot conveniently be used, however, since the X-values are not evenly spaced and ΣX does not usually equal zero. Nevertheless, using the symbol X_1 instead of Y, X_2 instead of X, and by considering the X^2-values as those of a separate variable X_3 we can rewrite the equation in the form

$$X_{1(23)} = a_{1(23)} + b_{12.3}X_2 + b_{13.2}X_3.$$

We may now regard our problem as a special case of multiple correlation. This permits us to use the convenient system of notation and methods of computation with which the student should by now be familiar. We can then carry through the computations in deviation form without any difficulties, thereby reducing the number of simultaneous normal equations that must be solved from three with three unknowns each, to two with two unknowns each. Thus, equation $Y_{X,X^2} = a + bX + cX^2$ requires three simultaneous equations:

(1) $na + b \Sigma x + c \Sigma X^2 = \Sigma Y;$

(2) $a \Sigma X + b \Sigma X^2 + c \Sigma X^3 = \Sigma XY;$

(3) $a \Sigma X^2 + b \Sigma X^3 + c \Sigma X^4 = \Sigma X^2 Y.$

But equation $X_{1(23)} = a_{1(23)} + b_{12.3}X_2 + b_{13.2}X_3$ can be put into deviation $x_{1(23)} = b_{12.3}x_2 + b_{13.2}x_3$ which requires only two simultaneous equations (35.4),

$$(2) \quad b_{12.3} \Sigma x_2^2 + b_{13.2} \Sigma x_2 x_3 = \Sigma x_1 x_2,$$

$$(3) \quad b_{12.3} \Sigma x_2 x_3 + b_{13.2} \Sigma x_3^2 = \Sigma x_1 x_3,$$

together with the single equation (35.5),

$$a_{1(23)} = \bar{X}_1 - b_{12.3}\bar{X}_2 - b_{13.2}\bar{X}_3.$$

Table 36.1—Output and Employment Costs of United States Steel Corporation, 1931–1941 and 1946–1955

Year	Output (millions of tons) (X)	Output squared (X²)	Employment costs (millions of dollars) (Y)
	X_2	X_3	X_1
1931	19.7	388.09	1,011
1932	9.8	96.04	609
1933	15.4	237.16	760
1934	16.2	262.44	822
1935	20.6	424.36	937
1936	30.8	948.64	1,241
1937	34.9	1,218.01	1,396
1938	17.8	316.84	881
1939	29.3	858.49	1,162
1940	37.9	1,436.41	1,395
1941	49.4	2,440.36	1,705
1946	36.5	1,332.25	1,333
1947	48.8	2,381.44	1,573
1948	49.9	2,490.01	1,663
1949	44.0	1,936.00	1,438
1950	54.1	2,926.81	1,741
1951	58.9	3,469.21	1,813
1952	50.6	2,560.36	1,575
1953	60.9	3,708.81	1,769
1954	48.6	2,361.96	1,504
1955	60.8	3,696.64	1,615
Total	794.9	35,490.33	27,943
Mean	37.85238	1,690.016	1,330.619

Source: United States Steel Corporation, *Annual Report*, 1955, pp. 30–31.

In Table 36.1 the data are shown, as well as the sums and means of the three variables. The symbols in the parentheses are those for the equation $Y_{X,X^2} = a + bX + cX^2$.

Following are the sums of squares and products, correction terms, and measures of variation and covariation, in symbolic form. This arrangement of the different cells facilitates substitution of values in the normal equations.

Sum of squares or products* ...	ΣX_2^2	$\Sigma X_2 X_3$	$\Sigma X_1 X_2$
Less: Correction term	$\dfrac{(\Sigma X_2)^2}{n}$	$\dfrac{(\Sigma X_2)(\Sigma X_3)}{n}$	$\dfrac{(\Sigma X_1)(\Sigma X_2)}{n}$
Variation or covariation	Σx_2^2	$\Sigma x_2 x_3$	$\Sigma x_1 x_2$
Sum of squares or products* ...	...	ΣX_3^2	$\Sigma X_1 X_3$
Less: Correction term	...	$\dfrac{(\Sigma X_3^2)}{n}$	$\dfrac{(\Sigma X_1)(\Sigma X_3)}{n}$
Variation or covariation	...	Σx_3^2	$\Sigma x_1 x_3$
Sum of squares*	...	...	ΣX_1^2
Less: Correction term	...	...	$\dfrac{(\Sigma X_1)^2}{n}$
Variation or covariation	...	...	Σx_1^2

* Note the following identities:

$$\Sigma X_2^2 = \Sigma X^2 \quad \Sigma X_2 X_3 = \Sigma X^3 \quad \Sigma X_1 X_2 = \Sigma XY$$
$$\Sigma X_3^2 = \Sigma X^4 \quad \Sigma X_1 X_3 = \Sigma X^2 Y$$
$$\Sigma X_1^2 = \Sigma Y^2$$

The alternative form for correction terms and the measures of variation and covariation are not given, because they would require notation with which the student is unfamiliar.

Finally, the numerical values corresponding to the above tabulation are shown. The squares and products of the individual items are not given, since that would involve needless repetition of a mechanical procedure with which the student is familiar. Also, modern calculating machines permit the series of multiplications to be made and cumulated without recording the individual products.

$$
\begin{array}{lll}
\quad\;\; 35{,}490.330 & \quad\;\; 1{,}734{,}667.565 & \quad\;\; 1{,}175{,}336.500 \\
\quad\;\; 30{,}088.858 & \quad\;\; 1{,}343{,}393.491 & \quad\;\; 1{,}057{,}709.081 \\
\Sigma x_2^2 = \overline{\;\;5{,}401.472\;} & \Sigma x_2 x_3 = \overline{\;\;391{,}274.074\;} & \Sigma x_1 x_2 = \overline{\;\;117{,}627.419\;}
\end{array}
$$

$$
\begin{array}{ll}
\quad\;\; 89{,}255{,}272.465 & \quad\;\; 55{,}511{,}267.590 \\
\quad\;\; 59{,}979{,}215.405 & \quad\;\; 47{,}224{,}109.104 \\
\Sigma x_3^2 = \overline{\;\;29{,}276{,}057.060\;} & \Sigma x_1 x_3 = \overline{\;\;8{,}287{,}158.486\;}
\end{array}
$$

$$
\begin{array}{l}
\quad\;\; 39{,}875{,}515.000 \\
\quad\;\; 37{,}181{,}488.048 \\
\Sigma x_1^2 = \overline{\;\;2{,}694{,}026.952\;}
\end{array}
$$

Substitutions are now made in the two simultaneous equations (35.4), page 547. All entries have been rounded to 7 digits, which are ample for our purpose.

$$(2) \quad 5{,}401.472b_{12.3} + 391{,}274.1b_{13.2} = 117{,}627.4;$$

$$(3) \quad 391{,}274.100b_{12.3} + 29{,}276{,}060.0b_{13.2} = 8{,}287{,}158.5.$$

Solving these equations gives $b_{12.3} = 39.917$ and $b_{13.2} = -0.25042$. To obtain $a_{1(23)}$ we substitute in equation (35.5), page 547.

$$a_{1(23)} = 1{,}330.619 - (39.917)(37.85238) + (0.25042)(1{,}690.016)$$
$$= 242.88.$$

Table 36.2—Computed Values for Employment Costs of the United States Steel Corporation, Based on Output
$(X_{1(23)} = 242.88 + 39.917X_2 - 0.25042X_3)$

X_2	X_3	$a_{1(23)} + b_{12.3}X_2$	$b_{13.2}X_3$	$X_{1(23)}$
(X)	(X^2)	$(a + bX)$	(cX^2)	$Y_{X,X2}$
10	100	642.05	−25.04	617
20	400	1,041.22	−100.17	941
30	900	1,440.39	−225.38	1,215
40	1,600	1,839.56	−400.67	1,439
50	2,500	2,238.73	−626.05	1,613
60	3,600	2,637.90	−901.51	1,736

Source: Computed from data of Table 36.1.

The estimating equation, therefore, is

$$X_{1(23)} = 242.88 + 39.917X_2 - 0.25042X_3$$

If we prefer, we can write it

$$Y_{X,X^2} = 242.88 + 39.917X - 0.25042X^2.$$

From this estimating equation are made the estimates of total employment costs shown in Table 36.2. The equation is plotted as a broken line on Chart 36.1.

Other measures of relationship. It is desirable to compute r_{12}, $r_{1(23)}$, and $r_{13.2}$. To obtain r_{12} we compute

$$b_{12} = \frac{\Sigma x_1 x_2}{\Sigma x_2^2} = \frac{117{,}627.4}{5{,}401.472} = 21.777;$$

$$\Sigma x_{1(2)}^2 = b_{12} \, \Sigma x_1 x_2 = (21.777)(117{,}627.4) = 2{,}561{,}572;$$

$$r_{12}^2 = \frac{\Sigma x_{1(2)}^2}{\Sigma x_1^2} = \frac{2{,}561{,}572}{2{,}694{,}027} = 0.9508;$$

$$r_{12} = +0.975.$$

r_{13} and $r_{12.3}$ are not computed, because we have no interest in the relationship between Y and X^2, or between Y and X after adjusting for X^2.

The measures of total variation and covariation required for $r_{1(23)}$ are given on page 548. The explained variation is found by use of formula (35.6).

$$\Sigma x_{1(23)}^2 = b_{12.3} \Sigma x_1 x_2 + b_{13.2} \Sigma x_1 x_3$$

$$= (39.917)(117,627.4) - (0.25042)(8,287,158)$$

$$= 2,620,063.$$

The unexplained variation is found by use of formula (35.7), subtracting the unexplained variation from the total variation:

$$\Sigma x_{1.23}^2 = \Sigma x_1^2 - \Sigma x_{1(23)}^2$$

$$= 2,694,027 - 2,620,063 = 73,964.$$

For the estimate of the standard error of estimate we use formula (35.8).

$$s_{1.23}^2 = \frac{\Sigma x_{1.23}^2}{n - 3}$$

$$= \frac{73,964}{18} = 4,109;$$

$$s_{1.23} = 64.10.$$

For the coefficient of nonlinear correlation we use formula (35.9).

$$r_{1(23)}^2 = \frac{\Sigma x_{1(23)}^2}{\Sigma x_1^2}$$

$$= \frac{2,620,063}{2,694,027} = 0.9725;$$

$$r_{1(23)} = 0.986.$$

No sign is attached to $r_{1(23)}$, since if the curve is extended sufficiently the slope will be positive in one part and negative in another.[2]

Since r_{12} is nearly as large as $r_{1(23)}$ one wonders whether $r_{13.2}$ can be significant.

---

[2] Therefore, in spite of the high correlation, and the fact that close estimates can be made within the range of the data, the type of equation is not completely logical for these data.

To compute $r_{13.2}$, we use formula (35.10).

$$r_{13.2}^2 = \frac{\Sigma\, x_{13.2}^2}{\Sigma\, x_{1.2}^2}.$$

$$\Sigma\, x_{13.2}^2 = \Sigma\, x_{1(23)}^2 - \Sigma\, x_{1(2)}^2 = 2{,}620{,}063 - 2{,}561{,}563 = 58{,}500;$$

$$\Sigma\, x_{1.2}^2 = \Sigma\, x_1^2 - \Sigma\, x_{1(2)}^2 = 2{,}694{,}027 - 2{,}561{,}563 = 132{,}464;$$

$$r_{13.2}^2 = \frac{58{,}500}{132{,}464} = 0.4416;$$

$$r_{13.2} = -0.6645.$$

The sign is negative because $b_{13.2}$ is negative.

Table 36.3—Analysis of Variance for Testing Significance of Relationship between Output and Employment Costs of United States Steel Corporation

Source of variation	Symbol	Amount of variation	Degrees of freedom	Estimate of variance*
Total	$\Sigma\, x_1^2$	2,694,030	20	...
Gross explained by X_2	$\Sigma\, x_{1(2)}^2$	2,561,560	1	$s_{1(2)}^2 = 2{,}561{,}600$
Unexplained by X_2	$\Sigma\, x_{1.2}^2$	132,470	19	$s_{1.2}^2 = 6{,}972$
Net explained by X_3	$\Sigma\, x_{13.2}^2$	58,500	1	$s_{13.2}^2 = 58{,}500$
Unexplained by X_2 and X_3 ...	$\Sigma\, x_{1.23}^2$	73,970	18	$s_{1.23}^2 = 4{,}109$
Explained by X_2 and X_3	$\Sigma\, x_{1(23)}^2$	2,620,060	2	$s_{1(23)}^2 = 1{,}310{,}000$

* Each of these is an unbiased estimate of the population variance if the population is uncorrelated.

If the student has understood the procedure that has been followed in this illustration, he will experience little difficulty in extending it to polynomials of higher order.

Testing significance. For testing the significance of r_{12} (and b_{12}), $r_{13.2}$ (and $b_{13.2}$), and $r_{1(23)}$, analysis of variance is convenient.

Table 36.3 summarizes the results of our analysis. Note that all entries for variation and degrees of freedom, except the last, can be obtained by cumulative subtraction. The tests are as follows:

Gross relationship of X_1 with X_2:

$$F_{1(2)} = \frac{s_{1(2)}^2}{s_{1.2}^2} = \frac{2{,}561{,}600}{6{,}972} = 367;$$

$$\nu_1 = 1, \quad \nu_2 = 19, \quad F_{.001} = 15.08.$$

Since there is a highly significant relationship between X_1 and X_2 (i.e., between Y and X), we may now proceed to test the net relationship between X_1 and X_3 i.e., between Y and X^2).

Net relationship of X_1 with X_3:

$$F_{13.2} = \frac{s_{13.2}^2}{s_{1.23}^2} = \frac{58,500}{4,109} = 14.2;$$

$$\nu_1 = 1, \quad \nu_2 = 18, \quad F_{.01} = 8.285 \quad \text{and} \quad F_{.001} = 15.38.$$

The relationship is significant. In each of the above cases we could compute $t = \sqrt{F}$, but it hardly seems worth the trouble. Since both the gross relationship with X_2 and the net relationship with X_3 are significant, we would intuitively expect the relationship with X_2 and X_3 combined to be significant.

Relationship of X_1 with X_2 and X_3 together:

$$F_{1(23)} = \frac{s_{1(23)}^2}{s_{1.23}^2} = \frac{1,310,000}{4,109} = 319;$$

$$\nu_1 = 2, \quad \nu_2 = 18, \quad F_{.001} = 10.39.$$

The relationship is highly significant.

Multiple Nonlinear Correlation

Suppose we have one dependent variable Y, and two independent variables W and X, and the relationship is of this type:

$$Y = a + bW + cW^2 + dX + eX^2 + fX^3.$$

Now let $X_1 = Y$, $X_2 = W$, $X_3 = W^2$, $X_4 = X$, $X_5 = X^2$, $X_6 = X^3$. The estimating equation can then be written

$$X_{1(23456)} = a_{1(23456)} + b_{12.3456}X_2 + b_{13.2456}X_3$$
$$+ b_{14.2356}X_4 + b_{15.2346}X_5 + b_{16.2345}X_6.$$

The problem can then be handled by a simple extension of the methods of Chapter 35.

If a chart similar to Chart 35.1 were drawn for the above relationship, with horizontal axes for W and X and a vertical axis for Y, all of the curves for vertical sections taken parallel to W and X would be nonlinear, but the curves for parallel sections would be parallel.

Joint Correlation

Sometimes the relationship between variables 1 and 2 may change as variable 3 changes. For example, the amount spent for some commodity may vary with age and income of the persons considered, and the effect of income on the amount spent may vary with age. An appropriate type of equation might be

$$Y_1 = a + bW + cX + dWX.$$

Now let $X_1 = Y$, $X_2 = W$, $X_3 = X$, $X_4 = WX$. The estimating equation can then be written

$$X_{1(234)} = a_{1(234)} + b_{12.34}X_2 + b_{13.29}X_3 + b_{14.23}X_4.$$

If a chart similar to Chart 35.1 were drawn for such a relationship, all of the slopes would be linear for vertical sections taken parallel to the X_2 or X_3 axis, but the steepness of the slope would depend on where the section was taken.

Sometimes relationships are both nonlinear and joint. For example,

$$Y = a + b_1W + b_2X + c_1W^2 + c_2WX + c_3X^2.$$

This may be written in the usual form with $X_1 = Y$, $X_2 = W$, $X_3 = X$, $X_4 = W^2$, $X_5 = WX$, and $X_6 = X^2$.

Deflation vs. Regression

The term *deflation* is sometimes used in a limited sense: to adjust for price changes. Thus, in analyzing the factors affecting the price of oranges we might adjust the price of oranges by dividing orange prices by an index of the price of competing commodities, say an index of food prices. Then we could correlate the deflated orange prices with the quantity of oranges produced. The alternative is to consider the price of oranges the independent variable with quantity produced and food prices the independent variables. The method of deflation has one advantage. Since the food price index is not used as a separate variable it does not result in the loss of a degree of freedom. On the other hand, deflation is an inflexible tool; the true relationship may be more complicated than can be expressed by dividing one variable by another.

The word deflation also has a broader meaning. Thus we may divide the production of oranges by the number of people in the United States, obtaining per capita production of oranges. Then we could find the relationship between price of oranges adjusted for the price of foodstuffs, and per capita production of oranges. The alternative is to consider the price of oranges as the independent variable, with production of oranges, population, and food prices the independent variables.

Adjustment for Trend

A common illustration of deflation is the adjustment for trend of the variables to be correlated. This is ordinarily done by *dividing* the different variables by their trend values. The alternative to deflation is to consider time as another independent variable, the different years being assigned integral values beginning with 0 for the first year and increasing by 1 for each year.

Another method of deflation is to *subtract* the trend values from the original data. This is not always an appropriate method, but it gets the same results as the method of regression. Let $Y =$ price $-$ price trend and $X =$ production $-$ production trend. The estimating equation is $Y_X = a + b_{YX}X$. To use the method of regression we let $X_1 =$ price, $X_2 =$ production, and $X_3 =$ time. The estimating equation is $X_{1(23)} = a_{1(23)} + b_{12.3}X_2 + b_{13.2}X_3$. In these two equations b_{YX} and $b_{12.3}$ have the same value. Also $r_{YX} = r_{12.3}$.

Whenever a series is adjusted for trend before correlating it with some other series, similarly adjusted, or whenever time is used as an independent variable, there is an implicit admission that the analysis is incomplete. There are factors affecting the variables that are unknown, or at least too numerous and too small to bother about. Time is a sort of waste-basket variable into which are thrown the actual causal factors. If we could take into consideration all of these factors, time could be left out of the equation.

It is not, of course, always appropriate to adjust for trend, or use time as a separate variable, when by so doing the results of the analysis are changed. It may be that the long-run effects of the independent variable are different from the short-run effects. If we are interested in the short-run effects, the data should be adjusted for trend or time considered as a separate variable. If we are interested in the long-run effects, neither of these things should be done. Variables which are short-run causes, and others which are long-run causes, should be included in the model.

Use of Logarithms with Time Series

If we wish to adjust for trend by division we could let

$$Y = \log \frac{\text{price}}{\text{price trend}} = \log \text{price} - \log \text{price trend};$$

$$X = \log \frac{\text{production}}{\text{production trend}} = \log \text{production} - \log \text{production trend}.$$

The estimating equation is $Y = a + b_{YX}X$. If time is considered an independent variable, let $X_1 = \log$ price, $X_2 = \log$ production, $X_3 =$ time. The estimating equation is $X_{1(23)} = a_{1(23)} + b_{12.3}X_2 + b_{13.2}X_3$. Again $b_{YX} = b_{12.3}$ and $r_{YX} = r_{12.3}$. Since it usually seems reasonable to deflate by division rather than by subtraction, it is often logical to employ logarithms throughout, as indicated in the present paragraph. The results of the two methods will be the same if the trends are exponential trends, obtained by fitting a straight line to the logarithms by the method of least squares.

If we wish to deflate the price series, not by its secular trend, but by a price index of competing commodities, the same considerations apply.

The Problem of Identification

When correlating time series data, especially when one series is a price series and the other a quantity series, it is sometimes difficult to interpret the meaning of an estimating equation fitted to the data by the method of least squares. It is generally admitted that the higher the price the smaller the amount that will be bought; on the other hand the higher the price the larger the amount that will be offered for sale. So when we have fitted an equation in which quantity is a function of price, especially when the adjustment of demand and supply to price is rapid, and all that is produced is also sold during each time period, it often is difficult to say whether it is a demand function, a supply function, or merely a line fitted to the intersection of different demand and supply curves at different times.

If it can be assumed that there has been no change in demand, then the relationship between price and quantity can be interpreted as a demand function. On the other hand, if the factors affecting supply can be assumed to be constant, the relation between price and quantity can be interpreted as a supply function.

In other cases the quantity produced depends on the price in the preceding year(s) and other factors; but not on the current price. If that is the case we can use two single equations to describe the relationship:

Supply function: quantity = function of price last year and perhaps other variables;

Demand function: quantity = function of current price and perhaps other variables.

Each equation can now be solved separately, by methods with which we are familiar.

Sometimes, however, it is necessary to set up not one single equation, but a system of equations. For example:

Supply function: quantity = function of (price; cost of production);
Demand function: quantity = function of (price; national income).

We now have two equations, each of which is *identified*. The criterion for identification is too difficult for an elementary book, but it should be noticed that national income appears in the demand equation but not in the supply equation; whereas cost of production appears in the supply equation, but not in the demand equation.

There are various ways of solving systems of equations that are identified, but they are all rather complicated, and beyond the scope of this book.

The Multiple-partial Correlation Coefficient

The multiple-partial correlation coefficient is the coefficient of multiple correlation of the dependent variable with two or more independent variables, when all of the variables have been adjusted for the effect of one or more other variables.[3] For example:

$r_{1(234).5}$ is the coefficient of multiple correlation of $x_{1.5}$ with $x_{2.5} x_{3.5}$ and $x_{4.5}$;

$r_{1(45).23}$ is the coefficient of multiple correlation of $x_{1.23}$ with $x_{4.23}$ and $x_{5.23}$.

In general,

(36.1)
$$r^2_{1i(jk...).tu...} = \frac{\Sigma\, x^2_{i(jk...).tu...}}{\Sigma\, x^2_{i.tu...}}.$$

Thus,

$$r^2_{1(345).2} = \frac{\Sigma\, x^2_{1(345).2}}{\Sigma\, x^2_{1.2}},$$

where
$$\Sigma\, x^2_{1(345).2} = x^2_{1(2345)} - x^2_{1(2)},$$

and
$$\Sigma\, x^2_{1.2} = \Sigma\, x^2_1 - \Sigma\, x^2_{1(2)}.$$

Similarly,

$$r^2_{1(45).23} = \frac{\Sigma\, x^2_{1(45)23}}{\Sigma x^2_{1.23}},$$

where
$$\Sigma\, x^2_{1(45).23} = \Sigma\, x^2_{1(2345)} - \Sigma\, x^2_{1(23)},$$

and
$$\Sigma\, x^2_{1.23} = \Sigma\, x^2_1 - \Sigma\, x^2_{1(23)}.$$

---

[3] For an expository article on this coefficient, see Dudley J. Cowden, "The Multiple-Partial Correlation Coefficient," *Journal of the American Statistical Association*, Vol. 47, September, 1952, pp. 442–456. A number of methods of computation are given in that article, including the method suggested in this text. Testing significance is also explained.

Chapter 37

CORRELATION OF TIME SERIES
AND FORECASTING

All businessmen are forced to make forecasts; and budgetary programs are one important type. Decisions are constantly being made in the light of anticipated economic conditions. All forecasting techniques are designed either to limit the reliance upon judgment, or to make judgment more reliable by providing significant facts and relationships. Although complete reliance cannot be placed upon any procedure, statistical or otherwise, any clue that may be helpful is worth noting.

The methods of forecasting discussed in this chapter are:

1. Forecasting a series by itself, sometimes referred to as the economic rhythm method.
2. Forecasting a series by other series, sometimes referred to as the cyclical sequence method.
3. Specific historical analogy.
4. Surveys of plans and opinions.
5. Cross-cut economic analysis.

Correlation of Cyclical Relatives

Before correlating time series it is usually desirable to eliminate trend and seasonal variations from both series, since ordinarily interest centers in comparisons of cyclical changes.[1] If the trend is not removed, the correlation coefficient will indicate partly whether or not the trends of the two series are similar.[2] This, however, can better be determined merely by comparing the trends directly, either mathematically or graphically.

If we are interested in long-run relationships, a plausible case can be made in favor of correlating the data without adjustment for trend. It should be

---

[1] Instead of removing trend the practice is sometimes followed of using time as a second independent variable. The observations representing time x_3 are usually consecutive numbers with 0 assigned to the central year or month. The numerical value of the *partial* correlation coefficient $r_{12.3}$ is the same that would be obtained if each of the two series were adjusted by *subtracting* the straight line trend values, and the *simple r* computed for the two *adjusted* series.

[2] If a pronounced seasonal is not removed from monthly data (and assuming that the trends are unimportant) the coefficient will indicate to a considerable extent the similarity or dissimilarity of the two seasonal indexes instead of the relationship between the cyclical movements.

**Chart 37.1—Two Artificial Time Series with
Identical Cycles, but with Trends
having Opposite Signs**

A. Original data

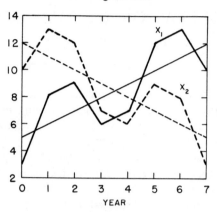

B. Cycles

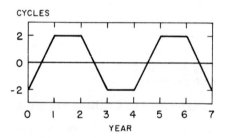

C. Scatter diagram of original data

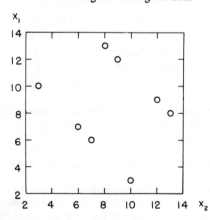

**Chart 37.2—Two Artificial Time Series
with Identical Trends, but Cycles
Negatively Correlated**

A. Original data

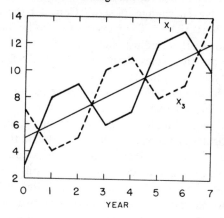

YEAR

B. Cycles

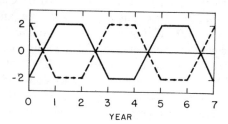

YEAR

C. Scatter diagram of original data

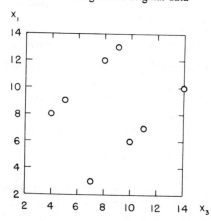

remembered, though, that similarity of trends is an extremely weak indication of causal relationship.[3]

Failure to adjust the data for trend (assuming no seasonal or that seasonal movements have been eliminated) may make the correlation coefficient larger or smaller, and may even change its sign. Consider the two artificial time series plotted as Chart 37.1A. Their cycles are similar but their trends are in opposite directions. If we adjust each series for trend (by subtracting its trend values[4]), we get the cycles shown by Chart 37.1B. Both series have exactly the same cycles, and the correlation between them is $r = +1.0$. If, however, we plot the *unadjusted* series as a scatter diagram, we get the results of Chart 37.1C. The correlation coefficient is $r = -0.135$. If we had correlated the unadjusted data for the years 2 through 5, the cycles would have been of more importance compared with the trend, and the correlation would have been positive. If, on the other hand, the series had been over a longer period of time, with the same tendencies in operation, the trend would have assumed even greater importance, compared with the cycles, and the correlation coefficient would have had a still larger negative value.

Consider also the two artificial times series plotted as Chart 37.2A. Their trends are the same but their cycles are contrasting. If we adjust each series for trend (by subtraction), we get the cycles shown by Chart 37.2B. Their cycles fluctuate in opposite directions at the same time, and the correlation between them is $r = -1.0$. If, however, we plot the *unadjusted* series as a scatter diagram, we get the results of Chart 37.2C. The correlation coefficient is $r = +.135$. If we had correlated the unadjusted data for the years 2 through 5, the trend would have been of more importance compared with the cycles, and the correlation would have been negative. If, on the other hand, the series had been over a longer period of time, with the same tendencies in operation, the trend would have assumed even greater importance, compared with the cycles, and the correlation coefficient would have had a still larger positive value.

Forecasting a Series by Itself

Most methods of forecasting a series by itself are naïve, in that they are lacking in theoretical basis.

Synthesis of projected time series components. It will be recalled that the components of an economic time series are: trend T; cycle C; seasonal S; and irregular I. Also, the components are usually considered to be multiplicative.

$$Y = TCSI.$$

---

[3] This should seem reasonable when we recall that a straight line trend has only one degree of freedom to fluctuate around the mean; a second-degree trend has only one additional degree of freedom; and so on.

[4] If we divide by the trend values, the results are slightly different, but the conclusions are similar.

If we can project the TC and S components, we can synthesize $Y - I$ by multiplication. We cannot, of course, project irregular movements, because their movements are not systematic.

Let us illustrate the mechanics of forecasting as of June, 1957, Sears, Roebuck and Company sales for 1957.

**Table 37.1—1957 Projection of Trend for Sears,
Roebuck and Company Monthly Sales**
(Sales are in millions of dollars.)

Month	X	$T = Y_X$
January	132	307.72
February	133	308.87
March	134	310.02
April	135	311.16
May	136	312.31
June	137	313.46
July	138	314.61
August	139	315.76
September	140	316.90
October	141	318.05
November	142	319.20
December	143	320.35

$Y_X = 156.159 + 1.14818X$ ($X = 0$ for January, 1946).

Trend projection. In Chapter 28, we found that the linear trend equation fitted to average monthly sales, by years, 1947–1956, with origin at January, 1946, was $Y_X = 156.159 + 1.14818X$. The value of X for January, 1957, is 132, and the trend value is

$$T = Y_X = 156.159 + (1.14818)(132) = \$307.72 \text{ million.}$$

The results for each month of 1957 are as shown in Table 37.1.

Trend projection for one year even on the basis of only 10 years is not unreasonable, but a projection becomes increasingly hazardous as the trend is projected further and further into the future. These difficulties should be kept in mind.

1. The economic causes affecting the trend may change after the type of trend equation has been determined.

2. The type of equation selected may not have been correct. There are many types of equations, and one of the bases of choosing among them is the way the trend behaves upon extension. Thus the trend is not used to forecast, but the forecast is used to select a trend.

3. The trend constants, and therefore the trend values, are subject to sampling error. The error in the trend values is a function of x, getting progressively larger as the trend is extended further from the chronological center of the data.

**Table 37.2—1957 Projection of Sears,
Roebuck and Company Monthly
Sales Moving Seasonal
Index Numbers
(Per cent.)**

Month	Index number
January	76.0
February	72.0
March	89.0
April	98.0
May	104.5
June	108.0
July	91.5
August	101.5
September	101.0
October	104.0
November	110.0
December	147.0

Source: Read from Chart 30.8.

**Table 37.3—1957 Projection of Sears, Roebuck and Company
Monthly Sales TS Values
(Sales are in millions of dollars.)**

Month	Trend T	Seasonal S (per cent)	TS
January	307.72	76.0	233.87
February	308.87	72.0	222.39
March	310.02	89.0	275.92
April	311.16	98.0	304.94
May	312.31	104.5	326.36
June	313.46	108.0	338.54
July	314.61	91.5	287.87
August	315.76	101.5	320.50
September	316.90	101.0	320.07
October	318.05	104.0	330.77
November	319.20	110.0	351.12
December	320.35	147.0	470.91

Source: Table 37.1 and 37.2.

Seasonal projection. The moving seasonal index numbers for 1957, read from Chart 30.8, are as given in Table 37.2.

This projection is fairly safe, provided a conscious effort has been exercised in the extensions to prevent the seasonal trends from turning sharply upward or downward for 1956 and 1957.

Projection of TS movements. This projection is shown in Table 37.3.

It is accomplished by multiplying the T projections of Table 37.1 by the S projections of Table 37.3.

Before monthly forecasts of actual sales can be made, some allowance must be made for cyclical influences.

Projection of cycle. Projection of the cyclical movements is the crucial part of the method of projection. Not only is it the most difficult component to project, but it is the most important one to do accurately. The other

Chart 37.3—Cyclical-Irregular and Cyclical Movements of Sears, Roebuck and Company Sales, and Projection of Cycle through 1957

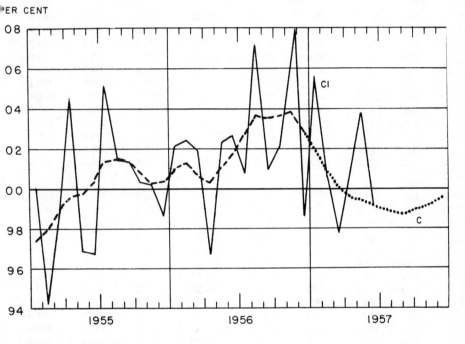

Source of data: Table 37.4.

methods considered in this chapter have to do, primarily, with forecasting cyclical movements.

In order to gain perspective, we shall go back to the beginning of 1955, and include also the data that are available for the first six months of 1957. The values of TCI are computed in Table 37.4, and the values in the other columns are the same, through 1956, as those of Tables 31.2 and 31.3. The values of CI and C_2, given in Table 37.4, are plotted on Chart 37.3. Projections of the C_2 values, given in Table 37.4, were read from Chart 37.3. It is to be noted that the projection of the cycle is not purely mechanical, as were those of T, S, and TS, but involve a considerable amount of judgment. Such projections should be made for forecasting purposes only by one who is thoroughly familiar with the business under consideration, and then only

Table 37.4—Computation of Deseasonalized Data for Sears, Roebuck and
Company Sales, January 1955–June 1957, Computation of Cyclical
Movements, 1955–1956, and Projection of Cyclical Movements
through 1957
(Sales are in millions of dollars.)

Year and month	Sales TCSI	Seasonal movements S	Deseasonalized data TCI	Trend T	Cyclical-irregular movements CI	First smoothing C_1	Cycle (second smoothing) C_2
1955:							
Jan.	212.9	76.0	280.13	280.16	100.0	96.3	97.4
Feb.	190.6	72.0	264.72	281.13	94.2	98.5	97.9
Mar.	242.8	87.0	279.08	282.46	98.8	99.5	98.8
Apr.	287.4	97.0	296.29	283.61	104.5	98.5	99.6
May	285.7	103.5	276.04	284.76	96.9	100.3	99.7
June	293.1	106.0	276.51	285.90	96.7	100.3	100.3
July	273.2	90.5	301.88	287.05	105.2	100.5	101.4
Aug.	293.8	100.5	292.34	288.20	101.4	102.2	101.5
Sep.	299.2	102.0	293.33	289.35	101.4	102.2	101.3
Oct.	311.7	107.0	291.31	290.50	100.3	99.9	100.7
Nov.	321.5	110.0	292.27	291.64	100.2	99.9	100.3
Dec.	424.2	147.0	288.57	292.79	98.6	100.3	100.4
1956:							
Jan.	228.1	76.0	300.13	293.94	102.1	101.6	101.0
Feb.	217.6	72.0	302.22	295.09	102.4	101.0	101.2
Mar.	265.6	88.0	301.82	296.24	101.9	100.9	100.7
Apr.	280.4	97.5	287.59	297.39	96.7	100.5	100.3
May	317.6	104.0	305.38	298.53	102.3	99.9	101.0
June	329.0	107.0	307.48	299.68	102.6	102.0	101.7
July	276.0	91.0	303.30	300.83	100.8	103.7	102.7
Aug.	326.9	101.0	323.66	301.98	107.2	102.6	103.6
Sep.	310.8	101.5	306.21	303.13	101.0	104.1	103.5
Oct.	327.6	105.5	310.52	304.27	102.1	103.5	103.6
Nov.	362.4	110.0	329.45	305.42	107.9	103.1	103.8
Dec.	445.0	147.0	302.72	306.57	98.7	003.9	102.8
1957:							
Jan.	246.9	76.0	324.87	307.72	105.6	102.2	102.0
Feb.	223.8	72.0	310.83	308.87	100.6	100.0	101.0
Mar.	269.8	89.0	303.15	310.02	97.8	101.2	100.0
Apr.	307.4	98.0	313.67	311.16	100.8	...	99.6
May	338.3	104.5	323.73	312.31	103.7	...	99.4
June	335.8	108.0	310.93	313.46	99.2	...	99.2
July	...	91.5	...	314.61	...	...	99.0
Aug.	...	101.5	...	315.76	...	...	98.8
Sep.	...	101.0	...	316.90	...	...	98.8
Oct.	...	104.0	...	318.05	...	...	99.0
Nov.	...	110.0	...	319.20	...	...	99.2
Dec.	...	147.0	...	320.35	...	...	99.6

Source of data: Tables 31.2 and 31.3.

Table 37.5—Computation of *TC* Values for Sears, Roebuck and Company Sales, 1955–1956, and Projection through 1957
(Sales are in millions of dollars.)

Year and month		TCI	T	C	TC
1955:	Jan.	280.13	380.16	97.4	272.9
	Feb.	264.72	281.13	97.9	275.2
	Mar.	279.08	282.46	98.8	279.1
	Apr.	296.29	283.61	99.6	282.5
	May	276.04	284.76	99.7	283.9
	June	276.51	285.90	100.3	286.8
	July	301.88	287.05	101.4	291.1
	Aug.	292.34	288.20	101.5	292.5
	Sep.	293.33	289.35	101.3	293.1
	Oct.	291.31	290.50	100.7	292.5
	Nov.	292.27	291.64	100.3	292.5
	Dec.	288.57	292.79	100.4	294.0
1956:	Jan.	300.13	293.94	101.0	296.9
	Feb.	302.22	295.09	101.2	298.6
	Mar.	301.82	296.24	100.7	298.3
	Apr.	287.59	297.39	100.3	298.3
	May	305.38	298.53	101.0	301.5
	June	307.48	299.68	101.7	304.8
	July	303.30	300.83	102.7	309.0
	Aug.	323.66	301.98	103.6	312.9
	Sep.	306.21	303.13	103.5	313.7
	Oct.	310.52	304.27	103.6	315.2
	Nov.	329.45	305.42	103.8	317.0
	Dec.	302.72	306.57	102.8	315.2
1957:	Jan.	324.87	...	...	313.9
	Feb.	310.83	...	...	312.0
	Mar.	303.15	...	...	310.0
	Apr.	313.67	...	...	309.9
	May	323.73	...	...	310.4
	June	310.93	...	...	311.0
	July	...	...	...	311.5
	Aug.	...	...	...	312.0
	Sep.	...	...	...	313.1
	Oct.	...	...	...	314.9
	Nov.	...	...	...	316.6
	Dec.	...	...	...	319.1

Source: Table 37.4, except that 1957 *TC* values were read from Chart 37.4.

after careful analysis. The cyclical projection of Chart 37.3 and Table 37.4 are intended solely as an illustration of the arithmetic of the procedure, and not as the writer's forecast.

Projection of TC movements. Many people feel that it is easier to project trend and cycle in combination than it is to do so separately. Table 37.5 shows the *TCI, T,* and *C* from Table 37.4. Through 1956, the *TC* values were computed by multiplying T by C. The TC values are extended subjectively through 1957 on Chart 37.4, their values being read from the chart and entered in the TC column of Table 37.5.

Final estimate of sales. Table 37.6 shows, for 1957, the trend values and the cyclical estimates of Table 37.4. The TC values are from Chart 37.4 and Table 37.5, but they may also be obtained by taking the product of the T values and C values of Table 37.4. The S values are the same as those of

Chart 37.4—*TCI* and *TC* Movements of Sears, Roebuck and Company Sales, and Projection of *TC* through 1957

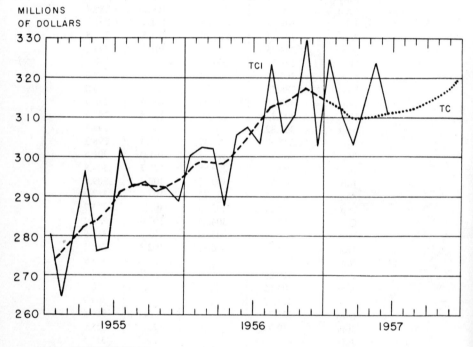

Source of data: Table 37.4.

Chart 30.8 and Table 37.4. The final estimates TCS are obtained by multiplying TC by S. No estimate is made of the irregular movements, since there is no basis for doing so.

Estimate of production and inventory. If a firm manufactures to stock, a manufacturing schedule can be set up permitting a fairly uniform rate of production throughout the year, but with fluctuating inventories. Let us assume that the sales forecast for 1947, by months, in physical units, is as indicated in Table 37.7. If it is advisable to have on hand at all times an inventory equal to two months' sales, the minimum inventory requirements at the beginning of each month are as indicated in column (3). If it is tentatively assumed that sales will remain 1,882 for January and February, 1948,

Table 37.6—Forecast of Sears, Roebuck and Company Sales for Second Half
of 1957 by Synthesis of Projected Components
(Sales are in millions of dollars.)

Month	T	C (per cent)	TC	S (per cent)	TCS
January	307.72	102.0	313.9	76.0	239
February	308.87	101.0	312.0	72.0	225
March	310.02	100.0	310.0	89.0	276
April	311.16	99.6	309.9	98.0	304
May	312.31	99.4	310.4	104.5	324
June	313.46	99.2	311.0	108.0	336
July	314.61	99.0	311.5	91.5	285
August	315.76	98.8	312.0	101.5	317
September	316.90	98.8	313.1	101.0	316
October	318.05	99.0	314.9	104.0	327
November	319.20	99.2	316.6	110.0	348
December	320.35	99.6	319.1	147.0	469

Source of data: Tables 37.4 and 37.5 and Chart 37.4.

Table 37.7—Budgeting Monthly Production and Inventories in Accordance
with Monthly Sales Forecast and Minimum Inventory Requirements

Month of year 1947 (1)	Sales forecast (2)	Minimum beginning inventory (3)	Production during month (4)	Estimated beginning inventory (5)
January	1,413	2,746	1,291	3,000
February	1,333	2,552	1,291	2,878
March	1,219	2,401	1,291	2,836
April	1,182	2,210	1,291	2,908
May	1,028	2,017	1,291	3,017
June	989	1,890	1,291	3,280
July	901	1,770	1,291	3,582
August	869	1,900	1,291	3,972
September	1,031	2,345	1,291	4,394
October	1,314	2,876	1,291	4,654
November	1,562	3,444	1,291	4,631
December	1,882	3,764	1,291	4,360
Total	14,723	...	15,492	...

the beginning inventory required at the end of December, 1947, will be the same as that required at the beginning of the month, namely 3,764. If the inventory on hand at the end of 1946 is 3,000, enough must be produced during the year to take care of expected sales during the year, and also to increase the inventory from 3,000 to 3,764. The average monthly production, therefore, should be

$$\frac{14,723 + 3,764 - 3,000}{12} = \frac{15,487}{12} = 1,291.$$

Consequently a monthly production of 1,291 is shown in column (4). The estimated inventory for the beginning of each month is obtained by subtracting from the beginning inventory of the preceding month the expected sales of that month, and adding the budgeted production. Thus, for the February 1 inventory we have

$$3,000 - 1,413 + 1,291 = 2,878.$$

For December 31, 1947, we would have

$$4,360 - 1,882 + 1,291 = 3,769.$$

This compares with the estimated requirement of 3,764. It should be noted that the estimated beginning inventory is larger than required for each month. If the preliminary estimates indicate that it will fall short for any month, it is necessary to build up the inventory for January 1 by the amount of the shortage, or else to increase the average production for the various months preceding that month by an amount sufficient to overcome the shortage. This type of planning is facilitated if the planning year is so selected that it will end with the seasonal peak.

*Harmonic analysis. The theory underlying harmonic analysis is that cycles are really periodic in nature, though their periodic nature may be masked because of the presence of two or more periodic waves of different lengths. The equation used in the harmonic analysis of a time series, where there is only one wavelike movement, is of the type

$$(37.1) \qquad Y_X = A \sin\left(360\frac{X}{T}\right) + B \cos\left(360\frac{X}{T}\right),$$

where $360\frac{X}{T}$ refers to the number of degrees, and T is the length of the cycle.

This equation is fitted to data that have been adjusted for trend. The amplitude of the curve, or distance from peak or trough of a wave to the mean value is

$$(37.2) \qquad R = \sqrt{A^2 + B^2}.$$

In fitting the curve, different trial values of T are used, and the value of T that gives the largest value of R is adopted.

Often an attempt is made to discover several periodic movements for a given time series, each of a different length. For example, one may be for 20 years, another for 10 years, and another for 4 years. There will then be 3 different equations, and three periodic curves. The cyclical movements are then taken as the sum of the 3 separate computed values for each month (or year). Though the separate curves will be periodic, the composite curve will not appear to be so.

The logical foundation for harmonic analysis is not very strong. External forces tend to disturb the inherent rhythm, if any; and when the wavelike movements are reestablished there is no reason for the peaks and troughs to coincide with extensions of the previous curve.

*Autoregression. One of the characteristics of most economic time series is that successive observations are interdependent; there is correlation between the values at time t and time $t - 1$, perhaps also between values at time t and time $t - 2$, and so on. If Y represents values of the series to be forecasted, the regression equation is

$$X_{0(12)} = a + b_{01.2}X_1 + b_{02.1}X_2,$$

where $X_{0(12)}$ is a value of Y at time t obtained from the estimating quotation;

X_1 is a value of Y at time $t - 1$;

X_2 is a value of Y at time $t - 2$.

Methods of Chapter 35 are used for obtaining the regression equation. The logical basis for the relationship indicated by the autoregression equation is not usually obvious.

Diffusion indexes. Let us consider a composite time series that is the sum or average of a large number of components. Usually all of the components will not reach cyclical peaks at the same time, nor will they reach cyclical troughs at the same time. On the other hand, the cyclical turning points will not be distributed at random over time, but most of the cyclical peaks will occur within a moderately short period of time (say a year), and most of the cyclical troughs also will occur within a moderately short period of time. This sort of behavior is perhaps inherent in a business economy, where industries are interdependent and the effects of any stimulus are gradually diffused over the entire economy.

Under the conditions stated, when approximately one half of the components have turned upward from their respective cyclical troughs, the composite series will also turn upward. Similarly, when approximately one half of the components have turned downward, the composite series will also turn downward. Therefore a *diffusion index* obtained by computing for each month the percentage of the number of series that are expanding[5] will lead

---

[5] A series is considered to be expanding if it is higher than its cyclical trough, but has not yet reached a cyclical peak.

the composite series. Chart 37.5 shows such an index computed by the National Bureau of Economic Research from approximately 700 time series. Notice that the diffusion index invariably turns up before the contraction period of general business (shaded area) is completed, and invariably turns down before the expansion period is completed.

An index of the type shown in Chart 37.5 is usually referred to as a *historical* diffusion index. The reason it is called a historical index is because

Chart 37.5—Historical Diffusion Index: Percentage of All-Inclusive Sample Undergoing Expansion

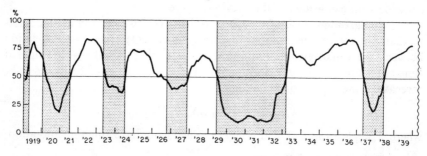

Source: *The American Statistician*, Vol. 8, April–May, 1954, p. 17. (Expansion measured by specific cycles. See Arthur F. Burns, *The Frontiers of Economic Knowledge*, Princeton University Press, 1954, p. 115. Shaded areas represent contraction of business cycles, according to NBER chronology.)

the turning points of each series are determined historically. Only after watching a series for several months can we have much basis for distinguishing a cyclical turning point from a random or other irregular fluctuation. This is the chief weakness of the historical diffusion index as a forecaster. By the time we know that a series has reached a cyclical turning point it is too late to use it as a forecaster.

Some experimentation has been made with *current* diffusion indexes. The simplest type is to count the number of series that are higher than the preceding month, and then express this number as a percentage of all series. In general, current diffusion indexes are so irregular in appearance that they are difficult to use. Since such an index typically ignores the relative magnitude of the change of indifferent series, and the relative importance of the different components, it is not apparent that one can forecast with such an index any better than by considering the behavior of the composite.

Percentage change in a time series. An economic time series does not ordinarily increase by a constant amount or percentage until it reaches its peak, and then decline by a constant amount or percentage until it reaches its trough. Rather there is some tendency to slacken its rate of growth or decline before it reaches a turning point. Therefore the percentage change in a time series will tend to change direction before the series itself. It might be thought that such a series of percentage changes would be useful for forecasting purposes. The difficulty is that the irregularities of a time series are accentuated by taking percentage changes. Therefore the series of percentage changes are very irregular in appearance, and hard to interpret.

The theory of equal areas. Since a least squares trend fitted to any time series equalizes the areas on a chart above and below the trend line, it is sometimes said that, in economic life, for every action there is an equal and opposite reaction. Going a step further, it is said that one can forecast the size of the next depression area from the size of the current prosperity area on a chart. The theoretical and practical weaknesses of this method are several.

1. It does not provide us any way of forecasting the next prosperity area. It is not claimed that each depression area is followed by an equal prosperity area.

2. It does not tell us when the current prosperity period will end, nor the duration or amplitude of the next depression. It can only foretell the product of duration and amplitude.

3. Each prosperity area is not necessarily followed by a prosperity area of the same magnitude. It is only the *total* areas that are equalized.

4. One must know the future behavior of cycles in order to obtain a trend which, *when projected*, will equalize areas above and below the line.

Forecasting a Series by Other Series

Since the cyclical turning points in all series do not occur at the same time, it is sometimes possible to predict the turning points, or even the values, of one series, if one or more forecasting series can be found that precede with some degree of regularity the one we wish to predict. There are various ways of estimating leads and lags of different series. The same results are not necessarily obtained by the different methods.

1. Compute the average number of months by which a given series precedes another at the cyclical turning points. The National Bureau of Economic Research has estimated the cyclical timing with respect to general business activity of 21 indicators. These are tabulated in Table 37.8, and the eight leading series shown graphically in Chart 37.6. Note that each of the 8 series turns up within the period of the 1949 recession.

2. Find the average behavior during several cycles for a specified period of time preceding and following the cyclical trough, cyclical peak, or other reference point, of the series used as a basis for comparison.

3. Find the number of months (or years) by which it is necessary to lag the forecaster in order to obtain the best correlation. A casual examination of Chart 37.7 suggests that it would be necessary to lag dwelling units started by three or four months in order to have the best correspondence

Chart 37.6—Eight Leading Series
Shaded areas represent contraction of business cycles, according to NBER chronology. Dots identify peaks and troughs of specific cycles.
(Arithmetic scale)

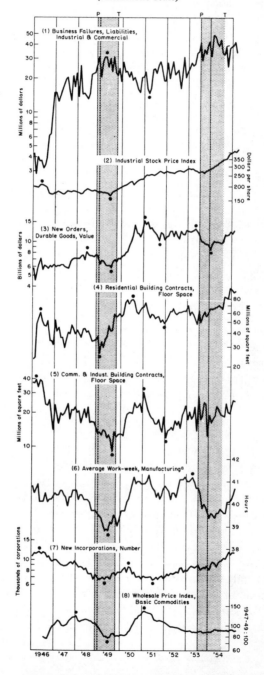

Source: Courtesy of Geoffrey H. Moore, National Bureau of Economic Research. For sources of current data, see "Analyzing Business Cycles," The *American Statistician*, April–May, 1954, Table 2.

of that series with the one for output of household durable goods. This is the method of *serial correlation*, and should be applied only to a time series for which the trend is relatively unimportant, or to one that has been adjusted for trend.

Table 37.8—Cyclical Timing of 21 Indicators

	Lead (−) or lag (+) in months at business cycle peaks and troughs			
Series	Average before 1939		At Nov. 1948 peak (3)	At Oct. 1949 trough (4)
	At peaks (1)	At troughs (2)		
Leading group:				
1 Business failures*	−10.5	−7.5	†	−7
2 Stock prices	−6.0	−7.2	−30	−4
3 New orders	−6.9	−4.7	−5	−3
4 Residential contracts	−6.2	−4.5	−30	−9
5 Commercial contracts ...	−5.2	−1.7	−32	−2
6 Work week	−3.8	−2.6	†	−6
7 Incorporations	−2.5	−3.5	−30	−6
8 Basic prices	−2.6	−3.2	−10	−4
Roughly coincident group:				
9 Employment	−0.2	−3.3	−1	0
10 Unemployment*	−1.5	+1.0	−11	0
11 Profits	−1.5	−1.8	−3	−5
12 Debits	+2.0	−4.3	0	−3
13 Carloadings	−0.3	−1.3	−21	0
14 Industrial production ...	+0.6	−2.2	−1	0
15 GNP	+2.5	+0.5	0	+1
16 Wholesale prices	−3.5	+3.7	0	−3
Lagging group:				
17 Personal income	+4.0	−0.2	−1	0
18 Retail sales	+3.8	+1.8	†	†
19 Installment debt	+5.0	+3.5	†	†
20 Rates on loans	+5.5	+4.8	−7	−5
21 Manufacturers' inventories	+6.5	+7.5	−4	−2

* Series 1 and 10 (business failures and unemployment) are compared invertedly with business cycles—that is, troughs in the series are compared with business cycle peaks, and peaks with business cycle troughs.
† No corresponding turn.
Source: *The American Statistician*, Vol. 8, April–May, 1954, p. 15. See also National Bureau of Economic Research, *Occasional Paper 31*, Tables 1 and 12, for the business cycle chronology, the historical series used for the timing record, and the periods covered before 1939.

Usually the data correlated are cyclical relatives, though other types of data are sometimes used, such as first differences or percentage changes. It is the percentage change in price, rather than the price level, that is likely to be correlated with sales or production data. Cumulated data are sometimes used as a forecaster, such as accumulated deficits or surpluses. Still another type of data which may be used consists of the ratio of one series to another. Ratios that have been used successfully are: new orders ÷ inventories; deposits ÷ loans; consumer expenditures ÷ disposable income.

Chart 37.7—Number of Dwelling Units Started, and Output of Major Household Durable Goods
(Seasonally adjusted, 1947–1949 = 100.)

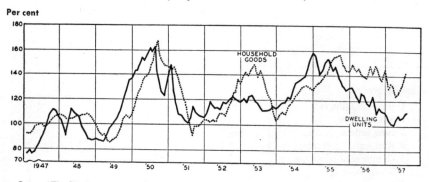

Source: The Cleveland Trust Company Business Bulletin, Vol. 38, October 16, 1957

The method of serial correlation (correlation with lagged independent variables) is apparently the method in greatest favor among forecasters. After forecasting the cyclical position it is, of course, necessary to multiply by the trend value and the seasonal index number, in order to forecast actual sales or production.

Serial correlation. For simplicity we shall apply the method of serial correlation to annual data, with Union Carbide and Carbon Company construction expenditures the series to be forecasted, and Union Carbide and Carbon Company sales the forecasting series. The data for each series are percentage deviations from trend. From inspection of Chart 37.8 it appears that although there is positive concurrent correlation between expenditures and sales, there is also some tendency for expenditures to lag about one year behind sales. To verify this hypothesis we correlate current expenditures with sales lagged no years, one year, and two years. See Table 37.9. The positive correlation Y and X_0, and between Y and X_1 suggests that the management of Union Carbide tends to increase construction expenditures when sales are currently large or have recently been large. The negative correlation between Y and X_2 does not, however, suggest that management

Chart 37.8—Union Carbide and Carbon Corporation Construction Expenditures, and Sales

A. Current sales

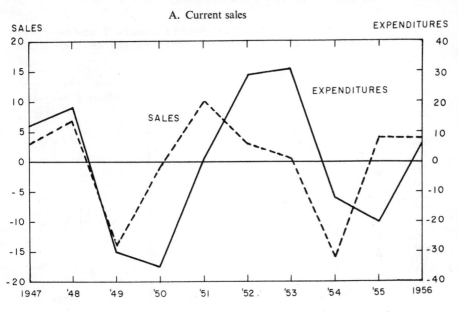

B. Sales lagged one year

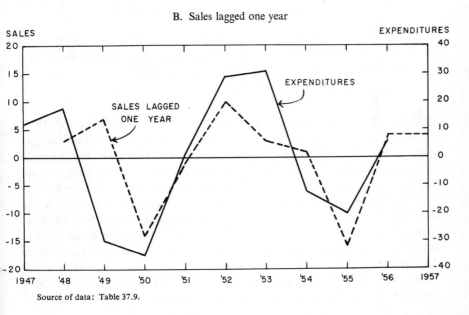

Source of data: Table 37.9.

cuts down on construction expenditures because of large sales 2 years previous. The negative correlation is a mechanical result of the shape and timing of the cycles in the two series.

Table 37.9—Union Carbide and Carbon Company Construction Expenditures, with Current Sales, Sales Lagged One Year, and Sales Lagged Two Years, and Correlation Coefficients

Year	Current expenditures Y	Current sales X_0	Current expenditures Y	Sales lagged one year X_1	Current expenditures Y	Sales lagged two years X_2
1947	12	3	..	..	..	..
1948	18	7	18	3	..	..
1949	−30	−14	−30	7	−30	3
1950	−35	−1	−35	−14	−35	7
1951	1	10	1	−1	1	−14
1952	29	3	29	10	29	−1
1953	31	1	31	3	31	10
1954	−12	−16	−12	1	−12	3
1955	−20	4	−20	−16	−20	1
1956	6	4	6	4	6	−16
r	$r_0 = +0.489$		$r_1 = +0.596$		$r_2 = -0.733$	

Source of data: Union Carbide and Carbon Corporation, *Annual Report for 1956*, pp. 38–39.

Forecasting the cyclical turning points is the important objective of forecasting, but in order to forecast actual sales we must have an estimating equation. Using the methods of Chapter 24, we obtain

$$Y_X = -0.7861 + 1.6415X_1.$$

Estimates are computed in Table 37.10, including a forecast for 1957. Chart 37.9 compares the actual and estimated expenditures. The broken line of this chart, which shows estimated expenditures, is substantially the same as the broken line of the Chart 37.8B, which shows lagged sales, except that the amplitude of fluctuation of the estimated expenditures is larger.

*Multiple serial correlation. Sometimes a forecast is based upon the correlation of a dependent variable with one lagged independent variable. Again, multiple regression may be used, involving several lagged independent variables. Often the forecast can be considerably improved by use of more than one lag for the independent variable or variables.

We can improve our estimates of construction expenditures by using a multiple estimating equation, including current sales X_0 as well as last years sales X_1. Using the methods of Chapter 35 we obtain

$$Y_X = -0.3325 + 1.6375X_0 + 1.9110X_1.$$

Table 37.10—Computation of Serial Regression Estimates of Union Carbide and Carbon Corporation Construction Expenditures from Union Carbide Sales

Year	Y	Sales X_0	Lagged sales X_1	Expenditure estimate Y_{X_1}	$a + b_0 X_0$	$b_1 X_1$	Expenditure estimate Y_{X_0, X_1}
1947	...	3	...	...	...	...	...
1948	18	7	3	4.14	11.13	5.73	16.86
1949	−30	−14	7	10.70	−23.26	13.38	−9.88
1950	−35	−1	−14	−23.77	1.97	−26.75	−28.72
1951	1	10	−1	−2.43	16.04	−1.91	14.13
1952	29	3	10	15.63	4.58	19.11	23.69
1953	31	1	3	4.14	1.305	5.73	7.03
1954	−12	−16	1	0.86	−26.53	1.91	−24.62
1955	−20	4	−16	−27.05	6.22	−30.58	−24.36
1956	6	4	4	5.78	6.22	7.64	13.86
1957	...	...	4	(5.78)	...	...	...
Total	12	...	...	−12.00*	...	...	−12.01

* Excluding 1957.
Regression equations:

$Y_{X_1} = -0.786 + 1.6415 X_1$;
$Y_{X_0, X_1} = -0.3325 + 1.6375 X_0 + 1.9110 X_1$.

Source of data: Table 37.9.

Chart 37.9—Union Carbide and Carbon Corporation Construction Expenditures and Estimates, Made from Regression Equations, with Sales the Independent Variable, and with Current Sales and Sales Lagged One Year the Independent Variables

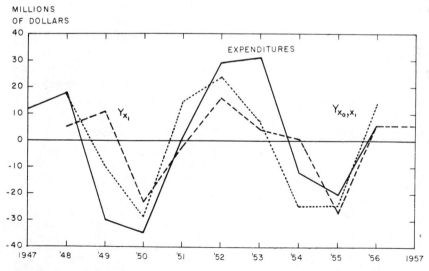

Source of data: Table 37.10.

Table 37.10 shows these estimates also, while on Chart 37.9 they are shown by a dotted line. Although the estimates are closer when we use the multiple regression equation, this equation cannot be used for forecasting purposes unless some way can be found of forecasting sales.

Serial correlation with monthly data. Since it would be very profitable to a businessman if he could predict, a number of months in advance, when business would pick up or recede, it is usually desirable to make forecasts more frequently than once a year. Usually percentages of trend are plotted on separate sheets of graph paper, with scales so chosen that the amplitudes of fluctuation will be about the same. These sheets are then placed together and held to a light, and when they are slid back and forth, some point is reached at which the correspondence appears to be closest. The correlation coefficient r is then computed, with the forecaster lagged the number of months L indicated by the chart, and also with the forecaster lagged $L - 2$, $L - 1$, $L + 1$, and $L + 2$ months. The lag that gives the largest value of r is the one used in the estimating equation.

Theoretical and practical difficulties. Several warnings concerning the use of this device in forecasting are in order.

1. The standard deviation of the errors made in actual forecasting is likely to be larger than the computed error of estimate, since the estimating equation applies to an era that is past. It is unlikely that the same set of causes will persist in future years. In particular,

    a. Consumer buying is affected by changes in the physical environment, by advertising appeals, and by the appearance of new products.

    b. Changes in methods of production affect the reaction of business to any stimulus.

    c. Changes in the social environment, such as business combinations, growth of pressure groups, and new legislation, are constantly affecting business behavior.

2 One should not mistake association for causation. Unless the regressional relationship has a causal basis, however, it is not likely to persist.

3. It is difficult, if not impossible, to determine the degree of significance to attach to our results. In the first place F and t tests are based upon the assumption that the data being analyzed are random samples of independent items drawn from a larger population. In economic time series, however, neither of these conditions is fulfilled. Each value in an economic time series is affected by preceding items and, in turn, affects the value of succeeding items. The number of degrees of freedom therefore is fewer than the number of observations, but exactly how many less it is difficult to say. Also, as indicated above, the economic order is progressively changing. Each period studied is a unique situation, not a random occurrence which might happen at any time; though it is possible to regard any given set of data as being a sample result of a given set of causes operating in a chance manner.

In the second place, the figures were juggled, so to speak, when the fore-casting series was lagged in order to get the best correlation. When there is no correlation for the synchronous data, some correlation can almost always be produced by such a procedure; and if there is some correlation, it is usually possible to increase it.[6] It is advisable, therefore, not only to include a considerable period of time in the series being correlated, but also to divide the period into two or more subperiods, comparing the results for the different subperiods, before coming to anything but the most tentative conclusion.

4. The degree of correlation obtained between two series depends on the nature of the trend around which the cyclical movements are measured. The timing of the cyclical movements may be similar (after adjustment for lag); but the relative amplitude of the deviations of the two series may vary over different segments of time. This difficulty may sometimes be overcome by using a more flexible trend. Another device is to correlate either differences between one month and the preceding, or percentages of the preceding month. When this is done the data are not previously adjusted for trend, since these methods partially eliminate the trend.

5. It is sometimes hard to tell which series is the forecaster. Although series A may precede series B at recessions, series B may typically precede series A at revivals. In other cases, series A when lagged may precede series B with positive correlation, but series B, when lagged, may precede series A with negative correlation.[7] Thus expanding business may bring about higher interest rates, but high interest rates may bring about a business decline.

6. Often the series we wish to forecast is one that moves early in the business cycle. Stock prices are an example of such a series.

7. Another factor that impairs the usefulness of this method is the scarcity of time series on a basis shorter than a month. It is quite possible that weekly, daily, or hourly data might bring to light relationships which are known and utilized only by a few "insiders." It does not seem logical that the cause-and-effect relationships which supposedly surround us on every side must take a month or more for their development. There must be many that work out in a few days, a few hours, or nearly instantaneously. As data are made available upon a weekly, daily, or more frequent basis, it is conceivable that very reliable lags and leads may be obtained. These may assist in accurate forecasting and improved control of business processes by the businessman.

---

[6] For an illustration of rather high correlation obtained by correlating chance data after adjusting for lag, see F. E. Croxton and D. J. Cowden, *Practical Business Statistics*, 1st ed. Prentice-Hall, Inc., Englewood Cliffs, N. J., 1934, pp. 457–460.

[7] It is even conceivable that a series representing the effect will precede a series representing the cause. Thus stock prices are a function of earnings and dividends; but in evaluating a stock one usually strongly considers his expectation of future earnings and dividends.

Specific Historical Analogy

Since all cycles are not uniform in amplitude or duration, some fore-casters make use of history, not by projecting any fancied economic rhythm into the future, or relying on any repetitive sequence, but by selecting some specific previous situation which has many of the earmarks of the present, and concluding that what happened in that previous situation will happen in the present one. As of the summer of 1945, a favorite analogy was that of the periods following World War I and World War II. It was pointed out that there was a short demobilization depression in 1919, a restocking boom in 1920 followed by a sharp deflation trough in 1921, and that business was carried forward by a revival of the durable goods industry in ensuing years. In the early part of 1957, the inflationary tendencies brought to some people's minds the fact that there were inflationary tendencies (though not entirely of the same type) also in 1929, and that they culminated in a stock market crash and business collapse.

Although it is undoubtedly true that partial analogies can be discovered in past history, one should be careful to take into consideration the differences, as well as the similarities, between past and present situations. The differences in the amount and type of government intervention in economic affairs should be especially noted.

Surveys of Plans and Opinions

By analysis of plans and/or opinions of economists, business executives, or consumers, as revealed by questionnaires, some idea of prospects for future months can be obtained. Among organizations using this technique are *Fortune* Magazine, United States Department of Commerce, Securities and Exchange Commission, and University of Michigan Survey Research Center.

Although considered helpful for forecasting purposes, two factors diminish somewhat the usefulness of the surveys of inclination to buy. First, a fairly large proportion of the respondents apparently do not take their answers seriously. Second, consumer plans are usually not very firm, and may be changed rather quickly. Consumer plans are not very responsive to small changes in price and income, but are unduly affected by spectacular occurrences.

It is not necessarily the case that best results are obtained by a representative sample. When sampling opinions, the sample should contain only those who are well informed and whose opinions are sound. In general, executives from large firms have means of obtaining better advice than do those of small firms. When sampling the plans of businessmen and consumers, a sample of people who will carry out their plans, and who have already made commitments is better than one of people who do not know what they will do, or who are likely to change their minds.

Some polls of opinions contain many answers that are uninformed, careless guesses. If included, such opinions tend to average out. There is evidence that many of the opinions are based on simple projections of recent patterns. The cyclical peaks and troughs are therefore not anticipated. Another tendency is to underestimate the extent of a cyclical rise or a cyclical fall.

Cross-cut economic analysis. This method is based upon the theory that no two cycles are alike, but that like causes always produce like results. All the factors bearing upon a given situation are assembled, and relying upon his knowledge of economic processes, the forecaster concludes whether the situation is favorable or unfavorable. Although the method is essentially nonstatistical, it is possible to develop a statistical technique by assigning weights to each factor and then counting the score to see whether the net result is favorable or unfavorable.

At the middle of 1957, the writer counted 6 favorable factors mentioned in business periodicals, and 11 unfavorable factors. Business economists were somewhat baffled by the mixed indications. However, some were impressed with the theory that the many built-in or managed stabilizing devices would avert a serious depression. The words "rolling adjustment" and "sideways movement" were in vogue. The majority opinion seemed to be that there would be little change in the fortunes of business until the last quarter, when most time series would show improving business! This view may perhaps be attributed to professional optimism, and partly to a psychological lag.

Chapter 38

GROWTH CURVES

A growth curve is here defined as one in which the amount or percentage of growth at any point of time (or during any period of time) is a function of the level attained at that point of time (or at the beginning of that period of time). In this chapter we shall consider these growth curves: exponential; second-degree exponential; modified exponential; Gompertz; logistic.

The procedure for fitting an exponential or second-degree exponential is to put the equation in linear form and then to use the method of least squares. For the Gompertz and logistic, the easiest procedure is to convert them into a modified exponential form and use the method of selected points. The method of partial totals is slightly more laborious.

Exponential

The exponential equation, which has the form

$$(38.1) \qquad Y_X = AB^X,$$

describes a series which is changing by a constant ratio B. Thus if $B = 1.10$ the trend value for each year is 110 per cent of the preceding year. The percentage rate of growth is $100(B - 1)$. Thus if $B = 1.10$, the rate of growth is 10 per cent. The exponential curve is often called a compound interest curve. On semi-logarithmic paper it is a straight line.

If we let $a = \log A$ and $b = \log B$, we can write the equation as a logarithmic straight line.

$$(38.2) \qquad \text{Log } Y_X = a + bX.$$

In the above equation X takes the values of $0, 1, 2, ..., n - 1$, if n is odd, and $0, 2, 4, ..., 2(n - 1)$ if n is even. In deviation form the logarithmic straight line equation is

$$(38.3) \qquad \text{Log } Y_x = \bar{Y}_{\log} + bx, \quad \text{where } \bar{Y}_{\log} = \frac{\Sigma (\log Y)}{n}.$$

In this equation x takes the values $..., -3, -2, -1, 0, 1, 2, 3, ...$, if n is odd and $..., -5, -3, -1, 1, 3, 5, ...$, if n is even.

Obviously the first differences of the log Y_X values have a constant value

b. Since equation (38.3) is in linear form we can use the usual least squares formula:[1]

$$(38.4) \qquad b = \frac{\Sigma \, (x \log Y)}{\Sigma \, x^2} \, .$$

To obtain a for equation (38.2) we compute

$$(38.5) \qquad a = \overline{Y}_{\log} - b\overline{X}.$$

For an illustration we shall use the Pittsburgh Plate Glass data of Table 38.1. The values needed for the preceding equations are also in Table 38.1.

Table 38.1—Sales of Pittsburgh Plate Glass Company and Computation of Exponential Trend, 1947–1956

(Sales are in millions of dollars.)

Year	X	x	Sales Y	$\log Y$	$x \log Y$	$\log Y_x$	Y_x
1947	0	−9	265.1	2.42341	−21.81069	2.40965	256.8
1948	2	−7	283.1	2.45194	−17.16358	2.45047	282.1
1949	4	−5	286.8	2.45758	−12.28790	2.49128	309.9
1950	6	−3	339.4	2.53071	−7.59213	2.53210	340.5
1951	8	−1	407.6	2.61023	−2.61023	2.57292	347.0
1952	10	1	407.5	2.61013	2.61013	2.61373	410.9
1953	12	3	457.1	2.66001	7.98003	2.65455	451.4
1954	14	5	435.7	2.63919	13.19595	2.69536	495.9
1955	16	7	586.9	2.76856	19.37992	2.73618	544.7
1956	18	9	604.6	2.78147	25.03323	2.77700	598.4
Sum	90	0	4,073.8	25.93323	6.73473	25.93324	4,064.6
Mean	9	0	...	2.593328	...	...	...

Source of data: Table 34.1.

$Y_x = 2.59332 + 0.020408x.$

Substituting, we have

$$\overline{Y}_{\log} = \frac{25.93323}{10} = 2.593323;$$

$$b = \frac{6.73473}{330} = 0.020408.$$

The trend equation is

$$Y_x = 2.593323 + 0.20408x.$$

---

[1] We use the method of selected points in a later section, when fitting the modified exponential. That method can be used for the exponential also. If the two selected Y-values are y_0 and y_1, then $A = y_0$, and $B^r = y_1/y_0$, where $r = n - 1$.

This equation may be used to compute the logarithmic values shown in the log Y_x column of Table 38.1. The total of this column agrees with the total of the log Y column. The trend values are obtained by looking up the antilogs of the values in the log Y_x column. Using equation (38.5) we find that

$$a = 2.593323 - (0.020408)(9) = 2.40965.$$

This is the 1947 value for log Y_x. Therefore the trend equation can be stated in either of these ways:

$$Y_x = 2.59332 + 0.020408x;$$
$$Y_X = 2.40965 + 0.020408x.$$

If we want the time units to be one year, we multiply b by 2, obtaining

$$Y_x = 2.59332 + 0.040816x;$$
$$Y_X = 2.40965 + 0.040816X.$$

If we wish, we can take the antilog of each side of the equation, $Y_X = 2.40965 + 0.40816X$, and obtain

$$Y_X = (256.83)1.0985^X,$$

with X-units one year. This indicates that Pittsburgh Plate Glass Company dollar sales have been growing at almost 10 per cent per year. If preferred, the trend values can be obtained by successive multiplication, thus eliminating the need of a column for log Y_x or log Y_X. Thus,

$$X = 0, \quad Y_X = 256.83;$$
$$X = 1, \quad Y_X = (256.83)(1.0985) = 282.13;$$
$$X = 2, \quad Y_X = (282.13)(1.0985) = 309.92;$$
$$X = 3, \quad Y_X = (309.92)(1.0985) = 340.45;$$

and so on.

It is worth noting that $\Sigma \log Y_X = \Sigma \log Y$, but $\Sigma Y_X \neq \Sigma Y$. See Table 38.1. However, the geometric mean of the Y_X and Y-values are equal. Also $\Sigma (\log Y - \log Y_X)^2$ is at a minimum, but not $\Sigma (Y - Y_X)^2$. This fact should not, however, be thought of as a disadvantage, if the amplitude of fluctuation of the log Y values around the log Y_X values is constant over time. By minimizing $\Sigma (\log Y - \log Y_X)^2$, cyclical deviations are allowed to exercise an influence on the trend more nearly equal to their relative magnitudes, and tend to cause the trend to run approximately through the centers of the cycles in early years when the cyclical fluctuations may be of small amplitude in an absolute sense, but large relative to the trend.

The exponential trend we have fitted is plotted on Chart 38.1 with an arithmetic scale, and on Chart 38.2 with a logarithmic vertical scale. If we compare Chart 38.1 with Chart 34.1 we can scarcely distinguish any difference between them. The exponential curve has slightly less curvature.

**Chart 38.1—Pittsburgh Plate Glass Company Sales and
Exponential Trend, 1947–1956**

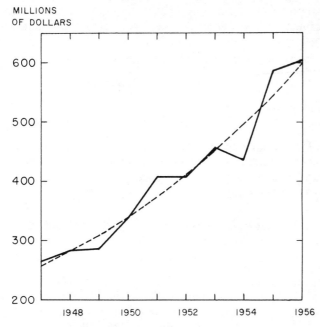

MILLIONS
OF DOLLARS

Source of data: Table 38.1.

**Chart 38.2—Pittsburgh Plate Glass Company Sales and
Exponential Trend, 1947–1956**
(Logarithmic vertical scale)

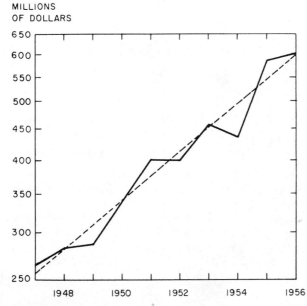

MILLIONS
OF DOLLARS

Source of data: Table 38.1.

The exponential trend has properties which make it logically superior to a second-degree trend in most cases. (1) It can never have negative values; rather, it approaches zero as x approaches $-\infty$. (2) It can not turn up both at the beginning and the end. On the other hand, many industries do not continue to grow indefinitely at a constant rate; but their trends flatten off sooner or later, and may eventually decline.

*Second-degree Exponential

A second-degree exponential has the equation form

$$(38.6) \qquad\qquad Y_X = AB^X C^{X^2}.$$

Typically, B and C are positive, with $B > 1$ and $C < 1$. If we take the ratios of successive values (first ratios), and then take successive ratios of these ratios (second ratios), we find that these second ratios have a constant value C^2 (see Table 38.4). The quantity $C^2 - 1$ is sometimes called the rate of retardation, because it is the percentage rate of decline in the first ratios.

If we let $a = \log A$, $b = \log B$, and $c = \log C$, the resulting equation is appropriately called a logarithmic parabola.

$$(38.7) \qquad\qquad \text{Log } Y_X = a + bX + cX^2.$$

The second differences of the logarithms have a constant value $2c$. The fitting of a logarithmic parabola is similar to the fitting of any second-degree equation, except that the first step is to look up the logarithms of the Y-values, and the last step is to look up the antilogs of the log Y_X values. Equations (38.6) and (38.7) may also be stated in deviation form, with x replacing X.

We shall illustrate the fitting of a logarithmic parabola trend to domestic consumption of rayon and acetate. The data are 5-year averages, and $n = 9$, the number of 5-year averages. Orthogonal polynomials are used for computational ease, and the equation type is

$$(38.8) \qquad\qquad \text{Log } Y_t = B_0 + B_1 t_1 + B_2 t_2.$$

Computation of the trend constants is in Table 38.2, and the resulting equation is

$$\text{Log } Y_t = 2.098371 + 0.325184 t_1 - 0.009958 t_2.$$

Conversion of this equation into simple polynomial form is easily accomplished by use of the formulas in Appendix 7.

$$\text{Log } Y_x = 2.098371 + 0.325184x - (0.009958)(3x^2 - 20);$$
$$\text{Log } Y_x = 2.297531 + 0.325184x - 0.029874x^2.$$

The trend values of Table 38.3 were computed by use of this equation. If we want trend values for each year, instead of at 5-year intervals, we must substitute $x/5$ for x in the equation.

$$\text{Log } Y_x = 2.297531 + 0.325184\left(\frac{x}{5}\right) - 0.029874\left(\frac{x}{5}\right)^2;$$

$$\text{Log } Y_x = 2.297531 - 0.065037x - 0.0011950x^2.$$

**Table 38.2—Domestic Consumption of Rayon and Acetate at Five-year Intervals
and Computations for Logarithmic Parabola Equations Using
Orthogonal Polynomials**
(Consumption is in millions of pounds.)

Center of 5-year period	X	t_1	t_2	Consumption Y	$\log Y$	$t_1 \log Y$	$t_2 \log Y$
1913	0	−4	28	4.14	0.61700	−2.46800	17.27600
1918	1	−3	7	7.48	0.87390	−2.62170	6.11730
1923	2	−2	−8	35.68	1.55242	−3.10484	−12.41936
1928	3	−1	−17	102.84	2.01216	−2.01216	−34.20672
1933	4	0	−20	197.64	2.29587	0.00000	−45.91740
1938	5	1	−17	379.52	2.57923	2.57923	−43.84691
1943	6	2	−8	668.70	2.82523	5.65046	−22.60184
1948	7	3	7	1,071.66	3.03006	9.09018	21.21042
1953	8	4	28	1,257.38	3.09947	12.39788	86.78516
Total	36	0	0	3,725.04	18.88534	19.51105	−27.60335
$\Sigma\, t_r^2$ or B_r	4	60	2,772	...	2.098371	0.325184	−0.009958

Source of data: Textile Economics Bureau, Inc., *Textile Organon*, Vol. XXVII, February, 1956, p. 20.

**Table 38.3—Computation of Logarithmic Parabola Trend Values at
Five-year Intervals, 1913–1953**

Center of 5-year period	t_1	t_2	$B_0 + B_1 t_1$	$B_2 t_2$	$\log Y_t$	Trend value Y_t
1913	−4	28	0.797635	−0.278824	0.51881	3.30
1918	−3	7	1.122819	−0.069706	1.05311	11.30
1923	−2	−8	1.448003	0.079664	1.52767	33.70
1928	−1	−17	1.773187	0.169286	1.94247	87.59
1933	0	−20	2.098371	0.199160	2.29753	198.39
1938	1	−17	2.423555	0.169286	2.59284	391.6
1943	2	−8	2.748739	0.079664	2.82840	673.6
1948	3	7	3.073923	−0.069706	3.00422	1,009.8
1953	4	28	3.399107	−0.278824	3.12028	1,319.1
Total	0	0	18.88534	0.00000	18.88533	3,728.4

Source: Trend equation is computed in Table 38.2. $\log Y_t = 2.098371 + 0.325184 t_1 - 0.009958 t_2$.

The data and trend are plotted on arithmetic paper in Chart 38.3, and on semi-logarithmic paper in Chart 38.4. Chart 38.3 shows that in an absolute sense the fit is very close, except possibly for the last two observations. Chart 38.4 shows that in a relative sense the fit is very close, except possibly for the first two observations. From the arithmetic chart one can see that the amount of growth has been increasing until 1948, after which the amount of growth started to decline. From the ratio chart one can see that

Chart 38.3—Domestic Consumption of Rayon and Acetate, at 5-Year Intervals, 1913–1953, and Second-Degree Exponential Trend

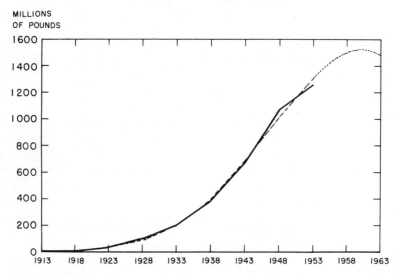

Source of data: Tables 38.2 and 38.3.

the percentage growth has been declining throughout. Each chart shows that the trend values will reach a maximum of 1,522 toward the end of 1960, and will then decline. The trend values can never reach zero no matter how far extended in either direction. Whether this trend is considered a good generalization depends in part on what one believes will be the future of rayon and acetate consumption. Another type of equation that would behave similarly to the second-degree exponential, within the range of the data, is a third-degree polynomial fitted to the Y-values. There are two ways, however, in which the third-degree polynomial is inferior: (1) if extended backward far enough the trend values would get larger; (2) if extended forward far enough the trend values would become negative.

To put the equation in exponential form, we take the logarithms of both sides, obtaining

$$Y_x = (198.39)1.16154^x 0.997253^{x^2}.$$

Chart 38.4—Domestic Consumption of Rayon and Acetate, at 5-Year Intervals, 1913–1953, and Logarithmic Parabola Trend
(Logarithmic vertical scale)

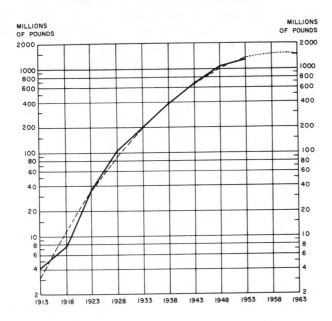

Source of data: Tables 38.2 and 38.3.

Table 38.4—Computation of Second-degree Exponential Trend Values, at One-year Intervals and their First and Second Ratios, 1933–1943

Year	x	x^2	B^x	AB^x	C^{x^2}	$\dfrac{Y_x}{AB^xC^{x^2}}$	Ratio to preceding year R_1	Ratio to preceding year R_2
1933	−5	25	0.47296	93.831	0.93355	87.596	...	...
1934	−4	16	0.54937	108.99	0.95695	104.30	1.1907	...
1935	−3	9	0.63811	126.59	0.97555	123.49	1.1840	0.9944
1936	−2	4	0.74119	147.04	0.98906	145.43	1.1777	0.9947
1937	−1	1	0.86093	170.80	0.99725	170.33	1.1712	0.9945
1938	0	0	1.00000	198.39	1.00000	198.39	1.1647	0.9945
1939	1	1	1.16154	230.44	0.99725	229.81	1.1584	0.9946
1940	2	4	1.34918	267.66	0.98906	264.73	1.1520	0.9945
1941	3	9	1.56713	310.90	0.97555	303.30	1.1457	0.9945
1942	4	16	1.82028	361.13	0.95695	345.58	1.1394	0.9945
1943	5	25	2.11433	419.46	0.93355	391.59	1.1331	0.9945

$Y_x = (198.39)1.16154^x\,0.997253^{x^2}$

This equation can also be used (though less conveniently) to obtain trend values for each year. Table 38.4 shows the computations for the years 1933–1943. This table shows computation also of the first ratios R_1 and the second ratios R_2. For example, the first R_1 value is $104.30 \div 87.596 = 1.1907$, and the first R_2 value is $1.1840 \div 1.1907 = 0.9944$. The second ratios have a constant value of approximately $0.9945 = 99.45$ per cent. The rate of retardation is therefore $100 - 99.45 = 0.55$ per cent. The growth ratio declines by a little more than $\frac{1}{2}$ per cent each year. The square root of the constant second ratio is 0.99725, which is C.

The second-degree exponential trend is one that is widely useful.

*Modified Exponential

Description of curve. The exponential equation,

$$Y_X = AB^X,$$

has these properties:

1. The first ratios have a constant value B.
2. The ratios of the first differences have a constant value B.

The modified exponential equation,[2]

$$(38.9) \qquad Y_X = k + AB^X,$$

has only one of these properties: the ratios of the first differences have a constant value B. The constant k is an *asymptote*, or limit which the trend values approach as X approaches ∞ (or $-\infty$). The asymptote may be either an upper or a lower limit, depending on the values of A and B.

Consider the equations

$$Y_X = 10 + (8)1.5^X;$$
$$Y_X = 10 + (8)0.5^X.$$

Both of these equations have positive values of A and k. Their trend values, first ratios (labeled R_1), first differences (labeled Δ), and the ratio of their first differences (labeled R_Δ), are computed in Table 38.5. As the Table shows: when $B > 1$, the first ratios are greater than 1, and the percentage growth is increasing; when $B < 1$, the first ratios are less than 1, and the percentage decline is decreasing. When $B > 1$, the first ratios approach B as X approaches ∞; when $B < 1$, the first ratios approach B as X approaches $-\infty$.

The shape of a modified exponential depends on the values of the constants k, A, and B. It especially depends on: whether k is positive or negative; whether A is positive or negative; whether B (which must be positive) is greater than 1 or less than 1. Chart 38.5 shows the general shapes that the

---

[2] The modified exponential equation can also be put in linear form:

$$\text{Log}\,(Y_X - k) = a + bX, \qquad \text{where } a = \log A \text{ and } b = \log B.$$

Table 38.5—Modified Exponential and its Properties when A and k are Positive

X	1.5^x	$(8)1.5^x$	$Y = 10 + (8)1.5^x$	R_1	ΔY	R_Δ
0	1.	8	18	...	...	...
1	1.5	12	22	1.222	4	...
2	2.25	18	28	1.273	6	1.5
3	3.375	27	37	1.321	9	1.5
4	5.0625	40.5	50.5	1.365	13.5	1.5

X	0.5^x	$(8)0.5^x$	$Y = 10 + (8)0.5^x$	R_1	ΔY	R_Δ
0	1.	8	18	...	...	...
1	0.5	4	14	0.778	4	...
2	0.25	2	12	0.857	2	0.5
3	0.125	1	11	0.917	1	0.5
4	0.0625	0.5	10.5	0.955	0.5	0.5

Chart 38.5—Modified Exponential Curves

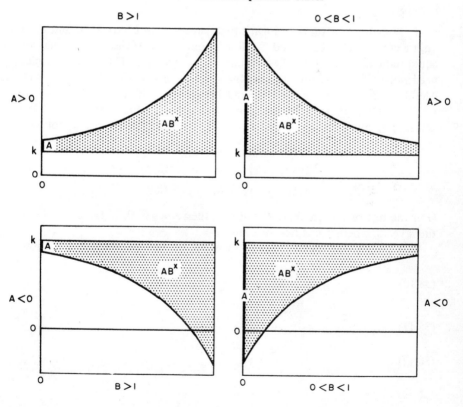

modified exponential can take when k is positive. Although it is mathematically possible for k to be negative, it is usually logically impossible.

For the two diagrams at the top, A is positive.
For the two diagrams at the bottom, A is negative.
For the two diagrams at the left, B is greater than 1.
For the two diagrams at the right, B is less than 1.

Although the modified exponential can take any of these shapes, typically $A > 0$ and $B > 1$, and so the upper left diagram is the most common.

The method of least squares is not often used for fitting a modified exponential because it is too difficult for practical use. Almost always one of two methods is used: (1) the method of partial totals; (2) the method of selected points. We shall use the method of selected points because of its simplicity, and shall use as an illustration general expenditures of state governments 1950–1956.

Fitting a modified exponential. For illustrative purposes we shall use general expenditures of state governments, 1950–1956. The data are given in Table 38.6. The procedure for fitting by the method of selected points is as follows:

1. Plot the data on semi-logarithmic paper, as in Chart 38.6, and draw on it a curve that gives a good fit. Read from the curve three values that are equidistant in time. Call these values y_0, y_1, and y_2. The values selected need not be, and usually are not, the same as any of the observed values. The distance between x_0 and x_1, and between x_1 and x_2 is r years, where $r = (n - 1)/2$. If possible, the years should be the first, middle, and last years. For our data $n = 7$ and $r = 3$. The selected points are as follows:

$$1950: \quad x_0 = 0; \quad y_0 = 12.3.$$
$$1953: \quad x_1 = 3; \quad y_1 = 14.7.$$
$$1956: \quad x_2 = 6; \quad y_2 = 18.9.$$

(For the rest of this chapter, X will take the values of $0, 1, 2, ..., n - 1$, for the n years, whether n is odd or even.)

2. Compute the trend constants by use of the first three equations below.

$$(38.10) \qquad\qquad B^r = \frac{y_2 - y_1}{y_1 - y_0} ;$$

$$(38.11) \qquad\qquad A = \frac{y_1 - y_0}{B^r - 1} ;$$

$$(38.12) \qquad\qquad k = y_0 - A;$$

$$(38.13) \qquad\qquad k = \frac{y_0 y_2 - y_1^2}{y_0 + y_2 - 2y_1} .$$

Table 38.6—General Expenditures by State Governments, 1950–1956, and
Modified Exponential Trend Fitted by Method of Selected Points
(Expenditures are in billions of dollars.)

Year	X	Expenditures Y	B^X	AB^X	$\dfrac{Y_x}{k + AB^X}$
1950	0	12.3	1.0000	3.20	12.30
1951	1	13.0	1.2051	3.86	12.96
1952	2	13.7	1.4522	4.65	13.75
1953	3	14.7	1.7500	5.60	14.70
1954	4	15.8	2.1089	6.75	15.85
1955	5	17.2	2.5413	8.13	17.23
1956	6	18.9	3.0625	9.80	18.90
1957	7	...	3.6905	11.88	20.91
1958	8	...	4.4473	14.23	23.33

$Y_X = 9.1 + (3.2)1.20507^X$.

Source of data: U.S. Census Bureau, as reported by *United States News and World Report*, Vol. XLIII, July 12, 1957, p. 56.

Chart 38.6—General Expenditures of State
Governments, 1950–1956, and
Free-Hand Trend

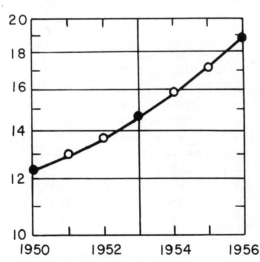

BILLIONS
OF DOLLARS

Source of data: Table 38.6.

For our data we have

$$B^3 = \frac{18.9 - 14.7}{14.7 - 12.3} = \frac{4.2}{2.4} = 1.75, \quad \text{and} \quad B = 1.20507;$$

$$A = \frac{2.4}{0.75} = 3.2;$$

$$k = 12.3 - 3.2 = 9.1.$$

The value of k obtained by use of equation (38.13) would, of course, be the same as that obtained by equation (38.12). The trend equation is

$$Y_X = 9.1 + (3.2)1.20507^X.$$

The trend values are computed in Table 38.6, and (rashly) extended through 1958. (The *United States News and World Report* on July 12, 1957, published a chart of the data, and made estimates for 1957 and 1958 of $20.6 million and $22.5 million, respectively.) Check marks after 1950, 1953, and 1956 indicate that the criterion of fit is satisfied: the trend passes through the selected points. The fit is almost perfect.

*Gompertz

The modified exponential,

$$Y_X = k + AB^X,$$

describes a trend the first differences of which have a constant ratio B. The Gompertz curve, which is usually stated in the form

(38.14) $$Y_X = kG^{B^X},$$

can also be stated in a form which is analogous to the modified exponential:[3]

(38.15) $$\text{Log } Y_X = \log k + AB^X,$$

where $A = \log G$.

The first differences of the log Y_X values have a constant ratio B. Typically the value of A is negative, and the value of B is between 0 and 1. Therefore the log Y_X values have the shape of diagram (4) of Chart 38.5. When plotted on semi-logarithmic paper, the Gompertz curve is concave downward, indicating that the percentage growth is getting smaller. Typically also, a Gompertz curve has the shape of a nonsymmetrical S curve when plotted on arithmetic paper. The lower asymptote is 0 and the upper asymptote is k.

---

[3] The Gompertz equation can also be written in linear form:

$$\log \log \frac{Y_x}{k} = a + bX.$$

For this equation, and also equation (38.15), logarithms to the base e, instead of the base 10, may be used. This changes the values of the equation constants, a, and b, but not the values of k or Y_x.

It is said to be nonsymmetrical because its behavior on opposite sides of its point of inflection is different. Because of its nonsymmetrical character, the first differences of Gompertz trend values resemble a positively skewed frequency distribution.

The Gompertz curve can be fitted by the method of selected points, obtaining B^r, A, $\log k$, and $\log Y_X$, by use of formulas indentical with formulas (38.10) through (38.13), except that $\log y$ is substituted for y throughout.

*Logistic

Description of curve. The logistic curve, which is usually stated in the form[4]

$$(38.16) \qquad Y_X = \frac{k}{1 + 10^{a' + bX}},$$

can also be stated in a form which is analogous to the modified exponential.[5]

$$(38.17) \qquad \frac{1}{Y_X} = \frac{1}{k} + AB^X,$$

where $A = \dfrac{A'}{k}$, and $A' = $ antilog a'.

For this equation, the first differences of the reciprocals of the trend values have a constant ratio B. Typically, the value of A is positive, and the value of B in between 0 and 1, and therefore the reciprocals of a logistic curve have the shape of diagram (2) of Chart 38.5. When plotted on semi-logarithmic paper, the logistic curve is concave downward, indicating that

---

[4] In this equation, e may be used instead of 10, where e is the base of the natural (Napierian) logarithmic system. This changes the values of a' and b, but not k or Y_X.

[5] The logistic equation can also be written in linear form in various ways.

$$(1) \quad \text{Log} \left(\frac{1}{Y} - \frac{1}{k} \right) = a + bX.$$

$$(2) \quad \text{Log} \left(\frac{k - Y}{Y} \right) = a' + bX.$$

In this second form it is sometimes said that the logit is a linear function of time.

$$(3) \quad \frac{1}{Y} \frac{dY}{dX} = p + qY.$$

In this form we can say that the relative growth is a linear function of the level attained. This is perhaps the most interesting concept of the logistic curve. Directions for obtaining values for the constants p and q are not given in this text. See, however, Harold Hotelling, "Differential Equations Subject to Error of Population Estimates," *Journal of the American Statistical Association*, Vol. 22, 1927, pp. 283–314. From equation (3) it follows that for annual data,

$$(4) \quad \frac{\Delta Y}{Y} \doteq p + qY.$$

the percentage growth is getting smaller. Typically, also, a logistic curve has the shape of a symmetrical S curve. The lower asymptote is 0 and the upper asymptote is k. It is symmetrical because its point of inflection is halfway between 0 and k, and its behavior on opposite sides of its point of inflection is the same. The first differences of a logistic curve resemble a normal curve rather closely.

Until the point of inflection is reached, the amount of growth of a logistic curve gets larger as Y_X gets larger, but eventually this is counteracted by another force; the amount of growth gets smaller as Y_X approaches its upper limit. This reminds one of the Mathusian law that population would grow geometrically if it were not for the limitation imposed by the scarce means of subsistence. For this and other reasons the logistic curve is often used to describe population growth and series closely connected with the size of the population.

The logistic curve can be fitted by the method of selected points, obtaining B^r, A, $1/k$, and $1/Y_X$, by use of formulas identical with formulas (38.10) through (38.13), except that $1/y$ is substituted for y throughout.

*Method of Partial Totals

The method of partial totals is more objective than the method of selected points, but the latter method is simpler and less laborious. The method of selected points is also more flexible because it is more subjective, and because it is more easily extended for use in fitting more complicated logistics (such as one with a lower asymptote that is not zero, or one which is a third-degree polynomial fitted to the log $(1/Y - 1/k)$ values).

For the method of partial totals, the data are divided into three parts, each of which has r observations, where $r = n/3$. The totals for the three parts are, respectively, $\Sigma_1 Y$, $\Sigma_2 Y$, and $\Sigma_3 Y$. The criterion of fit is satisfied when $\Sigma_1 Y_X = \Sigma_1 Y$, $\Sigma_2 Y_X = \Sigma_2 Y$, and $\Sigma_3 Y_X = \Sigma_3 Y$.

For the modified exponential:

$$(38.18) \qquad B^r = \frac{\Sigma_3 Y - \Sigma_2 Y}{\Sigma_2 Y - \Sigma_1 Y};$$

$$(36.19) \qquad A = (\Sigma_2 Y - \Sigma_1 Y)\frac{B-1}{(B^r-1)^2};$$

$$(38.20) \qquad k = \frac{1}{r}\left(\Sigma_1 Y - A\frac{B^r-1}{B-1}\right);$$

$$(38.21) \qquad k = \frac{1}{r}\left[\frac{\Sigma_1 Y \Sigma_3 Y - (\Sigma_2 Y)^2}{\Sigma_1 Y + \Sigma_3 Y - 2\Sigma_2 Y}\right]$$

For the Gompertz the equations are the same except that log Y is substituted for Y throughout, and log k is substituted for k.

For the logistic the equations are the same except that $1/Y$ is substituted for Y throughout, and $1/k$ is substituted for k.

Selection of Trend Type

In the selection of a curve to express the trend of a time series, a wide range of choice is possible; and it is not always easy to decide which type of curve is most appropriate. While not completely satisfactory, the following considerations are useful.

1. In general, a trend that can be expressed as an equation with time as the independent variable is to be preferred to a moving average. Even though it can not be said that the series conforms to an economic "law," such an equation is useful for purposes of description, summarization, and comparison.

2. Before undertaking any computations, the data should be plotted on arithmetic paper. If the points fall approximately on a straight line, a straight line equation is indicated. If there is one bend, a second-degree equation is indicated. If there is a point of inflection, a third-degree equation is indicated.

3. Also plot the data on semi-logarithmic paper. If the points fall approximately on a straight line, an exponential curve is indicated. If there is one bend, a logarithmic parabola is indicated.

4. If successive differences, or successive ratios, of the Y-values, the log Y values, or the $1/Y$ values, are approximately constant, the trend type is indicated. In order to determine whether an exponential, a second-degree exponential, a modified exponential, a Gompertz, or a logistic is appropriate, the following preliminary test is suggested.

First, plot the data on semi-logarithmic paper, and draw a freehand curve that gives a good fit. Read from the curve at least five values that are equidistant in time. The first, middle, and last points are those used in fitting a modified exponential, Gompertz, or logistic.

If the selected values fall on a straight line when plotted on semi-logarithmic paper, or the ratios of successive values fall on a horizontal straight line when plotted on arithmetic paper, an exponential is indicated.

If the ratios of successive values fall on a straight line when plotted on semi-logarithmic paper, or the second ratios fall on a horizontal straight line when plotted on arithmetic paper, a second-degree exponential is indicated.

If the ratios of the first differences (but not the ratios of successive values) fall on a horizontal straight line when plotted on arithmetic paper, a modified exponential is indicated.

If the ratios of the first differences of the logarithms fall on a horizontal straight line when plotted on arithmetic paper, a Gompertz curve is indicated.

If the ratios of the first differences of the reciprocals fall on a horizontal straight line when plotted on arithmetic paper, a logistic curve is indicated.

5. If the $(Y - k)$ values, $(\log Y - \log k)$ values, or $(1/Y - 1/k)$ values are approximately a straight line when plotted on semi-logarithmic paper, there is a strong presumption in favor of the modified exponential, the Gompertz, or the logistic, respectively. Experimentation with arbitrary values of k, $\log k$, and $1/k$ may reveal that the data are well described by one of the above curves over part, but not all, of the time covered.[6]

6. If a logical reason can be assigned for a series behaving in a manner described by a particular equation, preference should be given to that trend, even though it is not intended to project the trend. If the trend is to be projected ahead a short period (one or two years), it is particularly important that a trend be selected that will behave in a logical fashion. Thus, if the business is thought to be reaching a saturation point and will, when that point is reached, remain stationary, a trend should be selected that will flatten out at the top—not one that will continue upward or soon bend downward. If, on the other hand, it is believed that the rate of increase which has persisted will be continued, a compound interest curve should be chosen.

7. In order to determine the general shape of the curve desired, the statistician must understand the underlying economic factors. He must be able to distinguish trends from the various other movements present in the series. Having decided which variations are which, he is in a position to select a type of trend that will conform to these distinctions. If he can make up his mind which trend shows the cycles most accurately, he will have one criterion for deciding which trend to select.

8. Other things being equal, select a trend equation with as few constants as possible, bearing in mind that a trend is not satisfactory unless points 6 and 7 are satisfied. If there are too many constants in the equation selected, too many degrees of freedom will be used up, and the degrees of freedom remaining for the unexplained variation will be so few that some of the constants will not be significant. (In the extreme case, where there are as many constants as observations, the trend will go through each observation, but it will be meaningless.) One should also remember that the different observations in an economic time series are interdependent, and therefore there are never as many *independent* observations (degrees of freedom) as there are items to begin with.

Summary

We have defined a growth curve as a curve for which the growth is related in some systematic way to the level attained. The basic equation is the exponential. The family of curves considered in this chapter are related in various simple ways to the exponential.

---

[6] A complete graphic procedure for fitting the modified exponential, the Gompertz, and the logistic is given in Dudley J. Cowden, "Simplified Methods of Fitting Certain Types of Growth Curves," *Journal of the American Statical Association*, Vol. 42, December, 1947, pp. 585–590.

Logarithmic straight line:

$$\text{Log } Y_X = a + bX$$

Exponential:

$$Y_X = AB^X$$

Logarithmic parabola:

$$\text{Log } Y_X = a + bX + cX^2$$

Second-degree exponential:

$$Y_X = AB^X C^{X^2}$$

Modified exponential:

$$Y_X = k + AB^X$$

Gompertz:

$$\text{Log } Y_X = \log k + AB^X$$

Logistic:

$$\frac{1}{Y_X} = \frac{1}{k} + AB^X$$

The logarithmic parabola fits a wide variety of economic data rather closely. It has the disadvantage (or for some data the advantage) that it may become negatively inclined upon extension into the future. The Gompertz and logistic approach zero at one end and k at the other. The relative growth of the logistic is a linear function of Y_X. It has been widely used to describe the growth of biological data.

Chapter 39

TESTS OF HOMOGENEITY
AND INDEPENDENCE

Data are said to be homogeneous if all observations, or all samples, are governed by the same cause system. Different samples may be homogeneous with respect to their variances, but heterogeneous with respect to their means, or vice versa.

One can test specific items, means, ranges, etc., to see whether they differ too much from the others to be attributed to chance. These we refer to as specific tests. Alternatively, we can test the data as a whole. These tests we refer to as general tests.

Two probability distributions are said to be independent if the conditional probability distribution of the first variable is the same regardless of the value of the second variable, and vice versa. Symbolically, two events, A and B are independent if

$$\text{Prob (A)} = \text{Prob (A|B)} \quad \text{and} \quad \text{Prob (B)} = \text{Prob (B|A)}.$$

From this, it follows that

$$\text{Prob (AB)} = \text{Prob (A) Prob (B)}.$$

The first part of this chapter will be devoted to tests of homogeneity, mostly analysis of variance; the second part of the chapter will be devoted to tests of independence, mostly contingency tables.

Specific Tests of Homogeneity

Dixon's ratios involving extreme values. In conducting a time study the recorded observations, in hundredths of a minute, for engaging clutch to start lathe were as follows:

X	f
4	2
5	4
6	2
.	.
.	.
.	.
13	1
.	.
.	.
.	.
17	1
Total	10

600

In averaging these data to set a standard time should all 10 observations be averaged, or should the largest value, or two largest values, be excluded? The mean of all 10 items is 7 hundredths of a minute; the mean excluding the largest value is 5.9 hundredths of a minute; the mean excluding the two suspiciously large values is 5.0 hundredths of a minute.

A useful test, provided by W. J. Dixon, applied to the observations arrayed from X_1 (smallest) to X_n (largest), is

(39.1) $$r_{ij} = \frac{X_{1+i} - X_1}{X_{n-j} - X_1},$$

where the suspected outlier is the smallest in the array; and

(39.2) $$r_{ij} = \frac{X_n - X_{n-1}}{X_n - X_{1+j}},$$

where the suspected outlier is the largest in the array. The subscripts i and j refer to a specified rank, in practice either 1 or 2, depending on (1) whether one or more than one outliers are suspected, and (2) the sample size. Thus:

Number of items or samples	Number of outliers	
	1	2 or more
3–7	r_{10}	r_{20}
8–10	r_{11}	r_{20}
11–13	r_{21}	r_{21}
14–30	r_{22}	r_{22}

The tests can be supplied either to items, where the population is normal, or to sample means.

For the data tabulated above, $n = 10$, and the two largest values are suspected, so we use

$$r_{20} = \frac{X_{10} - X_8}{X_{10} - X_1} = \frac{17 - 6}{17 - 4} = \frac{11}{13} = .846.$$

Appendix 15 shows that when $n = 10$, the upper .005 probability point for r_{20} is .664. Since $.846 > .664$, we reject the hypothesis of homogeneity and discard the largest value, $X = 17$.

We have 9 values remaining in our sample, of which one, $X = 13$, is open to suspicion. We therefore compute

$$r_{11} = \frac{X_9 - X_8}{X_9 - X_2} = \frac{13 - 6}{13 - 4} = \frac{7}{9} = .778.$$

The upper .005 probability point for r_{11}, when $n = 9$, is .677. We therefore reject the observation $X = 13$. We conclude that the modified mean based on the remaining 8 items, which is $X = 5.0$ hundredths of a minute, provides the best estimate[1] of μ.

Table 2.1 gives the warp-breaking strength in pounds of 6 samples of 4 items each. It is repeated below as Table 39.1, together with values for the sum, mean, and range of each column. We want to decide whether the

Table 39.1—Warp-breaking Strength in Pounds of 6 Samples of 4 Items Each

Statistic	X_1	X_2	X_3	X_4	X_5	X_6	Row total
	70	68	66	67	71	62	
	68	66	64	66	68	59	
	68	66	63	65	66	59	
	62	63	60	60	57	56	
ΣX	268	263	253	258	262	236	1,540
$\bar{X}$	67.00	65.75	63.25	64.50	65.50	59.00	385.00
R	8	5	6	7	14	6	46

Source of data: Table 2.1.

data are homogeneous with respect to their means, or whether the sixth sample comes from a population with a smaller mean. Since $n = 6$ and there is only one suspected outlier, we compute

$$r_{10} = \frac{\bar{X}_2 - \bar{X}_1}{\bar{X}_6 - \bar{X}_1} = \frac{63.25 - 59.00}{67.00 - 59.00} = \frac{4.25}{8.00} = .531.$$

When $n = 6$, the upper probability points for r_{10} are:

.482 at the .10 point;
.560 at the .05 point.

If the criterion of significance is $\alpha = .05$, there is almost, but not quite, enough evidence to reject the hypothesis of homogeneity.

Control chart. From Table 39.1 we obtain

$$\bar{R} = \frac{46}{6} = 7.667.$$

The upper control limit for ranges is therefore

$$D_4\bar{R} = (2.282)(7.667) = 17.5.$$

---

[1] A different method of analysis was given in F. E. Croxton and D. J. Cowden, *Practical Business Statistics*, 2d ed., Prentice-Hall, Inc., Englewood Cliffs, N. J., 1948, pp. 171–176. That illustration is interesting because the analysis involves setting a standard for the 8 steps involved in the operation. The illustration in the present edition refers only to the second step.

No control chart is drawn since it is easy to see, from inspection of Table 39.1, that no range is beyond the upper control limit, even though the range for sample 5 is considerably out of line.

To obtain the control limits for means, we compute

$$\bar{X} \pm A_2 \bar{R} = \frac{1,540}{24} \pm (0.7285)(7.667)$$

$$= 64.167 \pm 5.585 = 58.58 \text{ and } 69.75.$$

No mean is beyond the control limits, though the mean of sample 6 is close to the lower control limit.[2] The control chart corroborates the testimony of Dixon's ratio r_{10}.

Analysis of Variance

This technique is sometimes referred to by the abbreviation ANOVA.

One basis of classification. In this section, we shall use F to test the hypothesis that the data are homogeneous with respect to their means, where F is the ratio of two independent estimates of the population variance.[3]

$$(39.3) \qquad\qquad F = \frac{s_1^2}{s_2^2}$$

Since several examples of analysis of variance will be used in this chapter, we shall present a somewhat detailed explanation. In this section there are k columns of n items each. The total numbers of items is N and $N = nk$, since $n_1 = n_2 = \ldots = n_k$. Symbolically, the sample is:

$$
\begin{array}{ccccc}
X_{11} & X_{12} & \cdots & X_{1j} & \cdots & X_{1k} \\
X_{21} & X_{22} & \cdots & X_{2j} & \cdots & X_{2k} \\
\cdot & \cdot & & \cdot & & \cdot \\
\cdot & \cdot & & \cdot & & \cdot \\
X_{i1} & X_{i2} & \cdots & X_{ij} & \cdots & X_{ik} \\
\cdot & \cdot & & \cdot & & \cdot \\
\cdot & \cdot & & \cdot & & \cdot \\
X_{n1} & X_{n2} & \cdots & X_{nj} & \cdots & X_{nk} \\
\end{array}
$$

---

[2] Though the analysis of the present chapter seems to be in conflict with that of Chapter 2, it should be realized that in Chapter 2, it was assumed that μ and σ were known. The knowledge assumed in Chapter 2 results in a more powerful test.

[3] More exactly,

$$F = \frac{\chi_1^2 / \nu_1}{\chi_2^2 / \nu_2},$$

where the degrees of freedom are ν_1 and ν_2, respectively, for the numerator and denominator.

As can be seen from the table, the subscripts refer to the row number and the columns number, in that order. The symbol X_{ij} means the ith X-value of column j.

Model. The population mean for each column is the grand mean plus the column effect. The relationship may be stated symbolically as

$$(39.4) \qquad \mu_j = \mu + K_j.$$

Thus, if $\mu = 50$ and $K_1 = -2$, $K_2 = 5$, and $K_3 = -3$, then $K_1 + K_2 + K_3 = 0$, and the column means are $\mu_1 = 48$, $\mu_2 = 55$, and $K_3 = 47$.

An X-value for any column is the column means plus a random element.

$$X_{ij} = \mu_j + E_{ij}.$$

Substituting $X_{ij} - E_{ij}$ for μ_j in equation (39.4), we obtain

$$(39.5) \qquad X_{ij} = \mu + K_j + E_{ij}.$$

Thus each X-value is made up of three additive components: the population mean, the column effect, and a random element.

The errors (residuals) are assumed to be distributed normally with mean of zero. If this hypothesis is not true, the true probabilities will not be those shown by the F table. It is often possible to put the data in approximately normal form by using the logarithms of the data, or by using some other transformation. However the F test is a "robust" test and mild departures from normality have only a minor effect. Another assumption is that the population variance is the same for each column:

$$\sigma_1^2 = \sigma_2^2 = \ldots = \sigma_k^2.$$

Equation (39.5) can also be stated in deviation form.

$$(39.6) \qquad (X_{ij} - \mu) = (\mu_j - \mu) + (X_{ij} - \mu_j).$$

Symbolic statement of test. The null hypothesis is that the column effect is zero:

$$K_1 = K_2 = K_k = 0, \quad \text{or} \quad \mu_1 = \mu_2 = \ldots = \mu_k.$$

If we substitute in equation (39.6) the estimates of μ and μ_j that are obtained from the sample, we have

$$(X_{ij} - \bar{\bar{X}}) = (\bar{X}_j - \bar{\bar{X}}) + (X_{ij} - \bar{X}_j).$$

If we square these deviations and sum them so that there are N squared deviations for each term, we have[3]

$$(39.7) \qquad \Sigma (X_{ij} - \bar{\bar{X}})^2 = \Sigma (\bar{X}_j - \bar{\bar{X}})^2 + \Sigma (X_{ij} - \bar{X}_j)^2.$$

[3] More explicitly:

$$\sum_1^N (X_{ij} - \bar{\bar{X}})^2 = \sum_1^k n(\bar{X}_j - \bar{\bar{X}})^2 + \sum_1^k \sum_1^n (X_{ij} - \bar{X}_j)^2.$$

These measures of variation, or sums of squared deviations, or simply sums of squares, may be abbreviated as

$$\Sigma\, x_T^2 = \Sigma\, x_K^2 + \Sigma\, x_{WK}^2,$$

and referred to verbally in this manner:

Total variation = column variation + within column variation.

The words "sum of squares" may be substituted for "variation" if so desired.

Each of the sums of squares of equation (39.7) has a number of degrees of freedom, which may also be put in equation form.

(39.8) $(N-1) = (k-1) + (N-k).$

It is easy to obtain the number of degrees of freedom by referring to equation (39.7). For total sum of squares, X_{ij} occurs N times and $\bar{\bar{X}}$ occurs once, so the number of degrees of freedom is $N-1$. For column sum of squares, $\bar{X}_j$ occurs k times and $\bar{\bar{X}}$ occurs once, so the number of degrees of freedom is $k-1$. For within column sum of squares, each X_{ij} occurs N times and $\bar{X}_j$ occurs k times, so the number of degrees of freedom is $N-k$. This can be put another way. There are $n-1$ degrees of freedom for each column, and there are k columns, so we have $k(n-1) = kn - k = N - k$ degrees of freedom altogether for within columns. The general rule is that an observation or statistic is limited in its freedom to vary by each restriction that is placed upon it. So we subtract from the number of values that are varying the number of restrictions imposed by the sample in order to determine the number of degrees of freedom to vary.

When any sum of squares is divided by its degrees of freedom we obtain a mean square, which is an unbiased estimate of the population variance σ^2 if the null hypothesis is true:

$$s_T^2 = \frac{\Sigma\, x_T^2}{N-1}; \quad s_K^2 = \frac{\Sigma\, x_K^2}{k-1}; \quad s_{WK}^2 = \frac{\Sigma\, x_{WK}^2}{N-k}.$$

Of the three estimates, s_K^2 and s_{WK}^2 are independent. It is possible to change the X-values in such a way that s_K^2 is changed without changing s_{WK}^2; and it is possible to change the X-values in such a way that s_{WK}^2 is changed without changing s_K^2; but if the X-values are changed in such a way as to change either s_K^2 but not s_{WK}^2, or s_{WK}^2 but not s_K^2, in either case s_T^2 will be affected.

In analysis of variance it is usually desirable to draw up an analysis of variance table. This is done symbolically in Table 39.2. Such a table enables one to observe the way in which the total variation is apportioned among its components. As the ruling of the table indicates, variation and degrees of freedom are additive, but variance is not.

To test the significance of the difference among columns we compute

$$F_K = \frac{s_K^2}{s_{WK}^2},$$

and evaluate the results by reference to the F table, Appendix 21.

Table 39.2—Symbolic Analysis of Variance Table

Source of variation	Amount of variation S.S.	Degrees of freedom d.f.	Estimate of variance M.S.
Total	Σx_T^2	$\nu_T = N - 1$	...
Columns ...	Σx_K^2	$\nu_K = k - 1$	$s_K^2 = \dfrac{\Sigma x_K^2}{\nu_K}$
Within columns	Σx_{WK}^2	$\nu_{WK} = N - k$	$s_{WK}^2 = \dfrac{\Sigma x_{WK}^2}{\nu_{WK}}$

Computational methods and numerical illustration. Efficient formulas for computation of the three measures of variation are as follows:

$$(39.9)\quad\begin{cases} \Sigma x_T^2 = \sum_1^N X^2 - \dfrac{\left(\sum\limits_1^N X\right)^2}{N}; \\[2em] \Sigma x_K^2 = \dfrac{\sum\limits_1^k\left(\sum\limits_1^n X\right)^2}{n} - \dfrac{\left(\sum\limits_1^N X\right)^2}{N}; \\[2em] \Sigma x_{WK}^2 = \Sigma x_T^2 - \Sigma x_K^2. \end{cases}$$

It is worthwhile also to notice

$$\Sigma x_{WK}^2 = \sum_1^k\left[\sum_1^n X^2 - \dfrac{\left(\sum\limits_1^n X\right)^2}{n}\right].$$

For convenience, the data of Table 39.1 are repeated as Table 39.3 and the sums and squares of sums are shown as the last two rows. $\sum\limits_1^N X^2 =$ $(70)^2 + (68)^2 + \ldots + (59)^2 + (56)^2 = 99{,}200.00$. From the values recorded in Table 39.3 we compute:

$$\frac{\left(\sum\limits_1^N X\right)^2}{N} = \frac{(1{,}540)^2}{24} = 98{,}816.67;$$

$$\frac{\sum\limits_1^k\left(\sum\limits_1^n X\right)^2}{n} = \frac{395{,}906}{4} = 98{,}976.50.$$

Table 39.3—Computations for Analysis of Variance
(Data of Table 39.1.)

Statistic	X_1	X_2	X_3	X_4	X_5	X_6	Row total
	70	68	66	67	71	62	
	68	66	64	66	68	59	
	68	66	63	65	66	59	
	62	63	60	60	57	56	
ΣX	268	263	253	258	262	236	1,540
$(\Sigma X)^2$	71,824	69,169	64,009	66,564	68,644	55,696	395,906

Table 39.4—Analysis of Variance Table
(Data of Table 39.1.)

Source of variation	Amount of variation S.S.	Degrees of freedom d.f.	Estimate of variance M.S.
Total	383.33	23	...
Columns	159.83	5	31.97
Within columns	223.50	18	12.42

The measures of variation are then easily obtained.

$$\Sigma x_T^2 = 99,200.00 - 98,816.67 = 383.33.$$
$$\Sigma x_K^2 = 98,976.50 - 98,816.67 = 159.83.$$
$$\Sigma x_{WK}^2 = 383.33 - 159.83 = 223.50.$$

Table 39.4 is the analysis of variance table. It follows the format of Table 39.2.

We now compute the variance ratio:

$$F_K = \frac{31.97}{12.42} = 2.574.$$

With degrees of freedom $\nu_1 = 5$ and $\nu_2 = 18$, the value of F at the 0.05 level is 2.773. The hypothesis that $\mu_1 = \mu_2 = \ldots = \mu_k$ is therefore accepted. The results of all of our tests of significance with respect to these data are in agreement.

Unequal sample sizes. This test can also be used when the number of observations in each column is not the same. We need only to substitute n_j for n in each formula, and in (39.9) use

$$\sum_1^k \frac{\left(\sum_1^{n_j} X\right)^2}{n_j} \quad \text{instead of} \quad \frac{\sum_1^k \left(\sum_1^n X\right)^2}{n}.$$

Special case when there are two columns. In Chapter 23, we tested the significance of the difference between two sample means, using the t test for the data of Tables 21.3 and 23.1. We can also use the method of analysis of variance.

$$\sum_1^N X = 6,932 + 4,383 = 11,315$$

$$\frac{\left(\sum_1^N X\right)^2}{N} = \frac{(11,315)^2}{100} = 1,280,292.25$$

$$\sum_1^N X^2 = 972,720 + 394,181 = 1,366,901$$

$$\Sigma x_T^2 = \sum_1^N x^2 = 1,366,901 - 1,280,292.25 = 86,608.75$$

$$\Sigma x_{WK}^2 = 11,668 + 9,967 = 21,635$$

$$\Sigma x_K^2 = 86,609 - 21,635 = 64,974$$

$$F = \frac{64,974 \div 1}{21,635 \div 99} = \frac{64,974}{219.54} = 296.0.$$

Now it is always true that $t = \sqrt{F}$ when $\nu_1 = 1$. Therefore,

$$t = \sqrt{296.0} = 17.2.$$

This is the same value of t that was obtained on page 354. The two methods are equivalent. The method of Chapter 23 is somewhat easier, and published t tables are more detailed than published F tables. But the method of analysis of variance can be extended not only to cases where there are more than 2 columns, but to many other cases as well.

*Two bases of classification. Five makes of cars were driven for four weeks, using a different brand of fuel each week, and a record was kept of miles per gallon. The results are shown in Table 39.6. We wish to know whether there is a significant difference among cars, and also among fuels.

For a problem of this type, there is another complication to consider. If a given car is driven by the same driver for four weeks, using a different brand of gasoline each week, then differences among weeks must be considered. Also, it is difficult to say whether differences in mileage are due to differences among cars or differences among drivers. If 20 different cars are each driven by 20 different drivers, all at one time, the statistical procedure is simplified, though the random variability is increased, and also the cost of the experiment. The procedure used in the present illustration is appropriate for this latter type of experiment.

Model. Three types of models are distinguishable in analysis of variance: random; fixed; mixed. In the present case if we select five makes of cars at random, and four brands of gasoline at random, we have a random model. The results of the analysis are applicable to cars in general, and to fuels in general. If, on the other hand, we select five makes of cars because we are interested in these makes, and four brands of gasoline becuase we are interested in those brands, we have a fixed model. The results of the analysis are

**Table 39.5—Arithmetic Illustration of Analysis of Variance Model:
Two Bases of Classification**

K_j / R_i	$K_1 = -2$	$K_2 = 5$	$K_3 = -3$	Row mean
$R_1 = 4$	$\mu_{11} = 52$	$\mu_{12} = 59$	$\mu_{13} = 51$	$\mu_{1.} = 54$
$R_2 = -4$	$\mu_{21} = 44$	$\mu_{22} = 51$	$\mu_{23} = 43$	$\mu_{2.} = 46$
Column mean	$\mu_{.1} = 48$	$\mu_{.2} = 55$	$\mu_{.3} = 47$	$\mu_{..} = 50$

applicable only to the selected makes of cars and the selected brands of gasoline. Finally, if we select four brands of gasoline because we are interested in those brands, but five makes of car at random, we have a mixed model. The results of the analysis are applicable to cars in general, but only to the brands of gasoline selected. The type of model does not affect the computations for tests of significance, but it affects the interpretation of the results.

The population mean for each cell is the grand population mean plus the row effect plus the column effect. The relationship may be stated symbolically as

(39.10) $$\mu_{ij} = \mu + R_i + K_j;$$

Thus, if $\mu = 50$; and there are two rows with $R_1 = 4$ and $R_2 = -4$; and there are three columns with $K_1 = -2$, $K_2 = 5$, and $K_3 = -3$, the cell means are as in Table 39.5. In this table:

$\mu_{i.}$ denotes mean of row i for all columns;

$\mu_{.j}$ denotes mean of column j for all rows;

$\mu_{..}$ denotes mean of all X-values.

This type of notation will be used whenever it is necessary for clarity. It is assumed that there is no interaction between columns and rows: the column effect is constant from row to row, and the row effect is constant from column to column. Notice that there is a constant difference of 8 between the row entries; there is a constant difference of -7 between the entries of column 1 and column 2, and a constant difference of 8 between column 2 and column 3.

An X-value for any cell is the cell mean plus a random element.

$$X_{ij} = \mu_{ij} + E_{ij}.$$

Substituting $X_{ij} - E_{ij}$ for μ_{ij} in equation (39.10), we obtain

$$X_{ij} = \mu + R_i + K_j + E_{ij},$$

or

(39.11) $$(X_{ij} - \mu) = R_i + K_j + (X_{ij} - \mu_{ij}).$$

From Table 39.5, it is apparent that $R_i = \mu_i - \mu$, $K_j = \mu_j - \mu$, and $\mu_{ij} = \mu_i + \mu_j - \mu$. Therefore, equation (39.12) can also be written in deviation form:

(39.12) $$(X_{ij} - \mu) = (\mu_i - \mu) + (\mu_j - \mu) + (X_{ij} - \mu_i - \mu_j + \mu).$$

As before, we have the assumption of normality and uniformity of variance.

Symbolic statement of test. The null hypothesis H_0 is that the column effect is zero, and the row effect is zero.

$$R_1 = R_2 = \ldots = R_r = 0; \quad K_1 = K_2 = \ldots = K_k = 0.$$

An equivalent statement is

$$\mu_{1.} = \mu_{2.} = \ldots = \mu_{r.} = \mu_{..}; \quad \mu_{.1} = \mu_{.2} = \ldots = \mu_{.k} = \mu_{..}.$$

If the sample estimates of μ, μ_i, and μ_j are substituted in equation (39.12), we obtain

$$(X_{ij} - \bar{\bar{X}}) = (\bar{X}_i - \bar{\bar{X}}) + (\bar{X}_j - \bar{\bar{X}}) + (X_{ij} - \bar{X}_i - \bar{X}_j + \bar{\bar{X}}).$$

The sums of squares are

(39.13) $$\Sigma (X_{ij} - \bar{\bar{X}})^2 = \Sigma (\bar{X}_i - \bar{\bar{X}})^2 + \Sigma (\bar{X}_j - \bar{\bar{X}})^2$$
$$+ \Sigma (X_{ij} - \bar{X}_i - \bar{X}_j + \bar{\bar{X}})^2,$$

which may be abbreviated to

$$\Sigma x_T^2 = \Sigma x_R^2 + \Sigma x_K^2 + \Sigma x_D^2$$

and stated verbally in this manner:

Total sum of squares = row sum of squares

+ column sum of squares + discrepance.

The degrees of freedom for the different sums of squares of equation (39.14) are additive:

$$(N - 1) = (r - 1) + (k - 1) + (N - r - k + 1), \quad \text{or}$$

(39.14) $$(N - 1) = (r - 1) + (k - 1) + (r - 1)(k - 1).$$

The mean squares are

$$s_R^2 = \frac{\Sigma x_R^2}{r - 1}; \quad s_K^2 = \frac{\Sigma x_K^2}{k - 1}; \quad s_D^2 = \frac{\Sigma x_D^2}{(r - 1)(k - 1)},$$

Finally the variance ratios are

$$F_R = \frac{s_R^2}{s_D^2}; \quad F_K = \frac{s_K^2}{s_D^2}.$$

Computational methods and numerical illustration. For efficient computation, the formulas are

$$(39.15) \begin{cases} \Sigma x_T^2 = \sum_1^N X^2 - \dfrac{\left(\sum_1^N X\right)^2}{N}\,; \\[2em] \Sigma x_R^2 = \dfrac{\sum_1^r \left(\sum_1^k X\right)^2}{k} - \dfrac{\left(\sum_1^N X\right)^2}{N}\,; \\[2em] \Sigma x_K^2 = \dfrac{\sum_1^k \left(\sum_1^r X\right)^2}{r} - \dfrac{\left(\sum_1^N X\right)^2}{N}\,; \\[2em] \Sigma x_D^2 = \Sigma x_T^2 - \Sigma x_R^2 - \Sigma x_K^2. \end{cases}$$

The quantity $\dfrac{\left(\sum_1^N X\right)^2}{N}$ is usually referred to as the general connection term.

**Table 39.6—Fuel Consumption of Five Makes of Car
Using Four Brands of Gasoline**

Fuel	Car					$\sum_1^k X$	$\left(\sum_1^k X\right)^2$
	(1)	(2)	(3)	(4)	(5)		
(1)	16.1	17.0	10.7	15.5	11.5	70.8	5,012.16
(2)	17.0	16.9	10.3	15.6	12.0	71.8	5,155.24
(3)	16.7	17.4	10.5	14.8	11.8	71.2	5,069.44
(4)	17.8	19.1	11.7	15.4	11.8	75.8	5,745.64
$\sum_1^r X$	67.6	70.4	43.2	61.3	47.1	289.6	20,982.96
$\left(\sum_1^r X\right)^2$	4,569.76	4,956.16	1,866.24	3,757.69	2,218.41	17,368.26	83,868.16*

* 83,868.16 = (289.6)².
Source: Freely adapted from data provided by Dail Frazier, The Standard Oil Company (Ohio).

From Table 39.6, we compute

$$\frac{\left(\sum_1^N X\right)^2}{N} = \frac{83,868.16}{20} = 4,193.41\,;$$

$$\sum_{1}^{N} X^2 = (16.1)^2 + (17.0)^2 + \dots + (71.2)^2 + (75.8)^2 = 4{,}348.38;$$

$$\Sigma\, x_T^2 = 4{,}348.38 - 4{,}193.41 = 154.97;$$

$$\Sigma\, x_R^2 = \frac{20{,}982.96}{5} - 4{,}193.41 = 4{,}196.59 - 4{,}193.41 = 3.18;$$

$$\Sigma\, x_K^2 = \frac{17{,}368.26}{4} - 4{,}193.41 = 4{,}342.065 - 4{,}193.408 = 148.66;$$

$$\Sigma\, x_D^2 = 154.97 - 3.18 - 148.66 = 3.13.$$

Table 39.7 is the analysis of variance table.
From the entries in the last column, we compute the variance ratios.

$$F_R = \frac{1.060}{0.2608} = 4.064, \qquad F_{.05;\,3,12} = 3.490$$

$$F_K = \frac{37.165}{0.2608} = 142.5; \qquad F_{0.001;\,4,12} = 9.63.$$

39.7—Analysis of Variance Table
(Data of Table 39.6)

Source of variation	Amount of variation S.S.	Degrees of freedom d.f.	Estimate of variance M.S.
Total	154.97	19	...
Rows (fuels)	3.18	3	1.060
Columns (cars) ..	148.66	4	37.165
Discrepance	3.13	12	0.2608

At the 0.05 level, there is a significant difference both among cars and among fuels. The difference among cars is especially convincing.

Special case where there are two columns. In Chapter 23, we tested the significance of the difference between 10 pairs of test cubes of concrete. We did this by taking the difference D for each pair, and testing whether $\bar{D}$ was significantly different from zero, using the t test. Note that D here means the difference $X_1 - X_2$, rather than "discrepance". The variance of the difference was estimated by computing

$$s_D^2 = \Sigma\, D^2 - \frac{(\Sigma\, D)^2}{n}.$$

It was also pointed out in a footnote that $s_D^2 = s_1^2 + s_2^2 - 2r_{12}s_1s_2$.

It is also possible to use analysis of variance. Using the data of Table 23.3, we obtain

$$\Sigma x_T^2 = 2{,}846.8$$

$$\Sigma x_R^2 = 1{,}842.8 \qquad s_R^2 = \frac{1{,}842.8}{9} = 204.8$$

$$\Sigma x_K^2 = 460.8 \qquad s_K^2 = \frac{460.8}{1} = 460.8$$

$$\Sigma x_D^2 = 543.2 \qquad s_D^2 = \frac{543.2}{9} = 60.36$$

$$F_K = \frac{460.8}{60.36} = 7.63$$

$$t = \sqrt{7.635} = 2.76.$$

The same value of t is obtained by all three procedures.

Chi-square Tests

Tests of homogeneity: goodness of fit. If data are homogeneous they should conform reasonably well to some probability distribution. Thus, in Chapter 19, the χ^2 test was applied to the life of wooden telephone poles, to test the hypothesis that the observations were normally distributed. When applying this test the number of degrees of freedom was the number of classes minus three, because the normal frequencies were made to conform to the observed distribution in three respects: number of frequencies; mean; standard deviation.

If the mean and standard deviation of the normal distribution are obtained from theoretical considerations, rather than the sample frequencies, the number of degrees of freedom for χ^2 is the number of classes minus one.

The χ^2 test can be used with other types of distributions as well. Thus, if the proportion of defective work is tabulated each day for 100 days, a binomial distribution can be obtained with $P = \bar{p}$. The observed distribution can be compared with the theoretical distribution, computing

$$\chi^2 = \sum \frac{(f - \hat{f})^2}{\hat{f}}$$

in the usual manner. The number of degrees of freedom is the number of classes minus two, since the observed and theoretical distributions are made to agree in two respects: $\Sigma \hat{f} = \Sigma f$ and $P = \bar{p}$. If a similar type of experiment is conducted for number of defects per unit, the Poisson distribution is used. The number of degrees of freedom is equal to the number of classes minus two, since the observed and theoretical distributions are made to agree in these respects: the total number of observations and the average number of defects.

The following is a simple illustration of the use of χ^2 with a probability distribution that does not conform to any of the types we have discussed. After being blindfolded, each of 60 persons was given 3 cigarettes, each of a different brand not disclosed to him, and asked to state which he liked best. If there is no difference among the brands, each brand should receive 20 first-choice votes. The actual votes were as in Table 39.8, column f.

Table 39.8—Theoretical and Observed Preferences for Three Brands of Cigarettes, and Computation of χ^2

Brand	P_i	$\hat{f}$ nP_i	f	$f - \hat{f}$	$(f - \hat{f})^2$	$\dfrac{(f - \hat{f})^2}{\hat{f}}$
A	.333	20	24	−4	16	0.800
B	.333	20	17	3	9	.450
C	.333	20	19	1	1	.050
Total	1.000	60	60	0		$\chi^2 = 1.300$

There are 2 degrees of freedom since the theoretical and observed frequencies have been made to agree in one respect: $\Sigma \hat{f} = \Sigma f$. Appendix 22 shows that when $\nu = 2$ and $\chi^2 = 1.386$, $P(\chi^2) = .50$. Thus the results are about what would be expected if the cigarettes were homogeneous with respect to flavor. That hypothesis must therefore be accepted.

Another interesting example of the use of χ^2 with a somewhat more complicated probability distribution is given in *Applied General Statistics*. Six cups of coffee, made from coffee as follows, were given to each of 52 tasters: A, fresh; a, fresh; B, 3 weeks old; b, 3 weeks old; C, 5 weeks old; c, 5 weeks old. The tasters were asked to match duplicate cups. Now $\binom{6}{2} = 15$, so 15 matchings are possible.

None correct	One correct
AB aC cb	Aa BC bc
AB ac Cb	Aa Bc Cb
Ab aC Bc	AB ab Cc
Ab ac BC	Ab aB Cc
AC aB bc	AC ac Bb
AC ab Bc	Ac aC Bb
Ac aB bC	*Three correct*
Ac ab BC	Aa Bb Cc

If there were no distinction as to taste among the different cups of coffee, 8/15 of the tasters would make no correct match, 6/15 of the tasters would make one correct match, and 1/15 would match all three pairs correctly.

The theoretical distribution and observed frequencies are in Table 39.9. The value of χ^2 is 46.08. As before there are 2 degrees of freedom. Appendix 22 shows that $P < .001$. Obviously the data are not homogeneous with respect to taste.

**Table 39.9—Theoretical and Observed Matching of Pairs
of Cups of Coffee by 52 Tasters**

Number of pairs correctly matched d	Prob (d)	Theoretical frequencies $\hat{f}$	Observed frequencies f
0	.5333	27.73	13
1	.4000	20.80	24
3	.0667	3.47	15
Total	1.0000	52.00	52

Source: F. E. Croxton and D. J. Cowden, *Applied General Statistics*, 2d ed., Prentice-Hall, Inc., Englewood Cliffs, N.J., p. 690.

Table 39.10—Computation of χ^2 for Test of Homogeneity: Two Classes
(Data of page 342)

Answer	P	$\dfrac{\hat{f}}{nP}$	f	$f - \hat{f}$	$(f - \hat{f})^2$	$\dfrac{(f - \hat{f})^2}{\hat{f}}$
Correct	.5	22	34	12	144	6.545
Incorrect	.5	22	10	−12	144	6.545
Total	1.0	44	44	0		$\chi^2 = 13.090$

Special case where there are two classes. In Chapter 22, another taste test was illustrated. Each of 44 persons was given a drink of R.C. Cola and a drink of Coca-Cola, and asked to state which was which. Of the 44 persons, 34 answered correctly. In Chapter 22, the test applied was

$$z = \frac{d - nP}{\sigma_d} = \frac{34 - 22}{3.317} = \frac{12}{3.317} = 3.62,$$

or with correction for continuity,

$$z = \frac{11.5}{3.317} = 3.5.$$

This problem can also be solved by use of χ^2, as in Table 39.10. Without correction for continuity the value of χ^2 is 13.090, and $\chi = 3.62$. Since χ is distributed normally when $v = 1$, the χ^2 (or χ) test is the same as the z test in such a case. If the correction for continuity is used

$$\chi^2 = 2(6.545 - 0.5) = 2(6.045) = 12.09,$$

and $\chi = 3.5$. This is the same as the value obtained for z when the correction for continuity was used.

Tests of independence using contingency tables. In Chapter 27 a 2×2 contingency table was used to illustrate correlation of qualitative data. In Table 27.5, 20 salesmen were classified into 2 categories, good and poor, according to flexibility and selling ability. Sometimes data are classified into more than 2 categories, with respect to one or both characteristics. Thus, the categories could be good, medium, and poor. A symbolic statement of the data is:

Category	1	2	$\ldots$	k	Total
1	f_{11}	f_{12}	$\ldots$	f_{1k}	$n_{1.}$
2	f_{21}	f_{22}	$\ldots$	f_{2k}	$n_{2.}$
.	.	.		.	.
.	.	.		.	.
.	.	.		.	.
r	f_{r1}	f_{r2}	$\ldots$	f_{rk}	$n_{r.}$
Total	$n_{.1}$	$n_{.2}$	$\ldots$	$n_{.k}$	N

If the probabilities for the cells in a given row are independent of the column in which they are located, and the probabilities for the cells in a given column are independent of the row in which they are located, then

$$P_{ij} = P_{i.}P_{.j},$$

and the expected frequencies are:

(39.16)

$\hat{f}_{11} = \dfrac{n_{1.}n_{.1}}{N}$	$\hat{f}_{12} = \dfrac{n_{1.}n_{.2}}{N}$	$\ldots$	$\hat{f}_{1k} = \dfrac{n_{1.}n_{.k}}{N}$	$n_{1.}$
$\hat{f}_{21} = \dfrac{n_{2.}n_{.1}}{N}$	$\hat{f}_{22} = \dfrac{n_{2.}n_{.2}}{N}$	$\ldots$	$\hat{f}_{2k} = \dfrac{n_{2.}n_{.k}}{N}$	$n_{2.}$
.	.		.	.
.	.		.	.
.	.		.	.
$\hat{f}_{r1} = \dfrac{n_{r.}n_{.1}}{N}$	$\hat{f}_{r2} = \dfrac{n_{r.}n_{.2}}{N}$	$\ldots$	$\hat{f}_{rk} = \dfrac{n_{r.}n_{.k}}{N}$	$n_{r.}$
$n_{.1}$	$n_{.2}$	$\ldots$	$n_{.k}$	N

Chi-square is computed as usual:

$$(39.17) \qquad \chi^2 = \sum \frac{(f - \hat{f})^2}{\hat{f}} = \frac{(f_{11} - \hat{f}_{11})^2}{\hat{f}_{11}} + \ldots + \frac{(f_{rk} - \hat{f}_{rk})^2}{\hat{f}_{rk}}.$$

The degrees of freedom are $(r-1)(k-1)$, the same as for a 2×2 table.
Special case: 2×2 table. Let us return now to the data of Table 27.5.

Category	(1)	(2)	Total
(1)	3	7	10
(2)	8	2	10
Total	11	9	20

The expected frequencies under the hypothesis of independence are

Category	(1)	(2)	Total
(1)	5.5	4.5	10
(2)	5.5	4.5	10
Total	11	9	20

With no correction for continuity:

$$\chi^2 = (f - \hat{f})^2 \sum \frac{1}{\hat{f}}$$

$$= (2.5)^2 \left(\frac{1}{5.5} + \frac{1}{4.5} + \frac{1}{5.5} + \frac{1}{4.5} \right)$$

$$= (6.25)(0.8080) = 5.050.$$

$$\chi = 2.247.$$

Using normal probabilities, we find that the probability of obtaining a value of χ as large as that obtained, or larger, is approximately 0.025. Using this method of analysis, then, the hypothesis of independence is rejected. The alternative hypothesis that selling ability depends partly on flexibility is accepted.

If we correct for continuity,

$$\chi^2 = (2.5 - 0.5)^2 \left(\frac{1}{5.5} + \frac{1}{4.5} + \frac{1}{5.5} + \frac{1}{4.5} \right)$$

$$= 4(0.8080) = 3.232.$$

$$\chi = 1.798.$$

The normal curve table indicates that the probability of obtaining a value of χ as large as 1.798 or larger is 0.072. If $\alpha = 0.05$, the hypothesis of independence is therefore accepted.

Exact test. Since the testimony of these two tests is contradictory, an exact test is desirable. First, consider the samples with the required marginal totals that result in a discrepancy for each cell as large as 2.5 or larger. These are

Sample			Discrepancy
3	7	10	2.5
8	2	10	
11	9	20	

2	8	10	3.5
9	1	10	
11	9	10	

1	9	10	4.5
10	0	10	
11	9	20	

8	2	10	2.5
3	7	10	
11	9	20	

9	1	10	3.5
2	8	10	
11	9	10	

10	0	10	4.5
1	9	10	
11	9	20	

We can use the hypergeometric distribution to obtain an exact test of significance.

$$(39.18) \qquad \text{Prob } (d) = \frac{\binom{D}{d}\binom{G}{g}}{\binom{N}{n}},$$

where there N items in the population, of which D are of one class (say defective) and G are of the other class (say effective). The corresponding frequencies for the sample are n, d, and g. The hypergeometric distribution is thus similar to the binomial distribution except that the population size is finite. As N approaches infinity, with $P = D/N$ remaining constant, the hypergeometric distribution approaches the binomial.

Consider the observed sample

3	7	10
8	2	10
11	9	20

or

$G - g = 3$	$D - d = 7$
$g = 8$	$d = 2$
$G = 11$	$D = 9$

$N - n = 10$
$n = 10$
$N = 20$

The probability of this sample is the probability that from a population of $N = 20$ with $D = 9$ and $G = 11$, and a sample of $n = 10$, we will obtain $d = 2$ and $g = 8$.

$$\text{Prob } (d = 2) = \frac{\binom{9}{2}\binom{11}{8}}{\binom{20}{10}}.$$

Using Appendix 5, we obtain

$$\text{Prob } (d = 2) = \frac{(36)(165)}{184,756} = \frac{5,940}{184,756} = .03215.$$

Similarly:

$$\text{Prob } (d = 1) = \frac{\binom{9}{1}\binom{11}{9}}{\binom{20}{10}} = \frac{(9)(55)}{184,756} = \frac{495}{184,756} = .00268;$$

$$\text{Prob } (d = 0) = \frac{\binom{9}{0}\binom{11}{10}}{\binom{20}{10}} = \frac{(1)(11)}{184,756} = \frac{11}{184,756} = .00006;$$

$$\text{Prob } (d = 7) = \frac{\binom{9}{7}\binom{11}{3}}{\binom{20}{10}} = \frac{(36)(165)}{184,756} = \frac{5,940}{184,756} = .03215;$$

$$\text{Prob } (d = 8) = \frac{\binom{9}{8}\binom{11}{2}}{\binom{20}{10}} = \frac{(9)(55)}{184,756} = \frac{495}{184,756} = .00268;$$

$$\text{Prob } (d = 9) = \frac{\binom{9}{9}\binom{11}{1}}{\binom{20}{10}} = \frac{(1)(11)}{184,756} = \frac{11}{184,756} = .00006.$$

Adding all of these probabilities together, we obtain

$$2(.03215 + .00268 + .00006) = 2(.03489) = .0698.$$

It is a little easier to combine all of these steps into one expression.

$$\frac{\binom{9}{2}\binom{11}{8} + \binom{9}{1}\binom{11}{9} + \binom{9}{0}\binom{11}{10} + \binom{9}{7}\binom{11}{3} + \binom{9}{8}\binom{11}{2} + \binom{9}{9}\binom{11}{1}}{\binom{20}{10}}$$

$$= \frac{5{,}940 + 495 + 11 + 5{,}940 + 495 + 11}{184{,}756} = \frac{12{,}892}{184{,}756} = .0698.$$

The probability obtained is virtually the same as the probability resulting from use of χ^2 corrected for continuity.

TABLES TO FACILITATE COMPUTATIONS

APPENDIX 1

Common Logarithms

Every logarithm has an integer, called the *characteristic*, and a decimal, called the *mantissa*. This table contains only mantissas. When $X \geq 1$, the characteristic is positive and is numerically one less than the number of places to the left of the decimal point. When $X < 1$, the characteristic is negative and is numerically one more than the number of zeros immediately to the right of the decimal point. Thus, the logarithm of 24.9 is 1.39620, and the logarithm of .0249 is $\bar{2}.39620$, or $8.39620 - 10$.

X	0	1	2	3	4	5	6	7	8	9	D
0	$-\infty$	00000	30103	47712	60206	69897	77815	84510	90309	95424	...
10	00000	00432	00860	01284	01703	02119	02531	02938	03342	03743	*
11	04139	04532	04922	05308	05690	06070	06446	06819	07188	07555	*
12	07918	08279	08636	08991	09342	09691	10037	10380	10721	11059	*
13	11394	11727	12057	12385	12710	13033	13354	13672	13988	14301	*
14	14613	14922	15229	15534	15836	16137	16435	16732	17026	17319	*
15	17609	17898	18184	18469	18752	19033	19312	19590	19866	20140	*
16	20412	20683	20952	21219	21484	21748	22011	22272	22531	22789	*
17	23045	23300	23553	23805	24055	24304	24551	24797	25042	25285	*
18	25527	25768	26007	26245	26482	26717	26951	27184	27416	27646	*
19	27875	28103	28330	28556	28780	29003	29226	29447	29667	29885	*
20	30103	30320	30535	30750	30963	31175	31387	31597	31806	32015	212
21	32222	32428	32634	32838	33041	33244	33445	33646	33846	34044	202
22	34242	34439	34635	34830	35025	35218	35411	35603	35793	35984	193
23	36173	36361	36549	36736	36922	37107	37291	37475	37658	37840	185
24	38021	38202	38382	38561	38739	38917	39094	39270	39445	39620	177
25	39794	39967	40140	40312	40483	40654	40824	40993	41162	41330	170
26	41497	41664	41830	41996	42160	42325	42488	42651	42813	42975	164
27	43136	43297	43457	43616	43775	43933	44091	44248	44404	44560	158
28	44716	44871	45025	45179	45332	45484	45637	45788	45939	46090	152
29	46240	46389	46538	46687	46835	46982	47129	47276	47422	47567	147
30	47712	47857	48001	48144	48287	48430	48572	48714	48855	48996	142
31	49136	49276	49415	49554	49693	49831	49969	50106	50243	50379	138
32	50515	50651	50786	50920	51055	51188	51322	51455	51587	51720	134
33	51851	51983	52114	52244	52375	52504	52634	52763	52892	53020	130
34	53148	53275	53403	53529	53656	53782	53908	54033	54158	54283	126
35	54407	54531	54654	54777	54900	55023	55145	55267	55388	55509	122
36	55630	55751	55871	55991	56110	56229	56348	56467	56585	56703	119
37	56820	56937	57054	57171	57287	57403	57519	57634	57749	57864	116
38	57978	58092	58206	58320	58433	58546	58659	58771	58883	58995	113
39	59106	59218	59329	59439	59550	59660	59770	59879	59988	60097	110
40	60206	60314	60423	60531	60638	60746	60853	60959	61066	61172	107
41	61278	61384	61490	61595	61700	61805	61909	62014	62118	62221	105
42	62325	62428	62531	62634	62737	62839	62941	63043	63144	63246	102
43	63347	63448	63548	63649	63749	63849	63949	64048	64147	64246	100
44	64345	64444	64542	64640	64738	64836	64933	65031	65128	65225	98
45	65321	65418	65514	65610	65706	65801	65896	65992	66087	66181	96
46	66276	66370	66464	66558	66652	66745	66839	66932	67025	67117	93
47	67210	67302	67394	67486	67578	67669	67761	67852	67943	68034	91
48	68124	68215	68305	68395	68485	68574	68664	68753	68842	68931	90
49	69020	69108	69197	69285	69373	69461	69548	69636	69723	69810	88

* Logarithms of numbers from 1,001 through 1,999 may be obtained, without interpolation, on pages 623–624.

X	0	1	2	3	4	5	6	7	8	9	D
50	69897	69984	70070	70157	70243	70329	70415	70501	70586	70672	86
51	70757	70842	70927	71012	71096	71181	71265	71349	71433	71517	84
52	71600	71684	71767	71850	71933	72016	72099	72181	72263	72346	83
53	72428	72509	72591	72673	72754	72835	72916	72997	73078	73159	81
54	73239	73320	73400	73480	73560	73640	73719	73799	73878	73957	80
55	74036	74115	74194	74273	74351	74429	74507	74586	74663	74741	78
56	74819	74896	74974	75051	75128	75205	75282	75358	75435	75511	77
57	75587	75664	75740	75815	75891	75967	76042	76118	76193	76268	76
58	76343	76418	76492	76567	76641	76716	76790	76864	76938	77012	74
59	77085	77159	77232	77305	77379	77452	77525	77597	77670	77743	73
60	77815	77887	77960	78032	78104	78176	78247	78319	78390	78462	72
61	78533	78604	78675	78746	78817	78888	78958	79029	79099	79169	71
62	79239	79309	79379	79449	79518	79588	79657	79727	79796	79865	70
63	79934	80003	80072	80140	80209	80277	80346	80414	80482	80550	68
64	80618	80686	80754	80821	80889	80956	81023	81090	81158	81224	67
65	81291	81358	81425	81491	81558	81624	81690	81757	81823	81889	66
66	81954	82020	82086	82151	82217	82282	82347	82413	82478	82543	65
67	82607	82672	82737	82802	82866	82930	82995	83059	83123	83187	64
68	83251	83315	83378	83442	83506	83569	83632	83696	83759	83822	63
69	83885	83948	84011	84073	84136	84198	84261	84323	84386	84448	62
70	84510	84572	84634	84696	84757	84819	84880	84942	85003	85065	62
71	85126	85187	85248	85309	85370	85431	85491	85552	85612	85673	61
72	85733	85794	85854	85914	85974	86034	86094	86153	86213	86273	60
73	86332	86392	86451	86510	86570	86629	86688	86747	86806	86864	59
74	86923	86982	87040	87099	87157	87216	87274	87332	87390	87448	58
75	87506	87564	87622	87679	87737	87795	87852	87910	87967	88024	58
76	88081	88138	88195	88252	88309	88366	88423	88480	88536	88593	57
77	88649	88705	88762	88818	88874	88930	88986	89042	89098	89154	56
78	89209	89265	89321	89376	89432	89487	89542	89597	89653	89708	55
79	89763	89818	89873	89927	89982	90037	90091	90146	90200	90255	55
80	90309	90363	90417	90472	90526	90580	90634	90687	90741	90795	54
81	90849	90902	90956	91009	91062	91116	91169	91222	91275	91328	53
82	91381	91434	91487	91540	91593	91645	91698	91751	91803	91855	53
83	91908	91960	92012	92065	92117	92169	92221	92273	92324	92376	52
84	92428	92480	92531	92583	92634	92686	92737	92788	92840	92891	51
85	92942	92993	93044	93095	93146	93197	93247	93298	93349	93399	51
86	93450	93500	93551	93601	93651	93702	93752	93802	93852	93902	50
87	93952	94002	94052	94101	94151	94201	94250	94300	94349	94399	50
88	94448	94498	94547	94596	94645	94694	94743	94792	94841	94890	49
89	94939	94988	95036	95085	95134	95182	95231	95279	95328	95376	49
90	95424	95472	95521	95569	95617	95665	95713	95761	95809	95856	48
91	95904	95952	95999	96047	96095	96142	96190	96237	96284	96332	48
92	96379	96426	96473	96520	96567	96614	96661	96708	96755	96802	47
93	96848	96895	96942	96988	97035	97081	97128	97174	97220	97267	47
94	97313	97359	97405	97451	97497	97543	97589	97635	97681	97727	46
95	97772	97818	97864	97909	97955	98000	98046	98091	98137	98182	46
96	98227	98272	98318	98363	98408	98453	98498	98543	98588	98632	45
97	98677	98722	98767	98811	98856	98900	98945	98989	99034	99078	45
98	99123	99167	99211	99255	99300	99344	99388	99432	99476	99520	44
99	99564	99607	99651	99695	99739	99782	99826	99870	99913	99957	44

X	0	1	2	3	4	5	6	7	8	9	D
100	000000	000434	000868	001301	001734	002166	002598	003029	003461	003891	432
101	4321	4751	5181	5609	6038	6466	6894	7321	7748	8174	428
102	8600	9026	9451	9876	010300	010724	011147	011570	011993	012415	424
103	012837	013259	013680	014100	4521	4940	5360	5779	6197	6616	420
104	7033	7451	7868	8284	8700	9116	9532	9947	020361	020775	416
105	021189	021603	022016	022428	022841	023252	023664	024075	4486	4896	412
106	5306	5715	6125	6533	6942	7350	7757	8164	8571	8978	408
107	9384	9789	030195	030600	031004	031408	031812	032216	032619	033021	404
108	033424	033826	4227	4628	5029	5430	5830	·6230	6629	7028	400
109	7426	7825	8223	8620	9017	9414	9811	040207	040602	040998	397
110	041393	041787	042182	042576	042969	043362	043755	044148	044540	044932	393
111	5323	5714	6105	6495	6885	7275	7664	8053	8442	8830	390
112	9218	9606	9993	050380	050766	051153	051538	051924	052309	052694	386
113	053078	053463	053846	4230	4613	4996	5378	5760	6142	6524	383
114	6905	7286	7666	8046	8426	8805	9185	9563	9942	060320	379
115	060698	061075	061452	061829	062206	062582	062958	063333	063709	4083	376
116	4458	4832	5206	5580	5953	6326	6699	7071	7443	7815	373
117	8186	8557	8928	9298	9668	070038	070407	070776	071145	071514	370
118	071882	072250	072617	072985	073352	3718	4085	4451	4816	5182	366
119	5547	5912	6276	6640	7004	7368	7731	8094	8457	8819	363
120	079181	079543	079904	080266	080626	080987	081347	081707	082067	082426	360
121	082785	083144	083503	3861	4219	4576	4934	5291	5647	6004	357
122	6360	6716	7071	7426	7781	8136	8490	8845	9198	9552	355
123	9905	090258	090611	090963	091315	091667	092018	092370	092721	093071	352
124	093422	3772	4122	4471	4820	5169	5518	5866	6215	6562	349
125	6910	7257	7604	7951	8298	8644	8990	9335	9681	100026	346
126	100371	100715	101059	101403	101747	102091	102434	102777	103119	3462	343
127	3804	4146	4487	4828	5169	5510	5851	6191	6531	6871	341
128	7210	7549	7888	8227	8565	8903	9241	9579	9916	110253	338
129	110590	110926	111263	111599	111934	112270	112605	112940	113275	3609	335
130	113943	114277	114611	114944	115278	115611	115943	116276	116608	116940	333
131	7271	7603	7934	8265	8595	8926	9256	9586	9915	120245	330
132	120574	120903	121231	121560	121888	122216	122544	122871	123198	3525	328
133	3852	4178	4504	4830	5156	5481	5806	6131	6456	6781	325
134	7105	7429	7753	8076	8399	8722	9045	9368	9690	130012	323
135	130334	130655	130977	131298	131619	131939	132260	132580	132900	3219	321
136	3539	3858	4177	4496	4814	5133	5451	5769	6086	6403	318
137	6721	7037	7354	7671	7987	8303	8618	8934	9249	9564	316
138	9879	140194	140508	140822	141136	141450	141763	142076	142389	142702	314
139	143015	3327	3639	3951	4263	4574	4885	5196	5507	5818	311
140	146128	146438	146748	147058	147367	147676	147985	148294	148603	148911	309
141	9219	9527	9835	150142	150449	150756	151063	151370	151676	151982	307
142	152288	152594	152900	3205	3510	3815	4120	4424	4728	5032	305
143	5336	5640	5943	6246	6549	6852	7154	7457	7759	8061	303
144	8362	8664	8965	9266	9567	9868	160168	160469	160769	161068	301
145	161368	161667	161967	162266	162564	162863	3161	3460	3758	4055	299
146	4353	4650	4947	5244	5541	5838	6134	6430	6726	7022	297
147	7317	7613	7908	8203	8497	8792	9086	9380	9674	9968	295
148	170262	170555	170848	171141	171434	171726	172019	172311	172603	172895	293
149	3186	3478	3769	4060	4351	4641	4932	5222	5512	5802	291

X	0	1	2	3	4	5	6	7	8	9	D
150	176091	176381	176670	176959	177248	177536	177825	178113	178401	178689	289
151	8977	9264	9552	9839	180126	180413	180699	180986	181272	181558	287
152	181844	182129	182415	182700	2985	3270	3555	3839	4123	4407	285
153	4691	4975	5259	5542	5825	6108	6391	6674	6956	7239	283
154	7521	7803	8084	8366	8647	8928	9209	9490	9771	190051	281
155	190332	190612	190892	191171	191451	191730	192010	192289	192567	2846	279
156	3125	3403	3681	3959	4237	4514	4792	5069	5346	5623	278
157	5900	6176	6453	6729	7005	7281	7556	7832	8107	8382	276
158	8657	8932	9206	9481	9755	200029	200303	200577	200850	201124	274
159	201397	201670	201943	202216	202488	2761	3033	3305	3577	3848	272
160	204120	204391	204663	204934	205204	205475	205746	206016	206286	206556	271
161	6826	7096	7365	7634	7904	8173	8441	8710	8979	9247	269
162	9515	9783	210051	210319	210586	210853	211121	211388	211654	211921	267
163	212188	212454	2720	2986	3252	3518	3783	4049	4314	4579	266
164	4844	5109	5373	5638	5902	6166	6430	6694	6957	7221	264
165	7484	7747	8010	8273	8536	8798	9060	9323	9585	9846	262
166	220108	220370	220631	220892	221153	221414	221675	221936	222196	222456	261
167	2716	2976	3236	3496	3755	4015	4274	4533	4792	5051	259
168	5309	5568	5826	6084	6342	6600	6858	7115	7372	7630	258
169	7887	8144	8400	8657	8913	9170	9426	9682	9938	230193	256
170	230449	230704	230960	231215	231470	231724	231979	232234	232488	232742	255
171	2996	3250	3504	3757	4011	4264	4517	4770	5023	5276	253
172	5528	5781	6033	6285	6537	6789	7041	7292	7544	7795	252
173	8046	8297	8548	8799	9049	9299	9550	9800	240050	240300	250
174	240549	240799	241048	241297	241546	241795	242044	242293	2541	2790	249
175	3038	3286	3534	3782	4030	4277	4525	4772	5019	5266	248
176	5513	5759	6006	6252	6499	6745	6991	7237	7482	7728	246
177	7973	8219	8464	8709	8954	9198	9443	9687	9932	250176	245
178	250420	250664	250908	251151	251395	251638	251881	252125	252368	2610	243
179	2853	3096	3338	3580	3822	4064	4306	4548	4790	5031	242
180	255273	255514	255755	255996	256237	256477	256718	256958	257198	257439	241
181	7679	7918	8158	8398	8637	8877	9116	9355	9594	9833	239
182	260071	260310	260548	260787	261025	261263	261501	261739	261976	262214	238
183	2451	2688	2925	3162	3399	3636	3873	4109	4346	4582	237
184	4818	5054	5290	5525	5761	5996	6232	6467	6702	6937	235
185	7172	7406	7641	7875	8110	8344	8578	8812	9046	9279	234
186	9513	9746	9980	270213	270446	270679	270912	271144	271377	271609	233
187	271842	272074	272306	2538	2770	3001	3233	3464	3696	3927	232
188	4158	4389	4620	4850	5081	5311	5542	5772	6002	6232	230
189	6462	6692	6921	7151	7380	7609	7838	8067	8296	8525	229
190	278754	278982	279211	279439	279667	279895	280123	280351	280578	280806	228
191	281033	281261	281488	281715	281942	282169	2396	2622	2849	3075	227
192	3301	3527	3753	3979	4205	4431	4656	4882	5107	5332	226
193	5557	5782	6007	6232	6456	6681	6905	7130	7354	7578	225
194	7802	8026	8249	8473	8696	8920	9143	9366	9589	9812	223
195	290035	290257	290480	290702	290925	291147	291369	291591	291813	292034	222
196	2256	2478	2699	2920	3141	3363	3584	3804	4025	4246	221
197	4466	4687	4907	5127	5347	5567	5787	6007	6226	6446	220
198	6665	6884	7104	7323	7542	7761	7979	8198	8416	8635	219
199	8853	9071	9289	9507	9725	9943	300161	300378	300595	300813	218

APPENDIX 2

Squares, Square Roots, and Reciprocals

Although these tables are for values of n with three or fewer digits, they can be used to extract the square root of a value of n containing more than three significant digits with an answer significant to five digits (usually), by the following simple device.

1. Let n' be the value of n recorded in Appendix Table 2.1 or 2.2 that is closest to the desired value of n. If n has an odd number of digits to the left of the decimal point, use Table 2.1; if n has an even number of digits to the left of the decimal point, use Table 2.2.
2. Look up $\sqrt{n'}$ in Table 2.1 or 2.2.
3. Compute

$$\sqrt{n} \doteq \frac{n + n'}{2\sqrt{n'}}.$$

Example A: Find the square root of 23,456.

1. Using Table 2.1, we find that $n' = 23,500$.
2. Table 2.1 shows that $\sqrt{23,500} = 153.2971$.
3. Therefore:

$$\sqrt{23,456} \doteq \frac{23,456 + 23,500}{2(153.2971)} = \frac{46,956}{306.5942} = 153.15.$$

Example B: Find the square root of 2,345.6.

1. Using Table 2.2 we find that $n' = 2,350$.
2. Table 2.2 shows that $\sqrt{2,350} = 48.47680$.
3. Therefore

$$\sqrt{2,345.6} \doteq \frac{2,345.6 + 2,350.0}{2(48.47680)} = \frac{4,695.6}{96.95360} = 48.431.$$

Appendix Table 2.1—Values of n^2, $\sqrt{n}$, and $1/n$ for Integral Values of n from 1 through 1,000

n	n^2	$\sqrt{n}$	$1/n$	n	n^2	$\sqrt{n}$	$1/n$
				50	2 500	7.071 068	.02000000
1	1	1.000 000	1.0000000	51	2 601	7.141 428	.01960784
2	4	1.414 214	.5000000	52	2 704	7.211 103	.01923077
3	9	1.732 051	.3333333	53	2 809	7.280 110	.01886792
4	16	2.000 000	.2500000	54	2 916	7.348 469	.01851852
5	25	2.236 068	.2000000	55	3 025	7.416 198	.01818182
6	36	2.449 490	.1666667	56	3 136	7.483 315	.01785714
7	49	2.645 751	.1428571	57	3 249	7.549 834	.01754386
8	64	2.828 427	.1250000	58	3 364	7.615 773	.01724138
9	81	3.000 000	.1111111	59	3 481	7.681 146	.01694915
10	100	3.162 278	.1000000	60	3 600	7.745 967	.01666667
11	121	3.316 625	.09090909	61	3 721	7.810 250	.01639344
12	144	3.464 102	.08333333	62	3 844	7.874 008	.01612903
13	169	3.605 551	.07692308	63	3 969	7.937 254	.01587302
14	196	3.741 657	.07142857	64	4 096	8.000 000	.01562500
15	225	3.872 983	.06666667	65	4 225	8.062 258	.01538462
16	256	4.000 000	.06250000	66	4 356	8.124 038	.01515152
17	289	4.123 106	.05882353	67	4 489	8.185 353	.01492537
18	324	4.242 641	.05555556	68	4 624	8.246 211	.01470588
19	361	4.358 899	.05263158	69	4 761	8.306 624	.01449275
20	400	4.472 136	.05000000	70	4 900	8.366 600	.01428571
21	441	4.582 576	.04761905	71	5 041	8.426 150	.01408451
22	484	4.690 416	.04545455	72	5 184	8.485 281	.01388889
23	529	4.795 832	.04347826	73	5 329	8.544 004	.01369863
24	576	4.898 979	.04166667	74	5 476	8.602 325	.01351351
25	625	5.000 000	.04000000	75	5 625	8.660 254	.01333333
26	676	5.099 020	.03846154	76	5 776	8.717 798	.01315789
27	729	5.196 152	.03703704	77	5 929	8.774 964	.01298701
28	784	5.291 503	.03571429	78	6 084	8.831 761	.01282051
29	841	5.385 165	.03448276	79	6 241	8.888 194	.01265823
30	900	5.477 226	.03333333	80	6 400	8.944 272	.01250000
31	961	5.567 764	.03225806	81	6 561	9.000 000	.01234568
32	1 024	5.656 854	.03125000	82	6 724	9.055 385	.01219512
33	1 089	5.744 563	.03030303	83	6 889	9.110 434	.01204819
34	1 156	5.830 952	.02941176	84	7 056	9.165 151	.01190476
35	1 225	5.916 080	.02857143	85	7 225	9.219 544	.01176471
36	1 296	6.000 000	.02777778	86	7 396	9.273 618	.01162791
37	1 369	6.082 763	.02702703	87	7 569	9.327 379	.01149425
38	1 444	6.164 414	.02631579	88	7 744	9.380 832	.01136364
39	1 521	6.244 998	.02564103	89	7 921	9.433 981	.01123596
40	1 600	6.324 555	.02500000	90	8 100	9.486 833	.01111111
41	1 681	6.403 124	.02439024	91	8 281	9.539 392	.01098901
42	1 764	6.480 741	.02380952	92	8 464	9.591 663	.01086957
43	1 849	6.557 439	.02325581	93	8 649	9.643 651	.01075269
44	1 936	6.633 250	.02272727	94	8 836	9.695 360	.01063830
45	2 025	6.708 204	.02222222	95	9 025	9.746 794	.01052632
46	2 116	6.782 330	.02173913	96	9 216	9.797 959	.01041667
47	2 209	6.855 655	.02127660	97	9 409	9.848 858	.01030928
48	2 304	6.928 203	.02083333	98	9 604	9.899 495	.01020408
49	2 401	7.000 000	.02040816	99	9 801	9.949 874	.01010101
50	2 500	7.071 068	.02000000	100	10 000	10.00000	.01000000

Appendix Table 2.1 (Cont'd)—Values of n^2, $\sqrt{n}$, and $1/n$ for Integral Values of n from 1 through 1,000

n	n^2	$\sqrt{n}$	$1/n$ .0	n	n^2	$\sqrt{n}$	$1/n$ .00
100	10 000	10.00000	10000000	150	22 500	12.24745	6666667
101	10 201	10.04988	09900990	151	22 801	12.28821	6622517
102	10 404	10.09950	09803922	152	23 104	12.32883	6578947
103	10 609	10.14889	09708738	153	23 409	12.36932	6535948
104	10 816	10.19804	09615385	154	23 716	12.40967	6493506
105	11 025	10.24695	09523810	155	24 025	12.44990	6451613
106	11 236	10.29563	09433962	156	24 336	12.49000	6410256
107	11 449	10.34408	09345794	157	24 649	12.52996	6369427
108	11 664	10.39230	09259259	158	24 964	12.56981	6329114
109	11 881	10.44031	09174312	159	25 281	12.60952	6289308
110	12 100	10.48809	09090909	160	25 600	12.64911	6250000
111	12 321	10.53565	09009009	161	25 921	12.68858	6211180
112	12 544	10.58301	08928571	162	26 244	12.72792	6172840
113	12 769	10.63015	08849558	163	26 569	12.76715	6134969
114	12 996	10.67708	08771930	164	26 896	12.80625	6097561
115	13 225	10.72381	08695652	165	27 225	12.84523	6060606
116	13 456	10.77033	08620690	166	27 556	12.88410	6024096
117	13 689	10.81665	08547009	167	27 889	12.92285	5988024
118	13 924	10.86278	08474576	168	28 224	12.96148	5952381
119	14 161	10.90871	08403361	169	28 561	13.00000	5917160
120	14 400	10.95445	08333333	170	28 900	13.03840	5882353
121	14 641	11.00000	08264463	171	29 241	13.07670	5847953
122	14 884	11.04536	08196721	172	29 584	13.11488	5813953
123	15 129	11.09054	08130081	1,3	29 929	13.15295	5780347
124	15 376	11.13553	08064516	174	30 276	13.19091	5747126
125	15 625	11.18034	08000000	175	30 625	13.22876	5714286
126	15 876	11.22497	07936508	176	30 976	13.26650	5681818
127	16 129	11.26943	07874016	177	31 329	13.30413	5649718
128	16 384	11.31371	07812500	178	31 684	13.34166	5617978
129	16 641	11.35782	07751938	179	32 041	13.37909	5586592
130	16 900	11.40175	07692308	180	32 400	13.41641	5555556
131	17 161	11.44552	07633588	181	32 761	13.45362	5524862
132	17 424	11.48913	07575758	182	33 124	13.49074	5494505
133	17 689	11.53256	07518797	183	33 489	13.52775	5464481
134	17 956	11.57584	07462687	184	33 856	13.56466	5434783
135	18 225	11.61895	07407407	185	34 225	13.60147	5405405
136	18 496	11.66190	07352941	186	34 596	13.63818	5376344
137	18 769	11.70470	07299270	187	34 969	13.67479	5347594
138	19 044	11.74734	07246377	188	35 344	13.71131	5319149
139	19 321	11.78983	07194245	189	35 721	13.74773	5291005
140	19 600	11.83216	07142857	190	36 100	13.78405	5263158
141	19 881	11.87434	07092199	191	36 481	13.82027	5235602
142	20 164	11.91638	07042254	192	36 864	13.85641	5208333
143	20 449	11.95826	06993007	193	37 249	13.89244	5181347
144	20 736	12.00000	06944444	194	37 636	13.92839	5154639
145	21 025	12.04159	06896552	195	38 025	13.96424	5128205
146	21 316	12.08305	06849315	196	38 416	14.00000	5102041
147	21 609	12.12436	06802721	197	38 809	14.03567	5076142
148	21 904	12.16553	06756757	198	39 204	14.07125	5050505
149	22 201	12.20656	06711409	199	39 601	14.10674	5025126
150	22 500	12.24745	06666667	200	40 000	14.14214	5000000

Appendix Table 2.1 (Cont'd)—Values of n^2, $\sqrt{n}$, and $1/n$ for Integral Values of n from 1 through 1,000

n	n^2	$\sqrt{n}$	$1/n$ .00	n	n^2	$\sqrt{n}$	$1/n$ .00
200	40 000	14.14214	5000000	250	62 500	15.81139	4000000
201	40 401	14.17745	4975124	251	63 001	15.84298	3984064
202	40 804	14.21267	4950495	252	63 504	15.87451	3968254
203	41 209	14.24781	4926108	253	64.009	15.90597	3952569
204	41 616	14.28286	4901961	254	64 516	15.93738	3937008
205	42 025	14.31782	4878049	255	65 025	15.96872	3921569
206	42 436	14.35270	4854369	256	65 536	16.00000	3906250
207	42 849	14.38749	4830918	257	66 049	16.03122	3891051
208	43, 264	14.42221	4807692	258	66 564	16.06238	3875969
209	43 681	14.45683	4784689	259	67 081	16.09348	3861004
210	44 100	14.49138	4761905	260	67 600	16.12452	3846154
211	44 521	14.52584	4739336	261	68 121	16.15549	3831418
212	44 944	14.56022	4716981	262	68 644	16.18641	3816794
213	45 369	14.59452	4694836	263	69 169	16.21727	3802281
214	45 796	14.62874	4672897	264	69 696	16.24808	3787879
215	46 225	14.66288	4651163	265	70 225	16.27882	3773585
216	46 656	14.69694	4629630	266	70 756	16.30951	3759398
217	47 089	14.73092	4608295	267	71 289	16.34013	3745318
218	47 524	14.76482	4587156	268	71 824	16.37071	3731343
219	47 961	14.79865	4566210	269	72 361	16.40122	3717472
220	48 400	14.83240	4545455	270	72 900	16.43168	3703704
221	48 841	14.86607	4524887	271	73 441	16.46208	3690037
222	49 284	14.89966	4504505	272	73 984	16.49242	3676471
223	49 729	14.93318	4484305	273	74 529	16.52271	3663004
224	50 176	14.96663	4464286	274	75 076	16.55295	3649635
225	50 625	15.00000	4444444	275	75 625	16.58312	3636364
226	51 076	15.03330	4424779	276	76 176	16.61325	3623188
227	51 529	15.06652	4405286	277	76 729	16.64332	3610108
228	51 984	15.09967	4385965	278	77 284	16.67333	3597122
229	52 441	15.13275	4366812	279	77 841	16.70329	3584229
230	52 900	15.16575	4347826	280	78 400	16.73320	3571429
231	53 361	15.19868	4329004	281	78 961	16.76305	3558719
232	53 824	15.23155	4310345	282	79 524	16.79286	3546099
233	54 289	15.26434	4291845	283	80 089	16.82260	3533569
234	54 756	15.29706	4273504	284	80 656	16.85230	3521127
235	55 225	15.32971	4255319	285	81 225	16.88194	3508772
236	55 696	15.36229	4237288	286	81 796	16.91153	3496503
237	56 169	15.39480	4219409	287	82 369	16.94107	3484321
238	56 644	15.42725	4201681	288	82 944	16.97056	3472222
239	57 121	15.45962	4184100	289	83 521	17.00000	3460208
240	57 600	15.49193	4166667	290	84 100	17.02939	3448276
241	58 081	15.52417	4149378	291	84 681	17.05872	3436426
242	58 564	15.55635	4132231	292	85 264	17.08801	3424658
243	59 049	15.58846	4115226	293	85 849	17.11724	3412969
244	59 536	15.62050	4098361	294	86 436	17.14643	3401361
245	60 025	15.65248	4081633	295	87 025	17.17556	3389831
246	60 516	15.68439	4065041	296	87 616	17.20465	3378378
247	61 009	15.71623	4048583	297	88 209	17.23369	3367003
248	61 504	15.74802	4032258	298	88 804	17.26268	3355705
249	62 001	15.77973	4016064	299	89 401	17.29162	3344482
250	62 500	15.81139	4000000	300	90 000	17.32051	3333333

Appendix Table 2.1 (Cont'd)—Values of n^2, $\sqrt{n}$, and $1/n$
for Integral Values of n from 1 through 1,000

n	n^2	$\sqrt{n}$	$1/n$ .00	n	n^2	$\sqrt{n}$	$1/n$ .00
300	90 000	17.32051	3333333	350	122 500	18.70829	2857143
301	90 601	17.34935	3322259	351	123 201	18.73499	2849003
302	91 204	17.37815	3311258	352	123 904	18.76166	2840909
303	91 809	17.40690	3300330	353	124 609	18.78829	2832861
304	92 416	17.43560	3289474	354	125 316	18.81489	2824859
305	93 025	17.46425	3278689	355	126 025	18.84144	2816901
306	93 636	17.49286	3267974	356	126 736	18.86796	2808989
307	94 249	17.52142	3257329	357	127 449	18.89444	2801120
308	94 864	17.54993	3246753	358	128 164	18.92089	2793296
309	95 481	17.57840	3236246	359	128 881	18.94730	2785515
310	96 100	17.60682	3225806	360	129 600	18.97367	2777778
311	96 721	17.63519	3215434	361	130 321	19.00000	2770083
312	97 344	17.66352	3205128	362	131 044	19.02630	2762431
313	97 969	17.69181	3194888	363	131 769	19.05256	2754821
314	98 596	17.72005	3184713	364	132 496	19.07878	2747253
315	99 225	17.74824	3174603	365	133 225	19.10497	2739726
316	99 856	17.77639	3164557	366	133 956	19.13113	2732240
317	100 489	17.80449	3154574	367	134 689	19.15724	2724796
318	101 124	17.83255	3144654	368	135 424	19.18333	2717391
319	101 761	17.86057	3134796	369	136 161	19.20937	2710027
320	102 400	17.88854	3125000	370	136 900	19.23538	2702703
321	103 041	17.91647	3115265	371	137 641	19.26136	2695418
322	103 684	17.94436	3105590	372	138 384	19.28730	2688172
323	104 329	17.97220	3095975	373	139 129	19.31321	2680965
324	104 976	18.00000	3086420	374	139 876	19.33908	2673797
325	105 625	18.02776	3076923	375	140 625	19.36492	2666667
326	106 276	18.05547	3067485	376	141 376	19.39072	2659574
327	106 929	18.08314	3058104	377	142 129	19.41649	2652520
328	107 584	18.11077	3048780	378	142 884	19.44222	2645503
329	108 241	18.13836	3039514	379	143 641	19.46792	2638522
330	108 900	18.16590	3030303	380	144 400	19.49359	2631579
331	109 561	18.19341	3021148	381	145 161	19.51922	2624672
332	110 224	18 22087	3012048	382	145 924	19.54483	2617801
333	110 889	18.24829	3003003	383	146 689	19.57039	2610966
334	111 556	18.27567	2994012	384	147 456	19.59592	2604167
335	112 225	18.30301	2985075	385	148 225	19.62142	2597403
336	112 896	18.33030	2976190	386	148 996	19.64688	2590674
337	113 569	18.35756	2967359	387	149 769	19.67232	2583979
338	114 244	18.38478	2958580	388	150 544	19.69772	2577320
339	114 921	18.41195	2949853	389	151 321	19.72308	2570694
340	115 600	18.43909	2941176	390	152 100	19.74842	2564103
341	116 281	18.46619	2932551	391	152 881	19.77372	2557545
342	116 964	18.49324	2923977	392	153 664	19.79899	2551020
343	117 649	18.52026	2915452	393	154 449	19.82423	2544529
344	118 336	18.54724	2906977	394	155 236	19.84943	2538071
345	119 025	18.57418	2898551	395	156 025	19.87461	2531646
346	119 716	18.60108	2890173	396	156 816	19.89975	2525253
347	120 409	18.62794	2881844	397	157 609	19.92486	2518892
348	121 104	18.65476	2873563	398	158 404	19.94994	2512563
349	121 801	18.68154	2865330	399	159 201	19.97498	2506266
350	122 500	18.70829	2857143	400	160 000	20.00000	2500000

Appendix Table 2.1 (Cont'd)—Values of n^2, $\sqrt{n}$, and $1/n$
for Integral Values of n from 1 through 1,000

n	n^2	$\sqrt{n}$	$1/n$ .00	n	n^2	$\sqrt{n}$	$1/n$ .00
400	160 000	20.00000	2500000	450	202 500	21.21320	2222222
401	160 801	20.02498	2493766	451	203 401	21.23676	2217295
402	161 604	20.04994	2487562	452	204 304	21.26029	2212389
403	162 409	20.07486	2481390	453	205 209	21.28380	2207506
404	163 216	20.09975	2475248	454	206 116	21.30728	2202643
405	164 025	20.12461	2469136	455	207 025	21.33073	2197802
406	164 836	20.14944	2463054	456	207 936	21.35416	2192982
407	165 649	20.17424	2457002	457	208 849	21.37756	2188184
408	166 464	20.19901	2450980	458	209 764	21.40093	2183406
409	167 281	20.22375	2444988	459	210 681	21.42429	2178649
410	168 100	20.24846	2439024	460	211 600	21.44761	2173913
411	168 921	20.27313	2433090	461	212 521	21.47091	2169197
412	169 744	20.29778	2427184	462	213 444	21.49419	2164502
413	170 569	20.32240	2421308	463	214 369	21.51743	2159827
414	171 396	20.34699	2415459	464	215 296	21.54066	2155172
415	172 225	20.37155	2409639	465	216 225	21.56386	2150538
416	173 056	20.39608	2403846	466	217 156	21.58703	2145923
417	173 889	20.42058	2398082	467	218 089	21.61018	2141328
418	174 724	20.44505	2392344	468	219 024	21.63331	2136752
419	175 561	20.46949	2386635	469	219 961	21.65641	2132196
420	176 400	20.49390	2380952	470	220 900	21.67948	2127660
421	177 241	20.51828	2375297	471	221 841	21.70253	2123142
422	178 084	20.54264	2369668	472	222 784	21.72556	2118644
423	178 929	20.56696	2364066	473	223 729	21.74856	2114165
424	179 776	20.59126	2358491	474	224 676	21.77154	2109705
425	180 625	20.61553	2352941	475	225 625	21.79449	2105263
426	181 476	20.63977	2347418	476	226 576	21.81742	2100840
427	182 329	20.66398	2341920	477	227 529	21.84033	2096436
428	183 184	20.68816	2336449	478	228 484	21.86321	2092050
429	184 041	20.71232	2331002	479	229 441	21.88607	2087683
430	184 900	20.73644	2325581	480	230 400	21.90890	2083333
431	185 761	20.76054	2320186	481	231 361	21.93171	2079002
432	186 624	20.78461	2314815	482	232 324	21.95450	2074689
433	187 489	20.80865	2309469	483	233 289	21.97726	2070393
434	188 356	20.83267	2304147	484	234 256	22.00000	2066116
435	189 225	20.85665	2298851	485	235 225	22.02272	2061856
436	190 096	20.88061	2293578	486	236 196	22.04541	2057613
437	190 969	20.90454	2288330	487	237 169	22.06808	2053388
438	191 844	20.92845	2283105	488	238 144	22.09072	2049180
439	192 721	20.95233	2277904	489	239 121	22.11334	2044990
440	193 600	20.97618	2272727	490	240 100	22.13594	2040816
441	194 481	21.00000	2267574	491	241 081	22.15852	2036660
442	195 364	21.02380	2262443	492	242 064	22.18107	2032520
443	196 249	21.04757	2257336	493	243 049	22.20360	2028398
444	197 136	21.07131	2252252	494	244 036	22.22611	2024291
445	198 025	21.09502	2247191	495	245 025	22.24860	2020202
446	198 916	21.11871	2242152	496	246 016	22.27106	2016129
447	199 809	21.14237	2237136	497	247 009	22.29350	2012072
448	200 704	21.16601	2232143	498	248 004	22.31591	2008032
449	201 601	21.18962	2227171	499	249 001	22.33831	2004008
450	202 500	21.21320	2222222	500	250 000	22.36068	2000000

Appendix Table 2.1 (Cont'd)—Values of n^2, $\sqrt{n}$, and $1/n$
for Integral Values of n from 1 through 1,000

n	n^2	$\sqrt{n}$	$1/n$ .00	n	n^2	$\sqrt{n}$	$1/n$ .00
500	250 000	22.36068	2000000	550	302 500	23.45208	1818182
501	251 001	22.38303	1996008	551	303 601	23.47339	1814882
502	252 004	22.40536	1992032	552	304 704	23.49468	1811594
503	253 009	22.42766	1988072	553	305 809	23.51595	1808318
504	254 016	22.44994	1984127	554	306 916	23.53720	1805054
505	255 025	22.47221	1980198	555	308 025	23.55844	1801802
506	256 036	22.49444	1976285	556	309 136	23.57965	1798561
507	257 049	22.51666	1972387	557	310 249	23.60085	1795332
508	258 064	22.53886	1968504	558	311 364	23.62202	1792115
509	259 081	22.56103	1964637	559	312 481	23.64318	1788909
510	260 100	22.58318	1960784	560	313 600	23.66432	1785714
511	261 121	22.60531	1956947	561	314 721	23.68544	1782531
512	262 144	22.62742	1953125	562	315 844	23.70654	1779359
513	263 169	22.64950	1949318	563	316 969	23.72762	1776199
514	264 196	22.67157	1945525	564	318 096	23.74868	1773050
515	265 225	22.69361	1941748	565	319 225	23.76973	1769912
516	266 256	22.71563	1937984	566	320 356	23.79075	1766784
517	267 289	22.73763	1934236	567	321 489	23.81176	1763668
518	268 324	22.75961	1930502	568	322 624	23.83275	1760563
519	269 361	22.78157	1926782	569	323 761	23.85372	1757469
520	270 400	22.80351	1923077	570	324 900	23.87467	1754386
521	271 441	22.82542	1919386	571	326 041	23.89561	1751313
522	272 484	22.84732	1915709	572	327 184	23.91652	1748252
523	273 529	22.86919	1912046	573	328 329	23.93742	1745201
524	274 576	22.89105	1908397	574	329 476	23.95830	1742160
525	275 625	22.91288	1904762	575	330 625	23.97916	1739130
526	276 676	22.93469	1901141	576	331 776	24.00000	1736111
527	277 729	22.95648	1897533	577	332 929	24.02082	1733102
528	278 784	22.97825	1893939	578	334 084	24.04163	1730104
529	279 841	23.00000	1890359	579	335 241	24.06242	1727116
530	280 900	23.02173	1886792	580	336 400	24.08319	1724138
531	281 961	23.04344	1883239	581	337 561	24.10394	1721170
532	283 024	23.06513	1879699	582	338 724	24.12468	1718213
533	284 089	23.08679	1876173	583	339 889	24.14539	1715266
534	285 156	23.10844	1872659	584	341 056	24.16609	1712329
535	286 225	23.13007	1869159	585	342 225	24.18677	1709402
536	287 296	23.15167	1865672	586	343 396	24.20744	1706485
537	288 369	23.17326	1862197	587	344 569	24.22808	1703578
538	289 444	23.19483	1858736	588	345 744	24.24871	1700680
539	290 521	23.21637	1855288	589	346 921	24.26932	1697793
540	291 600	23.23790	1851852	590	348 100	24.28992	1694915
541	292 681	23.25941	1848429	591	349 281	24.31049	1692047
542	293 764	23.28089	1845018	592	350 464	24.33105	1689189
543	294 849	23.30236	1841621	593	351 649	24.35159	1686341
544	295 936	23.32381	1838235	594	352 836	24.37212	1683502
545	297 025	23.34524	1834862	595	354 025	24.39262	1680672
546	298 116	23.36664	1831502	596	355 216	24.41311	1677852
547	299 209	23.38803	1828154	597	356 409	24.43358	1675042
548	300 304	23.40940	1824818	598	357 604	24.45404	1672241
549	301 401	23.43075	1821494	599	358 801	24.47448	1669449
550	302 500	23.45208	1818182	600	360 000	24.49490	1666667

Appendix Table 2.1 (Cont'd)—Values of n^2, $\sqrt{n}$, and $1/n$
for Integral Values of n from 1 through 1,000

n	n^2	$\sqrt{n}$	$1/n$ .00	n	n^2	$\sqrt{n}$	$1/n$ .00
600	360 000	24.49490	1666667	650	422 500	25.49510	1538462
601	361 201	24.51530	1663894	651	423 801	25.51470	1536098
602	362 404	24.53569	1661130	652	425 104	25.53429	1533742
603	363 609	24.55606	1658375	653	426 409	25.55386	1531394
604	364 816	24.57641	1655629	654	427 716	25.57342	1529052
605	366 025	24.59675	1652893	655	429 025	25.59297	1526718
606	367 236	24.61707	1650165	656	430 336	25.61250	1524390
607	368 449	24.63737	1647446	657	431 649	25.63201	1522070
608	369 664	24.65766	1644737	658	432 964	25.65151	1519757
609	370 881	24.67793	1642036	659	434 281	25.67100	1517451
610	372 100	24.69818	1639344	660	435 600	25.69047	1515152
611	373 321	24.71841	1636661	661	436 921	25.70992	1512859
612	374 544	24.73863	1633987	662	438 244	25.72936	1510574
613	375 769	24.75884	1631321	663	439 569	25.74879	1508296
614	376 996	24.77902	1628664	664	440 896	25.76820	1506024
615	378 225	24.79919	1626016	665	442 225	25.78759	1503759
616	379 456	24.81935	1623377	666	443 556	25.80698	1501502
617	380 689	24.83948	1620746	667	444 889	25.82634	1499250
618	381 924	24.85961	1618123	668	446 224	25.84570	1497006
619	383 161	24.87971	1615509	669	447 561	25.86503	1494768
620	384 400	24.89980	1612903	670	448 900	25.88436	1492537
621	385 641	24.91987	1610306	671	450 241	25.90367	1490313
622	386 884	24.93993	1607717	672	451 584	25.92296	1488095
623	388 129	24.95997	1605136	673	452 929	25.94224	1485884
624	389 376	24.97999	1602564	674	454 276	25.96151	1483680
625	390 625	25.00000	1600000	675	455 625	25.98076	1481481
626	391 876	25.01999	1597444	676	456 976	26.00000	1479290
627	393 129	25.03997	1594896	677	458 329	26.01922	1477105
628	394 384	25.05993	1592357	678	459 684	26.03843	1474926
629	395 641	25.07987	1589825	679	461 041	26.05763	1472754
630	396 900	25.09980	1587302	680	462 400	26.07681	1470588
631	398 161	25.11971	1584786	681	463 761	26.09598	1468429
632	399 424	25.13961	1582278	682	465 124	26.11513	1466276
633	400 689	25.15949	1579779	683	466 489	26.13427	1464129
634	401 956	25.17936	1577287	684	467 856	26.15339	1461988
635	403 225	25.19921	1574803	685	469 225	26.17250	1459854
636	404 496	25.21904	1572327	686	470 596	26.19160	1457726
637	405 769	25.23886	1569859	687	471 969	26.21068	1455604
638	407 044	25.25866	1567398	688	473 344	26.22975	1453488
639	408 321	25.27845	1564945	689	474 721	26.24881	1451379
640	409 600	25.29822	1562500	690	476 100	26.26785	1449275
641	410 881	25.31798	1560062	691	477 481	26.28688	1447178
642	412 164	25.33772	1557632	692	478 864	26.30589	1445087
643	413 449	25.35744	1555210	693	480 249	26.32489	1443001
644	414 736	25.37716	1552795	694	481 636	26.34388	1440922
645	416 025	25.39685	1550388	695	483 025	26.36285	1438849
646	417 316	25.41653	1547988	696	484 416	26.38181	1436782
647	418 609	25.43619	1545595	697	485 809	26.40076	1434720
648	419 904	25.45584	1543210	698	487 204	26.41969	1432665
649	421 201	25.47548	1540832	699	488 601	26.43861	1430615
650	422 500	25.49510	1538462	700	490 000	26.45751	1428571

Appendix Table 2.1 (Cont'd)—Values of n^2, $\sqrt{n}$, and $1/n$ for Integral Values of n from 1 through 1,000

n	n^2	$\sqrt{n}$	$1/n$ .00	n	n^2	$\sqrt{n}$	$1/n$ .00
700	490 000	26.45751	1428571	750	562 500	27.38613	1333333
701	491 401	26.47640	1426534	751	564 001	27.40438	1331558
702	492 804	26.49528	1424501	752	565 504	27.42262	1329787
703	494 209	26.51415	1422475	753	567 009	27.44085	1328021
704	495 616	26.53300	1420455	754	568 516	27.45906	1326260
705	497 025	26.55184	1418440	755	570 025	27.47726	1324503
706	498 436	26.57066	1416431	756	571 536	27.49545	1322751
707	499 849	26.58947	1414427	757	573 049	27.51363	1321004
708	501 264	26.60827	1412429	758	574 564	27.53180	1319261
709	502 681	26.62705	1410437	759	576 081	27.54995	1317523
710	504 100	26.64583	1408451	760	577 600	27.56810	1315789
711	505 521	26.66458	1406470	761	579 121	27.58623	1314060
712	506 944	26.68333	1404494	762	580 644	27.60435	1312336
713	508 369	26.70206	1402525	763	582 169	27.62245	1310616
714	509 796	26.72078	1400560	764	583 696	27.64055	1308901
715	511 225	26.73948	1398601	765	585 225	27.65863	1307190
716	512 656	26.75818	1396648	766	586 756	27.67671	1305483
717	514 089	26.77686	1394700	767	588 289	27.69476	1303781
718	515 524	26.79552	1392758	768	589 824	27.71281	1302083
719	516 961	26.81418	1390821	769	591 361	27.73085	1300390
720	518 400	26.83282	1388889	770	592 900	27.74887	1298701
721	519 841	26.85144	1386963	771	594 441	27.76689	1297017
722	521 284	26.87006	1385042	772	595 984	27.78489	1295337
723	522 729	26.88866	1383126	773	597 529	27.80288	1293661
724	524 176	26.90725	1381215	774	599 076	27.82086	1291990
725	525 625	26.92582	1379310	775	600 625	27.83882	1290323
726	527 076	26.94439	1377410	776	602 176	27.85678	1288660
727	528 529	26.96294	1375516	777	603 729	27.87472	1287001
728	529 984	26.98148	1373626	778	605 284	27.89265	1285347
729	531 441	27.00000	1371742	779	606 841	27.91057	1283697
730	532 900	27.01851	1369863	780	608 400	27.92848	1282051
731	534 361	27.03701	1367989	781	609 961	27.94638	1280410
732	535 824	27.05550	1366120	782	611 524	27.96426	1278772
733	537 289	27.07397	1364256	783	613 089	27.98214	1277139
734	538 756	27.09243	1362398	784	614 656	28.00000	1275510
735	540 225	27.11088	1360544	785	616 225	28.01785	1273885
736	541 696	27.12932	1358696	786	617 796	28.03569	1272265
737	543 169	27.14774	1356852	787	619 369	28.05352	1270648
738	544 644	27.16616	1355014	788	620 944	28.07134	1269036
739	546 121	27.18455	1353180	789	622 521	28.08914	1267427
740	547 600	27.20294	1351351	790	624 100	28.10694	1265823
741	549 081	27.22132	1349528	791	625 681	28.12472	1264223
742	550 564	27.23968	1347709	792	627 264	28.14249	1262626
743	552 049	27.25803	1345895	793	628 849	28.16026	1261034
744	553 536	27.27636	1344086	794	630 436	28.17801	1259446
745	555 025	27.29469	1342282	795	632 025	28.19574	1257862
746	556 516	27.31300	1340483	796	633 616	28.21347	1256281
747	558 009	27.33130	1338688	797	635 209	28.23119	1254705
748	559 504	27.34959	1336898	798	636 804	28.24889	1253133
749	561 001	27.36786	1335113	799	638 401	28.26659	1251564
750	562 500	27.38613	1333333	800	640 000	28.28427	1250000

Appendix Table 2.1 (Cont'd)—Values of n^2, $\sqrt{n}$, and $1/n$ for Integral Values of n from 1 through 1,000

n	n^2	$\sqrt{n}$	$1/n$ .00	n	n^2	$\sqrt{n}$	$1/n$ .00
800	640 000	28.28427	1250000	850	722 500	29.15476	1176471
801	641 601	28.30194	1248439	851	724 201	29.17190	1175088
802	643 204	28.31960	1246883	852	725 904	29.18904	1173709
803	644 809	28.33725	1245330	853	727 609	29.20616	1172333
804	646 416	28.35489	1243781	854	729 316	29.22328	1170960
805	648 025	28.37252	1242236	855	731 025	29.24038	1169591
806	649 636	28.39014	1240695	856	732 736	29.25748	1168224
807	651 249	28.40775	1239157	857	734 449	29.27456	1166861
808	652 864	28.42534	1237624	858	736 164	29.29164	1165501
809	654 481	28.44293	1236094	859	737 881	29.30870	1164144
810	656 100	28.46050	1234568	860	739 600	29.32576	1162791
811	657 721	28.47806	1233046	861	741 321	29.34280	1161440
812	659 344	28.49561	1231527	862	743 044	29.35984	1160093
813	660 969	28.51315	1230012	863	744 769	29.37686	1158749
814	662 596	28.53069	1228501	864	746 496	29.39388	1157407
815	664 225	28.54820	1226994	865	748 225	29.41088	1156069
816	665 856	28.56571	1225490	866	749 956	29.42788	1154734
817	667 489	28.58321	1223990	867	751 689	29.44486	1153403
818	669 124	28.60070	1222494	868	753 424	29.46184	1152074
819	670 761	28.61818	1221001	869	755 161	29.47881	1150748
820	672 400	28.63564	1219512	870	756.900	29.49576	1149425
821	674 041	28.65310	1218027	871	758 641	29.51271	1148106
822	675 684	28.67054	1216545	872	760 384	29.52965	1146789
823	677 329	28.68798	1215067	873	762 129	29.54657	1145475
824	678 976	28.70540	1213592	874	763 876	29.56349	1144165
825	680 625	28.72281	1212121	875	765 625	29.58040	1142857
826	682 276	28.74022	1210654	876	767 376	29.59730	1141553
827	683 929	28.75761	1209190	877	769 129	29.61419	1140251
828	685 584	28.77499	1207729	878	770 884	29.63106	1138952
829	687 241	28.79236	1206273	879	772 641	29.64793	1137656
830	688 900	28.80972	1204819	880	774 400	29.66479	1136364
831	690 561	28.82707	1203369	881	776 161	29.68164	1135074
832	692 224	28.84441	1201923	882	777 924	29.69848	1133787
833	693 889	28.86174	1200480	883	779 689	29.71532	1132503
834	695 556	28.87906	1199041	884	781 456	29.73214	1131222
835	697 225	28.89637	1197605	885	783 225	29.74895	1129944
836	698 896	28.91366	1196172	886	784 996	29.76575	1128668
837	700 569	28.93095	1194743	887	786 769	29.78255	1127396
838	702 244	28.94823	1193317	888	788 544	29.79933	1126126
839	703 921	28.96550	1191895	889	790 321	29.81610	1124859
840	705 600	28.98275	1190476	890	792 100	29.83287	1123596
841	707 281	29.00000	1189061	891	793 881	29.84962	1122334
842	708 964	29.01724	1187648	892	795 664	29.86637	1121076
843	710 649	29.03446	1186240	893	797 449	29.88311	1119821
844	712 336	29.05168	1184834	894	799 236	29.89983	1118568
845	714 025	29.06888	1183432	895	801 025	29.91655	1117318
846	715 716	29.08608	1182033	896	802 816	29.93326	1116071
847	717 409	29.10326	1180638	897	804 609	29.94996	1114827
848	719 104	29.12044	1179245	898	806 404	29.96665	1113586
849	720 801	29.13760	1177856	899	808 201	29.98333	1112347
850	722 500	29.15476	1176471	900	810 000	30.00000	1111111

Appendix Table 2.1 (Concl.)—Values of n^2, $\sqrt{n}$, and $1/n$ for Integral Values of n from 1 through 1,000

n	n^2	$\sqrt{n}$	$1/n$ .00	n	n^2	$\sqrt{n}$	$1/n$ .00
900	810 000	30.00000	1111111	950	902 500	30.82207	1052632
901	811 801	30.01666	1109878	951	904 401	30.83829	1051525
902	813 604	30.03331	1108647	952	906 304	30.85450	1050420
903	815 409	30.04996	1107420	953	908 209	30.87070	1049318
904	817 216	30.06659	1106195	954	910 116	30.88689	1048218
905	819 025	30.08322	1104972	955	912 025	30.90307	1047120
906	820 836	30.09983	1103753	956	913 936	30.91925	1046025
907	822 649	30.11644	1102536	957	915 849	30.93542	1044932
908	824 464	30.13304	1101322	958	917 764	30.95158	1043841
909	826 281	30.14963	1100110	959	919 681	30.96773	1042753
910	828 100	30.16621	1098901	960	921 600	30.98387	1041667
911	829 921	30.18278	1097695	961	923 521	31.00000	1040583
912	831 744	30.19934	1096491	962	925 444	31.01612	1039501
913	833 569	30.21589	1095290	963	927 369	31.03224	1038422
914	835 396	30.23243	1094092	964	929 296	31.04835	1037344
915	837 225	30.24897	1092896	965	931 225	31.06445	1036269
916	839 056	30.26549	1091703	966	933 156	31.08054	1035197
917	840 889	30.28201	1090513	967	935 089	31.09662	1034126
918	842 724	30.29851	1089325	968	937 024	31.11270	1033058
919	844 561	30.31501	1088139	969	938 961	31.12876	1031992
920	846 400	30.33150	1086957	970	940 900	31.14482	1030928
921	848 241	30.34798	1085776	971	942 841	31.16087	1029866
922	850 084	30.36445	1084599	972	944 784	31.17691	1028807
923	851 929	30.38092	1083424	973	946 729	31.19295	1027749
924	853 776	30.39737	1082251	974	948 676	31.20897	1026694
925	855 625	30.41381	1081081	975	950 625	31.22499	1025641
926	857 476	30.43025	1079914	976	952 576	31.24100	1024590
927	859 329	30.44667	1078749	977	954 529	31.25700	1023541
928	861 184	30.46309	1077586	978	956 484	31.27299	1022495
929	863 041	30.47950	1076426	979	958 441	31.28898	1021450
930	864 900	30.49590	1075269	980	960 400	31.30495	1020408
931	866 761	30.51229	1074114	981	962 361	31.32092	1019368
932	868 624	30.52868	1072961	982	964 324	31.33688	1018330
933	870 489	30.54505	1071811	983	966 289	31.35283	1017294
934	872 356	30.56141	1070664	984	968 256	31.36877	1016260
935	874 225	30.57777	1069519	985	970 225	31.38471	1015228
936	876 096	30.59412	1068376	986	972 196	31.40064	1014199
937	877 969	30.61046	1067236	987	974 169	31.41656	1013171
938	879 844	30.62679	1066098	988	976 144	31.43247	1012146
939	881 721	30.64311	1064963	989	978 121	31.44837	1011122
940	883 600	30.65942	1063830	990	980 100	31.46427	1010101
941	885 481	30.67572	1062699	991	982 081	31.48015	1009082
942	887 364	30.69202	1061571	992	984 064	31.49603	1008065
943	889 249	30.70831	1060445	993	986 049	31.51190	1007049
944	891 136	30.72458	1059322	994	988 036	31.52777	1006036
945	893 025	30.74085	1058201	995	990 025	31.54362	1005025
946	894 916	30.75711	1057082	996	992 016	31.55947	1004016
947	896 809	30.77337	1055966	997	994 009	31.57531	1003009
948	898 704	30.78961	1054852	998	996 004	31.59114	1002004
949	900 601	30.80584	1053741	999	998 001	31.60696	1001001
950	902 500	30.82207	1052632	1000	1 000 000	31.62278	1000000

Appendix Table 2.2—Values of $\sqrt{n}$ for Integral Values of n from 1,000 to 10,000 at Intervals of 10

n	$\sqrt{n}$	n	$\sqrt{n}$	n	$\sqrt{n}$	n	$\sqrt{n}$
1000	31.62278	1500	38.72983	2000	44.72136	2500	50.00000
1010	31.78050	1510	38.85872	2010	44.83302	2510	50.09990
1020	31.93744	1520	38.98718	2020	44.94441	2520	50.19960
1030	32.09361	1530	39.11521	2030	45.05552	2530	50.29911
1040	32.24903	1540	39.24283	2040	45.16636	2540	50.39841
1050	32.40370	1550	39.37004	2050	45.27693	2550	50.49752
1060	32.55764	1560	39.49684	2060	45.38722	2560	50.59644
1070	32.71085	1570	39.62323	2070	45.49725	2570	50.69517
1080	32.86335	1580	39.74921	2080	45.60702	2580	50.79370
1090	33.01515	1590	39.87480	2090	45.71652	2590	50.89204
1100	33.16625	1600	40.00000	2100	45.82576	2600	50.99020
1110	33.31666	1610	40.12481	2110	45.93474	2610	51.08816
1120	33.46640	1620	40.24922	2120	46.04346	2620	51.18594
1130	33.61547	1630	40.37326	2130	46.15192	2630	51.28353
1140	33.76389	1640	40.49691	2140	46.26013	2640	51.38093
1150	33.91165	1650	40.62019	2150	46.36809	2650	51.47815
1160	34.05877	1660	40.74310	2160	46.47580	2660	51.57519
1170	34.20526	1670	40.86563	2170	46.58326	2670	51.67204
1180	34.35113	1680	40.98780	2180	46.69047	2680	51.76872
1190	34.49638	1690	41.10961	2190	46.79744	2690	51.86521
1200	34.64102	1700	41.23106	2200	46.90416	2700	51.96152
1210	34.78505	1710	41.35215	2210	47.01064	2710	52.05766
1220	34.92850	1720	41.47288	2220	47.11688	2720	52.15362
1230	35.07136	1730	41.59327	2230	47.22288	2730	52.24940
1240	35.21363	1740	41.71331	2240	47.32864	2740	52.34501
1250	35.35534	1750	41.83300	2250	47.43416	2750	52.44044
1260	35.49648	1760	41.95235	2260	47.53946	2760	52.53570
1270	35.63706	1770	42.07137	2270	47.64452	2770	52.63079
1280	35.77709	1780	42.19005	2280	47.74935	2780	52.72571
1290	35.91657	1790	42.30839	2290	47.85394	2790	52.82045
1300	36.05551	1800	42.42641	2300	47.95832	2800	52.91503
1310	36.19392	1810	42.54409	2310	48.06246	2810	53.00943
1320	36.33180	1820	42.66146	2320	48.16638	2820	53.10367
1330	36.46917	1830	42.77850	2330	48.27007	2830	53.19774
1340	36.60601	1840	42.89522	2340	48.37355	2840	53.29165
1350	36.74235	1850	43.01163	2350	48.47680	2850	53.38539
1360	36.87818	1860	43.12772	2360	48.57983	2860	53.47897
1370	37.01351	1870	43.24350	2370	48.68265	2870	53.57238
1380	37.14835	1880	43.35897	2380	48.78524	2880	53.66563
1390	37.28270	1890	43.47413	2390	48.88763	2890	53.75872
1400	37.41657	1900	43.58899	2400	48.98979	2900	53.85165
1410	37.54997	1910	43.70355	2410	49.09175	2910	53.94442
1420	37.68289	1920	43.81780	2420	49.19350	2920	54.03702
1430	37.81534	1930	43.93177	2430	49.29503	2930	54.12947
1440	37.94733	1940	44.04543	2440	49.39636	2940	54.22177
1450	38.07887	1950	44.15880	2450	49.49747	2950	54.31390
1460	38.20995	1960	44.27189	2460	49.59839	2960	54.40588
1470	38.34058	1970	44.38468	2470	49.69909	2970	54.49771
1480	38.47077	1980	44.49719	2480	49.79960	2980	54.58938
1490	38.60052	1990	44.60942	2490	49.89990	2990	54.68089
1500	38.72983	2000	44.72136	2500	50.00000	3000	54.77226

Appendix Table 2.2 (Cont'd)—Values of $\sqrt{n}$ for Integral Values of n from 1,000 to 10,000 at Intervals of 10

n	$\sqrt{n}$	n	$\sqrt{n}$	n	$\sqrt{n}$	n	$\sqrt{n}$
3000	54.77226	3500	59.16080	4000	63.24555	4500	67.08204
3010	54.86347	3510	59.24525	4010	63.32456	4510	67.15653
3020	54.95453	3520	59.32959	4020	63.40347	4520	67.23095
3030	55.04544	3530	59.41380	4030	63.48228	4530	67.30527
3040	55.13620	3540	59.49790	4040	63.56099	4540	67.37952
3050	55.22681	3550	59.58188	4050	63.63961	4550	67.45369
3060	55.31727	3560	59.66574	4060	63.71813	4560	67.52777
3070	55.40758	3570	59.74948	4070	63.79655	4570	67.60178
3080	55.49775	3580	59.83310	4080	63.87488	4580	67.67570
3090	55.58777	3590	59.91661	4090	63.95311	4590	67.74954
3100	55.67764	3600	60.00000	4100	64.03124	4600	67.82330
3110	55.76737	3610	60.08328	4110	64.10928	4610	67.89698
3120	55.85696	3620	60.16644	4120	64.18723	4620	67.97058
3130	55.94640	3630	60.24948	4130	64.26508	4630	68.04410
3140	56.03570	3640	60.33241	4140	64.34283	4640	68.11755
3150	56.12486	3650	60.41523	4150	64.42049	4650	68.19091
3160	56.21388	3660	60.49793	4160	64.49806	4660	68.26419
3170	56.30275	3670	60.58052	4170	64.57554	4670	68.33740
3180	56.39149	3680	60.66300	4180	64.65292	4680	68.41053
3190	56.48008	3690	60.74537	4190	64.73021	4690	68.48357
3200	56.56854	3700	60.82763	4200	64.80741	4700	68.55655
3210	56.65686	3710	60.90977	4210	64.88451	4710	68.62944
3220	56.74504	3720	60.99180	4220	64.96153	4720	68.70226
3230	56.83309	3730	61.07373	4230	65.03845	4730	68.77500
3240	56.92100	3740	61.15554	4240	65.11528	4740	68.84766
3250	57.00877	3750	61.23724	4250	65.19202	4750	68.92024
3260	57.09641	3760	61.31884	4260	65.26868	4760	68.99275
3270	57.18391	3770	61.40033	4270	65.34524	4770	69.06519
3280	57.27128	3780	61.48170	4280	65.42171	4780	69.13754
3290	57.35852	3790	61.56298	4290	65.49809	4790	69.20983
3300	57.44563	3800	61.64414	4300	65.57439	4800	69.28203
3310	57.53260	3810	61.72520	4310	65.65059	4810	69.35416
3320	57.61944	3820	61.80615	4320	65.72671	4820	69.42622
3330	57.70615	3830	61.88699	4330	65.80274	4830	69.49820
3340	57.79273	3840	61.96773	4340	65.87868	4840	69.57011
3350	57.87918	3850	62.04837	4350	65.95453	4850	69.64194
3360	57.96551	3860	62.12890	4360	66.03030	4860	69.71370
3370	58.05170	3870	62.20932	4370	66.10598	4870	69.78539
3380	58.13777	3880	62.28965	4380	66.18157	4880	69.85700
3390	58.22371	3890	62.36986	4390	66.25708	4890	69.92853
3400	58.30952	3900	62.44998	4400	66.33250	4900	70.00000
3410	58.39521	3910	62.52999	4410	66.40783	4910	70.07139
3420	58.48077	3920	62.60990	4420	66.48308	4920	70.14271
3430	58.56620	3930	62.68971	4430	66.55825	4930	70.21396
3440	58.65151	3940	62.76942	4440	66.63332	4940	70.28513
3450	58.73670	3950	62.84903	4450	66.70832	4950	70.35624
3460	58.82176	3960	62.92853	4460	66.78323	4960	70.42727
3470	58.90671	3970	63.00794	4470	66.85806	4970	70.49823
3480	58.99152	3980	63.08724	4480	66.93280	4980	70.56912
3490	59.07622	3990	63.16645	4490	67.00746	4990	70.63993
3500	59.16080	4000	63.24555	4500	67.08204	5000	70.71068

Appendix Table 2.2 (Cont'd)—Values of $\sqrt{n}$ for Integral Values of n from 1,000 to 10,000 at Intervals of 10

n	$\sqrt{n}$	n	$\sqrt{n}$	n	$\sqrt{n}$	n	$\sqrt{n}$
5000	70.71068	5500	74.16198	6000	77.45967	6500	80.62258
5010	70.78135	5510	74.22937	6010	77.52419	6510	80.68457
5020	70.85196	5520	74.29670	6020	77.58866	6520	80.74652
5030	70.92249	5530	74.36397	6030	77.65307	6530	80.80842
5040	70.99296	5540	74.43118	6040	77.71744	6540	80.87027
5050	71.06335	5550	74.49832	6050	77.78175	6550	80.93207
5060	71.13368	5560	74.56541	6060	77.84600	6560	80.99383
5070	71.20393	5570	74.63243	6070	77.91020	6570	81.05554
5080	71.27412	5580	74.69940	6080	77.97435	6580	81.11720
5090	71.34424	5590	74.76630	6090	78.03845	6590	81.17881
5100	71.41428	5600	74.83315	6100	78.10250	6600	81.24038
5110	71.48426	5610	74.89993	6110	78.16649	6610	81.30191
5120	71.55418	5620	74.96666	6120	78.23043	6620	81.36338
5130	71.62402	5630	75.03333	6130	78.29432	6630	81.42481
5140	71.69379	5640	75.09993	6140	78.35815	6640	81.48620
5150	71.76350	5650	75.16648	6150	78.42194	6650	81.54753
5160	71.83314	5660	75.23297	6160	78.48567	6660	81.60882
5170	71.90271	5670	75.29940	6170	78.54935	6670	81.67007
5180	71.97222	5680	75.36577	6180	78.61298	6680	81.73127
5190	72.04165	5690	75.43209	6190	78.67655	6690	81.79242
5200	72.11103	5700	75.49834	6200	78.74008	6700	81.85353
5210	72.18033	5710	75.56454	6210	78.80355	6710	81.91459
5220	72.24957	5720	75.63068	6220	78.86698	6720	81.97561
5230	72.31874	5730	75.69676	6230	78.93035	6730	82.03658
5240	72.38784	5740	75.76279	6240	78.99367	6740	82.09750
5250	72.45688	5750	75.82875	6250	79.05694	6750	82.15838
5260	72.52586	5760	75.89466	6260	79.12016	6760	82.21922
5270	72.59477	5770	75.96052	6270	79.18333	6770	82.28001
5280	72.66361	5780	76.02631	6280	79.24645	6780	82.34076
5290	72.73239	5790	76.09205	6290	79.30952	6790	82.40146
5300	72.80110	5800	76.15773	6300	79.37254	6800	82.46211
5310	72.86975	5810	76.22336	6310	79.43551	6810	82.42272
5320	72.93833	5820	76.28892	6320	79.49843	6820	82.58329
5330	73.00685	5830	76.35444	6330	79.56130	6830	82.64381
5340	73.07530	5840	76.41989	6340	79.62412	6840	82.70429
5350	73.14369	5850	76.48529	6350	79.68689	6850	82.76473
5360	73.21202	5860	76.55064	6360	79.74961	6860	82.82512
5370	73.28028	5870	76.61593	6370	79.81228	6870	82.88546
5380	73.34848	5880	76.68116	6380	79.87490	6880	82.94577
5390	73.41662	5890	76.74634	6390	79.93748	6890	83.00602
5400	73.48469	5900	76.81146	6400	80.00000	6900	83.06624
5410	73.55270	5910	76.87652	6410	80.06248	6910	83.12641
5420	73.62065	5920	76.94154	6420	80.12490	6920	83.18654
5430	73.68853	5930	77.00649	6430	80.18728	6930	83.24662
5440	73.75636	5940	77.07140	6440	80.24961	6940	83.30666
5450	73.82412	5950	77.13624	6450	80.31189	6950	83.36666
5460	73.89181	5960	77.20104	6460	80.37413	6960	83.42661
5470	73.95945	5970	77.26578	6470	80.43631	6970	83.48653
5480	74.02702	5980	77.33046	6480	80.49845	6980	83.54639
5490	74.09453	5990	77.39509	6490	80.56054	6990	83.60622
5500	74.16198	6000	77.45967	6500	80.62258	7000	83.66600

Appendix Table 2.2 (Cont'd)—Values of $\sqrt{n}$ for Integral Values of n from 1,000 to 10,000 at Intervals of 10

n	$\sqrt{n}$	n	$\sqrt{n}$	n	$\sqrt{n}$	n	$\sqrt{n}$
7000	83.66600	7500	86.60254	8000	89.44272	8500	92.19544
7010	83.72574	7510	86.66026	8010	89.49860	8510	92.24966
7020	83.78544	7520	86.71793	8020	89.55445	8520	92.30385
7030	83.84510	7530	86.77557	8030	89.61027	8530	92.35800
7040	83.90471	7540	86.83317	8040	89.66605	8540	92.41212
7050	83.96428	7550	86.89074	8050	89.72179	8550	92.46621
7060	84.02381	7560	86.94826	8060	89.77750	8560	92.52027
7070	84.08329	7570	87.00575	8070	89.83318	8570	92.57429
7080	84.14274	7580	87.06320	8080	89.88882	8580	92.62829
7090	84.20214	7590	87.12061	8090	89.94443	8590	92.68225
7100	84.26150	7600	87.17798	8100	90.00000	8600	92.73618
7110	84.32082	7610	87.23531	8110	90.05554	8610	92.79009
7120	84.38009	7620	87.29261	8120	90.11104	8620	92.84396
7130	84.43933	7630	87.34987	8130	90.16651	8630	92.89779
7140	84.49852	7640	87.40709	8140	90.22195	8640	92.95160
7150	84.55767	7650	87.46428	8150	90.27735	8650	93.00538
7160	84.61678	7660	87.52143	8160	90.33272	8660	93.05912
7170	84.67585	7670	87.57854	8170	90.38805	8670	93.11283
7180	84.73488	7680	87.63561	8180	90.44335	8680	93.16652
7190	84.79387	7690	87.69265	8190	90.49862	8690	93.22017
7200	84.85281	7700	87.74964	8200	90.55385	8700	93.27379
7210	84.91172	7710	87.80661	8210	90.60905	8710	93.32738
7220	84.97058	7720	87.86353	8220	90.66422	8720	93.38094
7230	85.02941	7730	87.92042	8230	90.71935	8730	93.43447
7240	85.08819	7740	87.97727	8240	90.77445	8740	93.48797
7250	85.14693	7750	88.03408	8250	90.82951	8750	93.54143
7260	85.20563	7760	88.09086	8260	90.88454	8760	93.59487
7270	85.26429	7770	88.14760	8270	90.93954	8770	93.64828
7280	85.32292	7780	88.20431	8280	90.99451	8780	93.70165
7290	85.38150	7790	88.26098	8290	91.04944	8790	93.75500
7300	85.44004	7800	88.31761	8300	91.10434	8800	93.80832
7310	85.49854	7810	88.37420	8310	91.15920	8810	93.86160
7320	85.55700	7820	88.43076	8320	91.21403	8820	93.91486
7330	85.61542	7830	88.48729	8330	91.26883	8830	93.96808
7340	85.67380	7840	88.54377	8340	91.32360	8840	94.02127
7350	85.73214	7850	88.60023	8350	91.37833	8850	94.07444
7360	85.79044	7860	88.65664	8360	91.43304	8860	94.12757
7370	85.84870	7870	88.71302	8370	91.48770	8870	94.18068
7380	85.90693	7880	88.76936	8380	91.54234	8880	94.23375
7390	85.96511	7890	88.82567	8390	91.59694	8890	94.28680
7400	86.02325	7900	88.88194	8400	91.65151	8900	94.33981
7410	86.08136	7910	88.93818	8410	91.70605	8910	94.39280
7420	86.13942	7920	88.99438	8420	91.76056	8920	94.44575
7430	86.19745	7930	89.05055	8430	91.81503	8930	94.49868
7440	86.25543	7940	89.10668	8440	91.86947	8940	94.55157
7450	86.31338	7950	89.16277	8450	91.92388	8950	94.60444
7460	86.37129	7960	89.21883	8460	91.97826	8960	94.65728
7470	86.42916	7970	89.27486	8470	92.03260	8970	94.71008
7480	86.48699	7980	89.33085	8480	92.08692	8980	94.76286
7490	86.54479	7990	89.38680	8490	92.14120	8990	94.81561
7500	86.60254	8000	89.44272	8500	92.19544	9000	94.86833

Appendix Table 2.2 (Concl.)—Values of $\sqrt{n}$ for Integral Values of n from 1,000 to 10,000 at Intervals of 10

n	$\sqrt{n}$	n	$\sqrt{n}$
9000	94.86833	9500	97.46794
9010	94.92102	9510	97.51923
9020	94.97368	9520	97.57049
9030	95.02631	9530	97.62172
9040	95.07891	9540	97.67292
9050	95.13149	9550	97.72410
9060	95.18403	9560	97.77525
9070	95.23655	9570	97.82638
9080	95.28903	9580	97.87747
9090	95.34149	9590	97.92855
9100	95.39392	9600	97.97959
9110	95.44632	9610	98.03061
9120	95.49869	9620	98.08160
9130	95.55103	9630	98.13256
9140	95.60335	9640	98.18350
9150	95.65563	9650	98.23441
9160	95.70789	9660	98.28530
9170	95.76012	9670	98.33616
9180	95.81232	9680	98.38699
9190	95.86449	9690	98.43780
9200	95.91663	9700	98.48858
9210	95.96874	9710	98.53933
9220	96.02083	9720	98.59006
9230	96.07289	9730	98.64076
9240	96.12492	9740	98.69144
9250	96.17692	9750	98.74209
9260	96.22889	9760	98.79271
9270	96.28084	9770	98.84331
9280	96.33276	9780	98.89388
9290	96.38465	9790	98.94443
9300	96.43561	9800	98.99495
9310	96.48834	9810	99.04544
9320	96.54015	9820	99.09591
9330	96.59193	9830	99.14636
9340	96.64368	9840	99.19677
9350	96.69540	9850	99.24717
9360	96.74709	9860	99.29753
9370	96.79876	9870	99.34787
9380	96.85040	9880	99.39819
9390	96.90201	9890	99.44848
9400	96.95360	9900	99.49874
9410	97.00515	9910	99.54898
9420	97.05668	9920	99.59920
9430	97.10819	9930	99.64939
9440	97.15966	9940	99.69955
9450	97.21111	9950	99.74969
9460	97.26253	9960	99.79980
9470	97.31393	9970	99.84989
9480	97.36529	9980	99.89995
9490	97.41663	9990	99.94999
9500	97.46794	10000	100.00000

APPENDIX 3

Values of $\dfrac{1}{\sqrt{n}}$, $\dfrac{n}{n-1}$, and $\sqrt{\dfrac{n}{n-1}}$

n	$\dfrac{1}{\sqrt{n}}$	$\dfrac{n}{n-1}$	$\sqrt{\dfrac{n}{n-1}}$	n	$\dfrac{1}{\sqrt{n}}$	$\dfrac{n}{n-1}$	$\sqrt{\dfrac{n}{n-1}}$
1	1.00000	...	...	51	.14003	1.020	1.010
2	.70711	2.000	1.414	52	.13868	1.020	1.010
3	.57735	1.500	1.225	53	.13736	1.019	1.010
4	.50000	1.333	1.155	54	.13608	1.019	1.009
5	.44721	1.250	1.118	55	.13484	1.019	1.009
6	.40825	1.200	1.095	56	.13363	1.018	1.009
7	.37796	1.167	1.080	57	.13245	1.018	1.009
8	.35355	1.143	1.069	58	.13131	1.018	1.009
9	.33333	1.125	1.061	59	.13019	1.017	1.009
10	.31623	1.111	1.054	60	.12910	1.017	1.008
11	.30151	1.100	1.049	61	.12804	1.017	1.008
12	.28868	1.091	1.044	62	.12700	1.016	1.008
13	.27735	1.083	1.041	63	.12599	1.016	1.008
14	.26726	1.077	1.038	64	.12500	1.016	1.008
15	.25820	1.071	1.035	65	.12403	1.016	1.008
16	.25000	1.067	1.033	66	.12309	1.015	1.008
17	.24254	1.062	1.031	67	.12217	1.015	1.008
18	.23570	1.059	1.029	68	.12127	1.015	1.007
19	.22942	1.056	1.027	69	.12039	1.015	1.007
20	.22361	1.053	1.026	70	.11952	1.014	1.007
21	.21822	1.050	1.025	71	.11868	1.014	1.007
22	.21320	1.048	1.024	72	.11785	1.014	1.007
23	.20851	1.046	1.022	73	.11704	1.014	1.007
24	.20412	1.044	1.022	74	.11625	1.014	1.007
25	.20000	1.042	1.021	75	.11547	1.014	1.007
26	.19612	1.040	1.020	76	.11471	1.013	1.007
27	.19245	1.038	1.019	77	.11396	1.013	1.007
28	.18898	1.037	1.018	78	.11323	1.013	1.006
29	.18570	1.036	1.018	79	.11251	1.013	1.006
30	.18257	1.034	1.017	80	.11180	1.013	1.006
31	.17961	1.033	1.017	81	.11111	1.012	1.006
32	.17678	1.032	1.016	82	.11043	1.012	1.006
33	.17408	1.031	1.016	83	.10976	1.012	1.006
34	.17150	1.030	1.015	84	.10911	1.012	1.006
35	.16903	1.029	1.015	85	.10847	1.012	1.006
36	.16667	1.029	1.014	86	.10783	1.012	1.006
37	.16440	1.028	1.014	87	.10721	1.012	1.006
38	.16222	1.027	1.013	88	.10660	1.011	1.006
39	.16013	1.026	1.013	89	.10600	1.011	1.006
40	.15811	1.026	1.013	90	.10541	1.011	1.006
41	.15617	1.025	1.012	91	.10483	1.011	1.006
42	.15430	1.024	1.012	92	.10426	1.011	1.005
43	.15250	1.024	1.012	93	.10370	1.011	1.005
44	.15076	1.023	1.012	94	.10314	1.011	1.005
45	.14907	1.023	1.011	95	.10260	1.011	1.005
46	.14744	1.022	1.011	96	.10206	1.011	1.005
47	.14586	1.022	1.011	97	.10153	1.010	1.005
48	.14434	1.021	1.011	98	.10102	1.010	1.005
49	.14286	1.021	1.010	99	.10050	1.010	1.005
50	.14142	1.020	1.010	100	.10000	1.010	1.005

APPENDIX 4

Sums and Sums of Squares of Natural Numbers

Appendix Table 4.1—First 50 Natural Numbers

Natural number	Sum	Sum of squares
1	1	1
2	3	5
3	6	14
4	10	30
5	15	55
6	21	91
7	28	140
8	36	204
9	45	285
10	55	385
11	66	506
12	78	650
13	91	819
14	105	1 015
15	120	1 240
16	136	1 496
17	153	1 785
18	171	2 109
19	190	2 470
20	210	2 870
21	231	3 311
22	253	3 795
23	276	4 324
24	300	4 900
25	325	5 525
26	351	6 201
27	378	6 930
28	406	7 714
29	435	8 555
30	465	9 455
31	496	10 416
32	528	11 440
33	561	12 529
34	595	13 685
35	630	14 910
36	666	16 206
37	703	17 575
38	741	19 019
39	780	20 540
40	820	22 140
41	861	23 821
42	903	25 585
43	946	27 434
44	990	29 370
45	1 035	31 395
46	1 081	33 511
47	1 128	35 720
48	1 176	38 024
49	1 225	40 425
50	1 275	42 925

Appendix Table 4.2—First 50 Odd Natural Numbers

Odd natural number	Sum	Sum of squares
1	1	1
3	4	10
5	9	35
7	16	84
9	25	165
11	36	286
13	49	455
15	64	680
17	81	969
19	100	1 330
21	121	1 771
23	144	2 300
25	169	2 925
27	196	3 654
29	225	4 495
31	256	5 456
33	289	6 545
35	324	7 770
37	361	9 139
39	400	10 660
41	441	12 341
43	484	14 190
45	529	16 215
47	576	18 424
49	625	20 825
51	676	23 426
53	729	26 235
55	784	29 260
57	841	32 509
59	900	35 990
61	961	39 711
63	1 024	43 680
65	1 089	47 905
67	1 156	52 394
69	1 225	57 155
71	1 296	62 196
73	1 369	67 525
75	1 444	73 150
77	1 521	79 079
79	1 600	85 320
81	1 681	91 881
83	1 764	98 770
85	1 849	105 995
87	1 936	113 564
89	2 025	121 485
91	2 116	129 766
93	2 209	138 415
95	2 304	147 440
97	2 401	156 849
99	2 500	166 650

APPENDIX 5

Number of Combinations of N Things Taken n at a Time: Binomial Coefficients

$$\binom{N}{n} = \binom{N}{N-n} = \frac{N!}{n!(N-n)!}$$

N \\ n	1	2	3	4	5	6	7	8	9	10	11	12	13	14	15	16	17	18	19	20
0	1																			
1	1	1																		
2		2	1																	
3		1	3	1																
4			3	4	1															
5			1	6	5	1														
6				4	10	6	1													
7				1	10	15	7	1												
8					5	20	21	8	1											
9					1	15	35	28	9	1										
10						6	35	56	36	10	1									
6							21	70	84	120	11	12	13	14	15	16	17	18	19	20

N \\ n	6	7	8	9	10	11	12	13	14	15	16	17	18	19	20
6	1	7	28	84	210	462	924	1,716	3,003	5,005	8,008	12,376	18,564	27,132	38,760
7		1	8	36	120	330	792	1,716	3,432	6,435	11,440	19,448	31,824	50,388	77,520
8			1	9	45	165	495	1,287	3,003	6,435	12,870	24,310	43,758	75,582	125,970
9				1	10	55	220	715	2,002	5,005	11,440	24,310	48,620	92,378	167,960
10					1	11	66	286	1,001	3,003	8,008	19,448	43,758	92,378	184,756
11						1	12	78	364	1,365	4,368	12,376	31,824	75,582	167,960
12							1	13	91	455	1,820	6,188	18,564	50,388	125,970
13								1	14	105	560	2,380	8,568	27,132	77,520
14									1	15	120	680	3,060	11,628	38,760
15										1	16	136	816	3,876	15,504
16											1	17	153	969	4,845
17												1	18	171	1,140
18													1	19	190
19														1	20
20															1

Reprinted from Dudley J. Cowden, *Statistical Methods in Quality Control*, Prentice-Hall, Inc., Englewood Cliffs, N. J., 1957, pp. 652–653. Coefficients through $\binom{100}{50}$ are published in Appendix III of Thornton C. Fry, *Probability and its Engineering Uses*, D. Van Nostrand Co., Inc., New York, 1928. These coefficients are rounded to 8 digits, except $\binom{100}{50}$, which is rounded to 9 digits.

APPENDIX 6

Values of r and z_r

$$r = \tanh z_r \text{ and } z_r = \tanh^{-1} r$$

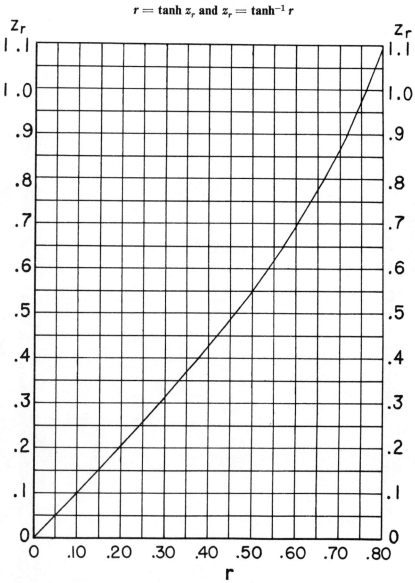

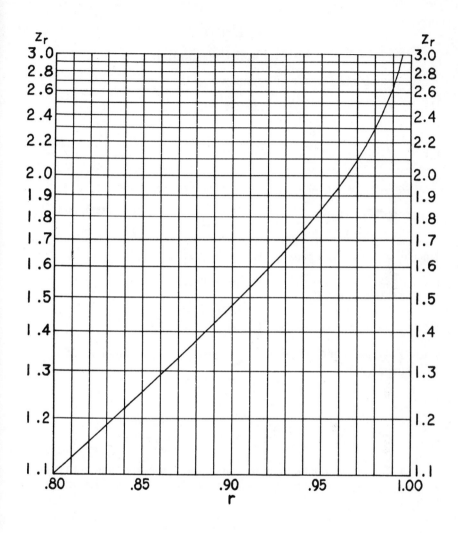

APPENDIX 7

Orthogonal Polynomials

An orthogonal polynomial equation is of the type

(1) $$Y_t = \Sigma\, B_r t_r = B_0 t_0 + B_1 t_1 + B_2 t_2 + \cdots,$$

where

(2) $$B_r = \frac{\Sigma\, t_r Y}{\Sigma\, t_r^2}.$$

By definition, $t_0 = 1$, and $t_1 = x$, where x takes the values

$$\ldots, -3, \quad -2, \quad -1, \quad 0, \quad 1, \quad 2, \quad 3, \ldots \text{ if } n \text{ is odd, and}$$
$$\ldots, \quad -5, \quad -3, \quad -1, \quad 1, \quad 3, \quad 5, \quad \ldots \text{ if } n \text{ is even.}$$

Since $t_0 = 1$, the orthogonal polynomial equation can also be written

(3) $$Y_t = \bar{Y} + B_1 t_1 + B_2 t_2 + \cdots.$$

For values of $r \geq 2$,

(4) $$t_r = t_1 q - \frac{q^2(n^2 - q^2)}{4(4q^2 - 1)} t_p,$$

where $q = r - 1$ and $p = q - 1$. For orthogonal polynomials of second and third degree:

(5) $$t_2 = t_1^2 - \frac{n^2 - 1}{12} = x^2 - \frac{n^2 - 1}{12};$$

(6) $$t_3 = t_1 t_2 - \frac{n^2 - 4}{15} t_1 = x^3 - \frac{3n^2 - 7}{20} x.$$

Equation (4) is to be thought of as a computational formula, rather than a definitional one. The property from which orthogonal polynomials derive their name is

(7) $$\Sigma\, t_i t_j = 0,$$

where i and j are any values of r, but $i \neq j$. If we let

$$x_0 = 1, \quad x_1 = x, \quad x_2 = x^2, \quad x_3 = x^3, \quad \text{etc.,}$$

then equation (7) is satisfied if

(8) $$t_0 = x_0, \quad t_1 = x_1, \quad t_2 = x_{2.1}, \quad t_3 = x_{3.12}.$$

(See Chapter 35.) These values are uncorrelated because of the fact that $x_{2.1}$ and $x_{3.12}$ are residuals. Thus, $x_{2.1}$ is x_2 adjusted for the effect of x_1, and $x_{3.12}$ is x_3 adjusted for the effect of x_1 and x_2.

To test significance of an orthogonal polynomial constant, it is necessary to compute the explained variation

$$(9) \qquad\qquad \Sigma\, y_{t(r)}^2 = B_r\, \Sigma\, t_r Y.$$

To obtain the orthogonal polynomials of this appendix table we may apply formulas (4), (5), (6), or (8) and then code them by multiplying results by a constant g_r in order to simplify them. Coding does not affect their orthogonal properties, and formulas (1), (2), (3), and (9) can be used without modification. At the bottom of the different columns are shown:

The sum of the squares $\Sigma\, t_r^2$ needed for computing the B_r;
The coding constant g_r.

Formulas for computing the coded t_r from the x^r, and for converting an orthogonal polynomial equation into a simple polynomial equation, are as follows.

n	t_2	t_3
5	$x^2 - 2$	$\dfrac{5x^3 - 17x}{6}$
6	$\dfrac{3x^2 - 35}{8}$	$\dfrac{5x^3 - 101x}{24}$
7	$x^2 - 4$	$\dfrac{x^3 - 7x}{6}$
8	$\dfrac{x^2 - 21}{4}$	$\dfrac{x^3 - 37x}{12}$
9	$3x^2 - 20$	$\dfrac{5x^3 - 89x}{6}$
10	$\dfrac{x^2 - 33}{8}$	$\dfrac{5x^3 - 293x}{24}$
11	$x^2 - 10$	$\dfrac{5x^3 - 89x}{6}$
12	$\dfrac{3x^2 - 143}{4}$	$\dfrac{x^3 - 85x}{12}$
13	$x^2 - 14$	$\dfrac{x^3 - 167x}{6}$
14	$\dfrac{x^2 - 65}{8}$	$\dfrac{5x^3 - 581x}{24}$
15	$3x^2 - 56$	$\dfrac{5x^3 - 167x}{6}$
16	$\dfrac{x^2 - 85}{4}$	$\dfrac{5x^3 - 761x}{12}$

Trend Equation: $Y_t = \Sigma B_r t_r$, where $B_r = \dfrac{\Sigma t_r Y}{\Sigma t_r^2}$. $\;t_0 = 1;\; t_1 = x.$

n = 5

t_1	t_2	t_3
-2	2	-1
-1	-1	2
0	-2	0
1	-1	-2
2	2	1
Σt_r^2: 10	14	10
g_r: 1	1	5/6

n = 6

t_1	t_2	t_3
-5	5	-5
-3	-1	7
-1	-4	4
1	-4	-4
3	-1	-7
5	5	5
Σt_r^2: 70	84	180
g_r: 2	3/2	5/3

n = 7

t_1	t_2	t_3
-3	5	-1
-2	0	1
-1	-3	1
0	-4	0
1	-3	-1
2	0	-1
3	5	1
Σt_r^2: 28	84	6
g_r: 1	1	1/6

n = 8

t_1	t_2	t_3
-7	7	-7
-5	1	5
-3	-3	7
-1	-5	3
1	-5	-3
3	-3	-7
5	1	-5
7	7	7
Σt_r^2: 168	168	264
g_r: 2	1	2/3

n = 9

t_1	t_2	t_3
-4	28	-14
-3	7	7
-2	-8	13
-1	-17	9
0	-20	0
1	-17	-9
2	-8	-13
3	7	-7
4	28	14
Σt_r^2: 60	2,772	990
g_r: 1	3	5/6

n = 10

t_1	t_2	t_3
-9	6	-42
-7	2	14
-5	-1	35
-3	-3	31
-1	-4	12
1	-4	-12
3	-3	-31
5	-1	-35
7	2	-14
9	6	42
Σt_r^2: 330	132	8,580
g_r: 2	1/2	5/3

$n = 11$

t_1	t_2	t_3
-5	15	-30
-4	6	6
-3	-1	22
-2	-6	23
-1	-9	14
0	-10	0
1	-9	-14
2	-6	-23
3	-1	-22
4	6	-6
5	15	30
Σt_r^2: 110	858	4,290
θ_r: 1	1	5/6

$n = 12$

t_1	t_2	t_3
-11	55	-33
-9	25	3
-7	1	21
-5	-17	25
-3	-29	19
-1	-35	7
1	-35	-7
3	-29	-19
5	-17	-25
7	1	-21
9	25	-3
11	55	33
572	12,012	5,148
2	3	2/3

$n = 13$

t_1	t_2	t_3
-6	22	-11
-5	11	0
-4	2	6
-3	-5	8
-2	-10	7
-1	-13	4
0	-14	0
1	-13	-4
2	-10	-7
3	-5	-8
4	2	-6
5	11	0
6	22	11
182	2,002	572
1	1	1/6

$n = 14$

t_1	t_2	t_3
-13	13	-143
-11	7	-11
-9	2	66
-7	-2	98
-5	-5	95
-3	-7	67
-1	-8	24
1	-8	-24
3	-7	-67
5	-5	-95
7	-2	-98
9	2	-66
11	7	11
13	13	143
910	728	78,240
2	1/2	5/3

$n = 15$

t_1	t_2	t_3
-7	91	-91
-6	52	-13
-5	19	35
-4	-8	58
-3	-29	61
-2	-44	49
-1	-53	27
0	-56	0
1	-53	-27
2	-44	-49
3	-29	-61
4	-8	-58
5	19	-35
6	52	13
7	91	91
280	37,128	39,780
1	3	5/6

$n = 16$

t_1	t_2	t_3
-15	35	-455
-13	21	-91
-11	9	143
-9	-1	267
-7	-9	301
-5	-15	265
-3	-19	179
-1	-21	63
1	-21	-63
3	-19	-179
5	-15	-265
7	-9	-301
9	-1	-367
11	9	-143
13	21	91
15	35	455
1,360	5,712	1,007,760
2	1	10/3

APPENDIX 8

a_1 Factors to be Applied to s or $\bar{s}$ to Obtain $\hat{\sigma}_1$

$\hat{\sigma}_1 = a_1 s$ when $k = 1$; $\hat{\sigma}_1 = a_1 \bar{s}$ when $k > 1$

($\hat{\sigma}_1$ is the most efficient unbiased estimator of σ.)

Sample size n	a_1 $\dfrac{\sigma}{E(s)}$	Sample size n	a_1 $\dfrac{\sigma}{E(s)}$
2	1.772	14	1.058
3	1.382	15	1.054
4	1.253	16	1.050
5	1.189	17	1.047
6	1.151	18	1.044
7	1.126	19	1.042
8	1.108	20	1.040
9	1.094	21	1.038
10	1.084	22	1.036
11	1.075	23	1.034
12	1.068	24	1.033
13	1.063	25	1.031

Source: Dudley J. Cowden, *Statistical Methods in Quality Control*, Prentice-Hall, Inc., Englewood Cliffs, N.J., 1957, p. 691.

The factor a_1 is the reciprocal of the quantity often referred to as c_2.

$$c_2 = \frac{\Gamma\left(\frac{n}{2}\right)}{\Gamma\left(\frac{n-1}{2}\right)} \sqrt{\frac{2}{n}}.$$

For a derivation of this formula see Dudley J. Cowden, *op., cit.*, pp. 78–79.

APPENDIX 9

b_i Factors to be Applied to X_i to Obtain $\hat{\sigma}_2$

$$\hat{\sigma}_2 = \Sigma\, b_i X_i, \quad X_1 \le X_2 \le \dots \le X_n$$

($\hat{\sigma}_2$ is the most efficient unbiased linear estimator of σ for a normal population.)

X_i \ n	2	3	4	5	6	7	8	9	10
X_1	-.88623	-.59082	-.45394	-.37238	-.31752	-.27781	-.24759	-.22373	-.20438
X_2	.88623	.00000	-.11018	-.13521	-.13856	-.13510	-.12945	-.12327	-.11720
X_3		.59082	.11018	.00000	-.04321	-.06246	-.07131	-.07510	-.07626
X_4			.45394	.13521	.04321	.00000	-.02296	-.03597	-.04358
X_5				.37238	.13856	.06246	.02296	.00000	-.01422
X_6					.31752	.13510	.07131	.03597	.01422
X_7						.27781	.12945	.07510	.04358
X_8							.24759	.12327	.07626
X_9								.22373	.11720
X_{10}									.20438

Computed (by subtraction) from Table 3, p. 99, of H. J. Godwin, "On the Estimation of Dispersion by Linear Systematic Statistics," *Biometrika*, Vol. 36, 1949, pp. 92-100.

APPENDIX 10

c_3 Factors to be Applied to $\bar{R}$ or R to Obtain $\hat{\sigma}_3$

$$\hat{\sigma}_3 = c_3 R \text{ when } k = 1; \quad \hat{\sigma}_3 = c_3\bar{R} \text{ when } k > 1$$

For $n \leq 15$, $\hat{\sigma}_3$ is the most efficient unbiased linear estimate of σ when only two values of X are used.

The most efficient size of sample is 8. It is nearly as efficient to use subsamples of 7 or 9 items each, and the loss of efficiency is small if the subsample size is 6 or 10. In subsampling it is essential that the items be assigned to the different samples *at random*.

Subsample size n	$c_3 = \dfrac{\sigma}{E(R)}$	Subsample size n	$c_3 = \dfrac{\sigma}{E(R)}$
2	0.8865	9	0.3667
3	.5907	10	.3249
4	.4857	11	.3152
5	.4299	12	.3069
6	.3946	13	.2998
7	.3698	14	.2935
8	.3512	15	.2880

Source: Taken, by permission, from American Society for Testing Materials, *A.S.T.M. Manual on Quality Control of Materials*, Philadelphia, 1951, p. 115. The factor c_3 is the reciprocal of a quantity often referred to as d_2.

APPENDIX 11

c_4 Factors to be Applied to Quasi-Range to Obtain $\hat{\sigma}_4$

$$\hat{\sigma}_4 = c_4 R_q$$

The quasi-range $R_q = X_j - X_i = X_{n-q} - X_{1+q}$; $j = n - i + 1$; $X_1 \leq \ldots \leq X_i \leq \ldots \leq X_j \leq \ldots \leq X_n$. Thus, q is the number of items excluded at each end.

The values of i and j given in this appendix are such that the quasi-range is the range that includes approximately 86 per cent of the observations. For $n > 16$, $\hat{\sigma}_4$ is the most efficient unbiased linear estimate of σ when only two values of X are used. When $n \leq 16$, use the c_3 values of Appendix 10.

The range of the middle 86 per cent is selected because this results in the most efficient unbiased linear estimate of σ when only two values of X are used. See Frederick Mosteller, "On Some Useful Inefficient Statistics," *Annals of Mathematical Statistics*, Vol. XVII, December, 1946, pp. 377–408.

In a normal distribution the area between $z = -1.476$ and $z = +1.476$ is 86 per cent of the entire area under the curve. The values of q selected for this table are those for which the expected value of $|z|$ is closest to 1.476. Values of $E|z_i|$ were obtained (sometimes by interpolation) from Table 28 of E. S. Pearson and H. O. Hartley (editors) *Biometrika Tables for Statisticians*, Vol. I, Cambridge University Press, Cambridge, 1954, p. 175. Values of n through 29 were checked by taking the reciprocals of the mean values given in Table I of J. H. Caldwell, "The Distribution of Quasi-Ranges in Samples from a Normal Population," *Annals of Mathematical Statistics*, Vol. XXIV, December, 1953, pp. 603–613. Caldwell also gives values for the variance, β_1, β_2, and selected percentage points. Values of c_4 given in the appendix table may in some cases be in error by one unit in the third decimal place.

APPENDIX 11 (Continued)

Values of i and j, and c_4 Factors to be Applied to Quasi-Range to Obtain $\hat{\sigma}_4$

$$\hat{\sigma}_4 = c_4 R_q; \quad R_q = X_j - X_i$$

(The number of extremes excluded at each end is q. The number of central values included is $n - 2q$.)

n	q	j $(n-q)$	i $(q+1)$	Per cent of central values included	c_4
16	1	15	2	87.5	0.389
17	1	16	2	88	.379
18	1	17	2	89	.370
19	1	18	2	89	.362
20	1	19	2	90	.355
21	1	20	2	90	.349
22	1	21	2	91	.343
23	1	22	2	91	.338
24	1	23	2	92	.333
25	1	24	2	92	.328
26	1	25	2	92	.324
27	1	26	2	93	.320
28	1	27	2	93	.316
29	1	28	2	93	.313
30	2	28	3	87	.368
31	2	29	3	87	.362
32	2	30	3	87.5	.357
33	2	31	3	88	.353
34	2	32	3	88	.350
35	2	33	3	89	.346
36	2	34	3	89	.342
37	2	35	3	89	.339
38	2	36	3	89	.336
39	2	37	3	90	.332
40	2	38	3	90	.329
41	2	39	3	90	.327
42	2	40	3	90	.325
43	2	41	3	91	.322
44	3	41	4	86	.357
45	3	42	4	87	.355
46	3	43	4	87	.352
47	3	44	4	87	.350
48	3	45	4	87.5	.347
49	3	46	4	88	.345
50	3	47	4	88	.342

For $n > 50$, compute range of central 86 per cent, approximately, and multiply 0.339. This will give a rough estimate of σ.

APPENDIX TABLES AND CHARTS FOR USE IN TESTING HYPOTHESES AND DETERMINING CONFIDENCE LIMITS

Tables of Probability Points

The probability point y_P is the value of the statistic y that has a probability $P(y)$ of being equalled or exceeded. The probability point y_P is sometimes referred to as an *upper* probability point. The corresponding *lower* probability point is y_Q, where $Q(y) = 1 - P(y)$. For a statistic that can take any value between[1] $-\infty$ and ∞:

$$P(y) = \int_{y}^{\infty} f(u)\, du;$$

$$Q(y) = \int_{-\infty}^{y} f(u)\, du.$$

The symbol y is here used to refer to any test statistic, such as z, t, F, or χ^2. For the normal distribution we have values of z_P and $P(z)$ tabulated.

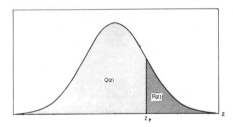

When there is no ambiguity P and Q may be used instead of $P(y)$ and $Q(y)$. $P + Q = 1$.

Use of tables in testing hypotheses. The null hypothesis H_0 is $Y = Y_0$, where Y is the unknown value of the parameter and Y_0 is its hypothetical parameter value. The required level of significance α is the probability of rejecting H_0 if H_0 is true. The first step in testing a hypothesis is to compute the test statistic y. The next step is to ascertain $P(y)$ from the appropriate appendix table and compare it with α. Alternatively, we may ascertain whether y falls in the acceptance region or the rejection region.

One-sided test, alternative hypothesis H_a: $Y > Y_0$. Reject H_0 if $P(y) \leq \alpha$. The critical value of y is $y_P = y_\alpha$. Reject H_0 if $y_P \geq y_\alpha$.

---

[1] If the limits are values other than $-\infty$ and ∞, we substitute the appropriate lower limit for $-\infty$ in the expression for $Q(y)$ and the appropriate upper limit for ∞ in the expression for $P(y)$. For F and χ^2 the limits are 0 and ∞.

One-sided test, alternative hypothesis H_a: $Y < Y_0$. Reject H_0 if $Q(y) \leqslant \alpha$. The critical value of y is $y_Q = y_\alpha$. Reject H_0 if $y_Q \leq y_\alpha$.

If the probability distribution is symmetrical about zero, as with z or t, the statement for this test can be simplified. Consider y to be positive. Then reject H_0 if $P(y) \geq \alpha$. Alternatively, reject H_0 if $|y| \geq |y_\alpha|$.

Two-sided test, alternative hypothesis H_a: $Y \neq Y_0$. If $Y > Y_0$, reject H_0 if $P(y) \leq \dfrac{\alpha}{2}$. If $Y < Y_0$, reject H_0 if $Q(y) \leq \dfrac{\alpha}{2}$. The critical values of y are $y_P = y_{\alpha/2}$ and $y_Q = y_{\alpha/2}$. Reject H_0 if $Y > Y_0$ and also $y_P \geq y_{\alpha/2}$. Reject H_0 if $Y < Y_0$ and also $y_P \leq y_{\alpha/2}$.

If the probability distribution is symmetrical about zero, the statement of the two-sided test is simpler. Consider y to be positive. Then reject H_0 if $P(y) \leq \alpha/2$, or $2P(y) \leq \alpha$. Alternatively, reject H_0 if $|y| > |y_{\alpha/2}|$.

Charts for Obtaining Confidence Limits for P in Binomial Sampling, Given d and $n\,(p = d/n)$

The confidence coefficient is always equal or less than that stated.

Appendix Chart 12.1—95 Per Cent Confidence Limits

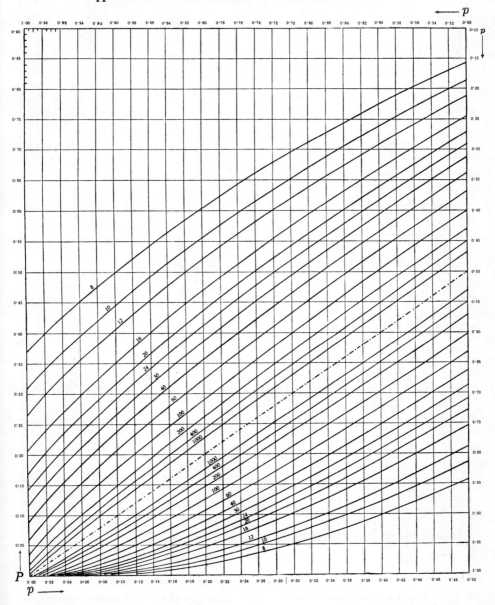

The numbers printed along the curves indicate the sample size n. If for a given value of the abscissa p, P_1 and P_2 are the ordinates read from (or interpolated between) the appropriate lower and upper curves, then $\Pr\{P_1 \leq P \leq P_2\} \leq \beta$.

Appendix Chart 12.2—99 Per Cent Confidence Limits for *P*

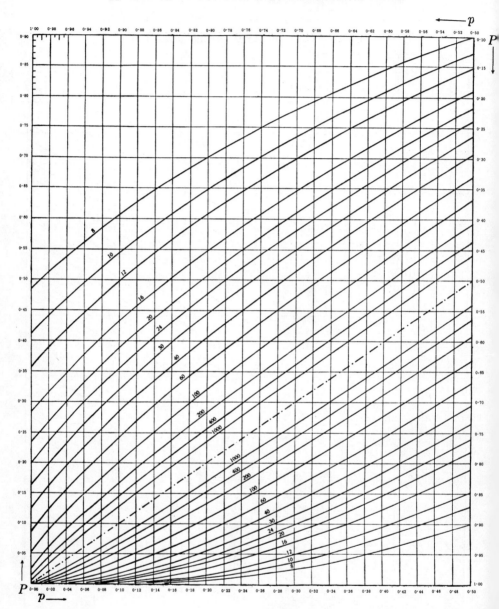

The numbers printed along the curves indicate the sample size of *n*.

Note: The process of reading from the curves can be simplified with the help of the right-angled corner of a loose sheet of paper or thin card, along the edges of which are marked off the scales shown in the top left-hand corner of each chart.

Taken, by permission, from E. S. Pearson and H. O. Hartley (editors), *Biometrika Tables for Statisticians*, Vol. I, Cambridge University Press, Cambridge, 1954, Table 41, pp. 204–205.

APPENDIX 13

Normal Curve Ordinates at Specified Values of z

$$f(z) \text{ and } \frac{Y_X}{Y_0}$$

Ordinates are values of $f(z) = \dfrac{1}{\sqrt{2\pi}} e^{-z^2/2}$.

The formula can also be written

$$f(z) = \frac{0.39894}{2.71828^{z^2/2}}.$$

The height of an ordinate to be erected at any value of z is obtained by multiplying the value of the ordinate shown as $f(z)$ in the appendix table by nc/σ. Assume that $\mu = 25$ pounds and $\sigma = 4$ pounds, and that we wish to erect an ordinate at 27 pounds for a distribution with sample size of 800 and class interval of 20 pounds.

$$\frac{nc}{\sigma} = \frac{(800)(20)}{4} = 4{,}000;$$

$$z = \frac{X - \mu}{\sigma} = \frac{27 - 25}{4} = 0.5.$$

The table value for the ordinate at $z = 0.5$ is 0.35207. The ordinate at $X = 27$ pounds is therefore $(4{,}000)(0.35207) = 1{,}408$.

Values of $\dfrac{Y_X}{Y_0} = e^{-z^2/2}$, the height of an ordinate relative to that of the maximum ordinate, are also shown in Appendix 13. For our data:

$$Y_0 = \frac{nc}{\sigma\sqrt{2\pi}} = \frac{(800)(20)}{(4)(2.50663)} = 1{,}595.77;$$

$$Y_X = (1{,}595.77)(0.88250) = 1{,}408.$$

APPENDIX 13 (Continued)

z	$f(z)$	$e^{-z^2/2}$	z	$f(x)$	$e^{-z^2/2}$
0.0	.39894	1.00000	2.0	.05399	.13534
0.1	.39695	.99501	2,1	.04398	.11025
0.2	.39104	.98020	2.2	.03547	.08892
0.3	.38139	.95600	2.3	.02833	.07100
0.4	.36827	.92312	2.4	.02239	.05614
0.5	.35207	.88250	2.5	.01753	.04394
0.6	.33322	.83527	2.6	.01358	.03405
0.7	.31225	.78270	2.7	.01042	.02612
0.8	.28969	.72615	2.8	.00792	.01984
0.9	.26609	.66698	2.9	.00595	.01492
1.0	.24197	.60653	3.0	.00443	.01111
1.1	.21785	.54607	3.1	.00327	.00819
1.2	.19419	.48675	3.2	.00238	.00598
1.3	.17137	.42956	3.3	.00172	.00432
1.4	.14973	.37531	3.4	.00123	.00309
1.5	.12952	.32465	3.5	.00087	.00219
1.6	.11092	.27804	3.6	.00061	.00153
1.7	.09405	.23575	3.7	.00042	.00106
1.8	.07895	.19790	3.8	.00029	.00073
1.9	.06562	.16448	3.9	.00020	.00050
			4.0	.00013	.00034
			4.5	.000016	.000040
			5.0	.000001	.000004

Normal Curve Areas

Appendix Table 14.1—Values of $P(z)$ for Specified Values of z

$P(z)$ is the probability of a value of z larger than that specified.

$$P(z) = \int_z^\infty f(u)\ du = \frac{1}{\sqrt{2\pi}} \int_z^\infty e^{-u^2/2}.$$

Graphically $P(z)$ is the area shaded in the diagram below.

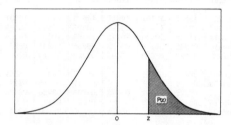

To illustrate the use of the table, assume that $\mu = 25$ pounds and $\sigma = 4$ pounds, and that we wish to find the probability of obtaining a value of X as large as 30 pounds or larger. Now $x = 5$ pounds and $z = 1.25$. From the appendix table it is seen that the probability of obtaining a value of z as large as 1.25 or larger is 0.10565. Therefore the probability that an item selected at random will be as large as 30 pounds or larger is 0.10565.

Appendix Table 14.1 (Cont'd)—Values of $P(z)$ for Specified Values of z

z	.00	.01	.02	.03	.04	.05	.06	.07	.08	.09
0.0	.50000	.49601	.49202	.48803	.48405	.48006	.47608	.47210	.46812	.46414
0.1	.46017	.45620	.45224	.44828	.44433	.44038	.43644	.43251	.42858	.42465
0.2	.42074	.41683	.41294	.40905	.40517	.40129	.39743	.39358	.38974	.38591
0.3	.38209	.37828	.37448	.37070	.36693	.36317	.35942	.35569	.35197	.34827
0.4	.34458	.34090	.33724	.33360	.32997	.32636	.32276	.31918	.31561	.31207
0.5	.30854	.30503	.30153	.29806	.29460	.29116	.28774	.28434	.28096	.27760
0.6	.27425	.27093	.26763	.26435	.26109	.25785	.25463	.25143	.24825	.24510
0.7	.24196	.23885	.23576	.23270	.22965	.22663	.22363	.22065	.21770	.21476
0.8	.21186	.20897	.20611	.20327	.20045	.19766	.19489	.19215	.18943	.18673
0.9	.18406	.18141	.17879	.17619	.17361	.17106	.16853	.16602	.16354	.16109
1.0	.15866	.15625	.15386	.15151	.14917	.14686	.14457	.14231	.14007	.13786
1.1	.13567	.13350	.13136	.12924	.12714	.12507	.12302	.12100	.11900	.11702
1.2	.11507	.11314	.11123	.10935	.10749	.10565	.10383	.10204	.10027	.09853
1.3	.09680	.09510	.09342	.09176	.09012	.08851	.08691	.08534	.08379	.08226
1.4	.08076	.07927	.07780	.07636	.07493	.07353	.07215	.07078	.06944	.06811
1.5	.06681	.06552	.06426	.06301	.06178	.06057	.05938	.05821	.05705	.05592
1.6	.05480	.05370	.05262	.05155	.05050	.04947	.04846	.04746	.04648	.04551
1.7	.04457	.04363	.04272	.04182	.04093	.04006	.03920	.03836	.03754	.03673
1.8	.03593	.03515	.03438	.03362	.03288	.03216	.03144	.03074	.03005	.02938
1.9	.02872	.02807	.02743	.02680	.02619	.02559	.02500	.02442	.02385	.02330
2.0	.02275	.02216	.02169	.02118	.02068	.02018	.01970	.01923	.01876	.01831
2.1	.01786	.01743	.01700	.01659	.01618	.01578	.01539	.01500	.01463	.01426
2.2	.01390	.01355	.01321	.01287	.01255	.01222	.01191	.01160	.01130	.01101
2.3	.01072	.01044	.01017	.00990	.00964	.00939	.00914	.00889	.00866	.00842
2.4	.00820	.00798	.00776	.00755	.00734	.00714	.00695	.00676	.00657	.00639
2.5	.00621	.00604	.00587	.00570	.00554	.00539	.00523	.00508	.00494	.00480
2.6	.00466	.00453	.00440	.00427	.00415	.00402	.00391	.00379	.00368	.00357
2.7	.00347	.00336	.00326	.00317	.00307	.00298	.00289	.00280	.00272	.00264
2.8	.00256	.00248	.00240	.00233	.00226	.00219	.00212	.00205	.00199	.00193
2.9	.00187	.00181	.00175	.00169	.00164	.00159	.00154	.00149	.00144	.00139
3.0	.00135	.00131	.00126	.00122	.00118	.00114	.00111	.00107	.00104	.00100
3.1	.00097	.00094	.00090	.00087	.00084	.00082	.00079	.00076	.00074	.00071
3.2	.00069	.00066	.00064	.00062	.00060	.00058	.00056	.00054	.00052	.00050
3.3	.00048	.00047	.00045	.00043	.00042	.00040	.00039	.00038	.00036	.00035
3.4	.00034	.00032	.00031	.00030	.00029	.00028	.00027	.00026	.00025	.00024
3.5	.00023	.00022	.00022	.00021	.00020	.00019	.00019	.00018	.00017	.00017
3.6	.00016	.00015	.00015	.00014	.00014	.00013	.00013	.00012	.00012	.00011
3.7	.00011	.00010	.00010	.00010	.00009	.00009	.00008	.00008	.00008	.00008
3.8	.00007	.00007	.00007	.00006	.00006	.00006	.00006	.00005	.00005	.00005
3.9	.00005	.00005	.00004	.00004	.00004	.00004	.00004	.00004	.00003	.00003
4.0	.00003	...	...	...	...	...	...	...	...	...
4.5	.000003	...	...	...	...	...	...	...	...	...
5.0	.0000003	...	...	...	...	...	...	...	...	...

Appendix Table 14.2—Values of $F(z)$ for Specified Values of z

$F(z)$ is the proportion of total area between μ and a given value of X, or between 0 and a given value of z.

$$F(z) = .5 - P(z) = \int_0^z f(u)\, du = \frac{1}{\sqrt{2\pi}} \int_0^z e^{-u^2/2}$$

Graphically $F(z)$ is the area shaded in the diagram below.

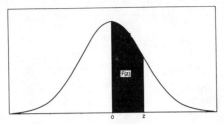

z	.00	.01	.02	.03	.04	.05	.06	.07	.08	.09
0.0	.00000	.00399	.00798	.01197	.01595	.01994	.02392	.02790	.03188	.03586
0.1	.03983	.04380	.04776	.05172	.05567	.05962	.06356	.06749	.07142	.07535
0.2	.07926	.08317	.08706	.09095	.09483	.09871	.10257	.10642	.11026	.11409
0.3	.11791	.12172	.12552	.12930	.13307	.13683	.14058	.14431	.14803	.15173
0.4	.15542	.15910	.16276	.16640	.17003	.17364	.17724	.18082	.18439	.18793
0.5	.19146	.19497	.19847	.20194	.20540	.20884	.21226	.21566	.21904	.22240
0.6	.22575	.22907	.23237	.23565	.23891	.24215	.24537	.24857	.25175	.25490
0.7	.25804	.26115	.26424	.26730	.27035	.27337	.27637	.27935	.28230	.28524
0.8	.28814	.29103	.29389	.29673	.29955	.30234	.30511	.30785	.31057	.31327
0.9	.31594	.31859	.32121	.32381	.32639	.32894	.33147	.33398	.33646	.33891
1.0	.34134	.34375	.34614	.34849	.35083	.35314	.35543	.35769	.35993	.36214
1.1	.36433	.36650	.36864	.37076	.37286	.37493	.37698	.37900	.38100	.38298
1.2	.38493	.38686	.38877	.39065	.39251	.39435	.39617	.39796	.39973	.40147
1.3	.40320	.40490	.40658	.40824	.40988	.41198	.41309	.41466	.41621	.41774
1.4	.41924	.42073	.42220	.42364	.42507	.42647	.42785	.42922	.43056	.43189
1.5	.43319	.43448	.43574	.43699	.43822	.43943	.44062	.44179	.44295	.44408
1.6	.44520	.44630	.44738	.44845	.44950	.45053	.45154	.45254	.45352	.45449
1.7	.45543	.45637	.45728	.45818	.45907	.45994	.46080	.46164	.46246	.46327
1.8	.46407	.46485	.46562	.46638	.46712	.46784	.46856	.46926	.46995	.47062
1.9	.47128	.47193	.47257	.47320	.47381	.47441	.47500	.47558	.47615	.47670
2.0	.47725	.47784	.47831	.47882	.47932	.47982	.48030	.48077	.48124	.48169
2.1	.48214	.48257	.48300	.48341	.48382	.48422	.48461	.48500	.48537	.48574
2.2	.48610	.48645	.48679	.48713	.48745	.48778	.48809	.48840	.48870	.48899
2.3	.48928	.48956	.48983	.49010	.49036	.49061	.49086	.49111	.49134	.49158
2.4	.49180	.49202	.49224	.49245	.49266	.49286	.49305	.49324	.49343	.49361
2.5	.49379	.49396	.49413	.49430	.49446	.49461	.49477	.49492	.49506	.49520
2.6	.49534	.49547	.49560	.49573	.49585	.49598	.49609	.49621	.49632	.49643
2.7	.49653	.49664	.49674	.49683	.49693	.49702	.49711	.49720	.49728	.49736
2.8	.49744	.49752	.49760	.49767	.49774	.49781	.49788	.49795	.49801	.49807
2.9	.49813	.49819	.49825	.49831	.49836	.49841	.49846	.49851	.49856	.49861
3.0	.49865	.49869	.49874	.49878	.49882	.49886	.49889	.49893	.49896	.49900
3.1	.49903	.49906	.49910	.49913	.49916	.49918	.49921	.49924	.49926	.49929
3.2	.49931	.49934	.49936	.49938	.49940	.49942	.49944	.49946	.49948	.49950
3.3	.49952	.49953	.49955	.49957	.49958	.49960	.49961	.49962	.49964	.49965
3.4	.49966	.49968	.49969	.49970	.49971	.49972	.49973	.49974	.49975	.49976
3.5	.49977	.49978	.49978	.49979	.49980	.49981	.49981	.49982	.49983	.49983
3.6	.49984	.49985	.49985	.49986	.49986	.49987	.49987	.49988	.49988	.49989
3.7	.49989	.49990	.49990	.49990	.49991	.49991	.49992	.49992	.49992	.49992
3.8	.49993	.49993	.49993	.49994	.49994	.49994	.49994	.49995	.49995	.49995
3.9	.49995	.49995	.49996	.49996	.49996	.49996	.49996	.49996	.49997	.49997
4.0	.49997	...	...	...	...	...	...	...	...	...
4.5	.499997	...	...	...	...	...	...	...	...	...
5.0	.4999997	...	...	...	...	...	...	...	...	...

To illustrate the use of the table, assume that $\mu = 25$ pounds and $\sigma = 4$

pounds, and that we wish to find the probability of obtaining a value of X between μ and 30 pounds. Now $x = 5$ pounds and $z = 1.25$. From the appendix table it is seen that 0.39435 of the area is between $z = 0$ and $z = 1.25$, i.e., between μ and $\mu + 1.25\sigma$. So the probability is 0.39435 that an item selected at random will be between 25 and 30 pounds.

Appendix Table 14.3—Values of z_P for Specified Values of P

$$z = \frac{X - \mu}{\sigma_X} \quad \text{or} \quad \frac{\overline{X} - \mu}{\sigma_{\overline{x}}}$$

P	z_P	P	z_P	P	z_P
0.0005	3.29053	0.005	2.57583	0.11	1.22653
.0010	3.09023	.010	2.32635	.12	1.17499
.0015	2.96774	.015	2.17009	.13	1.12639
.0020	2.87816	.020	2.05375	.14	1.08032
.0025	2.80703	.025	1.95996	.15	1.03643
.0030	2.74778	.030	1.88079	.16	0.99446
.0035	2.69684	.035	1.81191	.17	.95417
.0040	2.65207	.040	1.75069	.18	.91537
.0045	2.61205	.045	1.69540	.19	.87790
.0050	2.57583	.050	1.64485	.20	.84162
.006	2.51214	.06	1.55477	.25	.67449
.007	2.45726	.07	1.47579	.30	.52440
.008	2.40892	.08	1.40507	.35	.38532
.009	2.36562	.09	1.34076	.40	.25335
.010	2.32635	.10	1.28155	.45	.12566

Examples:

A probability of 0.025 is associated with a deviation from μ as large as $+1.9599\sigma$ or larger (area in upper tail is 0.025).

A probability of 0.025 is associated with a deviation from μ as small as -1.9599σ or smaller (area in lower tail is 0.025).

A probability of 0.05 is associated with a deviation from μ as large numerically as 1.9599 or larger (area in both tails is 0.05).

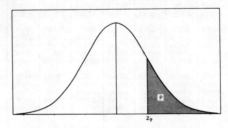

APPENDIX 15

Dixon's Ratios Involving Extreme Values

These ratios are for the purpose of testing the presence of one or more values from a different population. When a suspected outlier is the smallest value in the array

$$r_{ij} = \frac{X_{1+i} - X_1}{X_{n-j} - X_1},$$

where the items have been ranked in ascending order of magnitude. When a suspected outlier is the largest value in the array,

$$r_{ij} = \frac{X_n - X_{n-i}}{X_n - X_{1+j}}.$$

The ratios can be used to test outliers among n items or among k means.

The appropriate ratio to use depends on the sample size and on the number of suspected outliers at one end of the array. Thus

n or k	Number of outliers	
	1	2 or more
3–7	r_{10}	r_{20}
8–10	r_{11}	r_{20}
11–13	r_{21}	r_{21}
14–30	r_{22}	r_{22}

All these ratios may be applied repeatedly to the same data, to remove outliers other than the one first removed.

Appendix Table 15—Dixon's Ratios Involving Extreme Values at Selected Upper Probability Points: Values of r_{ij} for Specific Values of P

n or k	.10	.05	.01	.005	Statistic
3	0.886	0.941	0.988	0.994	
4	.679	.765	.889	.926	
5	.557	.642	.780	.821	r_{10}
6	.482	.560	.698	.740	
7	.434	.507	.637	.680	
8	.479	.554	.683	.725	
9	.441	.512	.635	.677	r_{11}
10	.409	.477	.597	.639	
4	.935	.967	.992	.996	
5	.782	.845	.929	.950	
6	.670	.736	.836	.865	
7	.596	.661	.778	.814	r_{20}
8	.545	.607	.710	.746	
9	.505	.565	.667	.700	
10	.474	.531	.632	.664	
11	.517	.576	.679	.713	
12	.490	.546	.642	.675	r_{21}
13	.467	.521	.615	.649	
14	.492	.546	.641	.674	
15	.472	.525	.616	.647	
16	.454	.507	.595	.624	
17	.438	.490	.577	.605	
18	.424	.475	.561	.589	
19	.412	.462	.547	.575	
20	.401	.450	.535	.562	
21	.391	.440	.524	.551	
22	.382	.430	.514	.541	r_{22}
23	.374	.421	.505	.532	
24	.367	.413	.497	.524	
25	.360	.406	.489	.516	
26	.354	.399	.486	.508	
27	.348	.393	.475	.501	
28	.342	.387	.469	.495	
29	.337	.381	.463	.489	
30	.332	.376	.457	.483	

Taken by permission of the author and publisher from W. J. Dixon,"Ratios Involving Extreme Values," *Annals of Mathematical Statistics*, Vol. 22, March, 1951, pp. 68–78.

APPENDIX 16

Values of t for Specified Probabilities

This table shows values of t when $P(t)$ have the values shown in the first row of the box head, or when $Q(-t) + P(t) = 2P(t)$ have the values shown in the second row of the box head. For example, if $\nu = 5$, the probability of obtaining a value of t as large as $+2.015$ or larger is $.05$; likewise, the probability of obtaining a value of t as small as -2.015 or smaller is $.05$; and the probability of obtaining a value of t as large, numerically, as 2.015 is $.10$.

For a one-sided test, reject H_0 if $P \leq \alpha$, (or $Q \leq \alpha$) which will be true if $|t| \geq t_\alpha$. Thus, if $\nu = 5$ and $\alpha = .05$, the appendix shows that $t_\alpha = t_{.05} = 2.015$. We reject H_0 if $|t| \geq 2.015$.

For a two-sided test, reject H_0 if $P + Q \leq \alpha$. But since $Q = P$, we may also say that we reject H_0 if $2P \leq \alpha$, or if $P \leq \alpha/2$. This will be true if $|t| \geq t_{\alpha/2}$. Thus, if $\nu = 5$ and $\alpha = .10$, the appendix shows that $t_{\alpha/2} = t_{.05} = 2.015$. We reject H_0 if $|t| \geq 2.015$.

As ν approaches ∞ the t distribution approaches the normal distribution. Compare the z-values in Appendix Table 14.3 with the t-values in the last row of Appendix 16 when the values of P are the same.

Appendix Table 16—Values of *t* for Specified Probabilities

ν	.45	.40	.35	.30	.25	.20	.15	.10	.05	.025	.01	.005	.0005	P
	.90	.80	.70	.60	.50	.40	.30	.20	.10	.05	.02	.01	.001	2P
1	.158	.325	.510	.727	1.000	1.376	1.963	3.078	6.314	12.706	31.821	63.657	636.619	
2	.142	.289	.445	.617	.816	1.061	1.386	1.886	2.920	4.303	6.965	9.925	31.598	
3	.137	.277	.424	.584	.765	.978	1.250	1.638	2.353	3.182	4.541	5.841	12.941	
4	.134	.271	.414	.569	.741	.941	1.190	1.533	2.132	2.776	3.747	4.604	8.610	
5	.132	.267	.408	.559	.727	.920	1.156	1.476	2.015	2.571	3.365	4.032	6.859	
6	.131	.265	.404	.553	.718	.906	1.134	1.440	1.943	2.447	3.143	3.707	5.959	
7	.130	.263	.402	.549	.711	.896	1.119	1.415	1.895	2.365	2.998	3.499	5.405	
8	.130	.262	.399	.546	.706	.889	1.108	1.397	1.860	2.306	2.896	3.355	5.041	
9	.129	.261	.398	.543	.703	.883	1.100	1.383	1.833	2.262	2.821	3.250	4.781	
10	.129	.260	.397	.542	.700	.879	1.093	1.372	1.812	2.228	2.764	3.169	4.587	
11	.129	.260	.396	.540	.697	.876	1.088	1.363	1.796	2.201	2.718	3.106	4.437	
12	.128	.259	.395	.539	.695	.873	1.083	1.356	1.782	2.179	2.681	3.055	4.318	
13	.128	.259	.394	.538	.694	.870	1.079	1.350	1.771	2.160	2.650	3.012	4.221	
14	.128	.258	.393	.537	.692	.868	1.076	1.345	1.761	2.145	2.624	2.977	4.140	
15	.128	.258	.393	.536	.691	.866	1.074	1.341	1.753	2.131	2.602	2.947	4.073	
16	.128	.258	.392	.535	.690	.865	1.071	1.337	1.746	2.120	2.583	2.921	4.015	
17	.128	.257	.392	.534	.689	.863	1.069	1.333	1.740	2.110	2.567	2.898	3.965	
18	.127	.257	.392	.534	.688	.862	1.067	1.330	1.734	2.101	2.552	2.878	3.922	
19	.127	.257	.391	.533	.688	.861	1.066	1.328	1.729	2.093	2.539	2.861	3.883	
20	.127	.257	.391	.533	.687	.860	1.064	1.325	1.725	2.086	2.528	2.845	3.850	
21	.127	.257	.391	.532	.686	.859	1.063	1.323	1.721	2.080	2.518	2.831	3.819	
22	.127	.256	.390	.532	.686	.858	1.061	1.321	1.717	2.074	2.508	2.819	3.792	
23	.127	.256	.390	.532	.685	.858	1.060	1.319	1.714	2.069	2.500	2.807	3.767	
24	.127	.256	.390	.531	.685	.857	1.059	1.318	1.711	2.064	2.492	2.797	3.745	
25	.127	.256	.390	.531	.684	.856	1.058	1.316	1.708	2.060	2.485	2.787	3.725	
26	.127	.256	.390	.531	.684	.856	1.058	1.315	1.706	2.056	2.479	2.779	3.707	
27	.127	.256	.389	.531	.684	.855	1.057	1.314	1.703	2.052	2.473	2.771	3.690	
28	.127	.256	.389	.530	.683	.855	1.056	1.313	1.701	2.048	2.467	2.763	3.674	
29	.127	.256	.389	.530	.683	.854	1.055	1.311	1.699	2.045	2.462	2.756	3.659	
30	.127	.256	.389	.530	.683	.854	1.055	1.310	1.697	2.042	2.457	2.750	3.646	
40	.126	.255	.388	.529	.681	.851	1.050	1.303	1.684	2.021	2.423	2.704	3.551	
60	.126	.254	.387	.527	.679	.848	1.046	1.296	1.671	2.000	2.390	2.660	3.460	
120	.126	.254	.386	.526	.677	.845	1.041	1.289	1.658	1.980	2.358	2.617	3.373	
∞	.126	.253	.385	.524	.674	.842	1.036	1.282	1.645	1.960	2.326	2.576	3.291	

This Table is reprinted from Table III of R. A. Fisher and F. Yates, *Statistical Tables for Biological, Agricultural and Medical Research*, 5th ed., Oliver and Boyd Ltd., Edinburgh, 1957, by permission of the author and publishers. A table of *t*, similar in arrangement to that of Appendix 15.1, but giving values of *Q(t)* for specified values of *t* and ν, may be found in E. S. Pearson and H. O. Hartley, editors, *Biometrika Tables for Statisticians*, Vol. 1, Table 9, Cambridge University Press, Cambridge, 1954.

APPENDIX 17

Values of G_1 for Use in Testing Hypothesis that $\mu = \mu_0$

If there are k subgroups of n items each,

$$G_1 = \frac{\bar{X} - \mu}{\bar{R}}.$$

If the data are not subgrouped, $k = 1$ and

$$G_1 = \frac{\bar{X} - \mu}{R}.$$

In general it is best to subgroup the data, at random, in such a way that each subsample size is approximately 8, not smaller than 6 or larger than 10. The statistic G_1 is a substitute for the statistic t; and although it is much easier to compute, its use involves loss of power.[1]

Taken, by permission, from Table I of J. Edward Jackson and Eleanor L. Ross, "Extended Tables for Use with the G test for Means," *Journal of the American Statistical Association*, Vol. 50, June, 1955, pp. 416–433. Jackson and Ross use the symbol m, rather than k, for the number of subgroups. They tabulated values at the 0.005 point (0.01 in both tails combined) also. Jackson and Ross computed their table directly from a table by Lord. See E. Lord, "The Use of Range in Place of Standard Deviation in the t-Test," *Biometrika*, Vol. 34, 1947, pp. 41–67.

Appendix Table 17.1—Values of G_1 at the 5 Per Cent Probability Point

$$P(G_1) = .05$$

For use in determining the 0.90 confidence limits for μ, and for the following tests of hypotheses. Reject H_0 if $G_1 \geq G_{1,\alpha}$.

Two-sided. $H_0: \mu = \mu_0;\ H_a: \mu \neq \mu_0;\ \alpha = 2P = .10$
One-sided. $H_0: \mu = \mu_0;\ H_a: \mu > \mu_0;\ \alpha = P = .05$
One-sided. $H_0: \mu = \mu_0;\ H_a: \mu < \mu_0;\ \alpha = P = .05$

n \ k	1	2	3	4	5	6	7	8	9	10	11	12	13	14	15
2	3.16	1.16	0.80	0.64	0.54	0.48	0.44	0.40	0.38	0.35	0.33	0.32	0.30	0.29	0.28
3	.88	.49	.37	.31	.27	.24	.22	.21	.19	.18	.17	.17	.16	.15	.15
4	.53	.32	.25	.21	.19	.17	.16	.15	.14	.13	.12	.12	.11	.11	.10
5	.39	.25	.19	.17	.15	.13	.12	.11	.11	.10	.10	.09	.09	.09	.08
6	.31	.20	.16	.14	.12	.11	.10	.10	.09	.08	.08	.08	.07	.07	.08
7	.26	.17	.14	.12	.11	.10	.09	.08	.08	.07	.07	.07	.06	.06	.07
8	.23	.15	.12	.10	.09	.09	.08	.07	.07	.07	.06	.06	.06	.06	.06
9	.20	.14	.11	.09	.08	.08	.07	.07	.06	.06	.06	.05	.05	.05	.05
10	.19	.12	.10	.09	.08	.07	.06	.06	.06	.05	.05	.05	.05	.05	.05
11	.17	.12	.09	.08	.07	.06	.06	.06	.05	.05	.05	.05	.04	.04	.04
12	.16	.11	.09	.07	.07	.06	.06	.05	.05	.05	.04	.04	.04	.04	.04
13	.15	.10	.08	.07	.06	.06	.05	.05	.05	.04	.04	.04	.04	.04	.04
14	.14	.09	.08	.07	.06	.05	.05	.05	.04	.04	.04	.04	.04	.04	.03
15	.13	.09	.07	.06	.06	.05	.05	.04	.04	.04	.04	.04	.03	.03	.03

Appendix Table 17.2—Values of G_1 at the 2.5 Per Cent Probability Point

$P(G_1) = 0.025$

For use in determining two-sided 0.95 confidence limits for μ, and for the following tests of hypotheses. Reject H_0 if $G_1 \geq G_{1,\alpha}$.

Two-sided. $H_0: \mu = \mu_0$; $H_a: \mu \neq \mu_0$; $\alpha = 2P = .05$
One-sided. $H_0: \mu = \mu_0$; $H_a: \mu > \mu_0$; $\alpha = P = .025$
One-sided. $H_0: \mu = \mu_0$; $H_a: \mu < \mu_0$; $\alpha = P = .025$

n \ k	1	2	3	4	5	6	7	8	9	10	11	12	13	14	15
2	6.36	1.72	1.08	0.83	0.70	0.61	0.55	0.50	0.46	0.44	0.41	0.39	0.37	0.36	0.34
3	1.30	.64	.47	.38	.33	.30	.27	.25	.24	.22	.21	.20	.19	.18	.18
4	.72	.41	.31	.26	.23	.21	.19	.18	.17	.16	.15	.14	.14	.13	.13
5	.51	.31	.24	.20	.18	.16	.15	.14	.13	.12	.12	.11	.11	.10	.10
6	.40	.25	.20	.17	.15	.13	.12	.11	.11	.10	.10	.09	.09	.09	.08
7	.33	.21	.17	.14	.13	.12	.11	.10	.09	.09	.08	.08	.08	.07	.07
8	.29	.19	.15	.13	.11	.10	.09	.09	.08	.08	.07	.07	.07	.07	.06
9	.25	.17	.13	.11	.10	.09	.08	.08	.07	.07	.07	.06	.06	.06	.06
10	.23	.15	.12	.10	.09	.08	.08	.07	.07	.06	.06	.06	.06	.05	.05
11	.21	.14	.11	.10	.08	.08	.07	.07	.06	.06	.06	.05	.05	.05	.05
12	.19	.13	.10	.09	.08	.07	.07	.06	.06	.06	.05	.05	.05	.05	.04
13	.18	.12	.10	.08	.07	.07	.06	.06	.05	.05	.05	.05	.05	.05	.04
14	.17	.11	.09	.08	.07	.06	.06	.05	.05	.05	.05	.04	.04	.04	.04
15	.16	.11	.09	.07	.07	.06	.06	.05	.05	.05	.04	.04	.04	.04	.04

APPENDIX 18

Values of G_2 for Use in Testing Hypothesis that $\mu_1 = \mu_2$:

$$G_2 = \frac{\overline{X}_1 - \overline{X}_2}{\overline{R}}.$$

In each of the two samples there are k subgroups of n items each. The statistic G_2 is a substitute for the statistic t; and although it is much easier to compute, its use involves loss of power.

Abridged, with permission from Table II of J. Edward Jackson and Eleanor L. Ross "Extended Tables for Use with the G test for Means," *Journal of the American Statistical Association*, Vol. 50 June, 1955, pp. 416–433. Jackson and Ross use the symbol m, rather than k, for the number of subgroups. They tabulate the .005 point (.01 in both tails) also, and their table provides for unequal numbers of subgroups in the two samples. Jackson and Ross computed their table directly from a table appearing in E. Lord, "The Use of Range in Place of Standard Deviation in the t-Test," *Biometrika*, Vol. 34, 1947, 41–67.

Appendix Table 18.1—Values of G_2 at the 5 Per Cent Probability Point

$$P(G_2) = .05$$

For use in two-sided test of hypothesis when $\alpha = 0.10$, or one-sided test of hypothesis when $\alpha = 0.05$. Reject H_0 if $G_2 \geq G_{2,\alpha}$.

n \ k	1	2	3	4	5	6	7	8	9	10	11	12	13	14	15
2	2.32	1.27	0.97	0.81	0.71	0.64	0.58	0.54	0.51	0.48	0.45	0.43	0.42	0.40	0.39
3	.97	.62	.49	.41	.37	.33	.31	.29	.27	.25	.24	.23	.22	.21	.21
4	.65	.42	.34	.29	.26	.24	.22	.20	.19	.18	.17	.16	.16	.15	.15
5	.49	.33	.27	.23	.20	.18	.17	.16	.15	.14	.14	.13	.12	.12	.12
6	.41	.28	.22	.19	.17	.15	.14	.13	.13	.12	.11	.11	.10	.10	.10
7	.35	.24	.19	.16	.15	.13	.12	.12	.11	.10	.10	.09	.09	.09	.08
8	.31	.21	.17	.15	.13	.12	.11	.10	.10	.09	.09	.08	.08	.08	.07
9	.27	.19	.15	.13	.12	.11	.10	.09	.09	.08	.08	.08	.07	.07	.07
10	.25	.17	.14	.12	.11	.10	.09	.08	.08	.08	.07	.07	.07	.06	.06
11	.23	.16	.13	.11	.10	.09	.08	.08	.07	.07	.07	.06	.06	.06	.06
12	.21	.15	.12	.10	.09	.08	.08	.07	.07	.06	.06	.06	.06	.06	.05
13	.20	.14	.11	.10	.09	.08	.07	.07	.06	.06	.06	.05	.05	.05	.05
14	.19	.13	.11	.09	.08	.07	.07	.06	.06	.06	.06	.05	.05	.05	.05
15	.18	.12	.10	.09	.08	.07	.07	.06	.06	.05	.05	.05	.05	.05	.04

Appendix Table 18.2—Values of G_2 at the 2.5 Per Cent Probability Point

$$P(G_2) = .025$$

For use in two-sided test of hypothesis when $\alpha = .05$, or one-sided test of hypothesis when $\alpha = .025$. Reject H_0 if $G_2 \geq G_{2,\alpha}$.

n \ k	1	2	3	4	5	6	7	8	9	10	11	12	13	14	15
2	3.43	1.67	1.22	1.00	0.87	0.78	0.71	0.66	0.61	0.58	0.55	0.52	0.50	0.48	0.46
3	1.27	.77	.60	.50	.45	.40	.37	.34	.32	.31	.29	.28	.27	.26	.25
4	.81	.52	.41	.35	.31	.28	.26	.24	.23	.22	.21	.20	.19	.18	.18
5	.61	.40	.32	.28	.24	.22	.21	.19	.18	.17	.16	.16	.15	.14	.14
6	.50	.33	.27	.23	.20	.19	.17	.16	.15	.14	.14	.13	.12	.12	.12
7	.43	.29	.23	.20	.18	.16	.15	.14	.13	.12	.12	.11	.11	.10	.10
8	.37	.25	.20	.18	.16	.14	.13	.12	.12	.11	.10	.10	.10	.09	.09
9	.33	.23	.18	.16	.14	.13	.12	.11	.10	.10	.09	.09	.09	.08	.08
10	.30	.21	.17	.14	.13	.12	.11	.10	.10	.09	.09	.08	.08	.08	.07
11	.28	.19	.16	.13	.12	.11	.10	.09	.09	.08	.08	.08	.07	.07	.07
12	.26	.18	.14	.12	.11	.10	.09	.09	.08	.08	.07	.07	.07	.07	.06
13	.24	.17	.14	.12	.10	.09	.08	.08	.08	.07	.07	.07	.06	.06	.06
14	.23	.16	.13	.11	.10	.09	.08	.08	.07	.07	.07	.06	.06	.06	.06
15	.22	.15	.12	.10	.09	.08	.08	.07	.07	.07	.06	.06	.06	.06	.05

Wilcoxon's Rank Totals for Testing Hypothesis that $\mu_1 = \mu_2$

Use Table 20, which gives values of T_2, when the two samples are independent; use Table 19, which gives values of T_1, when the data are matched pairs. In each case reject H_0 when $T \leq T_\alpha$.

Abridged, by permission from Frank Wilcoxon, *Some Rapid Approximate Statistical Procedures*, American Cyanamid Company, New York, 1949, p. 13.

APPENDIX 19

Values of T_1 for Matched Pairs for Specified Values of Q

T_1 is the smallest rank total of one sign, after ranking the *numerical* differences in ascending order and affixing the appropriate sign.

n	.025	.005	P
	.05	.01	$2P$
6	0	. .	
7	2	. .	
8	4	0	
9	6	2	
10	8	3	
11	11	5	
12	14	7	
13	17	10	
14	21	13	
15	25	16	
16	30	20	
17	35	23	
18	40	28	
19	46	32	
20	52	38	
21	59	43	
22	66	49	
23	73	55	
24	81	61	
25	89	68	

APPENDIX 20

Values of T_2 for Independent Samples for Specified Values of Q

T_2 is the rank total for the variable with the smallest rank total, after ranking the $2n$ observations in ascending order.

n	.025	.005	P
	.05	.01	2P
5	18	15
6	27	23
7	37	32
8	49	44
9	63	56
10	79	71
11	97	87
12	116	105
13	137	125
14	160	147
15	185	170
16	212	196
17	241	223
18	271	252
19	303	282
20	338	315

APPENDIX 21

The Variance Ratio: F

Values of F for Specified Values of $P(F)$

$$F = \frac{\chi_1^2/\nu_1}{\chi_2^2/\nu_2} = \frac{s_1^2}{s_2^2},$$ where s_1^2 and s_2^2 are two independent estimates of σ^2.

The degrees of freedom for the numerator and denominator are ν_1 and ν_2, respectively. The tables give upper probability points.

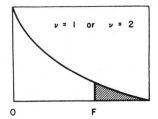 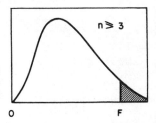

A lower probability point is the reciprocal of F with ν_1 and ν_2 interchanged. Thus if $\nu_1 = 5$ and $\nu_2 = 8$, the .05 upper probability point is 3.69. If $\nu_1 = 8$ and $\nu_2 = 5$ the lower probability point is $1/3.69 = .271$.

To estimate values of F for values of ν_1 or ν_2 not given in this table interpolate, using reciprocals of ν.

Values of F at the 0.05 and 0.01 points were abridged, by permission, from E. S. Pearson and H. O. Hartley (editors), *Biometrika Tables for Statisticians*, Volume I, Cambridge University Press, Cambridge, 1954, Table 18. The *Biometrika* tables are more extensive with respect to ν_1 and ν_2. Values of F at the .001 points were abridged from Table V of R. A. Fisher and F. Yates, *Statistical Tables for Biological, Agricultural, and Medical Research*, 5th ed., 1957, published by Oliver and Boyd, Ltd., Edinburgh, by permission of the authors and publishers.

Appendix Table 21.1—Upper 5 Per Cent Points of the F Distribution

v_2 \ v_1	1	2	3	4	5	6	8	10	12	20	24	30	40	60	120	∞
1	161.4	199.5	215.7	224.6	230.2	234.0	238.9	241.9	243.9	248.0	249.1	250.1	251.1	252.2	253.3	254.3
2	18.51	19.00	19.16	19.25	19.30	19.33	19.37	19.40	19.41	19.45	19.45	19.46	19.47	19.48	19.49	19.50
3	10.13	9.55	9.28	9.12	9.01	8.94	8.85	8.79	8.74	8.66	8.64	8.62	8.59	8.57	8.55	8.53
4	7.71	6.94	6.59	6.39	6.26	6.16	6.04	5.96	5.91	5.80	5.77	5.75	5.72	5.69	5.66	5.63
5	6.61	5.79	5.41	5.19	5.05	4.95	4.82	4.74	4.68	4.56	4.53	4.50	4.46	4.43	4.40	4.36
6	5.99	5.14	4.76	4.53	4.39	4.28	4.15	4.06	4.00	3.87	3.84	3.81	3.77	3.74	3.70	3.67
8	5.32	4.46	4.07	3.84	3.69	3.58	3.44	3.35	3.28	3.15	3.12	3.08	3.04	3.01	2.97	2.93
10	4.96	4.10	3.71	3.48	3.33	3.22	3.07	2.98	2.91	2.77	2.74	2.70	2.66	2.62	2.58	2.54
12	4.75	3.89	3.49	3.26	3.11	3.00	2.85	2.75	2.69	2.54	2.51	2.47	2.43	2.38	2.34	2.30
20	4.35	3.49	3.10	2.87	2.71	2.60	2.45	2.35	2.28	2.12	2.08	2.04	1.99	1.95	1.90	1.84
24	4.26	3.40	3.01	2.78	2.62	2.51	2.36	2.25	2.18	2.03	1.98	1.94	1.89	1.84	1.79	1.73
30	4.17	3.32	2.92	2.69	2.53	2.42	2.27	2.16	2.09	1.93	1.89	1.84	1.79	1.74	1.68	1.62
40	4.08	3.23	2.84	2.61	2.45	2.34	2.18	2.08	2.00	1.84	1.79	1.74	1.69	1.64	1.58	1.51
60	4.00	3.15	2.76	2.53	2.37	2.25	2.10	1.99	1.92	1.75	1.70	1.65	1.59	1.53	1.47	1.39
120	3.92	3.07	2.68	2.45	2.29	2.17	2.02	1.91	1.83	1.66	1.61	1.55	1.50	1.43	1.35	1.25
∞	3.84	3.00	2.60	2.37	2.21	2.10	1.94	1.83	1.75	1.57	1.52	1.46	1.39	1.32	1.22	1.00

Appendix Table 21.2—Upper 2.5 Per Cent Points of the F Distribution

v_2 \ v_1	1	2	3	4	5	6	8	10	12	20	24	30	40	60	120	∞
1	647.8	799.5	864.2	899.6	921.8	937.1	956.7	968.6	976.7	993.1	997.2	1001	1006	1010	1014	1018
2	38.51	39.00	39.17	39.25	39.30	39.33	39.37	39.40	39.41	39.45	39.46	39.46	39.47	39.48	39.49	39.50
3	17.44	16.04	15.44	15.10	14.88	14.73	14.54	14.42	14.34	14.17	14.12	14.08	14.04	13.99	13.95	13.90
4	12.22	10.65	9.98	9.60	9.36	9.20	8.98	8.84	8.75	8.56	8.51	8.46	8.41	8.36	8.31	8.26
5	10.01	8.43	7.76	7.39	7.15	6.98	6.76	6.62	6.52	6.33	6.28	6.23	6.18	6.12	6.07	6.02
6	8.81	7.26	6.60	6.23	5.99	5.82	5.60	5.46	5.37	5.17	5.12	5.07	5.01	4.96	4.90	4.85
8	7.57	6.06	5.42	5.05	4.82	4.65	4.43	4.30	4.20	4.00	3.95	3.89	3.84	3.78	3.73	3.67
10	6.94	5.46	4.83	4.47	4.24	4.07	3.85	3.72	3.62	3.42	3.37	3.31	3.26	3.20	3.14	3.08
12	6.55	5.10	4.47	4.12	3.89	3.73	3.51	3.37	3.28	3.07	3.02	2.96	2.91	2.85	2.79	2.72
20	5.87	4.46	3.86	3.51	3.29	3.13	2.91	2.77	2.68	2.46	2.41	2.35	2.29	2.22	2.16	2.09
24	5.72	4.32	3.72	3.38	3.15	2.99	2.78	2.64	2.54	2.33	2.27	2.21	2.15	2.08	2.01	1.94
30	5.57	4.18	3.59	3.25	3.03	2.87	2.65	2.51	2.41	2.20	2.14	2.07	2.01	1.94	1.87	1.79
40	5.42	4.05	3.46	3.13	2.90	2.74	2.53	2.39	2.29	2.07	2.01	1.94	1.88	1.80	1.72	1.64
60	5.29	3.93	3.34	3.01	2.79	2.63	2.41	2.27	2.17	1.94	1.88	1.82	1.74	1.67	1.58	1.48
120	5.15	3.80	3.23	2.89	2.67	2.52	2.30	2.16	2.05	1.82	1.76	1.69	1.61	1.53	1.43	1.31
∞	5.02	3.69	3.12	2.79	2.57	2.41	2.19	2.05	1.94	1.71	1.64	1.57	1.48	1.39	1.27	1.00

Appendix Table 21.3—Upper 1 Per Cent Points of the F Distribution

ν_2 \ ν_1	1	2	3	4	5	6	8	10	12	20	24	30	40	60	120	∞
1	4052	5000	5403	5625	5764	5859	5982	6056	6106	6209	6235	6261	6287	6313	6339	6366
2	98.50	99.00	99.17	99.25	99.30	99.33	99.37	99.40	99.42	99.45	99.46	99.47	99.47	99.48	99.49	99.50
3	34.12	30.82	29.46	28.71	28.24	27.91	27.49	27.23	27.05	26.69	26.60	26.50	26.41	26.32	26.22	26.13
4	21.20	18.00	16.69	15.98	15.52	15.21	14.80	14.55	14.37	14.02	13.93	13.84	13.75	13.65	13.56	13.46
5	16.26	13.27	12.06	11.39	10.97	10.67	10.29	10.05	9.89	9.55	9.47	9.38	9.29	9.20	9.11	9.02
6	13.75	10.92	9.78	9.15	8.75	8.47	8.10	7.87	7.72	7.40	7.31	7.23	7.14	7.06	6.97	6.88
8	11.26	8.65	7.59	7.01	6.63	6.37	6.03	5.81	5.67	5.36	5.28	5.20	5.12	5.03	4.95	4.86
10	10.04	7.56	6.55	5.99	5.64	5.39	5.06	4.85	4.71	4.41	4.33	4.25	4.17	4.08	4.00	3.91
12	9.33	6.93	5.95	5.41	5.06	4.82	4.50	4.30	4.16	3.86	3.78	3.70	3.62	3.54	3.45	3.36
20	8.10	5.85	4.94	4.43	4.10	3.87	3.56	3.37	3.23	2.94	2.86	2.78	2.69	2.61	2.52	2.42
24	7.82	5.61	4.72	4.22	3.90	3.67	3.36	3.17	3.03	2.74	2.66	2.58	2.49	2.40	2.31	2.21
30	7.56	5.39	4.51	4.02	3.70	3.47	3.17	2.98	2.84	2.55	2.47	2.39	2.30	2.21	2.11	2.01
40	7.31	5.18	4.31	3.83	3.51	3.29	2.99	2.80	2.66	2.37	2.29	2.20	2.11	2.02	1.92	1.80
60	7.08	4.98	4.13	3.65	3.34	3.12	2.82	2.63	2.50	2.20	2.12	2.03	1.94	1.84	1.73	1.60
120	6.85	4.79	3.95	3.48	3.17	2.96	2.66	2.47	2.34	2.03	1.95	1.86	1.76	1.66	1.53	1.38
∞	6.63	4.61	3.78	3.32	3.02	2.80	2.51	2.32	2.18	1.88	1.79	1.70	1.59	1.47	1.32	1.00

Appendix Table 21.4—Upper 0.1 Per Cent Points of the F Distribution

ν_2 \ ν_1	1	2	3	4	5	6	8	10	12	20	24	30	40	60	120	∞
1*	405.3	500.0	540.4	562.5	576.4	585.9	598.1	605.6	610.7	620.9	623.5	626.1	628.7	631.3	634.0	636.6
2	998.5	999.0	999.2	999.2	999.3	999.3	999.4	999.4	999.4	999.4	999.5	999.5	999.5	999.5	999.5	999.5
3	167.0	148.5	141.1	137.1	134.6	132.8	130.6	129.2	128.3	126.4	125.9	125.4	125.0	124.5	124.0	123.5
4	74.14	61.25	56.18	53.44	51.71	50.53	49.00	48.05	47.41	46.10	45.77	45.43	45.09	44.75	44.40	44.05
5	47.18	37.12	33.20	31.09	29.75	28.84	27.64	26.92	26.42	25.39	25.14	24.87	24.60	24.33	24.06	23.79
6	35.51	27.00	23.70	21.92	20.81	20.03	19.03	18.41	17.99	17.12	16.89	16.67	16.44	16.21	15.99	15.75
8	25.42	18.49	15.83	14.39	13.49	12.86	12.04	11.54	11.19	10.48	10.30	10.11	9.92	9.73	9.53	9.33
10	21.04	14.91	12.55	11.28	10.48	9.92	9.20	8.75	8.45	7.80	7.64	7.47	7.30	7.12	6.94	6.76
12	18.64	12.97	10.80	9.63	8.89	8.38	7.71	7.29	7.00	6.40	6.25	6.09	5.93	5.76	5.59	5.42
20	14.82	9.95	8.10	7.10	6.46	6.02	5.44	5.08	4.82	4.29	4.15	4.00	3.86	3.70	3.54	3.38
24	14.03	9.34	7.55	6.59	5.98	5.55	4.99	4.64	4.39	3.87	3.74	3.59	3.45	3.29	3.14	2.97
30	13.29	8.77	7.05	6.12	5.53	5.12	4.58	4.24	4.00	3.49	3.36	3.22	3.07	2.92	2.76	2.59
40	12.61	8.25	6.60	5.70	5.13	4.73	4.21	3.87	3.64	3.15	3.01	2.87	2.73	2.57	2.41	2.23
60	11.97	7.76	6.17	5.31	4.76	4.37	3.87	3.54	3.31	2.83	2.69	2.55	2.41	2.25	2.08	1.89
120	11.38	7.32	5.79	4.95	4.42	4.04	3.55	3.24	3.02	2.53	2.40	2.26	2.11	1.95	1.76	1.54
∞	10.83	6.91	5.42	4.62	4.10	3.74	3.27	2.96	2.74	2.27	2.13	1.99	1.84	1.66	1.45	1.00

APPENDIX 22

Values of χ^2 for Specified Values of P

This table shows the probability of obtaining a value of χ^2 as large as the sample value or larger. $P(\chi^2)$ is indicated by the black areas in the diagrams below.

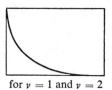

for $\nu = 1$ and $\nu = 2$

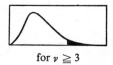

for $\nu \geq 3$

ν	Probability										
	.999	.995	.99	.98	.975	.95	.90	.80	.75	.70	.50
1	$.0^5157$	$.0^4393$	$.0^3157$	$.0^3628$	$.0^3982$	.00393	.0158	.0642	.102	.148	.455
2	.00200	.0100	.0201	.0404	.0506	.103	.211	.446	.575	.713	1.386
3	.0243	.0717	.115	.185	.216	.352	.584	1.005	1.213	1.424	2.366
4	.0908	.207	.297	.429	.484	.711	1.064	1.649	1.923	2.195	3.357
5	.210	.412	.554	.752	.831	1.145	1.610	2.343	2.675	3.000	4.351
6	.381	.676	.872	1.134	1.237	1.635	2.204	3.070	3.455	3.828	5.348
7	.598	.989	1.239	1.564	1.690	2.167	2.833	3.822	4.255	4.671	6.346
8	.857	1.344	1.646	2.032	2.180	2.733	3.490	4.594	5.071	5.527	7.344
9	1.152	1.735	2.088	2.532	2.700	3.325	4.168	5.380	5.899	6.393	8.343
10	1.479	2.156	2.558	3.059	3.247	3.940	4.865	6.179	6.737	7.267	9.342
11	1.834	2.603	3.053	3.609	3.816	4.575	5.578	6.989	7.584	8.148	10.341
12	2.214	3.074	3.571	4.178	4.404	5.226	6.304	7.807	8.438	9.034	11.340
13	2.617	3.565	4.107	4.765	5.009	5.892	7.042	8.634	9.299	9.926	12.340
14	3.041	4.075	4.660	5.368	5.629	6.571	7.790	9.467	10.165	10.821	13.339
15	3.483	4.601	5.229	5.985	6.262	7.261	8.547	10.307	11.036	11.721	14.339
16	3.942	5.142	5.812	6.614	6.908	7.962	9.312	11.152	11.912	12.624	15.338
17	4.416	5.697	6.408	7.255	7.564	8.672	10.085	12.002	12.792	13.531	16.638
18	4.905	6.265	7.015	7.906	8.231	9.390	10.865	12.857	13.675	14.440	17.338
19	5.407	6.844	7.633	8.567	8.907	10.117	11.651	13.716	14.562	15.352	18.338
20	5.921	7.434	8.260	9.237	9.591	10.851	12.443	14.578	15.452	16.266	19.337
21	6.447	8.034	8.897	9.915	10.283	11.591	13.240	15.445	16.344	17.182	20.337
22	6.983	8.643	9.542	10.600	10.982	12.338	14.041	16.314	17.240	18.101	21.337
23	7.529	9.260	10.196	11.293	11.688	13.091	14.848	17.187	18.137	19.021	22.337
24	8.085	9.886	10.856	11.992	12.401	13.848	15.659	18.062	19.037	19.943	23.337
25	8.649	10.520	11.524	12.697	13.120	14.611	16.473	18.940	19.939	20.867	24.337
26	9.222	11.160	12.198	13.409	13.844	15.379	17.292	19.820	20.843	21.792	25.336
27	9.803	11.808	12.879	14.125	14.573	16.151	18.114	20.703	21.749	22.719	26.336
28	10.391	12.461	13.565	14.847	15.308	16.928	18.939	21.588	22.657	23.647	27.336
29	10.986	13.121	14.256	15.574	16.047	17.708	19.768	22.475	23.567	24.577	28.336
30	11.588	13.787	14.953	16.306	16.791	18.493	20.599	23.364	24.478	25.508	29.336

For large values of v,

$$\chi^2 \doteq v\left(1 - \frac{2}{9v} \pm z_P \sqrt{\frac{2}{9v}}\right)^3,$$

where z_P is the normal deviate cutting off the corresponding tails of a normal distribution. Thus if $z_P = 1.96$, we obtain values of χ^2 for $P = .975$ and .025, or $Q = .025$ and .975.

For very large values of v,

$$\chi^2 \doteq \tfrac{1}{2}(z_P \pm \sqrt{2v - 1})^2.$$

This table is abridged from Table 8 of E. S. Pearson and H. O. Hartley (editors) *Biometrika Tables for Statisticians*, Volume I, Cambridge University Press, Cambridge, 1954; and Table IV of R. A. Fisher and F. Yates, *Statistical Tables for Biological, Agricultural, and Medical Research*, 5th ed., 1957, published by Oliver and Boyd, Ltd., Edinburgh, by permission of the authors and publishers.

Probability										v
.30	.25	.20	.10	.05	.025	.02	.01	.005	.001	
1.074	1.323	1.642	2.706	3.841	5.024	5.412	6.635	7.879	10.827	1
2.408	2.773	3.219	4.605	5.991	7.378	7.824	9.210	10.597	13.815	2
3.665	4.108	4.642	6.251	7.815	9.348	9.837	11.345	12.838	16.268	3
4.878	5.385	5.989	7.779	9.488	11.143	11.668	13.277	14.860	18.465	4
6.064	6.626	7.289	9.236	11.070	12.832	13.388	15.086	16.750	20.517	5
7.231	7.841	8.558	10.645	12.592	14.449	15.033	16.812	18.548	22.457	6
8.383	9.037	9.803	12.017	14.067	16.013	16.622	18.475	20.278	24.322	7
9.524	10.219	11.030	13.362	15.507	17.535	18.168	20.090	21.955	26.125	8
10.656	11.389	12.242	14.684	16.919	19.023	19.679	21.666	23.589	27.877	9
11.781	12.549	13.442	15.987	18.307	20.483	21.161	23.209	25.188	29.588	10
12.899	13.701	14.631	17.275	19.675	21.920	22.618	24.725	26.757	31.264	11
14.011	14.845	15.812	18.549	21.026	23.337	24.054	26.217	28.300	32.909	12
15.119	15.984	16.985	19.812	22.362	24.736	25.472	27.688	29.819	34.528	13
16.222	17.117	18.151	21.064	23.685	26.119	26.873	29.141	31.319	36.123	14
17.322	18.245	19.311	22.307	24.996	27.488	28.259	30.578	32.801	37.697	15
18.418	19.369	20.465	23.542	26.296	28.845	29.633	32.000	34.267	39.252	16
19.511	20.489	21.615	24.769	27.587	30.191	30.995	33.409	35.718	40.790	17
20.601	21.605	22.760	25.989	28.869	31.526	32.346	34.805	37.156	42.312	18
21.689	22.718	23.900	27.204	30.144	32.852	33.687	36.191	38.582	43.820	19
22.775	23.828	25.038	28.412	31.410	34.170	35.020	37.566	39.997	45.315	20
23.858	24.935	26.171	29.615	32.671	35.479	36.343	38.932	41.401	46.797	21
24.939	26.039	27.301	30.813	33.924	36.781	37.659	40.289	42.796	48.268	22
26.018	27.141	28.429	32.007	35.172	38.076	38.968	41.638	44.181	49.728	23
27.096	28.241	29.553	33.196	36.415	39.364	40.270	42.980	45.558	51.179	24
28.172	29.339	30.675	34.382	37.652	40.646	41.566	44.314	46.928	52.620	25
29.246	30.434	31.795	35.563	38.885	41.923	42.856	45.642	48.290	54.052	26
30.319	31.528	32.912	36.741	40.113	43.194	44.140	46.963	49.645	55.476	27
31.391	32.620	34.027	37.916	41.337	44.461	45.419	48.278	50.993	56.893	28
32.461	33.711	35.139	39.087	42.557	45.722	46.693	49.588	52.336	58.302	29
33.530	34.800	36.250	40.256	43.773	46.979	47.962	50.892	53.672	59.703	30

Values of $v = \dfrac{\Delta}{\sigma}$ from a Normal Population at Selected Probability Points

Values of v for other probability points and other degrees of freedom can be computed from tables of χ^2 or F.

$$\chi^2 = \frac{n\Delta^2}{\sigma^2}, \quad \text{and} \quad \frac{\Delta}{\sigma} = \sqrt{\frac{\chi^2}{n}}.$$

When $v_2 = \infty$,

$$F = \frac{s^2}{\sigma^2} = \frac{n}{n-1}\frac{\Delta^2}{\sigma^2}, \quad \left(\frac{\Delta}{\sigma}\right)^2 = \frac{n-1}{n}F, \quad \text{and} \quad \frac{\Delta}{\sigma} = \sqrt{\frac{n-1}{n}F}.$$

Assume, for example, that $n = 6$, and we wish the 0.1 per cent points. Using the χ^2 table (Appendix 22) with $v = 5$:

$$\text{Upper point:} \quad \frac{\Delta}{\sigma} = \sqrt{\frac{\chi^2_{0.001}}{n}} = \sqrt{\frac{20.517}{6}} = 1.849;$$

$$\text{Lower point:} \quad \frac{\Delta}{\sigma} = \sqrt{\frac{\chi^2_{0.999}}{n}} = \sqrt{\frac{0.210}{6}} = 0.187.$$

Using the F table (Appendix 21), we find that $F_{.001;5,\infty} = 4.10$. Also $F_{.001;\infty,5} = 23.79$, and so $F_{.999;5,\infty} = 1/23.79 = 0.0423$. Therefore:

$$\text{Upper point:} \quad \left(\frac{\Delta}{\sigma}\right)^2 = \frac{n-1}{n}F_{.001;5,\infty} = \frac{5}{6}(4.10) = 3.417, \quad \text{and}$$

$$\frac{\Delta}{\sigma} = 1.849;$$

$$\text{Lower point:} \quad \left(\frac{\Delta}{\sigma}\right)^2 = \frac{n-1}{n}F_{.999;5,\infty} = \frac{5}{6}(0.04203) = .03502, \quad \text{and}$$

$$\frac{\Delta}{\sigma} = 0.187.$$

In computing probability points for values of v when $n > 30$, a close approximation is given by

$$\frac{\Delta}{\sigma} \doteq \sqrt{\frac{v(1 - 2/9v \pm z_P\sqrt{2/9v})_3}{n}},$$

where $v = n - 1$, and z_P is the normal deviate cutting off the corresponding tails of a normal distribution. Thus, if $z_P = 1.96$, this expression gives the upper and lower .025 points.

Probability points for s/σ can be obtained from the values of Δ/σ given in this table by multiplying them by $\sqrt{n/(n-1)}$. Values of $\sqrt{n/(n-1)}$ are given in Appendix 3.

Except for the .001 and .999 probability points, the values of v in this table were computed from Catherine M. Thompson, "Tables of Percentage Points of the χ^2 distribution," *Biometrika*, Vol. 33, Pt. 2, pp. 187 ff. The values at the 0.001 points are from Frederick E. Croxton and Dudley J. Cowden, "Tables to Facilitate Computation of Sampling Limits of s and Fiducial Limits of σ," *Industrial Quality Control*, Vol. III, July, 1946, p. 20, and are reprinted by permission.

APPENDIX 24

Values of $w = \dfrac{R}{\sigma}$ from a Normal Population at Selected Probability Points

(For sample sizes greater than 12 it is advisable to use Δ/σ.)

n	Lower probability point							.50	Upper probability point						
	.001	.005	.01	.025	.05	.10	.25		.25	.10	.05	.025	.01	.005	.001
2	0.0009	0.0044	0.0089	0.0222	0.0443	0.0889	0.225	0.477	0.813	1.163	1.386	1.585	1.821	1.985	2.327
3	.0258	.0578	.0819	.130	.185	.265	.438	.680	.961	1.239	1.413	1.568	1.752	1.879	2.146
4	.0779	.134	.169	.232	.297	.382	.551	.769	1.013	1.250	1.398	1.529	1.684	1.792	2.017
5	.135	.203	.244	.311	.377	.461	.620	.819	1.038	1.247	1.378	1.493	1.630	1.724	1.922
6	.187	.262	.304	.372	.437	.518	.668	.852	1.051	1.241	1.358	1.462	1.586	1.671	1.849
7	.233	.311	.353	.420	.483	.561	.703	.874	1.058	1.233	1.341	1.437	1.550	1.628	1.791
8	.274	.352	.394	.460	.520	.595	.729	.891	1.063	1.226	1.326	1.415	1.520	1.592	1.744
9	.309	.386	.428	.492	.551	.623	.751	.903	1.066	1.218	1.313	1.396	1.494	1.562	1.704
10	.339	.417	.457	.520	.577	.646	.768	.913	1.067	1.212	1.301	1.379	1.472	1.536	1.670
11	.367	.443	.482	.543	.599	.665	.783	.922	1.068	1.206	1.290	1.365	1.453	1.513	1.640
12	.391	.466	.504	.564	.617	.682	.795	.928	1.069	1.200	1.280	1.352	1.435	1.493	1.614
13	.413	.486	.524	.582	.634	.696	.806	.934	1.069	1.195	1.272	1.340	1.420	1.475	1.591
14	.432	.505	.542	.598	.649	.709	.815	.939	1.069	1.190	1.264	1.329	1.406	1.459	1.570
15	.450	.521	.557	.613	.662	.721	.823	.943	1.068	1.185	1.257	1.320	1.394	1.445	1.552
16	.467	.536	.572	.626	.674	.731	.831	.947	1.068	1.181	1.250	1.311	1.382	1.432	1.535
17	.482	.550	.585	.637	.684	.740	.837	.950	1.067	1.177	1.244	1.303	1.372	1.420	1.520
18	.495	.563	.597	.648	.694	.749	.843	.953	1.067	1.173	1.238	1.295	1.362	1.409	1.505
19	.508	.574	.608	.658	.703	.756	.848	.955	1.066	1.170	1.233	1.288	1.353	1.398	1.492
20	.520	.585	.618	.667	.711	.763	.853	.958	1.066	1.166	1.228	1.282	1.345	1.389	1.480
21	.531	.595	.627	.676	.719	.770	.858	.960	1.065	1.163	1.223	1.276	1.337	1.380	1.469
22	.541	.604	.636	.684	.726	.776	.862	.961	1.065	1.160	1.219	1.270	1.330	1.372	1.458
23	.551	.613	.644	.691	.732	.781	.866	.963	1.064	1.157	1.214	1.265	1.324	1.364	1.449
24	.560	.621	.652	.698	.739	.787	.869	.965	1.063	1.155	1.211	1.260	1.317	1.357	1.439
25	.569	.629	.659	.704	.744	.791	.873	.966	1.063	1.152	1.207	1.255	1.311	1.350	1.431
26	.577	.636	.666	.710	.750	.796	.876	.967	1.062	1.150	1.203	1.250	1.306	1.343	1.423
27	.584	.643	.672	.716	.755	.800	.879	.969	1.062	1.148	1.200	1.246	1.300	1.337	1.415
28	.592	.649	.678	.721	.759	.804	.881	.970	1.061	1.146	1.197	1.242	1.295	1.332	1.408
29	.599	.656	.684	.727	.764	.808	.884	.971	1.061	1.143	1.194	1.238	1.290	1.326	1.401
30	.605	.661	.689	.731	.768	.812	.886	.972	1.060	1.141	1.191	1.235	1.286	1.321	1.394

Taken by permission from E. S. Pearson, "The Probability Integral of the Range in Samples of n Observations from a Normal Population," *Biometrika*, Vol. 32, Parts III and IV (1942), pp. 301–310. Values for the .25 and .50 probability points, and all values with 3 decimal places were obtained, by linear interpolation, from Table 1. All other values were taken directly from Table 2. Since $R = 2\Delta$ when $n = 2$, the values of the first row of this appendix table are twice as large as those of Appendix 23.

Factors for Obtaining Control Limits for Means and Ranges

n	A $\dfrac{3\sigma_{\bar{x}}}{\sigma}$	A_2 $\dfrac{3\sigma_{\bar{x}}}{E(R)}$	D_1 $\dfrac{E(R) - 3\sigma_R}{\sigma}$	D_2 $\dfrac{E(R) + 3\sigma_R}{\sigma}$	D_3 $\dfrac{E(R) - 3\sigma_R}{E(R)}$	D_4 $\dfrac{E(R) + 3\sigma_R}{E(R)}$
2	2.1213	1.881	...	3.686	...	3.267
3	1.7321	1.023	...	4.358	...	2.575
4	1.5000	0.7285	...	4.698	...	2.282
5	1.3416	.5768	...	4.918	...	2.115
6	1.2247	.4833	...	5.078	...	2.004
7	1.1339	.4193	0.204	5.204	0.076	1.924
8	1.0607	.3726	.388	5.306	.136	1.864
9	1.0000	.3367	.547	5.393	.184	1.816
10	0.9487	.3082	.687	5.469	.223	1.777
11	.9045	.2851	.811	5.535	.256	1.744
12	.8660	.2658	.923	5.593	.284	1.716
13	.8321					
14	.8018					
15	.7746					
16	.7500					
17	.7276					
18	.7071					
19	.6882					
20	.6708					
21	.6547					
22	.6396					
23	.6255					
24	.6124					
25	.6000					

There can be no lower control limit for ranges when $n < 7$, because then $E(R) - 3\sigma_R < 0$.

$D_1 = d_2 - D$ and $D_2 = d_2 + D$, where $D = 3\sigma_w$. Values of σ_w may be found in E. S. Pearson and H. O. Hartley, editors, *Biometrika Tables for Statisticians*, Table 20. Cambridge University Press, 1954.

The D_3 and D_4 values were taken, by permission, from American Society for Testing Materials, *A.S.T.M. Manual on Quality Control of Materials*, Table B2, 1951, p. 115. $D_3 = \dfrac{D_1}{d_2} = c_3 D_1$; $D_4 = \dfrac{D_2}{d_2} = c_3 D_2$. Note that $D_3 + D_4 = 2$. See Appendix 10 for values of c_3.

APPENDIX 26

Table for Testing Significance of Kendall's τ

$$\tau = \frac{S}{\binom{n}{2}}$$

This table shows the smallest value of S for which the probability is less than P. The distribution of S is symmetrical, and this table refers only to positive values of S.

$$\sigma_S^2 = \frac{n(n-1)(2n+5)}{18}.$$

The distribution of τ tends to normality as n approaches infinity, and when $n > 10$ it is satisfactory to test τ by considering z_S to be a normal deviate, where

$$z_S = \frac{S-1}{\sigma_S}.$$

In the numerator for z_S, the subtraction of 1 from S is a correction for continuity.

n	$P < .2$	$P < .1$	$P < .05$	$P < .025$	$P < .01$	$P < .005$	$P < .001$
3	3	...	...	...	...	...	...
4	4	6	6	...	...	...	...
5	6	8	8	10	10	...	...
6	7	9	11	13	13	...	...
7	7	11	13	15	17	19	21
8	8	12	16	18	20	22	24
9	10	14	18	20	24	26	30
10	11	17	21	23	27	29	35

Source: Derived from Maurice G. Kendall, *The Advanced Theory of Statistics*, Vol. I, Charles Griffin & Company Ltd., London, 1945, p. 405.

APPENDIX 27

Flexible Calendar of Working Days

Calendar Days, Sundays, Saturdays, and Holidays, by Months, 1898–1976

There are 14 distinct calendar patterns, referred to in the calendar by code number. In the code table below the years are arranged consecutively within columns. Any year can be located by reading down the proper column. Then read across to ascertain the code number. For instance, 1945 is located by reading down in the fifth column, and the code number is seen to be IV. Row IV of the calendar gives information concerning 1945, as well as concerning 1900, 1906, 1917, 1923, 1934, 1951, 1962, and 1973.

Code Table

Year								Code number
1898	1910fe	1921fe	1927	1938	1949	1955	1966	I
...	...	...	1928*	...	...	1956*f	...	II
1899f	1911	1922	...	1939	1950	...	1967fe	III
1900†	...	1923f	...	...	1951fe	...	...	IV
...	1912*	...	...	1940*fe	...	...	1968*	V
1901	...	...	1929fe	...	...	1957	...	VI
1902fe	1913fe	...	1930	1941	...	1958	1969	VII
...	...	1924*	...	...	1952*	...	...	VIII
1903	1914	1925	1931	1942	1953	1959fe	1970fe	IX
...	1915	1926	...	1943	1954	...	1971	X
1904*	...	...	1932*fe	...	...	1960*	...	XI
...	1916*	...	...	1944*	...	...	1972*f	XII
1905	...	...	1933	...	...	1961f	...	III
1906	1917	...	1934f	1945f	...	1962	1973	IV
1907fe	1918fe	...	1935	1946	...	1963	1974	VI
1908*	...	...	1936*	...	...	1964*fe	...	XIII
...	1919	...	...	1947	...	...	1975fe	VII
1909	...	...	1937fe	...	...	1965	...	X
...	1920*	...	...	1948*fe	...	...	1976*	XIV

* Leap Year; February has 29 days.
† 1900 was not a Leap Year.
f Good Friday occurred in March.
e Easter occurred in March.

Calendar

The first row for each year gives the number of Sundays in parentheses ( ) and Saturdays in brackets [ ] in each month. The second row shows the occurrence of holidays. Holidays occurring on Sundays are enclosed in parentheses; those on Saturdays are enclosed in brackets. For information concerning the states in which specific holidays are observed, see *The World Almanac and Book of Facts* (published annually by the New York *World-Telegram and Sun*, New York City).

Following is a key to the symbols used on the calendar:

N New Year's Day—January 1.
L Lincoln's Birthday—February 12.
W Washington's Birthday—February 22.
F Good Friday.
E Easter.
M Memorial Day—May 30.
J Independence Day—July 4.

D Labor Day—First Monday in September.
C Columbus Day—October 12.
V Election Day—First Tuesday after First Monday in November.
A Veteran's Day—November 11 (beginning 1918).
T Thanksgiving Day.
X Christmas Day—December 25.

Code number	Jan 31	Feb 28	Mar 31	Apr 30	May 31	Jun 30	Jul 31	Aug 31	Sep 30	Oct 31	Nov 30	Dec 31
I	(5) [5] [N]	(4) [4] [L] W	(4) [4]	(4) [5] F (E)	(5) [4] M	(4) [4]	(5) [5] J	(4) [4]	(4) [4] D	(5) [5] (C)	(4) [4] V A T	(4) [5] (X)
II	(5) [4] (N)	(4) [4] L W	(4) [5]	(4) [4] F (E)	(4) [4] M	(4) [5],	(5) [4] J	(4) [4]	(5) [5] D	(4) [4] C	(4) [4] V (A) T	(5) [5] X
III	(5) [4] (N)	(4) [4] (L) W	(4) [4]	(5) [5] F (E)	(4) [4] M	(4) [4]	(5) [5] J	(4) [4]	(4) [5] D	(5) [4] C	(4) [4] V [A] T	(5) [5] X
IV	(4) [4] N	(4) [4] L W	(4) [5]	(5) [4] F (E)	(4) [4] M	(4) [5]	(5) [4] J	(4) [4]	(4) [5] D	(4) [4] C	(4) [4] V (A) T	(5) [5] X
V	(4) [4] N	(4) [4] L W	(5) [5]	(4) [4] F (E)	(4) [4] M	(5) [5]	(4) [4] J	(4) [5]	(5) [4] D	(4) [4] [C]	(4) [5] V A T	(5) [4] X
VI	(4) [4] N	(4) [4] L W	(5) [5]	(4) [4] F (E)	(4) [4] M	(4) [5]	(4) [4] J	(4) [5]	(5) [4] D	(4) [4] [C]	(4) [5] V A T	(5) [4] X
VII	(4) [4] N	(4) [4] L [W]	(5) [5]	(4) [4] F (E)	(4) [5] M	(5) [4]	(4) [4] J	(4) [4]	(5) [4] D	(4) [4] (C)	(5) [5] V A T	(4) [4] X
VIII	(4) [4] N	(4) [4] L W	(5) [5]	(4) [4] F (E)	(4) [5] M	(5) [4]	(4) [4] J	(4) [4]	(5) [5] D	(4) [4] (C)	(5) [5] V A T	(4) [4] X
IX	(4) [5] N	(4) [4] L (W)	(5) [4]	(4) [4] F (E)	(5) [5] [M]	(4) [4]	(4) [4] [J]	(5) [5]	(4) [4] D	(4) [4] C	(5) [4] V A T	(4) [4] X
X	(5) [5] N	(4) [4] L W	(4) [4]	(4) [4] F (E)	(5) [5] (M)	(4) [4]	(4) [5] (J)	(5) [4]	(4) [4] D	(5) [5] C	(4) [4] V A T	(4) [4] [X]
XI	(5) [5] N	(4) [4] L W	(4) [4]	(4) [5] F (E)	(5) [4] M	(4) [4]	(5) [5] J	(4) [4]	(4) [4] D	(5) [5] C	(4) [4] V A T	(4) [5] (X)
XII	(5) [5] N	(4) [4] [L] W	(4) [4]	(5) [5] F (E)	(4) [4] M	(4) [4]	(5) [5] J	(4) [4]	(4) [5] D	(5) [4] C	(4) [4] V A T	(5) [5] X
III	(5) [4] (N)	(4) [4] (L) W	(4) [4]	(5) [5] F (E)	(4) [4] M	(4) [4]	(5) [5] J	(4) [4]	(4) [5] D	(5) [4] C	(4) [4] V [A] T	(5) [5] X
IV	(4) [4] N	(4) [4] L W	(4) [5]	(5) [4] F (E)	(4) [4] M	(4) [5]	(5) [4] J	(4) [4]	(4) [5] D	(4) [4] C	(4) [4] V (A) T	(5) [5] X
VI	(4) [4] N	(4) [4] L W	(5) [5]	(4) [4] F (E)	(4) [4] M	(5) [5]	(4) [4] J	(4) [5]	(5) [4] D	(4) [4] [C]	(4) [5] V A T	(5) [4] X
XIII	(4) [4] N	(4) [5] L [W]	(5) [4]	(4) [4] F (E)	(5) [5] [M]	(4) [4]	(4) [4] [J]	(5) [5]	(4) [4] D	(4) [5] C	(5) [4] V A T	(4) [4] X
VII	(4) [4] N	(4) [4] L [W]	(5) [5]	(4) [4] F (E)	(4) [5] M	(5) [4]	(4) [4] J	(4) [4]	(5) [4] D	(4) [4] (C)	(5) [5] V A T	(4) [4] X
X	(5) [5] N	(4) [4] L W	(4) [4]	(4) [4] F (E)	(5) [5] (M)	(4) [4]	(4) [5] (J)	(5) [4]	(4) [4] D	(5) [5] C	(4) [4] V A T	(4) [4] [X]
XIV	(4) [5] N	(5) [4] L (W)	(4) [4]	(4) [4] F (E)	(5) [5] (M)	(4) [4]	(4) [5] J	(5) [4]	(4) [4] D	(5) [5] C	(4) [4] V A T	(4) [4] [X]

APPENDIX 28

Random Numbers

1581922396	2068577984	8262130892	8374856049	4637567488
0928105582	7295088579	9586111652	7055508767	6472382934
4112077556	3440672486	1882412963	0684012006	0933147914
7457477468	5435810788	9670852913	1291265730	4890031305
0099520858	3090908872	2039593181	5973470495	9776135501
7245174840	2275698645	8416549348	4676463101	2229367983
6749420382	4832630032	5670984959	5432114610	2966095680
5503161011	7413686599	1198757695	0414294470	0140121598
7164238934	7666127259	5263097712	5133648980	4011966963
3593969525	0272759769	0385998136	9999089966	7544056852
4192054466	0700014629	5169439659	8408705169	1074373131
9697426117	6488888550	4031652526	8123543276	0927534537
2007950579	9564268448	3457416988	1531027886	7016633739
4584768758	2389278610	3859431781	3643768456	4141314518
3840145867	9120831830	7228567652	1267173884	4020651657
0190153442	4800088084	1165628559	5407921254	3768932478
6766554338	5585265145	5089052204	9780623691	2195448096
6315116284	9172824179	5544814339	0016943666	3828538786
3908771938	4035554324	0840126299	4942059208	1475623997
5570024586	9324732596	1186563397	4425143189	3216653251
2999997185	0135968938	7678931194	1351031403	6002561840
7864375912	8383232768	1892857070	2323673751	3188881718
7065492027	6349104233	3382569662	4579426926	1513082455
0654683246	4765104877	8149224168	5468631609	6474393896
7830555058	5255147182	3519287786	2481675649	8907598697
7626984369	4725370390	9641916289	5049082870	7463807244
4785048453	3646121751	8436077768	2928794356	9956043516
4627791048	5765558107	8762592043	6185670830	6363845920
9376470693	0441608934	8749472723	2202271078	5897002653
1227991661	7936797054	9527542791	4711871173	8300978148
5582095589	5535798279	4764439855	6279247618	4446895088
4959397698	1056981450	8416606706	8234013222	6426813469
1824779358	1333750468	9434074212	5273692238	5902177065
7041092295	5726289716	3420847871	1820481234	0318831723
3555104281	0903099163	6827824899	6383872737	5001682626
9717595534	1634107293	8521057472	1471300754	3044151557
5571564123	7344613447	1129117244	3208461091	1699403490
4674262892	2809456764	5806554509	8224980942	5738031833
8461228715	0746980892	9285305274	6331989646	8764467686
1838538678	3049068967	6955157269	5482964330	2161984904
1834182305	6203476893	5937802079	3445280195	3694915658
1884227732	2923727501	8044389132	4611203081	6072112445
6791857341	6696243386	2219599137	3193884236	8224729718
3007929946	4031562749	5570757297	6273785046	1455349704
6085440624	2875556938	5496629750	4841817356	1443167141
7005051056	3496332071	5054070890	7303867953	6255181190
9846413446	8306646692	0661684251	8875127201	6251533454
0625457703	4229164694	7321363715	7051128285	1108468072
5457593922	9751489574	1799906380	1989141062	5595364247
4076486653	8950826528	4934582003	4071187742	1456207629

Reproduced from Appendix IV of Dudley J. Cowden and Mercedes S. Cowden, *Practical Problems in Business Statistics*, Prentice-Hall, Inc., Englewood Cliffs, N. J., 1948.

INDEX